KU-048-539

1978 Yearbook of Science and the Future

Encyclopædia Britannica, Inc.

Chicago Toronto London
Geneva Sydney Tokyo
Manila Seoul

1978
Yearbook of Science and the Future

MANAGING EDITOR
Lawrence K. Lustig

EDITOR
David Calhoun

EDITORIAL CONSULTANT
Howard J. Lewis, Director, Office of Information,
National Academy of Sciences—National Academy
of Engineering—National Research Council

EDITORIAL STAFF
Charles Cegielski, Daphne Daume,
Arthur Latham

ART DIRECTOR
Cynthia Peterson

DESIGN SUPERVISOR
Ron Villani

SENIOR PICTURE EDITOR
Catherine Judge

PICTURE EDITORS
Jeannine Deubel, Julie A. Kunkler

LAYOUT ARTIST
Richard Batchelor

ILLUSTRATOR
John L. Draves

ART PRODUCTION
Richard Heinke

CARTOGRAPHER
Gerzilla Leszczynski

COMPUTER TYPESETTING SERVICES
Robert Dehmer, Supervisor; Ronald J. Laugeman,
Melvin E. Stagner, Gilberto Valle, Elaine Yost

EDITORIAL PRODUCTION MANAGER
J. Thomas Beatty

PRODUCTION COORDINATOR
Ruth Passin

PRODUCTION STAFF
Kathryn Blatt, Susan Goodfellow, Laura Grad,
Marilyn Klein, Larry Kowalski, Juanita L. Murphy,
John Park, Nancy W. Pask, Julian Ronning,
Harry Sharp, Melinda Shepherd, Joyce P. Walker,
Coleen Withgott

COPY CONTROL
Mary Srodon, Supervisor; Mayme Cussen

INDEX
Frances E. Latham, Supervisor;
Judith Anderson, Rosa E. Casas, Mary Neumann,
Helen Peterson, Mary Reynolds

LIBRARIAN
Terry Miller

SECRETARY
Karen Justin

MANUSCRIPT TYPING
Sherri L. Shaffer

Editorial Administration

MANAGING EDITOR
ENCYCLOPÆDIA BRITANNICA, INC.
Margaret Sutton

DIRECTOR OF BUDGETS
Verne Pore

COPYRIGHT © 1977 BY ENCYCLOPÆDIA BRITANNICA, INC.
Copyright under International Copyright Union. All Rights Reserved under
Pan American and Universal Copyright Conventions by Encyclopaedia Britannica, Inc.

Library of Congress Catalog Card Number: 69-12349
International Standard Book Number: 0-85229-333-X
International Standard Serial Number: 0096-3291

No part of this work may be reproduced or utilized in any form or by any means,
electronic or mechanical, including photocopying, recording, or by any information
storage and retrieval system, without permission in writing from the publisher.

(Trademark Reg. U.S. Pat. Off.) Printed in U.S.A.

THE UNIVERSITY OF CHICAGO
The Yearbook of Science and the Future
is published with the editorial advice of the faculties of
the University of Chicago.

Encyclopædia Britannica, Inc.

CHAIRMAN OF THE BOARD
Robert P. Gwinn

PRESIDENT
Charles E. Swanson

VICE-PRESIDENT, EDITORIAL
Charles Van Doren

Editorial Advisory Board

Louis J. Battan, past president of the American Meteorological Society, is professor of atmospheric sciences and director of the Institute of Atmospheric Physics at the University of Arizona.

George W. Beadle, president emeritus and distinguished professor of biology at the University of Chicago, was awarded the Nobel Prize in 1958 for his achievements in genetics.

Lewis M. Branscomb, chief scientist of IBM and former director of the National Bureau of Standards, is a physicist and member of the National Academy of Sciences.

Kenneth O. Emery is a marine geologist at the Woods Hole Oceanographic Institution.

Jesse L. Greenstein, a member of the National Academy of Sciences, is the Lee A. DuBridge professor of astrophysics at the California Institute of Technology and on the staff of the Hale Observatories.

Richard H. Kessler, M.D., is professor of medicine and associate dean of the Medical School at Northwestern University.

Joshua Lederberg, professor of genetics and biology and chairman of the department of genetics at the Stanford University School of Medicine, received the Nobel Prize in 1958 for his work in genetics.

Anthony L. Turkevich, professor of chemistry and distinguished professor of the Enrico Fermi Institute, University of Chicago, is a principal investigator of the geochemistry of lunar materials.

Science and the Unknown

When the two Viking spacecraft became the first probes to soft-land successfully on Mars, they dramatically extended man's reach into the unknown. Soon, the two craft were sending photographs of the planet's surface back to the Earth. Once again, scientists had ventured into uncharted territory in their continuing effort to increase man's knowledge of the universe.

The *1978 Yearbook of Science and the Future* recounts the journeys and discoveries of the Martian probes in the article "The Viking Mission to Mars." This feature joins several others in the volume in dealing with explorations of the unknown. "Other Civilizations in Space: The Search for Extraterrestrial Life" discusses the probability of the existence of other intelligent life in the universe and describes the efforts to detect signals from extraterrestrial civilizations. "The Second Generation of Astronauts" portrays the men and women who have volunteered to be the pioneers on missions in the new space shuttle. "Once More, Into the Loch" tells of the latest expeditions to Loch

Ness in Scotland, where scientists are trying to determine whether there is a creature within the lake that resembles the legendary "Monster." Finally, a premier adventurer into the unknown, Thor Heyerdahl, describes in "Primitive Navigation and the Settlement of Polynesia" how his ocean crossings on a balsa raft and in reed boats have convinced him that the Pacific islands of Polynesia were settled by explorers from the Americas.

Other feature articles in this volume deal with a wide range of subjects. Man's earliest beginnings as determined by the painstaking work of anthropologists and other scientists are discussed in "Antiquity of Man in Africa"; the glories of one of the great early civilizations are vividly illustrated in the pictorial essay "Treasures of Ancient Egypt."

The biological sciences are represented by "The Flight of Birds" and "The Role of Zoos in Wildlife Conservation." Scientists are using wind tunnels and allied devices to try to determine the physiological mechanisms that make flight possible for birds and a few other vertebrates. In the latter arti-

cle, the author describes how a number of animals would be extinct had they not been preserved in zoological parks, and predicts that the dwindling of natural habitats may require zoos in the future to save more varieties of wildlife.

In the physical sciences, "Plate Tectonics: Past, Present, and Future" discusses one of the major discoveries of recent times, that the Earth's surface consists of an interlocking mosaic of huge rocky plates. The motion of these plates generates such geological phenomena as earthquakes and mountain building. "The Catalysis of Chemical Reactions" describes how catalysis, the acceleration of chemical reactions by certain substances, is a significant factor in the production of goods worth $100 billion per year in the United States. In "Nature's Nuclear Reactor" the discovery by French scientists of the first nuclear reactor to be found in nature is recounted. During its lifetime it generated enough energy to supply a major city for several years. "Nuclear Waste Disposal" strongly presents the case for developing safe and effective means

for getting rid of the life-threatening waste products of nuclear electric power plants.

Finally, in categories of their own are "The Limits to Computation" and "Plastic Surgery." The former describes problems that have long been classified as "undecidable" or "intractable" by mathematicians and discusses the limitations of even the most powerful new computers in resolving them. "Plastic Surgery" tells of the remarkable advances that have recently occurred in this surprisingly ancient branch of medicine.

Full-color photographs and drawings abundantly illustrate the articles. Distinguished authorities have been selected to write these features, as well as the Year in Review entries, which discuss the developments that have taken place in individual disciplines within science and technology. Also included is a section on Scientists of the Year, covering obituaries and major awards to individuals.

THE EDITOR

Contents

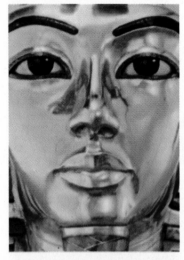

250

431

Treasures of Ancient Egypt

by Ann Stewart Anderson and Lawrence K. Lustig

The civilization of the age of the pharaohs is revealed by
artifacts, tombs, and statues found throughout Egypt. One of
the richest collections is at the Egyptian Museum in Cairo.

Ann Stewart Anderson

The Egyptian Museum in Cairo houses approximately 100,000 paintings, statues, and other treasures from Egypt's ancient civilizations.

ANN STEWART ANDERSON *has taught at the School of the Art Institute of Chicago, and* **LAWRENCE K. LUSTIG** *is a former university professor and research scientist with a special interest in Egyptology.*

(Overleaf) Photograph—Kodansha Ltd.

Approximately 7,000 years ago groups of Neolithic hunters and fishermen lived in settlements along the Nile Valley. They grew and stored grain, made pottery and stone implements, and used woven straw for a variety of purposes. The isolation of these people from other cultures, and the relative separation of those in the north from those in the south, led gradually to the emergence of different burial customs, tools and ornaments, and deities and religious practices in Upper and Lower Egypt. Moreover, the people themselves differed somewhat in facial characteristics and body structure. The dominant group in each region developed its own center of power and had its own ruler, a situation that persisted until a clash ultimately occurred around 3100 BC.

At that time a southern king, named Menes or Narmer, succeeded in unifying Upper and Lower Egypt by force of arms, despite the apparent cultural superiority of the northern people. This may fairly be said to be the single most important event in the history of Egypt, for after the unification King Menes became the first pharaoh and he ushered in an age that produced one of the most splendid archaeological chronicles of any known civilization.

The antiquity of Egyptian civilization is truly astonishing and requires some reference points for proper perspective. Egypt flourished as a nation for a thousand years before the Minoans built and inhabited their magnificent palace at Knossos on Crete. And Herodotus, historian of the Greeks, marveled at the wonder of the pyramids in the 5th century BC, in much the same manner that we would view the Acropolis in Athens or the Roman Forum today. Both Alexander the Great and Napoleon led their armies into the Nile Valley and there found evidence that a legion of generals had preceded them across that desert terrain. King Menes died some 30 centuries before the beginning of the Christian era, and the hieroglyphs that record his reign were carved nearly 5,000 years before the establishment of government in the New World. The age of the pharaohs is ancient indeed, when considered from a modern vantage point.

10

Our knowledge of the chronology involved stems from several sources. The historian Manetho, writing in the 3rd century BC, divided into 30 dynasties the period from the reign of King Menes to the death of the last pharaoh in 343 BC. Within this framework of reference he organized the succession of pharaohs over the centuries. Similar listings have been derived from the so-called Pyramid Texts, which are wall inscriptions at Saqqarah, Karnak, and Abydos dating from the 19th and 18th dynasties, and from the Turin Canon, which is a papyrus document of the same nature.

Basically, however, the details of the chronology rest upon excavations of tombs following Napoleon's expedition to Egypt in 1798. In the campaign of 1799, while digging trenches at Rashid, the French unearthed a slab of black basalt that is known as the Rosetta Stone. Inscribed on the stone — in Greek, hieroglyphs, and in an ancient Egyptian script — is a proclamation in praise of Ptolemy V that was written in 196 BC. The significance of this carved document resides in the fact that the parallelism of the text permitted a French linguist to decipher the meaning of the Egyptian hieroglyphs, a language lost literally in the sands of time. Jean-François Champollion labored more than 20 years to accomplish this task, for which success he deserves the construction of a pyramid in his honor. The ability to understand hieroglyphic inscriptions proved to be the key to comprehending the significance of ancient Egyptian civilization. Subsequent scholars not only determined the proper listing of successive rulers and their dates of reign but were permitted an extraordinary glimpse of the way of life and nature of society during the age of the pharaohs.

The 30 dynasties of Manetho may also be organized as the Early Dynastic Period (c. 3100–2686 BC), the Old Kingdom (c. 2686–2160 BC), Middle Kingdom (c. 2040–1786 BC), New Kingdom (c. 1567–1085 BC), and the Late Dynastic Period (c. 1085–343 BC). Together with the intervening periods, this overall era witnessed stonework and construction efforts on palaces, tombs, and monuments unrivaled before or since. Combined with funerary objects of art and other artifacts that have been discovered, this unique archaeological record forms the subject of this pictorial essay. Excluded is the so-called Ptolemaic Dynasty, a subsequent period of Greek domination that extended through 30 BC.

The Egyptian Museum
The artifacts, tombs, and colossi referred to above are scattered throughout Egypt at many sites, but a veritable treasure trove is to be found at the Egyptian Museum in Cairo. This substantial but unpretentious ocher-colored building contains thousands of discoveries from Egypt's incomparable past. Its halls and corridors are crowded with huge statues of standing and seated royal figures, mummies and sarcophagi, relief paintings and stelae, and golden funerary treasures as well as the utensils used by housewives 40 centuries ago.

The number of finds exhibited or housed approximates 100,000 and these objects represent an unparalleled record of all aspects of

Giraudon

The Narmer Palette, carved from slate, depicts the union of Upper and Lower Egypt. Cosmetics were mixed for ceremonial uses on such palettes during the Early Dynastic Period.

pharaonic time. They reveal a people characterized by grace and serenity, who developed writing, sculpture, and other art forms, who measured time and played music, who danced and tilled fields, who built ships and made linen, who went to war and worshiped their gods. No other people of ancient times have left such rich documentation of their varied activities.

The Egyptian Museum, quite fittingly, is the oldest national museum in the Middle East. Its establishment stems from the appointment of a Frenchman, Auguste Mariette, as the first director of antiquities in 1858. Mariette began his excavations in Egypt in 1850, and his discoveries included several important tombs in the great necropolis of ancient Memphis at Saqqarah, site of the Step Pyramid of King Djoser. The museum has grown enormously from its humble beginnings, when a deserted mosque and a few rat-infested sheds housed Mariette's finds. Archaeological teams produce new discoveries each year and the collection grows, seemingly without limit. Indeed, the greatest problem confronting the fortunate visitor to the Egyptian Museum is the abundance of the materials on display. Fifty or more marvelous figurines may be found in a few cases in a single room, any one of which would be presented in solitary splendor in a lesser collection.

Most of the objects to be described in this article are housed in the Egyptian Museum. True representation of the museum's collection, or of Egyptian archaeology generally, is impossible within the space constraints imposed here. What follows may best be considered a mere sampling of some of the more instructive items, treated within a chronological framework.

Early Dynastic Period (c. 3100–2686 BC)

The political unity achieved by King Menes in 3100 BC coincided with a seemingly abrupt flowering of Egyptian civilization. The capital city of Memphis was built, near present-day Saqqarah, and hieroglyphic texts and a calendar came into use. Irrigation works also were undertaken, and during the 2nd dynasty, about 2890 BC, the skillful use of stone in minor sculpture and construction works began, as did the artistic working of lapis lazuli, ivory, metal, and wood.

Widely used throughout the period were palettes carved from slate on which cosmetics were mixed for ceremonial use. The most famous of these is the Narmer Palette, which pictorially documents the union of Upper and Lower Egypt. On one side King Menes is shown wearing traditional royal garb—the crown of Upper Egypt, a false beard, and a classical kilt from which is suspended the tail of an animal. Raising his mace, the king clutches the hair of the traditional enemy of the east, a Syrian with pointed beard. Above are heads of the cow goddess, Hathor, flanking the royal palace, and in the lower register are two floating figures, probably indicating their subjugation.

The reverse side is in four bands, and again the Hathor heads appear at the top. The king is shown wearing the captured crown of Lower Egypt, and he is preceded by a priest and four standard-bearers. Two rows of horizontal decapitated enemies appear in front of them. Below this triumphal scene appear two long-necked beasts held by keepers, and at the bottom a bull tramples a nude Asian.

In addition to its symbolic importance, the Narmer Palette established an aesthetic formula subsequently used for 30 centuries. The division into horizontal bands, the juxtaposition of figures of different scale to indicate relative importance, and the patterning that unites elements and holds them to the picture plane—all these became characteristic of Egyptian artistic expression. The unselfconscious combining of human and animal forms and the fractured position of the body, in which the shoulders are frontal while buttocks, thighs, and feet are in profile, also continued as basic elements in Egyptian wall reliefs and other depictions.

Old Kingdom (c. 2686–2160 BC)

The Old Kingdom includes the 3rd through the 6th dynasties, and it was during this period that large-scale funerary monuments were first erected in Egypt. The pyramids represent admirable stonecutting and engineering skills, of course, but they also reflect a high degree of organization of people and resources. Beyond this, the pyramids are an

The Step Pyramid of Saqqarah, the burial place of King Djoser of the 3rd dynasty, is next to an enclosure that housed the life-sized statue of the king (opposite page).

artistic expression of the age of the pharaohs and are important religious shrines.

King Djoser, a ruler during the 3rd dynasty, commissioned his principal architect, Imhotep, to design his burial place. Djoser was dissatisfied with the traditional outcome, and the ruler and planner agreed on four subsequent changes. The Step Pyramid of Saqqarah, with its associated complex of buildings, courts, and walls, was the result. Archaeologists believe that the enclosure wall resembles that which originally surrounded Memphis, capital of Old Kingdom Egypt.

One of the most fascinating aspects of the Step Pyramid complex is that it exemplifies the transition from vegetable building materials to the use of stone. Ceilings carved from rock to resemble palm logs lie across papyrus bundle columns of limestone. Unfamiliar with the possibilities of this building material, the architect did not trust the strength of free-standing columns and so buttressed them against a wall. The entire complex is a life-sized model frozen in stone. Stone doors on stone hinges are set eternally ajar, and stone leaves flutter from atop replicas of trees.

Subsequent Old Kingdom rulers also built pyramids as part of their burial complexes, and more than eighty now exist in Egypt. But most of them differ greatly in form and concept from Imhotep's design, which was unique. To date, it is the only one that has been proven conclusively to include a Heb-Sed court, an area used in prehistoric time for the pharaoh to demonstrate his physical ability to continue his reign. Another departure in the Step Pyramid design involved Imhotep's location of the serdab, a cellarlike enclosure containing the Ka statue in which the deceased's double could dwell. Imhotep placed the serdab outside the pyramid, abutting its north face, and in this small stone room the life-sized Ka statue of King Djoser was found.

Seated on a simple throne, the figure still bears some traces of ancient paint. There are fragments of red ocher on the face and blue-black

14

Peter Clayton

Photos, Ann Stewart Anderson

Wall scenes from the tomb of Nefer: making wine (top) and carrying ducks on the end of a pole.

on the wig. The eye sockets, which once held false eyes of quartzite, are now empty. Although the ancient thief who removed them mutilated the king's face in his efforts, Djoser remains a figure of dignity. A great king, a god on earth, he was confident of his place in the cosmos and, like an ice sculpture frozen forever, he waits out eternity.

Aside from the Step Pyramid of King Djoser and his Ka statue, the necropolis at Saqqarah is also of great archaeological significance. The ancient Egyptians were concerned that their burial places include beautiful representations of those activities that had been important to the dead person. They viewed death not as an ending of the life they loved, but as a continuation of the same good things for eternity. They carefully portrayed those activities from which they intended to derive unending pleasure, believing that, through incantations and traditional magical formulas, the scenes on the tomb walls could be vitalized in the next life. As a result their carvings and drawings were highly accurate and convey much information about daily life in pharaonic time.

The tomb of Nefer, who is thought to have been a choir director and court overseer, was discovered in 1965 in a remarkable state of preservation. The wall scenes, as in all Egyptian tombs, are intended to be read from bottom to top and right to left. This banded composition is thought by some to be derived from the cylinder seals of Mesopotamian civilizations, but others argue that it reflects the terrain of Egypt, which is arrayed in bands parallel to the Nile and extending from the river's banks to the desert.

16

Photos, Ann Stewart Anderson

In any case, the bottom register or band in the general scene from the tomb of Nefer shows the trapping of wildfowl with nets, the preparation of the birds for cooking, the building of fires, and the washing of a pot. In the band above, cattle are led through a marsh in which tall papyrus stalks grow. Above this, wild birds fly from the papyrus thicket while two men carry bundles of heavy reed. They are obviously engaged in the process of transplanting, because they have wrapped the cumbersome roots that they struggle to lift. Each of these representations portrays for us across the centuries of time vivid aspects of everyday life in ancient Egypt. The same is true of the four detailed wall reliefs that are shown here.

The man carrying his catch of ducks on one end of his pole bends forward, straining slightly under the weight of his load. As he swings his shoulder forward to support it, he takes a step for balance. Surely the artist must have known a duck trapper who was middle-aged and slightly bald, as is this man.

Similarly, the scene of wine making shows four men trampling grapes with their bare feet. Working in a dancelike rhythm, they achieve balance by grasping the bar above the vat or holding each other about the waist. Should one doubt that the ancient Egyptians engaged in such activity, there is evidence that the chief vintner in modern times in Egypt always searched for traces of pharaonic vine roots when selecting a site for his vineyards.

And the last two details are likewise believable. Cattle have always

Wall scenes from the tomb of Nefer: stroking a cow (top) and washing a bowl in an irrigation canal.

17

(Top) Peter Clayton; (bottom) Hirmer Fotoarchiv, Munich

Hirmer Fotoarchiv, Munich

Limestone carvings from ancient Egypt include (top) the dwarf Seneb, a 4th-dynasty court official and his family, and (above) a woman making beer. At the right is a black diorite statue of King Chephren, builder of the second pyramid at Giza.

loomed large in importance as providers of milk, meat, and labor. The owner who stroked his beast in Nefer's day, thus encouraging it to eat, most assuredly has his modern counterpart. So too, the ancient Egyptian portrayed while scrubbing his bowl in an irrigation canal.

In addition to wall scenes such as those from Nefer's tomb, hundreds of carved and painted models provide information on commonplace activities and Egyptian sensitivities. The 12-inch limestone model of a woman making beer marvelously captures the action of pressing the mash. This clearly was a common endeavor in ancient Egypt, for currency was not used and various goods took its place. Accordingly, stonemasons, painters, and other workers were paid for their daily efforts in bread or vegetables—and beer.

The small model of the dwarf Seneb and his family seems best to illustrate personality traits among the ancient Egyptians. One cannot gaze upon this sculpture without sensing the tenderness and love that

18

Photos, Hirmer Fotoarchiv, Munich

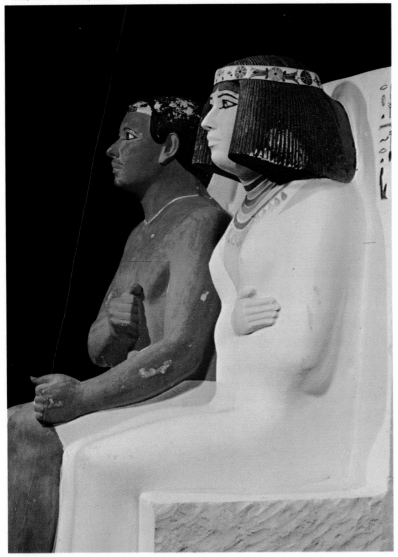

surely existed between Seneb and his wife. Her right arm behind Seneb, she gently clasps his shoulder while placing her other hand on his elbow. The positioning of her arms has been employed as a device to physically intertwine this couple for eternity. The artist's placement of their children beneath Seneb's figure adds to the harmony of the composition; they stand where a normal man's legs would have been and thus deemphasize Seneb's small physique.

Dwarfs were respected members of Egyptian society and were traditionally trusted as goldsmiths. Seneb was not a smith, however, but a court official of Cheops (Khufu), pharaoh in the 4th dynasty and builder of the Great Pyramid at Giza. The model shown here, carved from limestone at the end of his fortunate life, around 2560 BC, was found in Seneb's tomb.

Two final examples of Old Kingdom sculptures are the massive black diorite statues of King Chephren, builder of the second pyramid at Giza,

Painted limestone statues of Prince Ra Hotep and his wife Nofret demonstrate the ability of 4th-dynasty artists to make their works lifelike and individualistic.

19

Wooden model from the Middle Kingdom shows owner reviewing his cattle.

and the painted Ka statues of Prince Ra Hotep and his wife Nofret. The Ka statues, like all Egyptian sculptures, are remarkably lifelike and individualistic. The faces of Ra Hotep and Nofret, like those of Seneb and his wife, are quite distinctive and represent people who must have looked exactly as they are here depicted in stone. This realism is everywhere evident in ancient Egyptian art, though it is often combined with political and religious symbolism. This is, of course, particularly true when rulers were portrayed. The seated figure of King Chephren demonstrates this fact.

The sides of the king's throne exhibit the traditional symbols of the union of Upper and Lower Egypt. Stems of the lotus plant, symbolizing the kingdom of the south, are tied with that of the papyrus, symbol of the north. This image reinforces the fact that the pharaoh is the ruler of both lands, continuing in the tradition of King Menes.

Another symbol, one that makes this magnificent sculpture unique, is the elegant hawk which rests behind Chephren's head. Ancient mythology tells of the god Osiris, who, after having been murdered by his evil brother Seth, is restored to life by a loving wife, Isis, who then gives birth to their son, Horus. Eventually Osiris succumbs to death and retires to the next world to rule over the dead, leaving his son to reign in the domain of the living. Ancient Egyptians believed that the pharaoh was the earthly incarnation of Horus, and each ruler bore, as one of his

20

names, a "Horus name." Thus, a hawk, the animal form of Horus, stands on the high back of the royal throne, its wings enclosing the back of Chephren's head so that their tips end exactly at the edge of the royal headdress.

Middle Kingdom (*c.* 2040–1786 BC)

The Middle Kingdom includes the second half of the 11th dynasty and the 12th dynasty, under a succession of pharaohs, the most notable of whom was Sesostris III. Continued consolidation of political power, accompanied by armed forays to secure the kingdom's frontiers, led to a period of peace, prosperity, and a so-called golden age of culture under this ruler. The arts flourished, particularly literature and sculpture, monument building and construction works kept pace, and trade with the outside world became extensive.

The latter fact is demonstrated by the prevalence of wooden models among Middle Kingdom relicts. Logs for use in boatbuilding and other large works were imported from Lebanon. Models were sometimes carved from remnants, although native trees also served this purpose. The wooden model of a cattle review shown here is one of 24 discovered in the tomb of Meket-Re, a nobleman of Thebes in the 11th dynasty. Although somewhat imperfect in execution, it is the largest of those found, and again illustrates an important aspect of everyday ancient life, in the manner of the Old Kingdom tomb paintings described earlier.

Cattle raising was important in ancient Egypt, and it is estimated that one Old Kingdom herd numbered 1,300 animals. Periodically, the cattle had to be reviewed by the owner and the numbers recorded by a scribe for tax purposes. In this model, Meket-Re is accompanied by his son who sits to his left, resting one elbow on his knee. They are on the raised platform of a black pavilion. A tiny stairway leads up one side and four green-and-ocher-striped papyrus-bud columns support the roof, from which rainspouts protrude. Tiny wooden scribes sit on the platform in the traditional position, right legs resting on the floor. Against their raised left knees they prop white rolls of papyrus, which also are carved from wood. A stand in front of each scribe holds a case containing red and black ink. These were used by officials for writing.

The orderliness of the figures on the pavilion contrasts with the activity on the ground. Nineteen animals are led in review and some require restraint or gentle prodding. In the lower section each man moves individually and the cattle march irregularly, thus increasing the sense of action.

New Kingdom (*c.* 1567–1085 BC)

The New Kingdom includes the 18th, 19th, and 20th dynastic periods. The 18th was a continuation and expansion of the golden age of Sesostris III and other Middle Kingdom pharaohs, whereas, in marked contrast, the 20th dynastic period witnessed a considerable decline in Egyptian fortunes. Outstanding craftsmanship and literary activity

Kodansha Ltd.

Amenhotep II, an 18th-dynasty pharaoh, is suckled by the cow goddess Hathor.

occurred at the beginning of New Kingdom time, and world famous temples and tombs of this period ultimately were constructed at Luxor, Abu Simbel, and Karnak. Moreover, the military forces were expanded and improved, and notable victories were achieved in Libya, Palestine, and Syria during the 18th and 19th dynasties. Even into the 20th dynasty the Egyptians successfully repelled invading Sea Peoples, but by the end of New Kingdom time the frontiers had shrunk, the copper and turquoise mines in the Sinai had been lost, Libyan invaders appeared in Thebes, and increasing poverty among the inhabitants provoked widespread lawlessness and disorder. Tombs and royal temples were looted and pillaged and some works of art were lost forever.

The archaeological evidence for this history is abundant, but the decline of the New Kingdom will not be illustrated here because other aspects of this period virtually cry out for attention. The painted limestone Hathor cow, among the oldest of Egyptian deities, is one of these.

In the middle of the 18th dynasty a series of deaths led to doubt over rightful ascension to the throne. The issue was resolved when a young princess, Hatshepsut, seized power and became the ruling queen. This marked the only time that a woman had worn the double crown of the two kingdoms, and to prove her right to do so Hatshepsut resorted to a shrewd device. Claiming that she was directly descended from the great god Amon-Re, Hatshepsut had the legend of her mother's impregnation by the god carved on the walls of her temple at Dayr al-Bahri, and showed herself being suckled by the cow goddess Hathor.

22

Photos, Ann Stewart Anderson

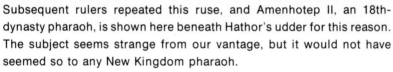

Subsequent rulers repeated this ruse, and Amenhotep II, an 18th-dynasty pharaoh, is shown here beneath Hathor's udder for this reason. The subject seems strange from our vantage, but it would not have seemed so to any New Kingdom pharaoh.

Religious beliefs during the 18th dynasty underwent a dramatic reversal during the reign of Amenhotep IV and, in fact, may well have brought about creation of the splendid funerary treasures of Tutankhamen, to be later described. Amenhotep IV, for reasons veiled by time, rejected the traditional religion of the preceding 17 dynasties. He changed his name to Akhenaton, and, with his wife Nefertiti and their daughters, abandoned the capital at Thebes and founded a new religion based on the solar disk. Akhenaton attempted to establish this form of monotheism throughout the realm, much to the dismay of the priests and traditionalists.

Change was reflected in art forms during this radical reign, as illustrated by relief carvings from the tomb of Ramose, an official under Akhenaton. Artists were encouraged to produce freer, rounded, and less stylized shapes in their depictions. The bending figure shown here accords with Egyptian art of this Amarna style, so named because the capital founded by Akhenaton is now known as Tell el-Amarna. Worthy of note is the absence of typical body fracturing that dominates Old and Middle Kingdom wall carvings; this man is shown with both shoulders forward, his hands on his knees, in a relatively natural position.

The tomb of Ramose also contains some of the finest hieroglyphic

Bending figure (left) from the tomb of Ramose shows the influence in Egyptian art of the Amarna style, which was marked by freer and more rounded shapes. Hieroglyphic carvings (above) are also from the tomb of Ramose.

23

Courtesy, Metropolitan Museum of Art, N.Y.; photos, Lee Boltin

(Top) The throne of Tutankhamen was carved from wood and coated with gold. (Below) On Tutankhamen's gold-stamped leather sandals are ancient Egypt's traditional enemies, the Asians and the Nubians.

carving in the Theban necropolis. The intricately detailed figures shown here are not only aesthetically pleasing but, as deduced by Champollion, they also record a message for succeeding generations, one that is imperishable and unchanging.

Religious beliefs die hard, and though Akhenaton did much to undermine worship of the traditional deities, the old cult of Amon was revived at Thebes within four years of the pharaoh's death. It was the boy-king Tutankhamen, pharaoh from 1361 to 1352 BC, who restored orthodoxy and returned the capital to Thebes. Some scholars argue that the richness of his tomb reflects principally the gratitude of the priests, for Tutankhamen was not one of the most powerful or eminent pharaohs.

The tomb of Tutankhamen was discovered by Howard Carter, an English archaeologist, in 1922 and the find ranks with the most splendid ever unearthed. After Carter and his team had excavated 16 steps and a corridor, they found a door fastened with a seal that bore Tutankhamen's name. A hole was dug through the door, and when Carter looked into the tomb, in his own words:

> At first I could see nothing, the hot air escaping from the chamber causing the candle flame to flicker, but presently, as my eyes grew accustomed to the light, details of the room within emerged slowly from the mist, strange animals, statues, and gold—everywhere the glint of gold. For the

24

moment—an eternity it must have seemed to the others standing by—I was struck dumb with amazement, and when Lord Carnarvon, unable to stand the suspense any longer, inquired anxiously, "Can you see anything?" it was all I could do to get out the words, "Yes, wonderful things."

Perhaps the most wonderful of the treasures found by Carter, all of which are housed in the Egyptian Museum in Cairo, is the royal throne. Carved from wood, coated with gold, and decorated with faience, glass, stones, and silver, it exemplifies the magnificent mastery of material and concept and the ability to combine all elements into perfect harmony that characterize Egyptian art at its best.

On the back, the king is shown seated on a chair, one hand resting lightly on his knee. He is faced by his wife, the third daughter of Akhenaton, who touches her husband lightly on the shoulder. Their relaxed positions, the scarves which flutter in the air, and the emphasis on curving forms indicate that the style followed was that prevalent in the court of Akhenaton. Above the couple, the solar disk, worshiped by their heretical ancestor, sends down its blessing rays. The royal names are written in their traditional Amon form, but the use of Akhenaton's solar symbol makes this throne a significant as well as elegant work.

The linkage of symbolism with practical objects is also illustrated by the king's sandals. The Egyptians believed that enemies would be trampled if representations of them were placed beneath the feet of the pharaoh. Tutankhamen's gold-stamped leather sandals show such enemies bound back to back. The Asian wears a pointed beard and the Nubian is shown in a loincloth.

Carter thought that the painted chest found in the tomb constituted the single greatest artistic treasure. Made from wood, its white gesso surface polished to resemble ivory, it presents scenes of battles with traditional enemies, again Asians and Nubians, and hunting episodes involving the king. The chest contained an assortment of sandals and garments, among which was a child's robe bearing the royal cartouche. This reflects Tutankhamen's youth at the time of his coronation.

The ancient Egyptians were sailors of some skill, and they traveled the length of the Nile by boat from earliest times. They believed that access to the next world was by boat and commonly included ship models in tombs to assure the deceased of transportation.

Several model boats were found in Tutankhamen's tomb, each so placed that the bow faced west, toward the setting sun and the netherworld. The graceful funeral boat shown here is constructed of wood and has a linen sail and rigging. On deck are two golden pavilions bearing silhouettes of animals, a sphinx on the bow and a bull in the stern. The two white stern paddles are lashed with ropes and are topped with curious gilded heads. Oars and paddles seem to have had particular significance for the Egyptians. Carter discovered full-sized magic oars in the burial chamber and concluded that their purpose was to ferry the king's bark across the waters to the next world.

Egyptian jewelry was not created for ornamentation as such but for symbolic or magical reasons. Predynastic Egyptians wore amulets

Peter Clayton

Model boats displayed in the Egyptian Museum are believed to be replicas of those that sailed the Nile during the reign of Tutankhamen.

25

Courtesy, Metropolitan Museum of Art, N.Y.; photo, Lee Boltin

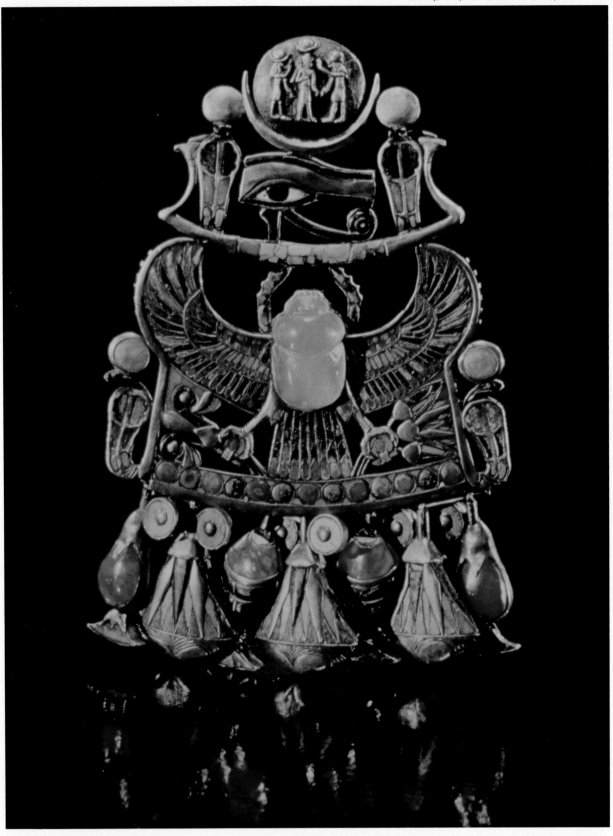

Peter Clayton

around their necks to ensure protection and fertility, and the elaborate pectorals, or chest pendants, worn by the pharaohs were outgrowths of this practice. The pectoral shown here from the tomb of Tutankhamen was part of his coronation regalia and is particularly rich in symbolic meaning.

Across the bottom of this pendant are three open lotus blossoms symbolizing the kingdom of the south, and its inclusion in this piece emphasized the pharaoh's sovereignty over that region. Above a row of 13 blue and red disks is a chalcedony scarab with falcon wings, tail, and claws. Thus two of the strongest symbols of ancient Egypt are united: the scarab, Kaphre, who pushes the solar disk across the morning sky in order to bring life, and the vulture, who spreads its protective wings over god and mortal alike. Flanking the scarab and integrated with the vulture wings are two sacred cobras that bear the disk of the Sun on their heads.

Normally, the scarab would be depicted pushing the Sun. But here, the solar disk has been replaced by a symbolic representation of the

Pectoral or chest pendant (opposite page), worn by the pharaohs to ensure protection and fertility, was found in the tomb of Tutankhamen. Stag circlet (left) belonged to a princess of the 18th dynasty.

27

Courtesy, Metropolitan Museum of Art, N.Y.; photo, Lee Boltin

Kodansha Ltd.

Selket (opposite page), one of the four goddesses whose figures were placed in Tutankhamen's tomb to guard the pharaoh's viscera in the canopic chest, stands in an attitude of protection. On her head is her emblem, the scorpion. The canopic chest is at the left. (Below) A life-sized wooden statue of Tutankhamen, covered with black resin and partly gilded; the statue was one of two that stood guard on each side of the entrance to the burial chamber.

Sun and the Moon. Upon the deep blue lunar orb Tutankhamen is shown with the Sun disk and Moon crescent above his head. To his right stands the Moon god, Thoth, in the form of an ibis, and to his left is Horus, his head mounted by his emblem, the Sun.

The materials used in Tutankhamen's pectoral include carnelian, calcite, lapis lazuli, turquoise, and obsidian, combined with variously colored glass and set in gold and silver. The pectoral exemplifies not only the craftsmanship of the ancient jewelers but also the essential amuletic purposes of the adornment of the pharaohs.

By way of contrast, the magnificent stag circlet of a princess of the 18th dynasty betrays probable foreign influences. Despite the supreme beauty of the piece it fails to relate to any known Egyptian symbols, and, in fact, the stag was not native to the region.

Other wonders from Tutankhamen's tomb clearly must include the standing guardian figures, placed as sentinels before the burial room; the canopic chest, containing the pharaoh's viscera; and the Anubis shrine, guardian of the mummy and portrayed as a recumbent jackal. Most widely known, however, are the golden sarcophagus and death mask of the young king.

The sarcophagus weighs more than one ton and is the largest gold object ever created. It is embellished and decorated with various symbols and gods, such as the two sisters Isis and Nephthys at the legs.

Hirmer Fotoarchiv, Munich

Courtesy, Metropolitan Museum of Art, N.Y.; photo, Lee Boltin

Hirmer Fotoarchiv, Munich

According to myth, Isis used her wings to fan the breath of life into her husband, Osiris, and thus revive him. The presence of these lovely golden goddesses with wings outstretched assured enduring life to the deceased king.

The death mask of Tutankhamen is the most beautiful funerary relic known, and it is, in effect, the portrait by which this pharaoh is best identified. So exact is the mask that it has been used by scholars attempting to prove the blood relationship between Akhenaton and Tutankhamen. But the work principally reflects the Egyptians' religious belief about death and seemingly conveys their placid acceptance of the concept of eternity.

The last of the pharaohs to be considered here is Ramses II, who, like Tutankhamen and Cleopatra, is one of the best-known figures of ancient Egypt. He undertook prodigious monument building throughout the region, erecting temples dedicated to himself and to his wife, Nefertari, between the Nile Delta and the Nubian border. He was active in war but ultimately was forced to conclude a treaty of peace with the Hittites, ending a stalemate. Following his reign, Ramses III ascended to the throne in 1198 BC and became the last of the great pharaohs. He gained some brilliant victories over the Libyans and Sea Peoples, but upon his death around 1166 BC the assortment of evils that accompanied the end of the New Kingdom came to pass.

It is perhaps fitting to represent the reign of Ramses II by means of his mummy. The process of mummification was an essential part of the funerary rites of pharaohs and notables, and embalmers were an important professional group in ancient Egypt. These men performed 13 processes over a period of 70 days to assure the preservation of the flesh. Ramses II and his fellow pharaohs from the Valley of the Tombs of the Kings now rest peacefully in simple wooden boxes in a gallery of the Egyptian Museum. They bear mute testimony to the skill of their embalmers—and to the reality of that great civilization that flourished along the Nile from the beginning of recorded time.

Funerary mask of Tutankhamen (opposite page), made of beaten and burnished solid gold, was placed directly over the bandaged face of the mummy. (Above) Anubis, the god of the dead, in the form of a jackal crouches on a gilded chest containing jewelry and amulets. (Below) A portion of the mummy of Ramses II.

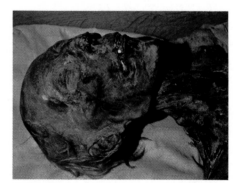

SIPA/Black Star

Primitive Navigation and the Settlement of Polynesia

by Thor Heyerdahl

Ocean crossings on a balsa raft and in reed boats along with a study of the prevailing winds and currents provide support for the theory that the Pacific islands of Polynesia were settled by explorers sailing westward from the Americas.

© Horst Munzig—Woodfin Camp

Modeled after the earliest known ships, "Ra I" (overleaf) was built near Egypt's ancient pyramids from bundles of papyrus stalks. On the opposite page are the paddles (top left) used in the boat and steps in its construction (center left and top right). The vessel is readied for its journey to the sea (bottom). Thor Heyerdahl and a small crew sailed "Ra I" part of the way across the Atlantic Ocean in 1969.

THOR HEYERDAHL *is an ethnologist and adventurer who organized and led the "Kon-Tiki" and "Ra" expeditions to prove the possibility of transoceanic contacts between ancient civilizations. His books include* Kon-Tiki; Aku-Aku: The Secret of Easter Island; *and* The Ra Expeditions. *A member of the Norwegian Academy of Sciences, Heyerdahl is chairman of the board of the Kon-Tiki Museum in Oslo.*

There was a time when a scholar could be referred to as an anthropologist and one would know what his profession was. Not so today. One anthropologist may study human blood groups, while another may be a linguist or an archaeologist. Anthropology has, indeed, become so vast in scope that it covers anything man is and does, was and did, anywhere at any time. Even subgroups within the discipline are splitting up, and an archaeologist whose field is Hittite culture in the Middle East knows little more than a layman about the archaeology of the Olmec culture in Mexico. As each specialist picks his restricted field, certain topics are bound to receive comparatively little attention. One of these is primitive navigation.

In view of its paramount importance to the understanding of cultural relations, it is surprising that primitive navigation has not been studied extensively. The fact that the navigation is primitive does not mean that the topic is so elementary that one can cope with it through intuition and surmises. Other aspects of primitive culture, whether arrowheads, potsherds, or flint scrapers, are cautiously investigated by scholars, yet important early watercraft such as papyrus boats and balsa rafts have erroneously been deemed not seaworthy for lack of adequate research. Whereas scientists carefully avoid transgressions into other specialists' domains, the field of primitive navigation has remained a scientific no-man's-land where any scholar feels free to express his opinion.

Most people are prejudiced in their ideas about the ocean and what is needed to cross it. They are brought up to believe that security at sea increases with the size of the vessel and the height of the deck above sea level; that a craft with a watertight hull is safer than one with a wash-through bottom; that it is safer to hug the continental coast than to venture into the open ocean; that the mileage across the sea can be measured directly on a map like mileage on land; and that survival empty-handed in the ocean is a greater hazard than in the wilderness ashore. None of these beliefs is true, and the present writer had to sail ocean voyages in many types of small craft before he was able to perceive fully how far the modern concepts of security at sea are removed from reality.

What is seaworthy?

It is a popular belief that early man after crossing rivers astride a log got the idea of scooping out the trunk to sit dry in a dugout canoe and that by next adding planks to the hull he developed the first ships. This is a truth with modifications. Simple reed floats and plain canoes undoubtedly go back to the earliest period of human inventions. However, the earliest known ships were not built from wood but from bundles of papyrus stalks. In fact, sophisticated reed ships are familiar motifs among the pre-dynastic petroglyphs in Egypt, and are also elaborately depicted on the oldest Sumerian cylinder seals. The pre-dynastic Egyptian papyrus ships are often shown with mast and sail, one or two cabins on deck, and even livestock on board, indicating considerable size. One of them is shown being pulled up the river by thirty people.

34

(Photos) © Horst Munzig—Woodfin Camp

Courtesy, Kon-Tiki Museum

The reed boat "Ra II" was sailed across the Atlantic Ocean from Morocco to Barbados by Heyerdahl and a crew in 1970.

Not until the times of the pharaohs, after 3000 BC, does one find the first evidence of wooden ships, which then appeared side by side with the earlier reed boats. With the papyrus vessel as a clear prototype, the boat builders of the inner Mediterranean began splitting timber to construct plank ships. The oldest known examples are the entombed Nile vessel of the pharaoh Khufu (Cheops) and the first sailing ships depicted in Hittite and Phoenician art. These early forerunners of Greek and Roman ships were all papyroform; that is, although timbered by

36

carpenters, they closely followed the conventionalized lines of the earlier papyrus vessel with its sickle shape and lofty, often encurved stern terminating in a symbolic papyrus flower.

Reed vessels and canoes continued to flourish side by side in all continents until modern times. The oceangoing canoe reached its most impressive dimensions among the American Northwest Coast Indians and the Polynesians, who each constructed vessels in which up to one hundred men could travel. Both of these peoples sometimes sewed on sideplanks to enlarge the dugout hull, but nowhere is there evidence of dugout canoes developing into ships with plank-covered ribs.

Medieval Europe preferred to adopt the principle of the watertight

Rock carvings found in Scandinavia, dating from the first and second millennia BC, depict boats with a sickle shape similar to that of the ancient Egyptian reed craft (bottom).

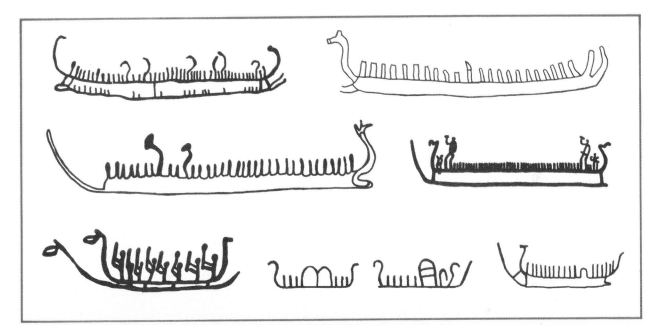

(Drawings) from Philip Banbury, *Man and the Sea: From the Ice Age to the Norman Conquest,* © 1975; (photo) Collection Bibliovisuelle

Courtesy, Kon-Tiki Museum

hull, not only because of the local shortage of suitable reeds but also because a hardwood ship had far superior longevity, went faster, and could easily be pulled ashore for maintenance and repair. Admitting this, however, one should not forget that the ancient reed ships were at least equal to hardwood vessels in carrying capacity, as well as being much steadier and greatly superior in security at sea. Pharaoh Khufu's spectacular wooden ship, in spite of perfect maritime lines borrowed from the reed ships, would break and sink had it left the Nile for the Mediterranean, and even Phoenician and Viking ships were threatened by breaking seas and cracking planks in storms or shallows, and would sink if bailing failed.

No bailing was needed on a reed boat or a balsa raft; entering water runs out through the bottom and leaves the vessel on top of the waves as before. The compact body, shallow draft, and flexibility of such craft permit them to float like seabirds in any storm, to venture among shoals and shallows, and to manage crash landings on reefs and coasts which no hulled vessel could approach. These advantages explain why the mariners of the advanced civilizations of ancient Peru preferred reed boats and balsa rafts in the open sea, even though they knew about hulls and used them on rivers.

The "Kon-Tiki" (above) is a balsa raft on which Heyerdahl and a small crew sailed from the Pacific coast of South America to Polynesia in 1947. The leather boat in which St. Brendan is said to have sailed from Ireland to the Canary Islands in the 6th century AD is re-created (right). (Opposite page) Map of the Pacific Ocean shows the prevailing currents and countercurrents.

Homer Sykes—© Daily Telegraph Magazine/Woodfin Camp

Because an ocean liner is safer than a small lifeboat, the common conclusion is that safety at sea increases with the size of the vessel. This is not always true. Testings of primitive craft have shown that it is a great advantage for a vessel to be small enough to move freely and tackle the waves one at a time. If a vessel is long enough to bridge two wave crests, it may crack through strain or be filled as one wave bursts onboard while another is tilting up the opposite end of the boat. From experience the writer has learned that a primitive craft less than thirty feet long is able to ride the ocean swells drier and with greater ease than longer vessels.

Winds and currents

Even more misleading is the common assumption that navigation is safe as long as the primitive voyager can hug a continental coastline. Unless it refers to sheltered ports and inlets, this belief is unjustified. Dangers diminish with the distance from land. Nowhere are the oceans more treacherous to a primitive navigator than near coasts and shallows. Nowhere do the seas dig up steeper, more ferocious waves than where ocean rollers meet backwash from cliffs and increase in chaotic interference with tides and deflected currents. In the mid-ocean there are no obstacles to interfere with the progress of either waves or watercraft; the swells, therefore, are drawn long and regular, and perils of wreckage are at minimum. The only imminent danger during the Pacific

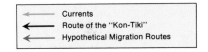

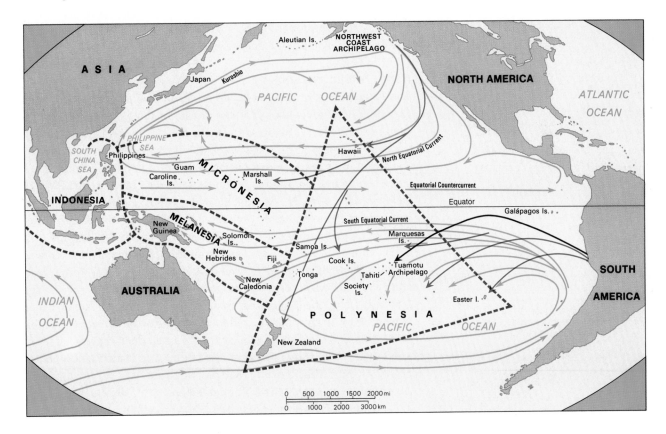

crossing with the balsa raft "Kon-Tiki" occurred when the voyagers came within sight of reefs and islands inside Polynesia. In the two Atlantic crossings with the reed boats "Ra I" and "Ra II" the crew felt a profound relief when, after sailing some 600 miles along the threatening coast of North Africa, they finally headed into the long and regular swells of the open Atlantic.

A fundamental difference between land and sea travel is that at sea the speed of the watercraft determines the distance to be overcome to get from one point to another. For example, the distance from Peru to the Tuamotu Islands is 4,000 miles when measured on any map, but after traveling only about 1,000 miles the slow-moving "Kon-Tiki" raft had already completed the entire crossing. The reason was that the ocean surface had displaced itself by about 3,000 miles in the direction of travel during the 101 days of the voyage. If a primitive vessel had been able to return to Peru in a straight line with the same speed, it would therefore have had to cover 7,000 miles of moving surface. In addition, because the permanent trade winds blow along with the west-bound current the Peru-bound vessel would have had to tack in a zig-zag course, thus adding another couple of thousand miles to the voyage. To a fast-moving ocean liner the actual traveling distance between Peru and Polynesia is almost the same in both directions, but to a raft or canoe the distance is about nine times longer one way than the other, depending upon the speed of the vessel. Thus, Pacific Ocean distances are highly deceptive on a map, a factor that is commonly overlooked even though it had a decisive influence on European discoveries in Polynesia, Melanesia, and Micronesia.

Early Pacific voyages

The Asian coasts of the Pacific were known to Europeans more than two centuries before the American coasts of the same ocean. Marco Polo reached the coasts of China and Indonesia in the 1290s, whereas Vasco Núñez de Balboa first saw the Pacific from the American side in 1513. Yet, in spite of the early establishment of important Portuguese and Spanish trading ports in Indonesia, not a single European vessel sailed into the open Pacific from that side; winds and currents repelled all attempts. But soon after Christopher Columbus led the Europeans to America the natural gateway to the Pacific was open. Even the part of Oceania nearest Asia was discovered from America. In 1521 Guam, flanking the Philippine Sea and yet unknown to the nearby Portuguese and Japanese, was found by Ferdinand Magellan coming from South America. Next, the Spaniards crossed the Isthmus of Panama and reached Peru, where they experienced the seaworthiness of the Inca balsa rafts and learned of islands said to be inhabited by black men, which fleets of Inca merchants and explorers had visited far out in the ocean. Álvaro de Mendaña de Neira set out from Peru to look for these islands and discovered the Solomon Islands in Melanesia in 1567. He had bypassed Polynesia, which he discovered when he reached the Marquesas group on a second voyage, also from Peru, in 1595.

40

Loren McIntyre—Woodfin Camp

These initial discoveries of Micronesia, Melanesia, and Polynesia opened a 200-year period of Pacific exploration, always with entry from the American side and with exit in Indonesia. The Tuamotu Archipelago and the New Hebrides (1606), the Tonga Islands (1616), Easter Island (1722), the Cook Islands (1765), and Tahiti and the Society Islands (1767) were all hit upon by Europeans sailing from South America.

For 500 years, from Marco Polo's travels in the 1290s to Capt. James Cook's voyages in the 1770s, nature alone determined all European movements in the South Pacific. The extremely strong and permanent trade winds accompanied from America by the mighty and fast-floating North and South Equatorial currents were too powerful to be outwitted until the coming of truly modern sailing ships. Embracing all the South Pacific island groups in its broad sweep, the South Equatorial current, also known as the Humboldt or Peru Current, sweeps up the South American coast and turns westward south of the Galápagos group toward all of Polynesia and Melanesia. Correspondingly, the North Equatorial Current, in another wide belt north of the Equator, flows down the North American coast and sweeps westward from Mexico straight across the Pacific to the Philippine Sea, embracing all of Micronesia en route.

Between these two westward-moving giants, which dominate all the tropic and temperate Pacific, lies a belt of doldrums with confused

Reed boats similar to those used during the time of the Incas still provide transportation on Lake Titicaca, which straddles the border of Bolivia and Peru. "Ra II" was built by boatmakers from this area.

41

eddies and upwellings, often given the misleading name of the Equatorial Countercurrent. In reality it is no continuous current at all, and the doldrums were more dreaded than helpful to sailors no matter where they wanted to go.

In 1527 Hernán Cortés, Mexico's conqueror, ordered an expedition to sail from Mexico to the Philippines, which it did. When the expedition was ordered to return, it tried in vain for two years to reenter the Pacific, but wind and current always forced the vessels back to Indonesia. These and subsequent attempts to enter Oceania from Indonesia failed, and America could only be reached by Europeans sailing westward across the Atlantic.

Not until 1565 did Andrés de Urdaneta discover that by sailing northward along Japan he would get favorable winds and currents back to America in the high latitudes below the Aleutian Island chain. This opened the so-called caravel route followed by all Spanish and Portuguese sailing vessels for over two centuries: westward from Mexico to Indonesia in the sweep of the North Equatorial Current and eastward back again by means of the Japan Current (Kuroshio) high above Hawaii. Even the two Mendaña expeditions with their South Pacific home port in Peru, upon discovering Melanesia and Polynesia, had to return to South America by the far northern route between the Aleutian Islands and Hawaii.

Origins of the Polynesians: migration theories

In these days of engine travel the hard lessons of five centuries of Pacific exploration are too easily overlooked by theorists island-hopping on maps. As a logical consequence of the erroneous assumption that the reed boats and balsa rafts of South America were not seaworthy, investigators turned all their attention to Southeast Asia in a search for possible embarkation points for the different peoples of the Pacific islands. Because at least one component in the composite Polynesian stock appeared to have primary roots in that general area, straight and crooked lines were drawn from Indonesia to any distant corner of the Pacific to postulate hypothetical migration routes.

The first to put these theories to a practical test was the French navigator Eric de Bisschop prior to World War II. He attempted to sail a Chinese junk from Indonesia to Polynesia, but gave up after three years of futile effort without even reaching Micronesia and concluded that such a migration route by primitive craft was inconceivable. He next sailed a canoe with the greatest ease in the opposite direction, from Polynesia to Indonesia. In 1947 the "Kon-Tiki" raft sailed with equal ease from Peru to Polynesia, and since then no fewer than 13 manned rafts have left South America, all of them reaching islands in Oceania. Two landed in the Galápagos group, and all the others reached Polynesia; five balsa rafts passed both Polynesia and Melanesia, and continued across the Pacific to Australia.

Challenged by this excessive demonstration of feasible South American influence in Oceania, the supporters of the orthodox migration

Steve McCutcheon

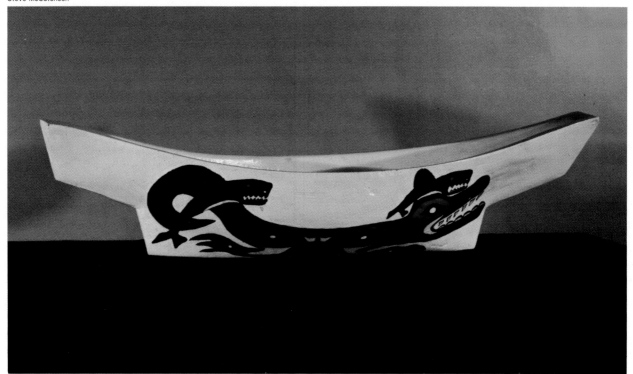

theory sponsored in 1947 an elaborate attempt to sail a primitive craft in the opposite direction, from Southeast Asia across the Pacific. A Vienna anthropologist, Kuno Knöbl, built an authentic Asian junk after a ceramic model from the first century AD, and sailed into the Pacific from the China Sea. The junk, named "Tai Ki," could no more resist the combined forces of wind and current than could the early caravels and was helplessly dragged northward along the coast of Japan. The plank-built vessel then began to sink as the hull was drilled through by Pacific boring worms. In the extreme North Pacific, the crew sent an SOS and were rescued by aircraft, and the abandoned wreck was subsequently observed drifting off the coast of Alaska.

The evidence of these experiments points to the Northwest Coast of America, *i.e.*, the continental archipelago of British Columbia—and not the tropic island belt—as the geographical threshold to the New World for Asian seafarers. From this threshold the winds and currents of the North Pacific turn directly down upon Hawaii in northern Polynesia in the same way that elements in the South Pacific deflect from Peru to all the islands south of the Equator. Early explorers found large canoes in Hawaii which were carved from pine trees that had drifted from the Northwest American coast, and the feasibility of a corresponding canoe voyage was shown half a century ago by Capt. J. C. Voss, who sailed a Northwest Coast Indian canoe directly from Vancouver Island to central Polynesia.

It has been argued that the original settlers of Polynesia might have been castaways driven there by storms that occasionally blow contrary to prevailing winds. Recently, a computer simulation testing these

Replica of a war canoe built from a solid log; such a boat was typical of oceangoing craft of the Indians on the Northwest Coast of North America. The painted ornamentation resembles that on similar canoes in Polynesia.

43

theories of accidental drifts was carried out by M. Levison, R. G. Ward, and J. W. Webb. More than 100,000 simulated Pacific drifts and over 8,000 guided voyages were run through computers. The result showed that the chance of drifts to Polynesia was nil, not only from Asia but also from any part of nearby Micronesia. The computer study otherwise confirmed what was already known from experience: voyagers from South America need only turn their stern to the wind and the chance of landing in Polynesia is indisputable. If drifts were made from North America, the Northwest Coast archipelago was found to be the most favorable starting point.

A further problem in all attempts to trace Asian migration routes to Polynesia is that the intervening 4,000-mile-wide Micronesian-Melanesian territory shows only archaeologic and linguistic evidence of some late Polynesian arrivals from the opposite direction — from Polynesia. In spite of a century of scholarly research no traces have been found of any passage through Micronesia and Melanesia of proto-Polynesians from Asia, whereas racial and cultural evidence precluding such transit have been demonstrated in abundance. These admitted obstacles have been thought overcome by those who have proposed that perhaps the Polynesians passed through the intervening area so fast that they left no traces. Others, refusing to believe in nonstop Asian sailings through the 4,000-mile-wide region, have postulated that the Polynesians never lived in Asia at all but developed locally in the marginal area of their present domain.

Polynesian-Northwest Coast Indian similarities

All such speculations, however, collide with existing physiological and genetic evidence. The Polynesians have always been known to contrast with the Indonesians in physical appearance, having an extremely tall body build, long heads, relatively fair skin, beard and body hair, tendency to narrow and aquiline nose, thin lips, and sometimes fine and wavy hair. All of these features are rare or absent in the Pacific basin, with the marked exception of the island population of Northwest America. In recent years geneticists have also shown that the Polynesian blood groups differ from those of the Indonesians, Micronesians, and Melanesians, whereas they closely resemble those of the Northwest Coast Indians.

Inside Polynesia the many analogies to the Northwest Coast Indians have been particularly noticeable in New Zealand. There, the Maori isolated themselves in the early settlement period, missing the cultural impulses that subsequently diffused into Polynesia from the nearby Melanesians on Fiji. Such secondary Polynesian acquisitions as the Melanesian pig, the chicken, and the outrigger thus never reached any Maori tribe. The Maori deep-sea canoe closely followed the Northwest American type, without outrigger, oarlocks, or keel, and lashed together as a double canoe in case of ocean voyages; it had no permanent mast, being equipped instead with a clumsy matting sail that was only hoisted before the wind. The canoes of both regions had separate

44

Nicholas deVore III—Bruce Coleman Inc.

The 60-foot twin-hulled sailing canoe "Hokuleʻa," reconstructed from sketches of similar craft made by Capt. James Cook and others in the 1700s, successfully journeyed 3,000 nautical miles from Hawaii to Tahiti in 1976. The voyage supported the belief that ancient Polynesians could have made the journey.

bow and stern pieces sewed on and ornamented with carvings, paint, and inlays of abalone shell. Strong resemblances have also been pointed out between the forts of the two areas, the peculiar plank houses with an ancestor figure often straddling the door, the carved posts with superimposed figures raised in the open, the bark blankets that served both as clothing and as the local currency, and the tools and other implements. Investigators also noted similarities in religion and tribal organization.

If one were to pick out the truly pan-Polynesian culture elements on which the Polynesian ancestors must have based their subsistence

45

(Photos courtesy, top) Hutchinson et al., 1906; (bottom) American Museum of Natural History

Strong facial resemblances can be seen between the Polynesians and the Indians from the Northwest Coast of North America. At the top, above, is a Maori from New Zealand, and below is a Nitinat Indian from the Northwest Coast. On the opposite page, a Polynesian from the Marquesas Islands (top) is paired with a Northwest Coast Indian.

prior to their dispersal over the islands, it would be the aforesaid canoe, three basic types of fishhooks, the elbow adze, the poi pounder, the bark beater, and the earth oven. The art of fishing with hook and line was unknown in Southeast Asia and Indonesia, and the origin of the Polynesian fishhook must be sought elsewhere. It has long been pointed out that both the Polynesian one-piece encurved shell hook and the highly specialized composite hook with stone shank and bone barb were present in South America long before they existed in Oceania, but only recently have archaeologists discovered that the same peculiar stone-shanked hook belonged to the Northwest Coast archipelago as well. The Northwest Coast Indians were also the only extra-Oceanic people to make use of the third type of fishhook found in Polynesia; this was the forked wooden ruvettus or halibut hook with bone barb.

Archaeologists have shown that prototypes of the Polynesian polished stone adze blades occur in very early remains from the Philippines and continental Southeast Asia, while completely alien forms dominated the intervening territories of Melanesia and Micronesia. The same special forms of elbow adzes and blades had found their way from early Southeast Asia to Northwest America, where they were the principal tool of the coast Indians.

The typical food-preparing implements of Polynesia, considered the apogee of Pacific island stone-shaping art, are the three conventional and beautifully executed types of polished poi pounders: the bell-shaped type with a tall, slender handle terminating in a disk or bulb; the T-shaped type, with a horizontal grip and upturned ears; and the less common D-shaped variety. All three reappear as the principal food-preparing tool among the Northwest Coast Indians. The American form has a flat and the Polynesian a slightly convex base, but evolutionary forms ranging from the former (pestle) to the latter (pounder) have been found in Hawaii.

The Polynesian custom of beating the inner bark of trees with grooved wooden or whalebone mallets for the manufacture of bark cloth reflects the islanders' peculiar ignorance of the loom. Their universal custom of baking their food in stone-lined underground earth ovens is a consequence of their equally puzzling ignorance of pottery making. From early Neolithic times the loom and pottery were familiar culture traits among all but the most isolated and backward tribes in the circum-Pacific area. The only striking exception outside Polynesia was the entire area of the Northwest American coast, where the otherwise highly inventive Indians produced bark cloth with the same kinds of wooden and whalebone mallets as in Polynesia and baked their food in the same kind of earth oven. The inner bark of breadfruit and paper mulberry trees of the tropic islands was turned into coherent tapa cloth by the mere beating in layers, but that of New Zealand and Northwest American forest trees split into fibres that had to be united through "finger-weaving." Captain Cook pointed out that the making of bark cloth was exactly the same in New Zealand as on the Northwest Ameri-

46

(Photos) Bottom, courtesy, American Museum of Natural History; top, Thor Heyerdahl

can coast, and subsequent museum investigators have found bark cloaks from the two areas to be so alike that they could be distinguished only upon close inspection.

Whereas race and culture unconditionally conform with geographical considerations in suggesting the Northwest American Coast Indians as the missing link between the early Asian mariners and the Polynesians, linguistic evidence pinpoints no route. The long-sought Malayo-Polynesian relationship in languages has upon thorough study been found too indistinct and diffused to indicate any area of contact, a fact that has permitted some modern linguists to propose the theory of Polynesian micro-evolution on the Polynesian side of the Micronesian-Melanesian buffer territory. Others have proposed that the Malay and Polynesian languages must have separated at an extremely early period, while the parental stocks still lived in continental Asia, after which the Malays and Polynesians followed entirely different migration routes to their respective island domains. Either of these theories would be compatible with a Polynesian sailing route by way of Northwest America, especially since it is generally accepted that the Northwest Coast Indians must have had their parental home in coastal Asia.

Many scholars have attempted to show a common origin for the Northwest Coast Indian and Oceanic languages. However, although all the tribes in the mountain-girt valleys and severed islands of the Northwest American coast maintained their own common and distinctive stamp in race and culture, they managed to alter their speech so drastically that even neighboring tribes spoke quite different languages. This is assumed to be partly due to the local custom of word taboo and partly to centuries of close contact with adjacent continental tribes. It is, at any rate, not surprising if the Polynesians in their island isolation have maintained more of the Asian linguistic roots than have any semi-continental tribe.

The Pacific curves. It covers half the globe, and the equatorial line between the coasts of Southeast Asia and South America arches as a complete semicircle. It is our medieval concept of a flat earth that survives when we look at a map and speak of the Equator as the "straight line" across the Pacific. A wire that is bent across the globe from Indonesia to South America can be twisted freely with its midpoint touching Alaska, and this is the route that primitive ocean travelers followed.

Antiquity of Man in Africa
by Bernard Wood

Discoveries in eastern and southern Africa indicate that ancestors of modern man lived in those regions as long ago as 3,750,000 years.

© National Geographic Society, photos by David Brill

When only half a jaw is found, a mirror is used (above) to reveal the shape of the whole bone. Geologist James Aronson (right) uses equipment to release atoms of argon from Ethiopian volcanic rock in order to date the rock. Aronson measures the argon that has accumulated in the rock as a result of the radioactive decay of potassium and is therefore able to determine the dates of volcanic eruptions that formed the rock. This in turn places age limits on fossils deposited above and below the rock.

BERNARD WOOD *is Senior Lecturer in the Department of Anatomy at the Middlesex Hospital Medical School in London.*

(Overleaf) Painting by Eraldo Carugati

During recent years Africa has been the focus of interest for all who study human origins. This is not to say that important progress has not been made elsewhere, but the sheer volume of fossil evidence found in Africa cannot be matched in any other continent. During the past ten years nearly 600 fossil hominid specimens have been recovered from sites in southern and eastern Africa, and more limited but significant progress has been made at sites in the northern part of the continent.

Important advances have also been made in the ways scientists use the rich fossil and archaeological evidence. Archaeologists, geologists, and paleontologists have combined their attempts to investigate the biological context of the hominids, the bipedal primate ancestors of modern man. Where did they live? What did they eat? Did they live in family groups? How far could they travel? By amalgamating evidence from existing hunter-gatherer societies with information from the sites of the fossils, scientists are slowly accumulating knowledge of early hominid subsistence patterns and societies. Advances have also been made in geochronology (the science of dating rocks) and in the ability of geologists to reconstruct the paleoenvironment. Potassium-argon, argon-40/argon-39, fission-track, and magnetic dating methods allow scientists to date rocks at the fossil sites without having to rely on the fossils themselves.

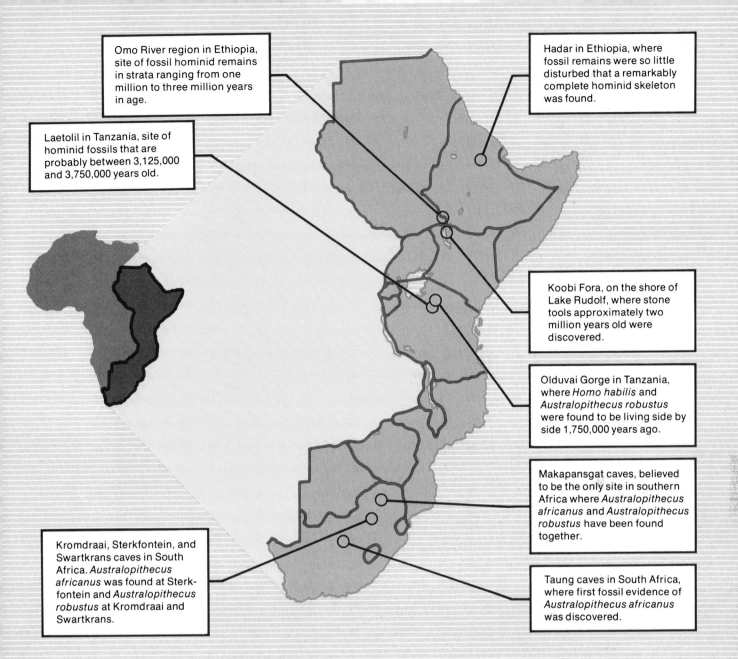

Omo River region in Ethiopia, site of fossil hominid remains in strata ranging from one million to three million years in age.

Hadar in Ethiopia, where fossil remains were so little disturbed that a remarkably complete hominid skeleton was found.

Laetolil in Tanzania, site of hominid fossils that are probably between 3,125,000 and 3,750,000 years old.

Koobi Fora, on the shore of Lake Rudolf, where stone tools approximately two million years old were discovered.

Olduvai Gorge in Tanzania, where *Homo habilis* and *Australopithecus robustus* were found to be living side by side 1,750,000 years ago.

Makapansgat caves, believed to be the only site in southern Africa where *Australopithecus africanus* and *Australopithecus robustus* have been found together.

Kromdraai, Sterkfontein, and Swartkrans caves in South Africa. *Australopithecus africanus* was found at Sterkfontein and *Australopithecus robustus* at Kromdraai and Swartkrans.

Taung caves in South Africa, where first fossil evidence of *Australopithecus africanus* was discovered.

The South African caves

Prior to the 1920s no important fossil evidence of man had been found in Africa. During the first three quarters of the 19th century Europe was the focus of interest for students of ancient man. Starting with the discovery of a skull at Gibraltar in 1848, the notion of a fossil record for man gradually became accepted. In the last decade of the 19th century the discoveries of a Dutch army surgeon, Eugène Dubois, shifted attention to Indonesia, and then Canadian anthropologist Davidson Black redirected it to China with his exciting finds in the 1920s at the Chou-k'ou-tien cave near Peking.

In 1924 Raymond Dart, a South African anthropologist, made an epochal discovery of a child's skull in rock samples that had been sent to

51

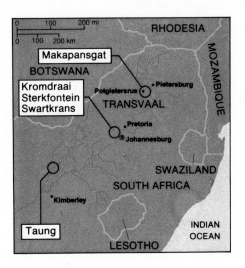

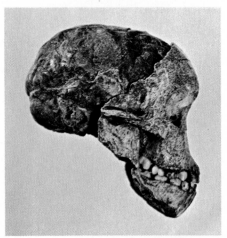

Fossil evidence of ancient man has been found in southern Africa, especially in caves at Taung, Sterkfontein, Swartkrans, Kromdraai, and Makapansgat (above). Below is a child's skull found in rock samples from a mine at Taung; Raymond Dart interpreted the skull as being the first fossil evidence of Australopithecus africanus.

P. V. Tobias and A. R. Hughes, University of the Witwatersrand, South Africa

him from a mine at Taung, near Kimberley. The skull had come from the solidified rubble or breccia that had accumulated in numerous caves in the limestone plateaus of South Africa. Despite the difficulties of interpreting the shape of a juvenile skull (the specimen was as mature as a six-year-old child of today), Dart was perspicacious enough to understand the significance of the find. Though the braincase was small, Dart interpreted the Taung child as being the first fossil evidence of a man-ape, and he called it *Australopithecus africanus*, the southern ape of Africa.

Scientists greeted Dart's ideas with extreme skepticism. Their reaction is more understandable when it is realized that at that time Piltdown man, with its modern cranium and ape jaw, now known to be an elaborate forgery but then considered to be authentic fossil evidence, greatly influenced the thinking of contemporary scientists. Dart's new skull had the opposite characteristics, an apelike braincase and human-looking teeth.

Dart did have at least one loyal supporter, Robert Broom, who in his retirement had started to take an interest in hominid fossils. In 1935 Broom set about the task of finding specimens to support Dart's bold hypothesis. A year later he found fossils at a cave near Johannesburg called Sterkfontein, and he secured from the breccia the fossil hominid evidence he had been seeking. Broom and Dart were instrumental, along with their students, in locating caves at Kromdraai, Makapansgat, and Swartkrans, all of which were to provide fossil evidence of the australopithecines. Work at the sites reached its peak immediately after World War II and then declined. The cave at Taung was destroyed by mining, and the Kromdraai cave has lain unexplored for 20 years. In the mid-1960s intensive excavations were resumed at Swartkrans by Charles K. Brain and at Makapansgat and Sterkfontein by Phillip V. Tobias and Alun R. Hughes, and the fossil hominid specimens recovered from these sites exceed one thousand.

As each new cave was explored, the hominids it contained were given new and different names. The nomenclature has since been clarified so that now most workers think that all the South African early hominid fossils should be placed in a single genus, *Australopithecus*. The main subdivision in the genus is into "gracile" (slender) and "robust" forms, the former called *Australopithecus africanus* and the latter, *Australopithecus robustus*. It is a peculiarity of the cave sites that within each major geological subdivision in the caves there is only one type of hominid represented; Makapansgat may prove to be an exception, for scientists have suggested that both forms of the australopithecines are found there. The gracile form is found at Taung, Sterkfontein, and Makapansgat, and the robust at Swartkrans and Kromdraai. The robust specimens in the two separate caves are usually placed in the same species, but it is possible that differences between the Kromdraai and Swartkrans samples deserve the original specific distinction that they were accorded by Broom when he described the first fossils from Swartkrans in 1949.

(Top and bottom right) P. V. Tobias and A. R. Hughes, University of the Witwatersrand, South Africa; (center and bottom left) John T. Robinson, University of Wisconsin

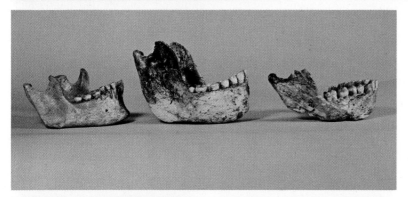

Terrain at Taung (top), the site of important fossil discoveries. At the left are mandibles from (left to right) modern man and the robust and gracile forms of Australopithecus. *An incomplete* Telanthropus *skull from Swartkrans is at the bottom left, and at the bottom right are fragments of a skull of the genus* Homo *found in 1976 at Sterkfontein.*

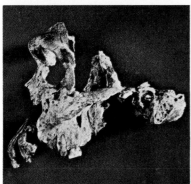

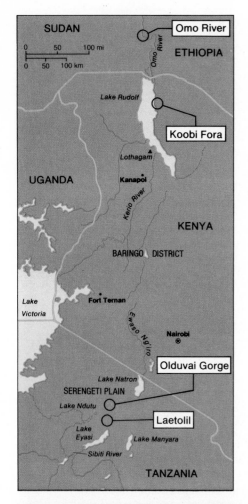

In 1949 and subsequent years John Robinson found several fossils at the Swartkrans cave that appeared to differ from the main samples of robust australopithecines. These were called *Telanthropus* by Broom and Robinson. Stone tools were also found at Swartkrans, but there was no certainty that the tools, *Telanthropus*, and the robust australopithecines were all the same age. It was vital to know this because, to judge from the scanty remains, *Telanthropus* looked much more like modern humans than did the australopithecines. Stone tools and small humanlike teeth were found together at Sterkfontein but in a layer of breccia that postdates the main australopithecine-bearing stratum.

Recent geological research at these cave sites is helping to resolve the relationships of the more human-looking fossils to the main australopithecine breccias. Several of the Swartkrans specimens were found to fit together to make up a cranium that supports the earlier evidence for *Telanthropus* being a more humanlike ancestor. An exciting fossil skull found in August 1976 at Sterkfontein by Hughes is expected to help clarify the story of man and the australopithecines in the caves.

East African evidence

In recent times fossil sites in East Africa have yielded remarkable collections of fossil hominids. The first hominid specimens of any importance in this region were found at Olduvai Gorge in Tanzania in the early 1930s. Since then fossil hominids have been discovered elsewhere in Tanzania as well as in Kenya and Ethiopia. Sites that ten years ago were unknown or only partly explored have yielded nearly 500 hominid specimens, including partial skeletons and almost complete skulls. These sites are all related to the Rift Valley; the instability of the

© National Geographic Society, photo by David Brill

(Left) Jerry Lesser—Bruce Coleman Inc.; (top right) © National Geographic Society, photo by Des Bartlett; (bottom right) Bernard Wood

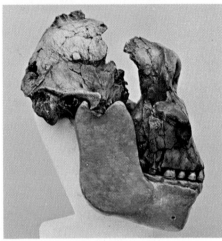

Major East African fossil sites (opposite page top) include Laetolil, the Olduvai Gorge, Koobi Fora, and the Omo River. Severed tusks lie on sedimentary strata in Ethiopia (opposite page bottom) that are typical of those rich in fossil remains. The Olduvai Gorge (left), the scene of many fossil discoveries, exposes layer upon layer of ancient lake beds. At the top is a partial skullcap of Chellean man found at Olduvai by L. S. B. Leakey and identified as Homo erectus. *Below is the skull of an* Australopithecus (Zinjanthropus) boisei, *a robust australopithecine found at Olduvai.*

Earth's crust in this region is responsible both for the volcanic debris called tuffs (which helped not only to preserve the fossils but also to provide one of the clues to their dating) and for the Earth movements that altered the land surface sufficiently to cause the erosion and eventual exposure of the fossils contained in the strata.

Fossil sites in East Africa differ markedly in size from those in the south. At Hadar in Ethiopia and Koobi Fora on the eastern shores of Lake Rudolf (also called Lake Turkana) in Kenya, fossil-rich sediments are exposed over an area of more than 1,000 square kilometers (about 385 square miles) — a dramatic contrast to the confined South African cave localities.

While not as large as some Kenyan and Ethiopian localities, Olduvai Gorge has vertebrate fossil sites exposed in the walls of most of the 30-kilometer-long gorge that has been cut into the sediments on the edge of the Serengeti Plain. The first major discovery was a cranium of

55

(Top left) Russ Kinne—Photo Researchers; (top right) © National Geographic Society, photo by Robert Campbell; (bottom left) © National Museums of Kenya

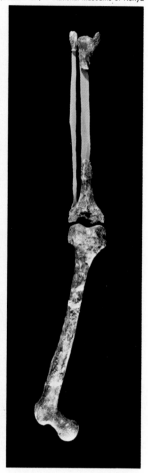

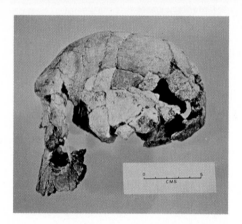

The shore of Lake Rudolf (top) was the site of the skull "1470" (above) and the limb bones (top right) of a hominid that fashioned primitive stone tools some two million years ago.

a robust australopithecine, found in 1959. It was called *Zinjanthropus boisei* and brought recognition to Louis and Mary Leakey, who had been conducting painstaking archaeological and paleontological research in Olduvai Gorge for many years before their famous discovery.

In the early 1960s a series of discoveries by the Leakeys at Olduvai Gorge provided evidence of a gracile hominid, resembling *Australopithecus africanus* but with a larger braincase, slightly modified teeth, and more advanced limb bones. It was named *Homo habilis* and was found at the same level as the robust australopithecine specimens, in strata about 1,750,000 years old, thereby providing the first and important evidence that *Homo* and *Australopithecus* were living side by side. Discoveries in later strata provided the first firm evidence of *Homo erectus* in Africa south of the Sahara. Archaeological evidence at Olduvai complemented the fossil discoveries, for the stone tools recovered in higher strata were more varied and complex than those in the lowest layers.

The sediments exposed at Olduvai Gorge correspond to those that border nearby Lake Ndutu. In 1973 excavations conducted at Lake Ndutu by the Tanzanian Department of Antiquities exposed a hominid skull. This was skillfully restored and provided further evidence of

56

Homo erectus populations in East Africa. There are no firm dates for the site, but anthropologists have suggested an age of approximately 500,000 years.

The Laetolil area in Tanzania, near the Olduvai Gorge, has been known as a fossil site for nearly 40 years. Part of a hominid upper jaw was collected there in 1939, but no more intensive prospecting was undertaken until 1974 when work was resumed under the direction of Mary Leakey. More than a dozen fossil hominid specimens have been found, all either teeth or lower jaws. First assessments of the specimens indicate that only one hominid population is being sampled, and the proportions of the teeth and the shape and size of the mandible indicate that it has an affinity with early *Homo* and the gracile australopithecines. The fossils at Laetolil probably date from between 3,125,-000 and 3,750,000 years, and their great antiquity may well explain why they share features with both later *Homo* populations and *Australopithecus africanus*.

Confirmation of the coexistence of *Homo* and *Australopithecus* in the period between one million and two million years ago was provided by another member of the Leakey family, Richard E. Leakey, when he pioneered research in the fossil-rich deposits on the northeastern shore of Lake Rudolf. The discovery of authentic stone artifacts in strata more than two million years old pushed even further back in time the first tangible evidence of human activity.

In 1972 the first of a series of skull remains and limb bones were found at the Lake Rudolf site. They probably belonged to the hominids who had fashioned the very early, primitive tools. The surprise to scientists was not only the remarkably advanced appearance of the remains but also their age, which on the dating evidence then available was between 2.5 million and 3 million years. Later, a different set of dating experiments indicated a younger age for the strata that bore skull "1470" and the limb bones. Results from fission-track dating methods supported the earlier date, and only additional experimentation will resolve the debate.

Even if they are less than two million years old, however, the Lake Rudolf fossils represent remarkable evidence of early *Homo* populations. Further exploration has been rewarded with braincases, teeth, and lower jaws that confirm evidence of a reasonably large-brained (600–800 cubic centimeters) hominid with teeth larger but similarly proportioned to those of modern humans. From later strata a new skull, "3733," provides evidence that hominids resembling *Homo erectus* were living in Africa as early as 1.5 million years ago.

Ethiopian sites

Fossil animals had been found in sediments along the banks of the Omo River in Ethiopia as early as 1933. Exploration was begun in earnest in 1967 by teams from the U.S., led by F. Clark Howell; France, led by Yves Coppens; and Kenya, led by Richard Leakey. Fossil hominid remains were found in strata ranging in age from three million to one

Fossil hominid mandible from Laetolil in Tanzania, held by its discoverer, M. Maunda, has been dated between 3,500,000 and 3,750,000 years.

© Mary D. Leakey

57

F. Clark Howell, University of California, Berkeley

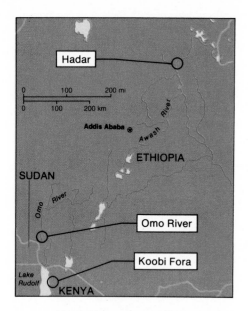

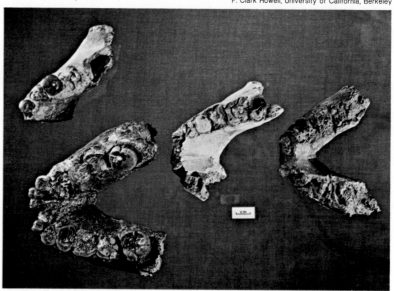

Hominid fossils have been found in Ethiopia in sediments along the Omo River and at Hadar alongside the Awash River. They include (right) mandibles of Australopithecus africanus *(far right) and* Australopithecus boisei, *all from the Omo River area. The finds have been dated at between 1.9 million and 2.7 million years.*

million years. Dating from the middle part of this period were the remains of robust australopithecines. In the earlier layers teeth and jaws were found that were similar to those of the gracile australopithecines in South Africa; in the uppermost strata the fossils resembled more closely *Homo habilis* remains from Olduvai. Thus, as in the hominid collection from Koobi Fora, there is evidence at the Omo River sites for two hominid lineages, one resembling *Homo* and the other the robust australopithecines.

The most recently discovered fossil hominid site is at Hadar, a locality in a large expanse of exposed fossil-bearing rocks alongside the Awash River in northeastern Ethiopia. There Donald C. Johanson and Maurice Taieb were spectacularly successful in their search for hominid fossils. The bodies of dead animals were apparently subject to little disturbance during burial so that fossils from this area are among the most complete specimens known. The hominid fossils are no exception to this remarkable preservation process, and in addition to jawbones and skulls a remarkably complete skeleton was found. Recent explorations uncovered the remains of a group of hominids that were apparently buried and fossilized together. This collection will enable scientists to judge much more accurately how much hominid populations varied in size and shape; at present, only modern populations of apes or humans can be used as models.

Preliminary reports on the growing fossil collection from Hadar suggest that the majority of the remains represent the early ancestors of man and should be included in the genus *Homo*. In addition, it is claimed that the preserved skeleton resembles material from Sterkfontein in South Africa and may represent an East African variant of *Australopithecus africanus*. There are also a few fossils that could well belong to robust australopithecines. Preliminary radiometric dating evidence and assessments of the fauna point to an age of about three million years for most of the hominid material.

58

Ramapithecus: ancestor of the hominids?

As exciting as the evidence is from these fossil sites there remains a large gap in the story of human evolution in Africa. The vast bulk of the available evidence from comparative anatomy, protein sequencing studies, and paleontology points to a joint ancestor for the living African apes and humans. Fossil evidence suggests that this ancestor was more apelike, or pongid, than humanlike, or hominid. The problem is one of identifying the earliest hominids among the scanty fossil evidence. Although the structures of modern humans and apes differ considerably, as one approaches the point of their evolutionary divergence similarities between the two forms will inevitably increase.

At sites in Asia, Europe, the Middle East, and Africa there is steadily accumulating fossil evidence of an animal paleontologists call *Ramapithecus*. In the 1930s, among fossil ape specimens described from deposits in India, G. Edward Lewis identified jaws and teeth that he believed showed resemblances to humans rather than to the apes: a small canine tooth, a face with little projection, and no apelike gap between the incisor and canine teeth. Since then argument about the status of *Ramapithecus* has abounded. More specimens were collected in India and Pakistan, and these remains, consisting of jawbones, showed well-worn molar teeth lying in a rather low, squat, mandibular body; these features were cited as adaptations to a tough diet, a feature more indicative of hominids than of pongids.

Africa has also contributed remains of *Ramapithecus*. Jaw fragments were found at Fort Ternan in Kenya. Louis Leakey considered that they were distinct from the Asian *Ramapithecus*, but most observers now include them in the original Indian genus. With an age of about 14 million years, the Fort Ternan specimens are most likely the earliest examples of *Ramapithecus* known, since most of the Indian and Pakistan specimens range in time between 7 million and 14 million years. Fossil evidence from Turkey, Greece, and Hungary suggests that animals resembling the Asian and African *Ramapithecus* populations were widespread in Europe about 10 million years ago. It is unfortunate that these European specimens are mainly jaws and teeth, and that only at the Hungarian site and in West Pakistan is there the possibility that limb bones of *Ramapithecus* may have been recovered.

The evidence that *Ramapithecus* is a hominid is strong but by no means conclusive. Small canine teeth occur in another Asian fossil primate, *Gigantopithecus*. Most scientists, however, think that *Gigantopithecus* is an ape and that its small biting teeth are an example of "convergent" evolution, an ape looking like a hominid.

Early hominid habitats

Until about 20 million years ago the landmasses of Africa and Arabia were separate from Eurasia. Fossil evidence suggests that the earliest fossil apes were African and that they lived in an African terrain which was more forested than the relatively open savanna of today; climatic changes and recent human interference have much reduced the areas

Peter Andrews, British Museum of Natural History and Alan Walker, Harvard University

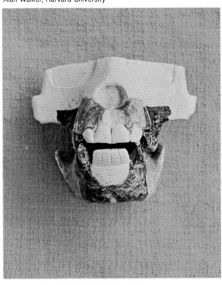

Reconstruction of Ramapithecus *jaw is based on remains of a left maxilla and a left mandible found at Fort Ternan in Kenya. These bones, from what many believe to be the earliest hominid, have an approximate age of 14 million years.*

59

© National Geographic Society, photo by David Brill

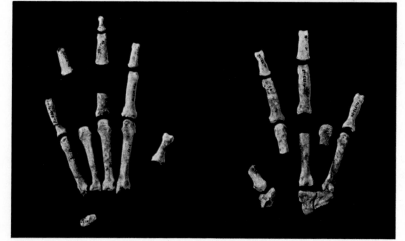

(Top) Remains of an elephant that lived during the Pliocene Epoch, from 7 million to 2.5 million years ago, share a site at Hadar with a large variety of other animal fossils, including such mammals as giraffes, pigs, antelopes, rhinoceroses, hyenas, otters, and big cats. Hand bones found at Hadar (right) resemble those of modern man.

© National Geographic Society, photo by Marie-Louise Brimberg

of tropical rain forest. Probably before their differentiation as hominids these ancestral ape populations spread into Europe and Asia, still dependent on a forest habitat.

Later, perhaps about 12 million years ago, there was a major evolutionary development. At this time, some of the animals looked less like apes and were probably adapted to a tougher diet, resulting in their large, well-worn, grinding teeth. From what is known of the habitat, these animals would have been more adapted to open woodland than forest, perhaps feeding much more on the ground than do modern apes. This is the "niche" that it is presumed *Ramapithecus* occupied, and it is surmised that the demands of crossing open spaces between patches of woodland would have provided the necessary spur to the development of a bipedal gait, the hands being used for clutching seeds or roots hastily collected in the exposed clearings.

This scenario of the earliest phase of hominid evolution is based more on guesswork than on hard fact. The truth is that in the crucial period between *Ramapithecus* and the earliest certain hominid remains there is a gap in the fossil record of about four million–six million years. Two molar teeth crowns from the Baringo District in Kenya, one of them ten million and the other six million years old, are tantalizing but ambiguous evidence. A mandible fragment from Lothagam and the lower end of an upper arm bone from Kanapoi, both sites to the southwest of Lake Rudolf, are both hominid and are between four million and five million years old but scarcely help to fill the gap. In many ways it would be more useful to find limb bone fossils rather than the remains of jaws and teeth. Modern apes have relatively long upper limbs, and the Hadar skeleton is complete enough to show that the relative length of the upper limbs of this early hominid was midway between that of modern humans and apes.

As Charles Darwin predicted in 1871, the scene of this critical missing phase of human evolution was probably Africa. Temperate zones were no place for a struggling hominid; seasonal fruiting would have severely limited the scope for subsistence on plants and trees, and the climate in India and Pakistan apparently cooled earlier than it did in Europe. Though recent studies on virus immunity point to a link between humans and the Asian apes, an African location for the post-*Ramapithecus* phase of human evolution is most likely.

The earliest true hominid

Leaving aside details of the different interpretations given to the fossil hominids from the East African sites, most schemes divide the material into a robust australopithecine group characterized by a heavily crested small-brained skull with a very expanded ear region, a robustly built jaw bearing relatively small incisor and canine teeth compared with large grinding teeth, and peculiar pelvic and lower limb bones, and a more gracile group which lacks these particular features. The robust group appears to have formed a specialized offshoot from the main hominid stem at some time between three million and five million

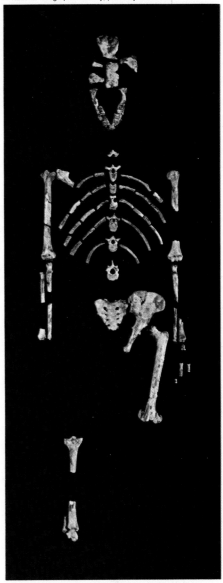

© National Geographic Society, photo by David Brill

"Lucy," a partial skeleton of an adult female primate, was assembled from remains found at Hadar. Believed to be three million years old, she walked upright and was less than four feet tall. The shape of the lower jaw and its narrow incisors resemble those of Australopithecus.

61

Photos, © National Museums of Kenya

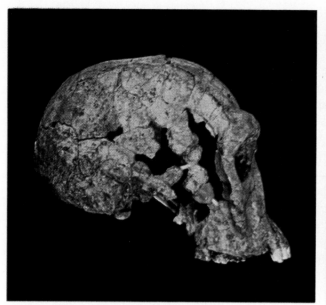

Found at Koobi Fora in 1973 were the skulls "1813" (above) and "1805" (right). Because they combined Homo-*like teeth with a brain size smaller than that of other* Homo *specimens, it was difficult to determine whether they belonged to the* Homo *or the* Australopithecus *line.*

years ago. Because no evidence of these robust specimens has been found later than about 1,125,000 years ago it is presumed that about that time they became extinct.

The remaining more gracile specimens, generally attributed to *Homo* in East Africa and *Australopithecus africanus* in South Africa, show a good deal of variation but tend to have a more balanced dental apparatus that evolved along with a gradually enlarging braincase. In many ways the South African gracile australopithecines look more like the robust forms than do the gracile *Homo* populations in East Africa. The earliest East African gracile fossils more closely resemble what is known of *Ramapithecus* and thus probably better indicate the common hominid ancestor than does *Australopithecus africanus*.

Discoveries at Koobi Fora in 1973 have prompted anthropologists to ask a new question—is *Australopithecus africanus* found along with *Homo* in East Africa? In 1973 a cranium "1813" and a skull "1805" were found at Koobi Fora. These two specimens combined *Homo*-like teeth with a brain size much smaller than that of other *Homo* specimens. Along with some small jawbones, these specimens posed the problem of whether they were part of a variable *Homo* lineage, represented a separate "small-brained" *Homo* lineage, or belonged to a "small-toothed" *Australopithecus africanus* group.

The finds at Koobi Fora caused scientists to look again at the gracile hominids from Olduvai: do they all belong to *Homo habilis*, or do some belong to a small-toothed australopithecine? As of 1977 the question remained unanswered. Clearly, if "1813" and "1805" are much later representatives of the type of hominids sampled at Hadar, their evolution had been more in the direction of *Homo* than toward the robust australopithecines.

It is clear from the evidence described above that the single-species hypothesis is no longer tenable. More of an axiom than a hypothesis,

62

Photos, © National Museums of Kenya

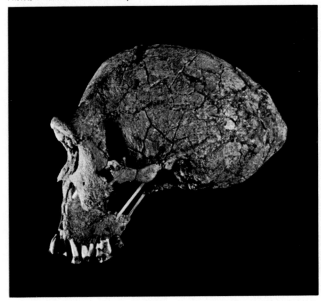 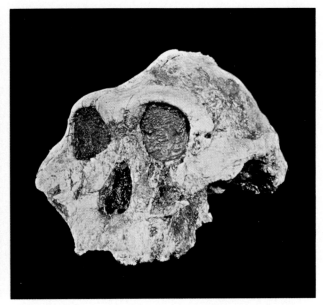

it stated that because of the principle of "competitive exclusion," hominids, once they had developed a tool culture, had insufficient ecological "space" for more than one lineage to survive. The recent discovery at Koobi Fora of an "erectus"-like skull, "3733," at the same general level in the stratigraphic sequence as "406," a typical robust australopithecine cranium, constitutes, however, a near-mortal blow for the proponents of the single-species principle.

(Left) A skull similar to that of Homo erectus *and (above) one of a robust australopithecine were found at Koobi Fora at the same general stratigraphic level.*

The future

It is certain that in the near future fossil evidence will be found that will enable hominid paleontologists to test current hypotheses about the phylogeny (evolution) of the hominids. The contributions of the Leakey family are unequaled in this field, and the careful fieldwork of Louis and Mary Leakey, continued by Richard Leakey, provides outstanding examples of African prehistory research.

Increasingly vigorous and novel archaeological techniques combined with the efforts of scientists who are seeking to understand the factors that control the preservation of fossils will enable new questions to be framed and answered that will deal with broader interpretations of the fossil and stone-tool evidence. What factors caused the diversification of hominid lineages? How did the strategies of the lineages differ? Was a stone culture limited to one lineage? Were there strong habitat preferences? These questions, all dealing more with evolutionary biology than with hominid phylogeny alone, represent the research problems of the future.

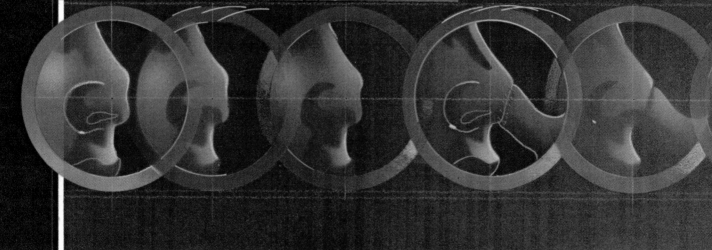

Plastic Surgery
by Peter McKinney

A worthy and surprisingly ancient branch of medicine, plastic surgery is shedding its unjustified reputation for catering exclusively to human vanity.

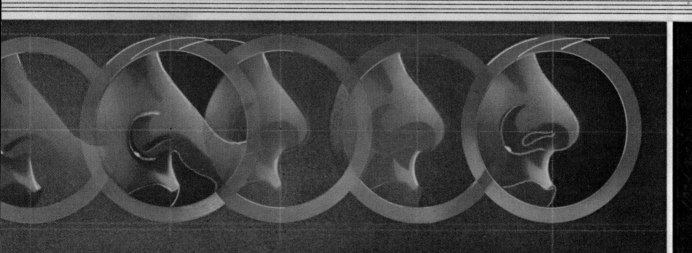

The public generally has a limited conception of the purpose and capabilities of plastic surgery. Yet from the earliest origins of its techniques, some of which predate 1000 BC, its foremost objectives have remained the same—the removal or improvement of disfiguring pathological conditions and the restoration of normal appearance. Even aesthetic or cosmetic surgery, a branch of plastic surgery that has received disproportionately large publicity, is sometimes misunderstood. It is often viewed as a purely mechanical—and miraculous—means to achieve a youthful appearance or an improvement in physical attractiveness, but its several limitations and its dependence for success on the expectations and psychological well-being of the patient are usually underemphasized.

Early history

As a specialty, plastic surgery is fairly young, and important advances have been made largely in response to the bodily damage wrought by major wars of the 20th century. The adjective "plastic" derives from the Greek, meaning "to form" or "to mold," and although synthetic plastics are employed in some of its procedures, use of the word as a medical term precedes its industrial usage by over half a century. The German surgeon Karl Ferdinand von Gräfe wrote the treatise *Rhinoplastik* in 1818, but coinage of the term "plastic surgery" has been attributed to Eduard Zeis, who published it in the title of his *Handbuch der plastischen Chirurgie* (1838).

The principles of plastic surgery were developed during thousands of years of trial and improvement. The first record of this knowledge has been traced to the famous Hindu surgeon Susruta, who described the reconstruction of noses using flaps of tissue from the adjacent cheeks; in Susruta's India (perhaps as early as 600 BC) the removal of a portion of the nose was a common punishment for female adultery. From China in the 3rd century BC emerged descriptions of surgery for the correction of such birth defects as split lips. Celsus in the 1st century AD and Galen in the following century described facial rebuilding techniques and are credited with the introduction of plastic surgery to Europe. Gaspare Tagliacozzi of Bologna, author of the first textbook of plastic surgery in 1597, gained fame for his rebuilding of noses using arm tissue. This was not an uncommon need at that time because the nasal tip was frequently damaged in sword fights.

Research in plastic surgery began in Italy in 1804 when Giuseppe Baronio experimented with grafts of skin, using sheep as an experimental model. Many 19th-century European and American surgeons published articles on topics that were to become the nucleus of the specialty, such as facial reconstruction, palate repairs, lip closure, and burn treatments. John Jones, the first professor of surgery at King's College (now Columbia University), New York City, introduced the techniques of plastic surgery to the American colonies with the publishing of his *Plain Concise Practical Remarks, on the Treatment of Wounds and Fractures* (1775).

PETER McKINNEY is Associate Professor of Clinical Surgery, Division of Plastic Surgery, Northwestern University Medical School, Chicago.

Illustrations by John Youssi

Much experience was gained from the treatment of casualties of the U.S. Civil War, during which was recorded the performance of 32 plastic operations. *Contributions to Reparative Surgery* (1876), written by New York surgeon Gurdon Buck, was based largely on his experiences as a consultant to the Union Army. John Roe of Rochester, N.Y., introduced aesthetic surgery to the U.S. in 1887, when he described a method of rhinoplasty, or plastic surgery of the nose, using internal incisions. The first full-time plastic surgeon, John Staige Davis of Baltimore, published *Plastic Surgery* in 1919, and a veritable explosion of information and advances followed the founding of the American Association of Plastic Surgeons two years later, the first such society in the world. *Plastic and Reconstructive Surgery*, the first journal devoted exclusively to the field, began publication in 1946.

Techniques of plastic surgery

Because of the high potential for rejection of another person's tissue through the immune response, the plastic surgeon employs material from the individual's own body whenever possible. In practice, this requires tissue to be transplanted from either adjacent or distant areas to correct a defect. A host of tissue substitutes also has been developed, but these foreign materials are never safely at rest in the human body, though many such substances have remained in humans for decades without complications. Living tissue is transplanted between sites in one of three basic forms—flaps, grafts, or free transfers.

A flap is thick tissue consisting usually of skin and underlying fat that is left partially attached to the body to maintain blood supply during all stages of its transfer. It is the preferred method because it provides a padding of flesh as well as skin coverage and most closely approximates the lost tissue. There are two methods of flap transfer, local and distant. By its nature, the transfer of a local flap must be made to an adjacent area; for instance, in Susruta's method of nasal reconstruction, tissue is shifted from the adjacent cheeks to mold a new nose. Part of the flap remains attached to its original location until such time as the tissue establishes new vascular connections with its recipient site, usually on the order of two to three weeks. The use of local tissue is preferred for several reasons: it is faster; the tissue is more likely to match the surrounding skin in color, texture, and thickness; and it is easier on both patient and surgeon. The planning and molding of local flap tissue is one of the greatest skills of a plastic surgeon.

If local tissue is inadequate, tissue must be transferred from a distance. This can be done in one stage—for example, the use of a flap from the chest to repair a hand—or it can be done in multiple stages using a carrier—for instance, abdomen to wrist to face—with adequate time at each stage for the flap to establish new blood-supply connections. The tube flap, a distant method first described in Great Britain and the Soviet Union just after World War I, is a closed, fat-filled tube of skin attached to the body only at its ends. It is transferred to a distant site in stages by "waltzing," or transplanting each of its ends in turn

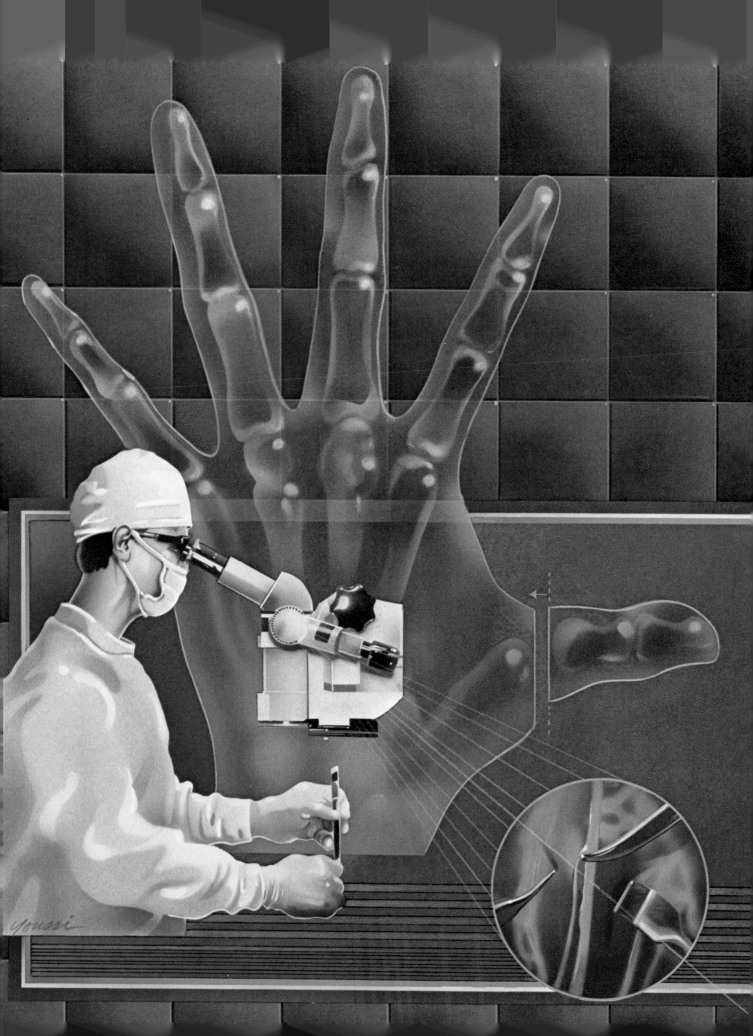

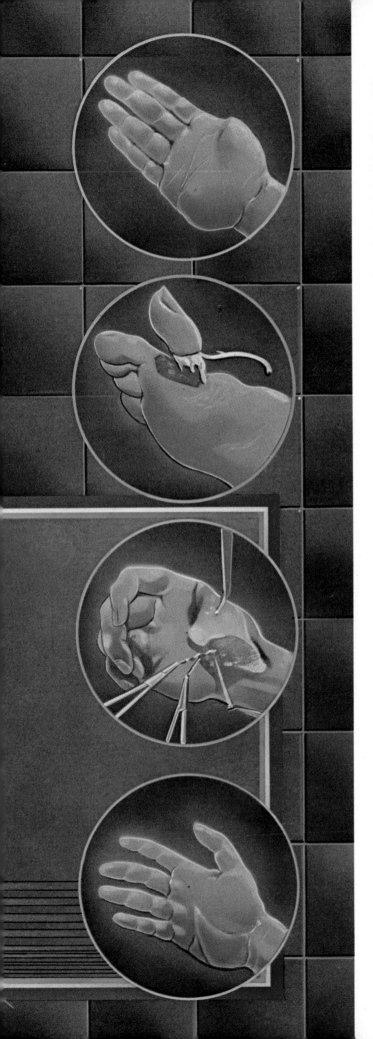

Reconstruction of a missing thumb by transplantation of a large toe has been made possible by the development of microsurgical techniques that allow anastomosis, or joining, of vessels and nerves between transplanted tissue and the recipient site. Careful planning of the venous supply and cutaneous tissue flaps is important. To facilitate connection with the hand, long strips (pedicles) of artery, vein, and nerve tissue, as well as generous lengths of extensor and flexor tendon, must be dissected with the toe. Simultaneous dissection of the recipient site in the hand involves locating the vascular supplies and nerves and tailoring any remaining portion of the proximal phalanx of the thumb (the bone between the knuckles) to fit into that of the large toe. Following relocation of the toe and vascular anastomoses, digital nerves are repaired and the tendons are threaded deep into the hand for connection at some distance from the transfer site.

toward the recipient area. In general, distant methods of transfer can be cumbersome and often require long periods of immobilization. The tube flap still has some limited applications, but it is a slow method of reconstruction and requires many months to complete the transfer.

A graft is tissue that is transferred devoid of blood supply and is totally dependent for nourishment upon rapid establishment of vascular connections with its new location. Hence, the graft is prepared as thin tissue that consequently cannot provide padding, but it offers an ease of transfer because it is completed in one stage. Skin, bone, fat, dermis, cornea (part of the eye covering), perichondrium (cartilage covering), and muscle (for restoration of motion to face, arm, and sphincters) all have been used as grafts. Grafting is most useful where large areas are to be covered, such as in burn cases, or where the skin is thin, such as a small defect on the eyelid or hand.

In 1906 Alexis Carrel and Charles Claude Guthrie reported on the replantation of a leg amputated at the thigh through anastomosis, or joining, of large vessels, a feat that paved the way for the development of free transfer of tissue. By the 1950s growing knowledge of the immunological response, facility in the handling of increasingly small vessels, and several successful organ transplants stimulated attempts to anastomose small vessels using the microscope and led to the development of suitable suturing equipment. By the late 1970s most major cities had a surgeon with the ability to match and join vessels less than one millimeter in diameter, allowing successful replantation of severed extremities as well as one-step transfer of tissue through immediate microsurgical anastomosis of arteries and veins. There would seem little question that in the future these techniques will supplant the older methods of transferring tissue via distant flaps.

Flaps, grafts, and free transfers all require a donor site, an area from which the tissue comes. Operations involving flap tissue or free transfer leave a large defect that requires closure and limits the size of the tissue that can be removed. In the case of grafts, the donor site will heal itself as would a scrape of the knee; the graft is thin tissue and thus leaves relatively little scar.

Implantable material
The search for an ideal tissue substitute has been investigated since the 16th century when canine bone was used for reconstruction of a defect in a soldier's skull; about the same period there were reports of silver plates for nasal prostheses. Over the years the silicones, metal, Teflon, the polyurethanes, and other materials have been developed and tested for suitability of implantation. The most widely used of these materials are the silicones, which have received notoriety because of their use and misuse in breast enlargement. Silicone compounds, which are polymers of silicon, oxygen, hydrogen, and carbon, can be made as oils or as gels or solids in long chains of high molecular weight. These materials are remarkably stable under heat and resistant to decomposition. Dimethylsiloxane, consisting of linear chains of silicon and oxy-

From "The Plastic-Surgery Boom," © *Newsweek*, Jan. 24, 1977

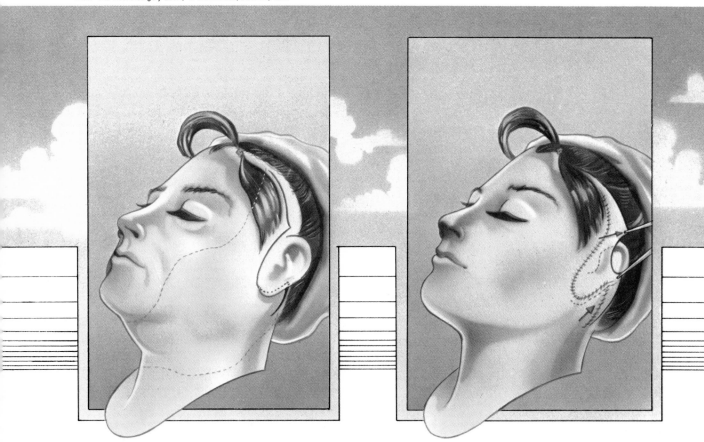

gen atoms with two methyl groups attached to each silicon atom, is most commonly used in its gel form for breast reconstruction, but is being favored increasingly for the correction of bony defects such as receding chins or the making of new finger joints for arthritics.

Other materials have been used for bone and joint replacement, heart pacemakers, and valves. A new material called proplast has been utilized for the replacement of bone to correct defects about the jaw and forehead. A porous weave of Teflon impregnated with carbon, proplast allows a certain amount of tissue ingrowth, permitting better fixation. Because of the dangers of spontaneous extrusion and infection inherent in the use of materials foreign to the body, the search for new substances continues. To date, none of these materials has demonstrated complete compatibility with human tissue; while offering immediate solutions, they may lead to future problems.

Aesthetic surgery

Aesthetic, or cosmetic, surgery is the most popular and well-known branch of plastic surgery. One can hardly find a leading general-interest magazine that has not written on this subject in the last few years. Much attention has been given to the correction of aging and the restoration of a more youthful appearance, not only for private reasons but also for job competition in an economic market that emphasizes youth.

The rhytidectomy, or face-lift operation, is designed to remove skin about the forehead, face, and neck that has lost its elasticity with age. On each side of the head a long vertical incision is made in the scalp of the temple region above the hairline, continuing down just forward of the ear and then up behind it. The skin along the side of the face and below the chin is separated by scalpel from underlying tissue and then pulled tight toward the back of the head until the sags and wrinkles disappear. Finally, the excess skin is trimmed and the free edges are sutured around the ears.

71

A change of appearance overlaps with psychological goals and thus offers difficult challenges in evaluating the suitability of candidates for aesthetic surgery. Roughly two-thirds of patients who request aesthetic procedures do so for sound reasons; that is, they have a physical deformity, they do not have psychological problems that impede their adjustment to society, and they wish correction for their own personal reasons. By contrast a small percentage of patients have very little physical deformity but tremendous mental problems. They may have a poor view of themselves and be seeking relief from chronic dissatisfaction with life through plastic surgery. Severe emotional problems may result when the surgery does not change their view of life. The group of patients who fall somewhere between these two categories is the most difficult to assess: these people have the combined problem of a noticeable physical deformity and an emotional abnormality. Several examples may provide some idea of the importance of the psychological aspects of this specialty. It is important to realize that the patient's own goals, be they conscious or unconscious, are the cornerstone of a successful overall result.

Case 1. A 16-year-old girl with juvenile diabetes sought relief from huge breasts. She had a difficult family situation: her parents were separated and her mother was an alcoholic. She would not attend gym or dances because of what she described as her freakish appearance. Because the patient was emotionally immature, there were serious reservations about operating, in spite of the reality of her deformity. However, technically successful surgery was performed, after which the patient outwardly made a dramatic psychological adjustment, becoming more outgoing. This sudden shift in her behavior was undoubtedly due to her youth and to relief from the embarrassment her large breasts had caused her. She still had some severe problems, but in this instance there was profound improvement.

Case 2. A middle-aged woman who requested a rhinoplasty revealed that she had been scheduled ten years previously for the procedure but had panicked at the last moment. Her nose overlapped her upper lip and her chin was small; physically her problem was obvious, but her life situation was in such upheaval that no prudent surgeon would operate on her. However, at the intervention of her internist surgery was done and was technically successful. Many months afterward the patient related how grateful she was that her surgery had relieved her of at least one of her many problems. To all appearances this patient had been a poor prospect for surgery because of her unstable home situation, her panic reaction several years before, and her age, as psychological problems are more hidden and complex in an older person. If surgery had been done before she had come to terms with her home situation, it most likely would not have made her happy; hence, her panic reaction at the time was probably quite fortunate.

Case 3. A 16-year-old black male requested correction of a wide, flared nose that he felt would impede a future acting career. He had a good record in school and had had a supportive family life, both of

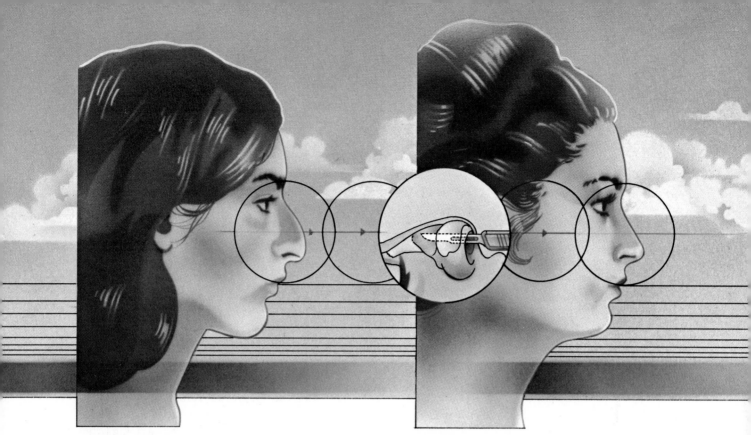

which indicated good emotional adjustment. Yet, despite a careful interview and a superb technical result in the appearance of his nose, he developed serious emotional problems five weeks after the surgery. Most interesting was the fact that as his mental state improved with psychiatric therapy, he requested correction of the appearance of his lips. It became apparent that the change in the appearance of the nose had removed some excuse in his life that for him explained why he had not been more successful. He then developed his new excuse—the appearance of his lips. Further surgical correction, of course, would have been a disaster.

The goal of aesthetic surgery is to restore contour that has been altered by age, trauma, or congenital defect. The most common types of aesthetic surgery are described below.

Blepharoplasty. This operation involves removal of excess fat and skin from the eyelids to correct a tired or baggy expression. Depending upon the extent of the problem, there are associated adjunctive procedures such as a brow lift, a temporal face lift, sectioning of the brow muscles to reduce the furrows between the eyes, or chemical peel for "crow's feet." Scars usually result in the folds of the eyelids or above the brow in the case of a brow lift. The operation is delicate and runs the risk of pulling the eyelid down if either too much skin is removed or if too much scar tissue forms.

Rhytidectomy. The face-lift operation removes extra skin about the forehead, face, and neck to correct the jowls developed in aging. This procedure produces a scar from the temple hairline around the ear into the neck hairline and shifts the hair slightly backward. It runs the risk of bleeding in the neck or of a wide scar in the hairline.

Among the most popular operations of aesthetic surgery is rhinoplasty, which corrects a hump on the nose and trims the cartilage in the nasal tip. By any of a variety of surgical techniques, a deflected or dislocated nasal septum or a deflection of the entire cartilaginous structure of the nose can also be remedied.

Correction of a tired or baggy expression around the eyes can be accomplished with a blepharoplasty. The specific procedure illustrated on the facing page is especially suited for the removal of excess fat below the eyes. An incision just below the lower eyelash margin is carried through skin and muscle to form a skin-muscle flap. Excess fat is extracted through a series of stab wounds in the orbital septum, and the incision is closed with several interrupted sutures.

Chemical peel. An old method revived for correction of fine wrinkles from exposure to the Sun, chemical peel, or chemosurgery, creates a controlled burn of the skin, allowing new skin to regrow in a smoother fashion. It runs the risk of a change in skin color or of scar formation if the burn is made too deeply.

Dermabrasion. Sanding of the skin helps deeper scars, pockmarks, and acne scars. While not completely removing the defects, it may smooth them out. Its risks are a change in skin color, inadequate removal of the scars, or increased scar formation.

Hair transplants. Moving small plugs of hair from the back of the head to the top of the head helps in very selected individuals to correct male pattern baldness. People with fine hair are poor candidates, because the bundle of hair shafts in each plug is not thick enough to cover the resultant scar.

Rhinoplasty. One of the most popular of aesthetic operations, it is done most commonly after age 16, when development of the nose is fairly complete. It corrects a bump, narrows the tip, and improves breathing if the nasal septum is deflected. Older techniques created a "surgical," ski-jump nose, but recent advances have eliminated such an artificial appearance. Although rhinoplasty often is done in the late teens, partial rhinoplasty is also a useful adjunct for correction of the aging face. The risks of the operation are bleeding or a subsequent operation to correct a fallen tip.

Chin augmentation. Often done in conjunction with a nose or face change, this procedure involves the placement of cartilage, bone, or an implantable material on the tip of the chin under the skin. A scar in the mouth or under the chin is required and there is risk of infection at the site of the implant.

Scar revisions. A scar always remains once the skin is cut by surgery or trauma. A plastic surgeon designs the incision to produce the least scarring in the majority of cases by taking advantage of normal skin creases, anatomical structures, and hair to camouflage scars, but they are always there if one searches for them. If a scar runs counter to elective lines of incision or is not repaired properly at the time of injury, revisions may offer improvement.

Otoplasty. Setting ears closer to the head can be of great relief to a schoolchild who suffers from derision by his or her classmates. In older people sometimes earlobes are made smaller in conjunction with face-lifting. Entire ears can be built to replace those either lost through trauma or absent at birth.

Abdominoplasty. Pregnancy or weight loss may leave redundant skin of the lower abdomen. This technique only partially removes stretch marks, requires transplantation of the umbilicus, and leaves a large scar. It is not a substitute for weight loss.

Thigh lift, arm lift. This technique leaves large scars around the thigh or arm and is less frequently done than the other procedures. It is useful after weight loss, in the aged, or in young women who have significant fullness of the hips. Again, it is not a substitute for weight loss.

Breast plasty. The uplifting of a breast either by surgically raising the nipple or by the insertion of a prosthesis is most often done after post-pregnancy collapse of the breast tissue. The first method leaves considerably more scar tissue but may be necessary if the nipple has fallen below the crease of the breast. Its risks are loss of a nipple or unacceptably large scars. Usually, however, the breast can be filled out with silicone gel or a saline-inflatable prosthesis, at the risk of numbness of the nipple or spontaneous loss of the implant.

Breast reduction. Done for hypertrophy of the breasts, it creates a lighter, more shapely breast but leaves large scars. The risks are similar to those of the breast uplift, and the results may interfere with subsequent nursing.

Reconstruction of breast. This procedure follows partial or total amputation and is becoming more commonplace as techniques improve. It may involve the insertion of a prosthesis, transfer of flap tissue to provide skin coverage, or complete nipple reconstruction in some instances. In cases of radical mastectomy, in which skin, gland, nipple, and ax¹llary lymph nodes are removed, and especially if radiation has been used for further treatment of the tumor, breast reconstruction presents a difficult challenge.

Some experts argue that no breast reconstructions should be performed that may hide or delay detection of a recurrence of the cancer. This thought, however, must be balanced by the patient's wishes and by any further type of therapy that could be offered for treatment of recurrence. By the beginning of 1977 fewer than 200 reconstructions had been attempted in the U.S. following radical mastectomy. Rebuilding the breast following a simple mastectomy or subcutaneous mastectomy (removal of the mammary gland with preservation of the nipple), although risky, is relatively easy. The results never replace the normal breast in shape or feel but, if successful, will obviate the necessity of an external prosthesis.

Trauma and hand surgery

Plastic surgery has always addressed itself to the correction of deformities through trauma. In times of peace this task consisted primarily of the management of facial fractures, the correction of scar formation, and coverage of large wounds. In times of war, particularly the major conflicts of the past century, plastic surgery experienced many significant improvements while correcting awesome wounds with which the solutions of peacetime could not cope.

As warfare evolved, the nature of its wounds also changed. World War I was a static, trench-based confrontation that produced teams of

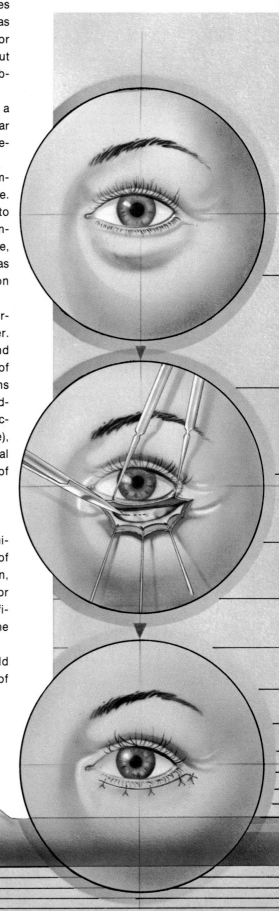

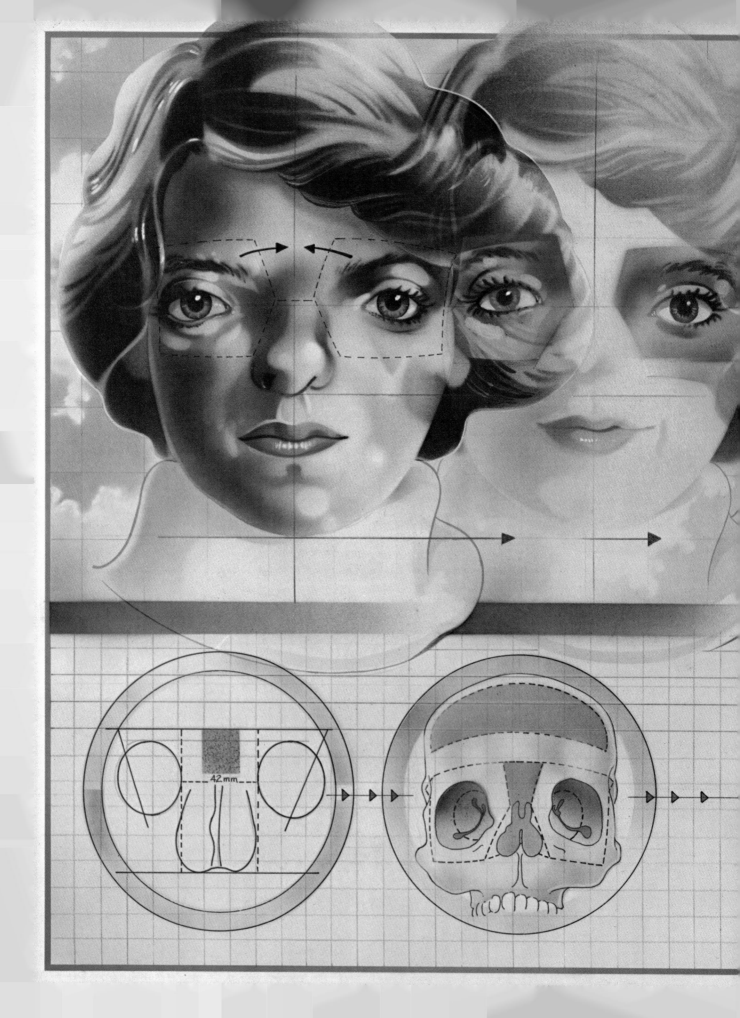

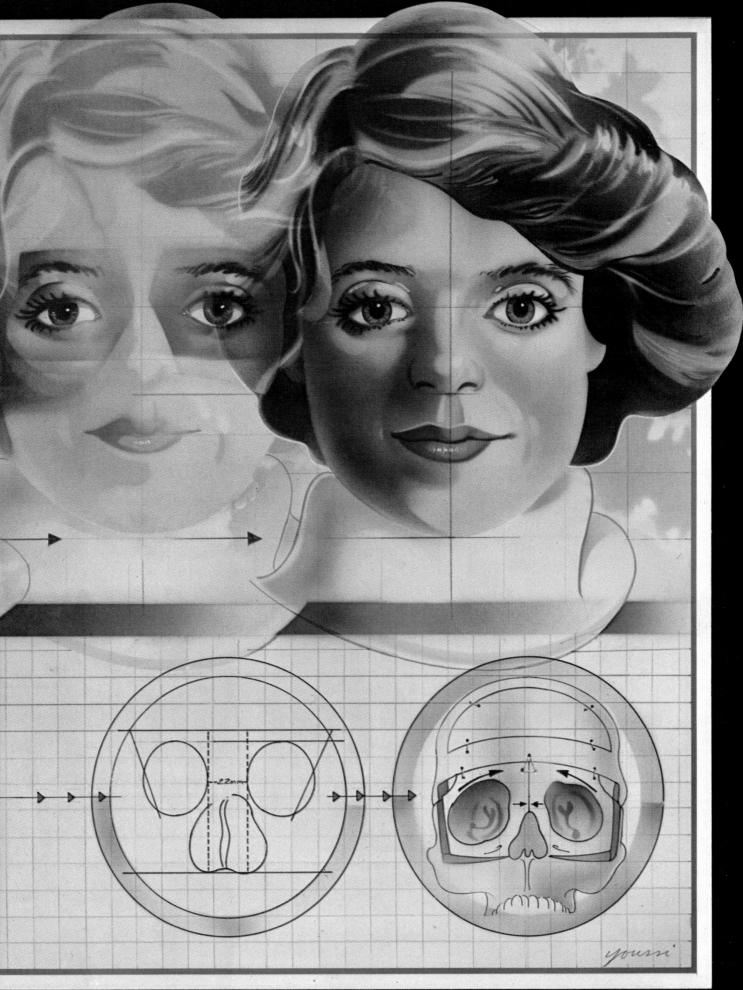

The past decade has witnessed development of a radical approach to the correction of a variety of severe cranial malformations using surgery that restructures the entire skeletal foundation of the face. One such congenital deformity, orbital hypertelorism (depicted on pp. 76–77), is an abnormally wide separation of the orbits of the skull that often occurs as a physical manifestation secondary to other birth defects. In one type of corrective surgery, following procedures for shrinking the brain and for exposure and removal of a large section of frontal bone, the associated structures of the eyes are detached from their orbits, and the orbits and surrounding bone are cut free from the skull in roughly rectangular segments. A measured central segment, representing the interorbital distance to be subtracted, is removed, and the two orbits are displaced laterally toward one another. Finally, the new orbital positions are fixed with wire, bone grafts are used to bridge remaining defects, and the section of frontal bone is replaced. Frequently an associated deformity of the nose is also corrected during this type of surgery.

surgeons and dentists to deal with severe facial injuries. Within this period bone grafting became a routine matter for correcting jawbone fractures that failed to knit. World War II, a war of mobility, produced injury to legs and hands requiring extensive tendon repair and soft-tissue coverage; improved methods for rapid coverage of wounds and repair of the hand were developed. In the Korean War, and particularly in the Vietnam conflict, improved tactical mobility allowed early evacuation of wounded, an advantage that enabled surgical salvage of more difficult problems. One medical challenge of the Vietnam conflict was the high-velocity injury; caused by the impact of a projectile traveling at speeds more than 2,500 feet per second, it was characterized by the presence of extensive tissue damage at a distance from the visible wound of entry.

Congenital anomalies, tumors, and sex assignment

The correction of congenital anomalies such as harelip and cleft palate, and the management of more severe congenital deformities of facial bone structures, has led to the development of a new division of plastic surgery, pediatric plastic surgery. The practitioners in this field have focused upon problems in the younger patient and have made significant contributions.

Plastic surgeons have always worked toward the correction of tumors, both of the skin and within the mouth, and more particularly toward the reconstruction of these deformities, such as restitution of jaw contour following removal of a portion of the mandible and reconstruction of facial contour. More recently, subcutaneous mastectomy has been pioneered by plastic surgeons as a possible means of reducing incidences of cancer of the female breast. For selected individuals who have cystic disease of the breast, who have a family history of tumors of the breast, and who have had numerous previous cancer-free biopsies, subcutaneous mastectomy with breast reconstruction may be indicated. It should be emphasized that the reconstructed breast is never as good in appearance or texture as the original and it is not a substitute for complete amputation for patients with proven carcinoma of the breast.

Since the celebrated cases of Christine Jorgensen in the 1950s and more recently Renee Richards, both intersexuality and sex-assignment surgery, directed toward producing either a male or female configuration from an intersexual body, have come to public attention. Although of questionable value in adults, this type of surgery is most useful in children born with abnormalities. Production of a female is favored in practically all situations, as male assignment, although surgically possible, has not proved as satisfactory with respect to psychological adjustment and later physical development.

Ongoing developments

Of the many aspects of plastic surgery that have blossomed in the 1970s, several hold great promise for the future. The ability to join vessels less than one millimeter in size with the use of the microscope has contributed to revolutionary techniques that allow both replantation and rapid one-stage transfer of tissue. Although many problems remain to be solved, in the hands of qualified individuals and with careful selection of patients success is improving.

Filling a defect by anastomosis of an artery and vein has allowed direct transfer of large blocks of tissue, and will gradually supplant older, cumbersome techniques of tissue transfer that rely on access to blood supply through the relatively slow process of vessel ingrowth. This technique allows the shifting of large blocks of tissue in one step, saving the patient considerable time and discomfort. It has particular application to reconstruction of portions of the body, rather than to aesthetic surgery, and is most useful following trauma or in patients who have had extensive tumor surgery. The most striking example of its use has been the successful building of a new thumb by the direct transfer of a large toe.

In the past, facially disfiguring congenital bone anomalies could be corrected only by a patchwork of grafts and tissue transfers, all of which were helpful but did nothing for the basic foundation. In the mid-1960s Paul Tessier of Paris boldly approached this problem by essentially reconstructing the entire foundation of the face. This type of operation requires extensive exposure of the facial bones. An incision in the hairline is used and the scalp is brought forward and down over the face. After pulling aside the brain and eyes, a saw is used to cut the bones free. These are wired into their new positions and the spaces filled with grafts of bone from the patient's hip. This technique allows the plastic surgeon to remodel the face with most of the scar hidden by the hair. Such a tremendous undertaking has considerable risk; nevertheless, it stands as an innovative and bold approach to a physical deformity that previously did not have a satisfactory correction and as a tremendous step forward for individuals who have a normal brain and a physically deformed body.

In recent years such advances in plastic surgery have followed lengthy courses of development that initiated in the laboratory. The availability of research grants has always waxed and waned, depending on the generosity of government and private sources. Current emphasis has been on the application of the fruits of past research with emphasis on the delivery of health care. However, it is possible that, for neglecting to lay a solid groundwork of basic medical research in the 1970s, society will pay a heavy price in the future.

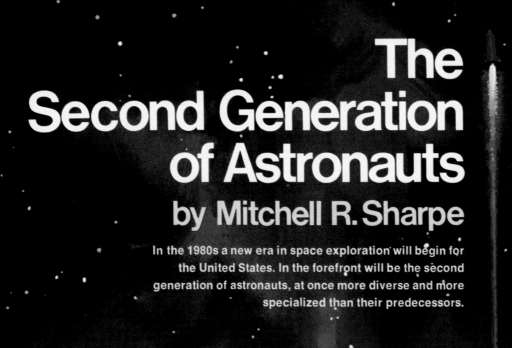

The
Second Generation
of Astronauts
by Mitchell R. Sharpe

In the 1980s a new era in space exploration will begin for
the United States. In the forefront will be the second
generation of astronauts, at once more diverse and more
specialized than their predecessors.

Courtesy, National Air and Space Museum, The
Smithsonian Institution, Washington, D.C.

*The first pressurized flying suit was
designed and worn by Wiley Post for
his high-altitude (35,000-48,000 feet)
airplane flights in the 1930s. A rubber
garment worn next to the skin is
covered by a suit of reinforced cotton.*

MITCHELL R. SHARPE *is Historian of
the Alabama Space and Rocket
Center, Huntsville, Alabama, and
consultant to the National Air and
Space Museum of the Smithsonian
Institution.*

Illustrations by Paul Alexander

In some ways the first generation of astronauts in the United States
resembled the early airplane pilots. While the leather helmet, goggles,
and silk scarf fluttering in the "prop wash" of the pilots had given way
to the plastic helmets and hermetically sealed, silver space suit of the
astronauts, both groups had much in common. They were adventurers
who caught the public's eye with their derring-do. In mounting to
heights beyond those possible for the ordinary man, they became at
once heroic and inspirational.

Also, the first generation of astronauts like the very early pilots was
predominantly male. When the names of the first seven U.S. astronauts
were revealed in April 1959, it was generally no surprise to the public
that women were not included. As John H. Glenn, one of the seven, put
it, "The men go off and fight the wars and fly the airplanes and come
back and help design and test them. The fact that women are not in this
field is a fact of our social order." Although a small group of highly
qualified women had tried to join the ranks of the nation's first astronauts, they were excluded from consideration by no less than U.S.
Pres. Dwight D. Eisenhower, who evidently shared Glenn's views.

By the coming of the second generation of U.S. astronauts in 1976,
the nation's goals in space had changed considerably. Scientists and
mission specialists were needed instead of the test-pilot adventurers of
the first era, and physical requirements were less demanding. Also, the
announcement in July 1976 by the National Aeronautics and Space
Administration (NASA) for positions as pilots and mission specialists
included the statement: "NASA is committed to an affirmative action
program with a goal of having qualified minorities and women among
the newly selected astronaut candidates."

The new vehicle

The space shuttle, in which the second generation of astronauts will
travel, is completely different in concept and operation from the rocket-
boosted and expendable spacecraft that carried the first men to the
Moon and back. Outwardly, the shuttle resembles an aircraft more than
a spaceship, and it has been designed so that it is far less taxing
physically on its passengers than were the first spacecraft.

The shuttle has been planned to be part of the space transportation
system for the 1980s and beyond. It consists of two major components,
the solid-propellant booster rockets and the orbiter; both are reusable,
with the exception of the propellant tank for the orbiter's engines. The
orbiter, which looks like an airplane and is about the size of a DC-9
jetliner, is 122 feet long and has a wingspan of 78.5 feet. Two hatches
running along its length on top open to receive payloads as long as 60
feet, as great as 15 feet in diameter, and weighing as much as 65,000
pounds. Thus, the orbiter can launch more than 90% of currently
planned or foreseen satellites into orbit around the Earth at a nominal
altitude of 110 miles. The first orbiter, named "Enterprise" after the
spaceship of the popular TV program "Star Trek," rolled out of the
factory on Sept. 17, 1976.

Courtesy, NASA

Women training to join the second generation of astronauts include (left to right) Carolyn S. Griner, Ann F. Whitaker, and Mary Helen Johnston. They are wearing space suits designed for the Apollo program. Below, a Mercury-Redstone rocket launches the first man into space for the U.S., Alan B. Shepard, Jr., on May 5, 1961.

The orbiter is boosted into space by two large solid-propellant rockets and its own three liquid-propellant rocket engines. During the launch, those on board will experience no greater acceleration forces than 3 G, and on reentry into the atmosphere the crew will experience only 1.5 G. (By comparison, a passenger aboard a 747 airliner experiences 0.25 G at takeoff; similarly, the DC-10 produces 0.33 G as it races down the runway.) At an altitude of approximately 28 miles, the two solid-propellant rockets burn out and are ejected from the orbiter. They return to Earth by parachute and are refurbished for future use. The orbiter then continues into orbit using its own three engines.

The orbiter, which is also reusable and has a lifetime of 100 missions or more, carries a crew of three astronauts consisting of the commander, pilot, and mission specialist. Additionally, accommodations are available for as many as four specialists on scientific experiments aboard the craft; they are called "payload specialists."

While the usual mission probably will last only seven days, missions of up to a month are possible. The three astronauts will occupy the flight deck at launch and return to Earth, while the payload specialists will sit in seats beneath the flight deck in small compartments that house the sleeping quarters, kitchen, and bathroom.

The pilot and mission specialist will have space suits available, but they will not wear them unless there is an emergency or a need to venture outside the orbiter. Unlike the expensive, "custom-tailored" space suits worn by the astronauts of Mercury, Gemini, Apollo, and Skylab, those of the second generation will be relatively inexpensive, "off the rack" garments. The helmet is the same as that used by the Skylab astronauts, but the suit itself is different. The upper torso is made of aluminum, and the lower torso and arms are of fabric. Because the torso is rigid, the backpack containing the life support system can be mounted directly on it with no cumbersome hoses needed. The fabric parts of the suit are also much more durable than were those of previous models.

The payload specialists and commander, while not furnished with

Courtesy, NASA

Courtesy, NASA

Courtesy, NASA

Above is the official emblem of Spacelab, a cooperative enterprise between the European Space Agency and the U.S. National Aeronautics and Space Administration. Darrell Arndt (right) tests the suction cup foot restraints to be used on the space shuttle. Below is a transparent model of the rescue sphere pictured on the opposite page.

space suits, will have access to a unique escape garment. It is a fabric sphere 34 inches in diameter into which the individual zips himself. The sphere is then inflated with oxygen. Inside, there is an independent oxygen supply and a small telephone. A plastic window is also provided. In case of an emergency evacuation of the orbiter, a space-suited crewman would assist the commander and payload specialists into their bags, inflate them, and then carry them to safety aboard the rescue orbiter. Alternately, a "clothesline" on pulleys could be rigged between the two vehicles and the "bagged" individuals transported over it.

Thus housed and equipped, the personnel aboard the orbiter will perform their duties. Each will have specific duties, and all will be specialists. The day of the "jack-of-all-trades" astronaut, who could do everything from pilot the spaceship to pull teeth, is past.

Spacelab, the successor to Skylab, will go into orbit within the cargo bay of "Enterprise." This manned spacecraft was designed and built by the European Space Agency (ESA), a multinational consortium of Belgium, Denmark, France, West Germany, Italy, The Netherlands, Spain, Sweden, Switzerland, and the United Kingdom, with the cooperation of Australia. While much smaller than Skylab, Spacelab is much more advanced technically and is reusable as well. It consists of a pressurized compartment and an unpressurized pallet. Personnel can work in the former without space suits, but a suit is needed to tend experiments mounted on the pallet. The total weight of Spacelab and its experiments is about 32,000 pounds.

Typical of the experiments that can be performed in Spacelab are those involving the effect of weightlessness on various forms of life, the processing of various materials and pharmaceuticals in zero gravity, surveys of the Earth, astronomical observations, and communications

Courtesy, NASA

Photos, courtesy, NASA

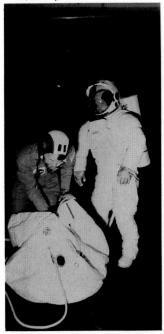  

and navigation studies. Such experiments will be performed by payload specialists. They will be highly qualified scientists or technicians in good health who will need only a few weeks of specialized spaceflight training, including familiarization with zero gravity and emergency procedures to be followed in case of some mishap.

The method of selecting payload specialists will be left to NASA and ESA. Basically, NASA wants to leave the task to the investigators who have experiments in the mission. Obviously, if physically qualified, the experimenter could be the payload specialist. While all details of selection by ESA are not firm, the organization probably will set up a screening committee and make tentative choices that will then be reviewed by NASA for physical aptitude and orientation. ESA and NASA will select both a primary and an alternate payload specialist by this means. The alternate, if not called upon to fly, will take an active part in the ground support operations for the mission.

While such selection and training procedures seem to open up the possibilities for space travel to a wide group of people previously denied it, at least one problem remains unsolved. The basic Spacelab mission is seen to be a week in length. What happens if the payload specialists, with their limited familiarization with weightlessness, need two or three days to adjust to it, as did several of the Skylab astronauts who had received extensive training for many months? Such a possibility presents a problem for mission planners.

Astronaut selection and training

With the advent of the space shuttle vehicle and Spacelab, NASA announced in July 1976 that it would accept applications for 15 commanders and pilots and 15 mission specialists. All are rated as

Astronauts in training demonstrate the rescue capsule designed for use on the space shuttle. If an orbiter becomes disabled, those crewmen not in space suits can zip themselves into fabric spheres that are 34 inches in diameter. Each sphere is then inflated with oxygen. In addition to an independent oxygen supply, each sphere also contains a telephone and has a plastic window.

85

Courtesy, NASA

Prototype of the 50-foot manipulator arm to be used on the space shuttle maneuvers a 32,000-pound payload at the Johnson Space Center in Houston, Texas (top right). The manipulator arm will be mounted on the shuttle orbiter and will launch and retrieve payloads from it while in Earth orbit. At the right, physiologist Charles F. Sawin (reclining) serves as a subject for a medical experiment monitored by scientist-astronaut Story Musgrave in the Spacelab simulator at the Johnson Space Center. Below, Joseph Engle (left) and Richard H. Truly (right), astronauts involved in testing the space shuttle orbiter, sit at the primary flight control station of the flight deck of the orbiter.

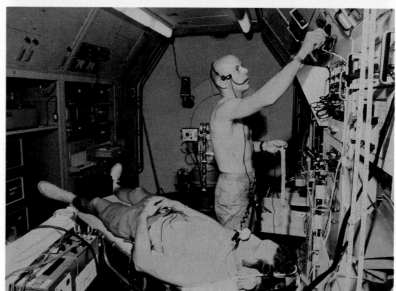

Courtesy, NASA

astronauts, but the mission specialist is not required to perform piloting duties.

The commander has responsibility for the space vehicle, its crew, mission success, and safety of the flight. Thus, he is much more akin to the contemporary airline captain than were the early astronauts, who were essentially engineers or test pilots trying out new craft. The pilot's duties are to assist the commander in controlling and operating the shuttle. The functions of the mission specialist, however, are not equivalent to those of the third officer or flight engineer on a commercial aircraft. The mission specialist is concerned mainly with the payload for a particular mission, whether it is the manned Spacelab or a satellite or probe. He operates the remote manipulator system, an articulated mechanical arm that can reach into the cargo bay of the orbiter and extract objects to be placed in space or can pick objects out of orbit and place them in the cargo bay for repair or return to Earth. The mission specialist will also be especially trained to perform tasks outside the orbiter while wearing a space suit.

Both pilot and mission specialist candidates will be selected for a two-year training and evaluation program at NASA's Johnson Space Center in Houston. This procedure is a departure from past practices of the space agency. The personnel selected will be candidates and not astronauts. All will be given responsible scientific or technical positions within the center, where they will work on jobs related to the space shuttle. They also will be permitted to continue their own particular skills when practicable. Additionally, they will undergo a basic astronaut training program to familiarize them with the space shuttle and the spaceflight environment. Pilot candidates will maintain their flight skills by using NASA jet airplanes. After a two-year period of training, a final selection for flight crews will be made. Those individuals not selected will be offered other jobs within the space agency.

The selection criteria for the shuttle crewmen is also in great contrast to that of the Mercury astronauts selected in 1959. At a minimum a candidate applying for the first team of U.S. astronauts had to be less than 40 years of age, less than 5 feet 11 inches tall, in excellent physical condition, a qualified jet pilot, and a graduate of a test-pilot school. Additional requirements included a bachelor's degree (or the equivalent) and 1,500 hours of flying time.

To apply for a candidate position of pilot today, individuals must be able to pass a NASA Class I flight physical examination (similar to a military Class I examination but much more extensive). Specifically, they must have a distant visual acuity of 20/50 unaided but correctable to 20/20 in each eye. Furthermore, they must have hearing with a loss not to exceed 30 decibels at 500 Hertz, 25 decibels at 1,000 Hertz, and 25 decibels at 2,000 Hertz. Additionally, the blood pressure must have a preponderant systolic not exceeding 140 nor a diastolic exceeding 90, measured in a sitting position. All applicants must be between 5 feet 4 inches and 6 feet 4 inches tall. They also must have a bachelor's degree in engineering, physical science, or mathematics or have completed all requirements for such a degree by Dec. 31, 1977. Higher degrees are desirable. They also must have a minimum of 1,000 hours of first pilot time (with 2,000 or more desirable), preferably in but not restricted to high-performance jet planes.

Mission specialist applicants must also possess a bachelor's degree in engineering, physical science, mathematics, or biological sciences or have completed all requirements for the degree by the same date. They must be able to pass a NASA Class II flight physical examination (equivalent to a military Class II examination, but more detailed). Specifically, they must have a visual acuity of 20/100 or better unaided but correctable to 20/20 in each eye. Their hearing acuity in the better ear must be the same as that specified for pilots. In the other ear, however, there can be a loss of 35 decibels at 500 Hertz, 30 decibels at 1,000 Hertz, and 30 decibels at 2,000 Hertz. The blood pressure

Courtesy, NASA

Twin-engine Gulfstream-2 airplane is used to train space shuttle orbiter pilots. Its engines and wings were modified so that it could be landed in the "no-power" mode that approximates the flight characteristics of the orbiter.

Cutaway drawing of the space shuttle orbiter shows the crew compartment, which consists of an upper flight deck containing the controls to pilot the craft and a lower deck furnished with sleeping quarters and storage lockers. Access to the payload bay, which houses the Spacelab, is through an airlock and pressurized tunnel at the rear of the lower deck.

Courtesy, NASA

Fred W. Haise, Jr., trains to become a space shuttle orbiter astronaut in the shuttle procedures simulator at the Johnson Space Center. This training facility simulates the primary flight control station of the flight deck of the orbiter.

requirements are the same as for pilot candidates. Mission specialists, on the other hand, can have a minimum height of 5 feet and a maximum height of 6 feet 4 inches.

The basic astronaut training program for the candidates will be far less demanding than for previous programs. The operation of the orbiter and Spacelab do not dictate such a strenuous preparation for missions. Neither vehicle will land on the Moon, as did Apollo, nor stay in orbit about the Earth for several months, as did Skylab. Thus, there will be no need for candidates to spend long hours in space suits deploying complex scientific equipment. Formal classes in academic subjects such as astronomy, space physics, physiology, and elementary mechanics and aerodynamics will probably not be required at all. Greater emphasis will be placed upon simulators of various types.

The shuttle procedures simulator is used to develop the general operational flight procedures for the crew as well as specific operational procedures for different types of missions. It is used mainly for training in guidance, control, navigation, and computer operation.

The crew procedures evaluation simulator is used to train only those pilots that will participate in the initial phases of the orbiter testing, the approach and landing tests to be made in 1978. Seated in a mock-up of the orbiter cockpit, the commander and pilot manipulate the controls in response to a view of the landing strip at Edwards Air Force Base (California) projected on the window in front of them. It is similar to devices used to train airline pilots.

The shuttle mission simulator is a complex and realistic replica of the orbiter's flight deck and crew station for training crews in all phases of vehicle operations. It includes simulations of all major systems of the vehicle. By 1978 the device will contain features such as color projections on windows of the actual sights the crew will see during various phases of a particular mission.

As the shuttle program matures, special simulators for training flight crews in the Spacelab and the interim upper stage will be added. The interim upper stage, being developed by the U.S. Air Force, is a second rocket stage carried in the orbiter's cargo bay. It permits satellites to be placed into geosynchronous orbits (remaining always over the same point on the Earth) or probes on trajectories into deep space.

There is also available at the Johnson Center a life-sciences payload development facility. It consists of a simulated orbiter flight deck and Spacelab. The unit has been used on several occasions to provide a means by which science, engineering, and operational evaluations can be made of the Spacelab and orbiter.

Also playing an important role in the training of astronauts is the airplane. It is used in three ways. Brief periods of weightlessness are produced by flying an aircraft through a parabolic path. Typically, a KC-135 flown in such a manner can produce about 30 seconds of zero gravity. During this period, trainees float about to become familiar with the state of weightlessness. They also perform tasks that they will later do in space.

Nik Wheeler/SIPA—Black Star

A modified Gulfstream-2 executive aircraft is used to train orbiter pilots in landing their craft. The jet engines of the plane were replaced with thrust-reversible models, and special aerodynamic surfaces were added to the underside of the wings. Thus equipped, the plane can be landed in the "dead stick" (no power) mode that approximates the flight characteristics of the orbiter.

Finally, a modified Learjet, a Lockheed C-141, and a Convair 990 are used to establish operational procedures involving scientific experiments that can be used in Spacelab. The program is called ASSESS (Airborne Science/Spacelab Experiments System Simulation), and it offers a means of identifying and training potential mission specialists and payload specialists. Between 1972 and 1977 a series of flights in such aircraft were made to simulate as far as possible the way in which payload and mission specialists will function aboard the Spacelab.

The new astronauts and some hopefuls

The first men to fly the "Enterprise" have already been selected. They will not, however, fly it from Earth into space and back. Fred W. Haise, Jr., and Charles G. Fullerton will conduct approach and landing test flights of the orbiter at Edwards Air Force Base. The two men and their orbiter will be mounted on top of a modified Boeing 747 jet and flown to an altitude of approximately 28,000 feet. There, the orbiter will be released, and Haise and Fullerton will guide it back to a landing. Haise was selected as an astronaut in 1966 and was the lunar module pilot on the ill-fated Apollo 13 mission in 1970. Fullerton joined the astronaut team in 1969 but has not been on a space mission.

Subsequent flights of the same type will be made by Joseph Engle, who became an astronaut in 1966 after having flown 16 missions in the X-15 rocket plane, and Richard H. Truly, who joined the astronaut

First space shuttle orbiter to leave the ground, the "Enterprise" was carried piggyback on a Boeing 747 over the Mojave Desert on Feb. 18, 1977. The two craft remained joined together throughout the flight, which lasted more than two hours and reached an altitude of approximately 16,000 feet.

91

Courtesy, NASA

John W. Young, chief of the Astronaut Office at the Johnson Space Center, checks out the orbiter aeroflight simulator. The controls and displays simulate the flight deck of a shuttle orbiter crew compartment.

group in 1969. Neither man has flown in space. Operational space missions will be made by men and women yet to be selected. Pilots and mission specialists finally selected and offered jobs with NASA will be expected to remain for at least five years. For civilians so accepted the pay will range between $11,000 and $35,000 a year with personnel becoming members of the federal civil service. U.S. military candidates selected will remain with their arm of service and be paid according to their rank.

Within a few weeks after the announcement of openings for astronauts, queries were arriving at the Johnson Space Center from all parts of the world. Each day's mail brought some 150 to 200 letters. Many of these wanted more information than given in the announcement, but a considerable number asked for applications. After three months approximately 5,500 queries had been received, not only from the U.S. but also from such countries as Canada, Mexico, Great Britain, West Germany, Australia, Sweden, Nigeria, New Zealand, and Brazil. One inquiry was received from a citizen of the U.S.S.R. By the beginning of 1977, NASA had received 225 applications for pilot, 922 for mission specialist, and 118 for both.

Among those determined to find a place in space were several women. Mrs. Ann F. Whitaker, who has a bachelor's and a master's degree in physics, has been with NASA's Marshall Space Flight Center (Alabama) since 1963. Specializing in the field of surface physics, she has conducted research into the effects of the space environment on semiconductors, lubrication, bearings, and gears. She wants to pursue her profession in space as a mission specialist or payload specialist but not as a "one shot affair." Whitaker summed up her reasons for wanting to become an astronaut: "Spacelab provides an excellent opportunity for the scientific community, both men and women, to conduct their own experiments in space. They can change their procedures in real-time, if necessary, and adjust to changing conditions. They can adjust or repair their equipment on the spot. I want to fly in Spacelab because I have some ideas I would like to test."

Mrs. Carolyn S. Griner, also of the Marshall Center, has a bachelor's degree in astronautical engineering and is pursuing graduate work in industrial and systems engineering. After joining the center in 1974, she specialized in the processing of materials in the space environment. Mary Helen Johnston, who has a Ph.D. in metallurgical engineering, works closely with Griner at the Marshall Center and specializes in research on the solidification of materials, crystal growth, and X-ray diffraction. She and Griner are interested in becoming either mission or payload specialists. Johnston and Griner collaborated in an experiment launched in December 1974 aboard a Black Brant sounding rocket at White Sands Missile Range in New Mexico. Their study of materials processing underwent about five minutes of weightlessness after the rocket burned out. Considering the experiment, Griner said, "Recent sounding rocket flights have confirmed our belief that certain materials processing can be done only under weightless conditions, or

Photos, courtesy, NASA

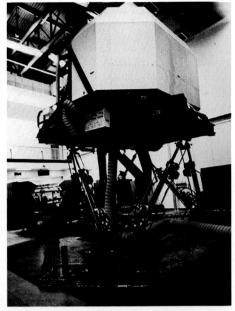

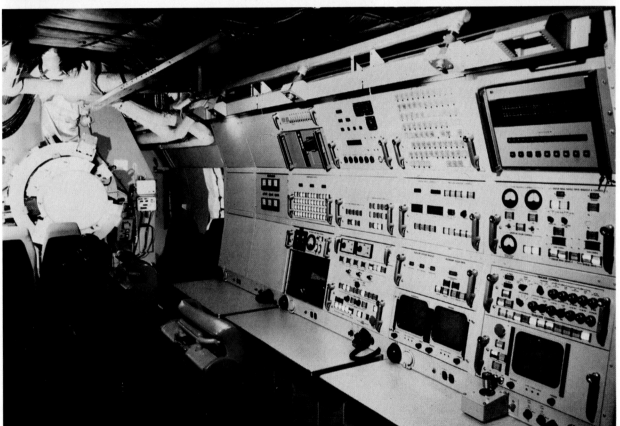

U.S. women astronauts undergo simulated weightlessness during scuba training in the neutral buoyancy simulator (top left). The exterior of the orbiter aeroflight simulator is at the top right. Above is the interior of the airborne infrared observatory, a Lockheed C-141 jet transport fitted with an infrared telescope.

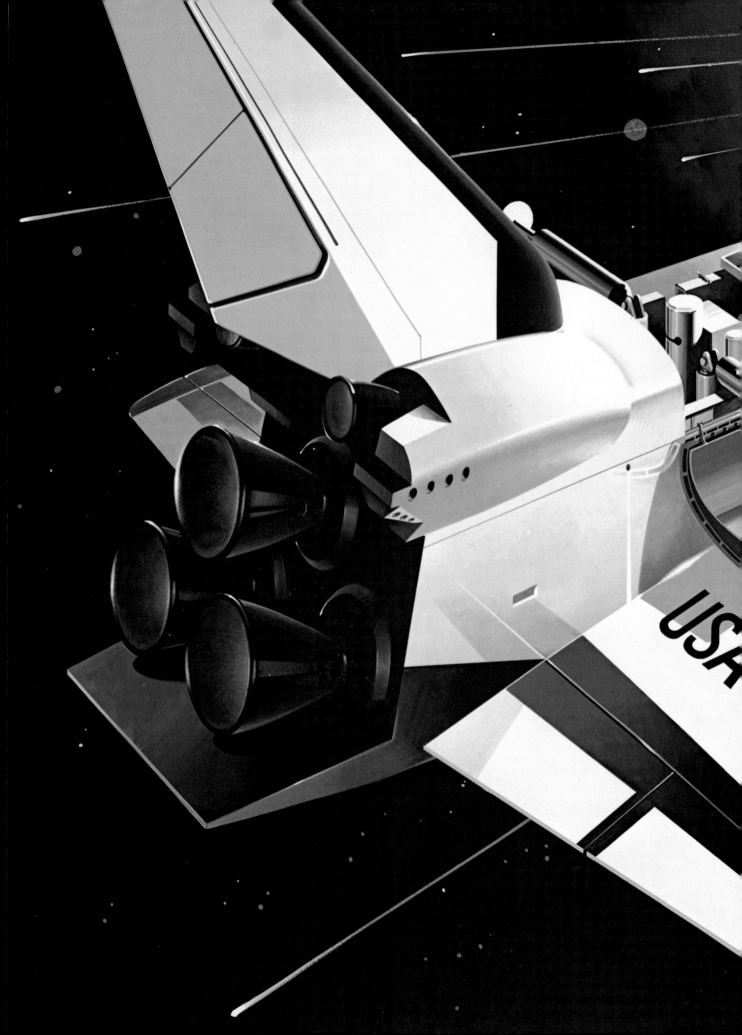

Cutaway drawing of the shuttle orbiter shows the location of Spacelab. Scientists and payload specialists work in the pressurized forward module, which is connected to the shuttle cabin by a pressurized tunnel. In the rear are two unpressurized pallet sections in which are mounted scientific instruments, including telescopes, sensors, and antennas. This equipment is operated remotely from the pressurized module.

(Top) Courtesy, NASA; (below) Tiziou—Sygma

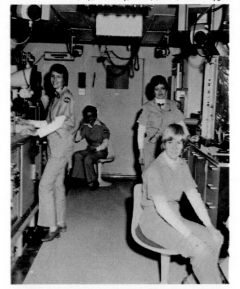

Top, Carolyn Griner, Doris Chandler, Ann Whitaker, and Mary Johnston (left to right) performed a five-day mission in the General Purpose Laboratory at the Marshall Space Flight Center in Huntsville, Alabama. They conducted materials-processing experiments of the type that could be performed in the Spacelab. Below (left to right) are Richard Truly, Joseph Engle, Fred Haise, and Charles Fullerton, the pilots selected to be the first to fly the shuttle orbiter "Enterprise" during the testing program.

at least under very low gravity influence. Spacelab offers the opportunity for us to develop this technology for the benefit of everyone on Earth. This, to me, is too important to be ignored. We must pursue this avenue of approach in space."

Typical of the women at the Johnson Space Center planning on a career in space are Mrs. Jeri Brown and Miss Marsha Ivins. While Brown is more interested in being a payload specialist, she intends to apply as mission specialist as well. Ivins has applied for pilot as well as mission specialist and will apply for payload specialist.

Brown has a degree in engineering science and works in the Johnson Center's human factors organization. During the Skylab mission, she worked with biomedical specialists to determine why astronauts grew a couple of inches during their flights. Joining the Johnson Center in 1974 with a degree in aerospace engineering, Ivins began specializing in the field of advanced control systems for manned spacecraft. During the Apollo/Soyuz Test Project, in 1974, she helped to operate the environmental control system console for the Apollo spacecraft in the mission control center at Houston. She has also been qualified in an Air Force high-altitude chamber and has experienced weightlessness in a KC-135 aircraft.

Equally as enthusiastic about the prospects for becoming astronauts were male employees of various NASA centers. Typical of them are Leon Weaver of the Marshall Space Flight Center, W. Carter Alexander of the Johnson Space Center, and Robert D. Price of the Goddard Space Flight Center (Maryland).

Like many of his competitors, Weaver has long been interested in flying. An aerospace engineer, he has a commercial pilot's license and has spent time in jets. At the Marshall Center, he is involved in defining and selecting experiments for the first Spacelab missions. He is primarily interested in becoming a payload specialist and wants a full-time role in space. Weaver expresses the desire "to follow a project from conception through design, development, test, and into orbit."

Alexander, a physiologist in the Life Sciences Astronaut Office, has been intimately involved in the training of astronauts. Indeed, he has developed and evaluated plans and concepts for training astronauts in the simulators and devices described above. He is interested in becoming a mission specialist because of its career status. "Should I fail to be selected on a career basis, I will seek assignment as a payload specialist, at such time as these selections are announced. My goal is a career appointment; however, the opportunity to fly in any capacity is acceptable to me," he says.

Price, the Landsat Results Manager at the Goddard Center, is an astrophysicist who has specialized in the field of high-energy radiation. He is interested in the position of mission specialist primarily because of his profession and his familiarity with the types of experiments that will be flown on the first two Spacelab missions.

There is no lack of highly qualified candidates for astronauts elsewhere in the world. Most of them come from the 11 member nations of

Jim Collison

the European Space Agency. Typical of such individuals is Francisco Costanzo, of Italy, who is a mechanical engineer with ESA's European Space Technology Center in The Netherlands. He specializes in problems of structural and thermal control systems and worked on such satellites as HEOS (Highly Eccentric Orbit Satellite), launched in 1971, and GEOS (Geodetic Earth Orbiting Satellite), launched in 1973.

Costanzo's motivation for entering Europe's space program came from an early fascination with science fiction, particularly books of Jules Verne, and from his interest in mountain climbing, gliding, flying, and parachuting. He spent a year at the Johnson Space Center on a one-year fellowship and worked on problems involving the remote manipulator system of the orbiter. While there, he applied for mission specialist after having earlier applied for payload specialist with ESA.

From these examples it can be seen that the motivation for those hoping to become the new generation of astronauts differs in many respects from that of the first generation. There is less emphasis on adventure and on the task of developing and testing spacecraft. Instead, the new generation wants to pursue professional goals and expand personal horizons and capabilities, increase knowledge generally, and benefit mankind by exploiting the space environment.

On a special 90-wheel trailer rig the "Enterprise" is moved 35 miles overland from the assembly plant at Palmdale, Calif., to the Dryden Flight Research Center at Edwards, Calif.

FOR ADDITIONAL READING

Melvin Calvin and Oleg G. Gazenko, *Foundations of Space Biology Medicine,* vol. iii, *Space Medicine and Biotechnology* (National Aeronautics and Space Administration, 1975).

James E. Oberg, "Testing the Space Shuttle . . . Piggyback Style!" in *Science Digest* (vol. 80, no. 4, 1976, pp. 54-61).

Evgeny Riabchikov, *Russians in Space* (Doubleday, 1971).

Mitchell R. Sharpe, *Living in Space: The Astronaut and His Environment* (Doubleday, 1969).

Wernher von Braun, *Space Frontier* (Rinehart & Winston, 1967).

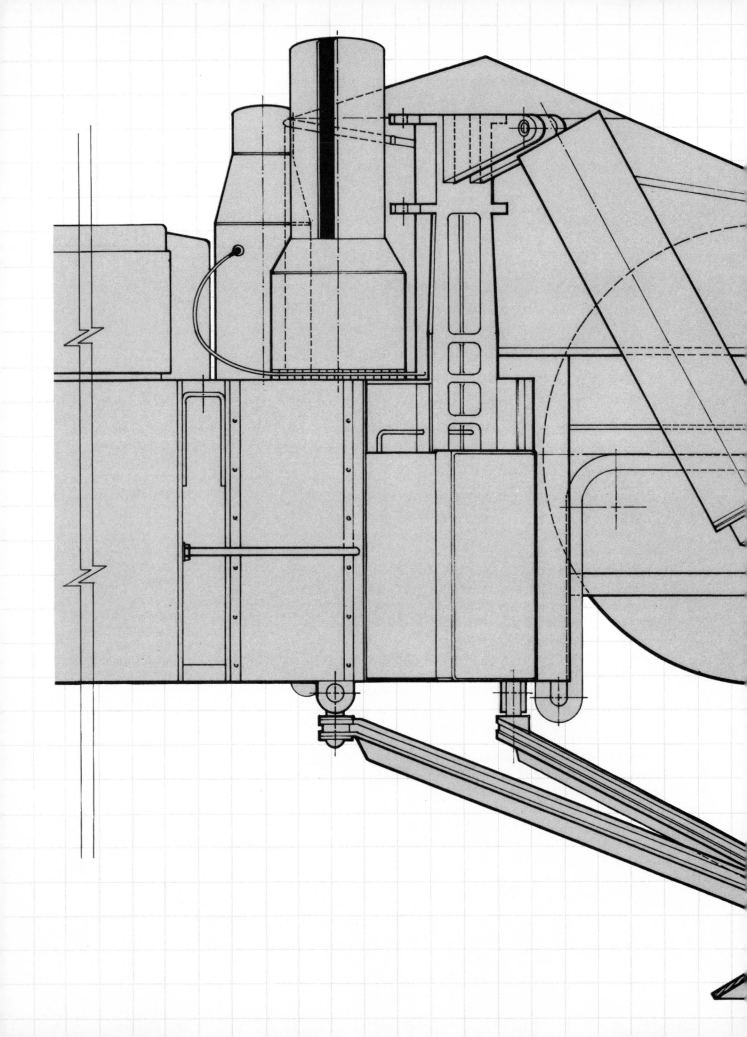

The Viking Mission to Mars

by Gerald A. Soffen

The first successful soft-landing of spacecraft on the surface of Mars was not only a remarkable feat of aerospace engineering but also has provided scientists with a wealth of fascinating data about our neighboring planet.

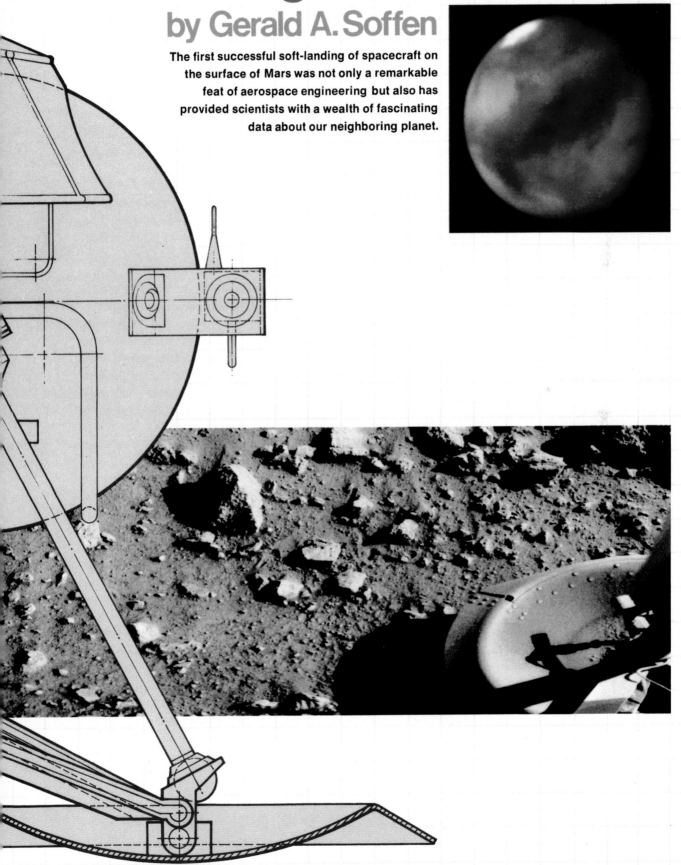

Courtesy, Martin Marietta

Titan IIIE Centaur, the launch vehicle for both Viking 1 and Viking 2.

GERALD A. SOFFEN *is a Viking Project Scientist at the Jet Propulsion Laboratory in Pasadena, California.*

(Overleaf) Photographs, Courtesy, NASA. Illustrations by Ben Kozak

A major achievement in the exploration of space took place in 1976 when the United States landed two unmanned spacecraft on the surface of Mars, 212 million miles from the Earth. For the first time scientists could study the planet at close range and possibly resolve the long debate as to whether or not it harbors life. The two spacecraft, Viking 1 (launched Aug. 20, 1975) and Viking 2 (launched Sept. 9, 1975), carried a wide range of scientific equipment designed to detect any traces of life and also to analyze other properties of the planet's surface and atmosphere.

The Vikings were the first spacecraft to land and fulfill their missions on the Martian surface. The U.S. had restricted its previous efforts to flybys, and the only Soviet craft to land transmitted for only 20 seconds. The landings climaxed a decade of planning and work by thousands of people; the cost of the project was approximately $1 billion.

The spacecraft

Each Viking spacecraft consisted of an orbiter, a lander capsule, and a lander support structure that was jettisoned by the orbiter after the landing. The orbiter was similar in construction and operation to the Mariner spacecraft, particularly Mariner 9, but it was considerably larger and had expanded capabilities for the storage and execution of commands and for the storage and transmission of data. Like their Mariner ancestors, the orbiters were powered by solar energy and carried two antennas (high-gain parabolic and low-gain omnidirectional) for two-way communication with the Earth. To accommodate its passenger, the lander, each orbiter had a relay antenna for receiving the lander's data transmissions from the Mars surface and facilities for supplying power and command information to the encapsulated lander and for accepting information from it so that the lander subsystems could be thoroughly checked out before separation.

Each Viking lander was a three-legged aluminum hexagonal structure weighing approximately 1,000 pounds. Within the body were the computer, power, data, thermal control, and scientific instrument systems. Mounted on top were the cameras, seismometer, antennas, and radioisotope thermoelectric generators to supply power. When attached to the orbiter, the lander was within a double capsule. One part of the inner capsule was an aeroshell within which the lander was nested during the descent, and the other part consisted of a bioshield and basecover and parachute system. The second and outer capsule consisted of a bioshield and base and cap.

Flight to Mars

Viking 1 was launched into an orbit that would bring it close to Mars in June 1976 but not so close as to entail a significant risk of landing on the planet. On the seventh day after the launch a maneuver to correct the orbit was executed; it was so precise that the spacecraft could have gone into orbit around Mars with no further adjustments than the single propulsive maneuver at the planet. A preliminary check-

Courtesy, NASA

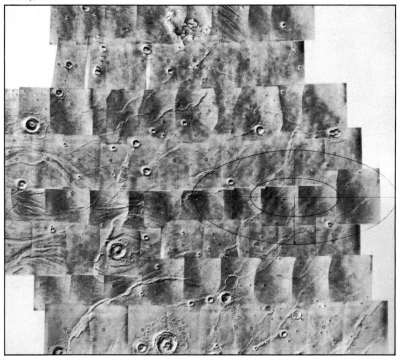

Courtesy, Martin Marietta

Drawn on the photomosaic (top) is the dispersion ellipse in the center of which is the landing site of Viking 1, in the Chryse Planitia basin. A similar picture had revealed potentially hazardous terrain in the originally designated landing site 740 kilometers (460 miles) to the southeast. At the left is a model of the Viking lander.

out of the subsystems in the lander was made soon after launch, and during the next few months several tests were run on the gas chromatograph-mass spectrometer and on the temperature sensors of the meteorology experiment. Certain engineering subsystems on the lander, including the gyroscopes and the tape recorder, were checked out periodically. The computers were programmed and batteries were conditioned by telemetered command, but the scientific instruments of the lander were otherwise dormant until the next to last day of the 304-day interplanetary cruise.

Sixty-one days after launch a picture of the Earth was taken with one orbiter camera, for purposes of calibration. During the next eight months several large sets of pictures of star fields were taken to provide geometric and photometric calibrations of the cameras and to determine accurately the pointing of the scan platform on which the orbiter's science instruments were mounted.

Fifty-seven days before insertion into orbit around Mars preparations for orbital operations began with the first of several lander battery conditioning sequences involving discharge and recharge of the batteries, with power supplied by the orbiter. Subsequently, both orbiter cameras recorded pictures of Jupiter to provide photometric calibration, and the other orbiter science instruments were also calibrated.

Three optical navigation sequences were performed in which one orbiter camera took pictures of Mars and the other took pictures of the star field close to Mars. These pictures were analyzed to determine the position of the Viking-Mars line, and this technique of optical navigation considerably increased the precision of the knowledge about the spacecraft's position.

The maneuver to insert Viking 1 into orbit around Mars began on June 19. The propulsion engine burned for 38 minutes, reducing the spacecraft velocity by 1.1 kilometers per second (1 kilometer = 0.62 mile). When the spacecraft was safely in orbit, the site certification phase of the mission began.

The site certification observations started with a set of widely dispersed pictures surrounding the preselected site at latitude 19.5° N, longitude 34° W. Swaths of contiguous pictures to cover the dispersion ellipse around the nominal landing site were laid down. These

infrared thermal mapper

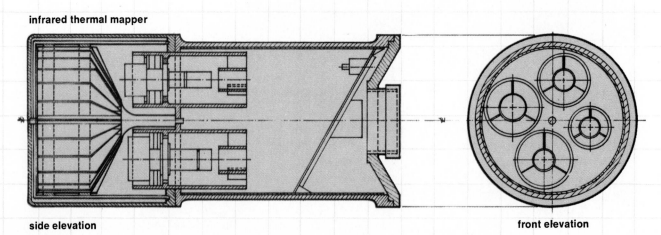

side elevation   **front elevation**

pictures showed unexpected detail and clearly indicated the presence of fluvial features and some mottled terrain, which appeared to be too hazardous to attempt a landing. Consequently, the picture sequences were retargeted to the northwest of the original site in the direction of the Chryse Planitia basin. These pictures also did not look reassuring; therefore, after a few days for replanning and redesigning, pictures were taken of areas to the west. A study of these pictures together with the results of radar data from the Arecibo Observatory in Puerto Rico concerning the area in early July resulted in selecting an acceptable landing site at latitude 22.4° N, longitude 47.5° W.

Landing the spacecraft

After separation from the orbiter, the lander aligned itself for the deorbit maneuver by using small attitude-control jets. At this time it was traveling at 4.6 kilometers per second. After deorbit and a three-hour coasting period, the braking was performed by three systems: an aeroshell, a supersonic parachute, and terminal descent rocket engines.

The lander entered the Martian atmosphere with its attitude still controlled by the jets. Its entry was made at an angle that allowed it to obtain a small amount of lift, which contributed to the deceleration needed for the soft landing. During the entry the ablation (burning away) of the aeroshell heat shield protected the capsule from atmospheric heating.

The landing radar system operated in conjunction with the onboard computers, gyroscopes, and accelerometers to determine the direction and distance to the surface. Peak deceleration occurred at 25 kilometers above the surface. At an altitude of 6 kilometers (descending at 250 meters per second) the parachute was deployed by a mortar, and seven seconds later the aeroshell was jettisoned. Eight seconds later the lander's legs were extended. The parachute operated for 45 seconds until the lander was 1.5 kilometers above the surface (descending at 60 meters per second). The terminal descent engine fired for 40 seconds to reduce the final velocity to 2 meters per second, and touchdown on the surface of Mars was made on July 20, 1976.

A switch on the lander footpad automatically shut off the descent engine when the first leg touched the surface. Honeycomb-aluminum shock absorbers in the legs helped to cushion the impact. The Viking 1 lander set down in a flat valley at an angle to the surface within 3° of vertical, its cameras facing to the southeast.

After 25 seconds on the surface one camera began to take a high-resolution picture of one of the lander's footpads. The slow-scanning camera performed in this mode for four minutes, and the first picture from Mars was obtained. During this time the lander activated itself. A high-gain antenna was erected and pointed for direct communication to the Earth. The meteorology boom with its sensors was deployed. The second picture of the 300° panoramic scene around the lander was taken in the next seven minutes. On the day after the landing the first color picture of the surface was taken.

Courtesy, NASA

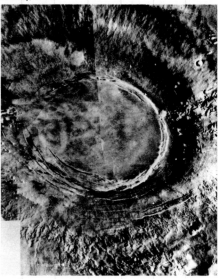

Mosaic of five photographs taken from the Viking 1 orbiter at an altitude of 6,000 kilometers (3,700 miles) reveals Arsia Mons, a Martian volcano that rises about 19 kilometers (12 miles) above the surrounding terrain. The central caldera, a circular collapse depression, is about 120 kilometers (75 miles) in diameter. The fine linear features outside the caldera are lava flows.

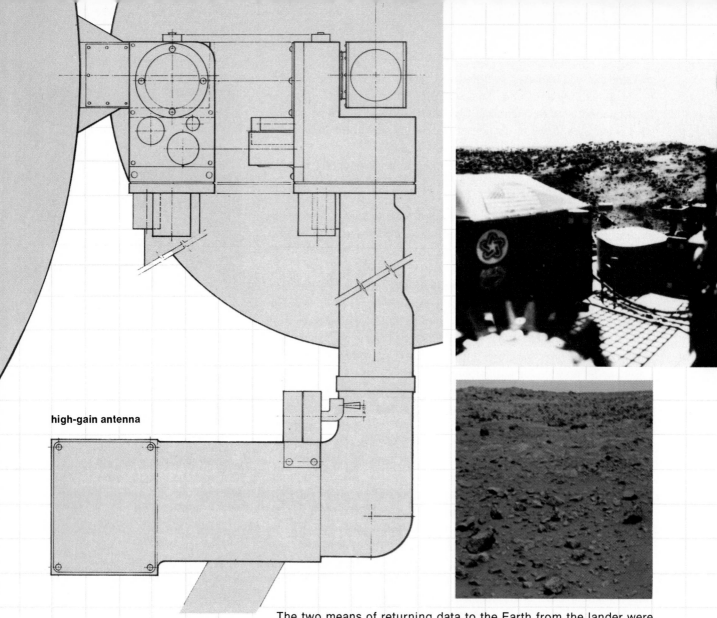

high-gain antenna

The two means of returning data to the Earth from the lander were by a relay link to the orbiter and back and by direct link to Earth. The relay link carried about ten times the data of the direct link. The capacity of the relay link was 10 million to 20 million bits per day, while that of the direct link was about 1 million bits per day.

The flight and landing procedures of Viking 2 were similar to those of Viking 1. Viking 2 was launched from the Earth on Sept. 9, 1975, and went into orbit around Mars on Aug. 7, 1976. The lander touched down on the planet on Sept. 3, 1976, north and west of Viking 1 at latitude 47.9° N, longitude 225.9° W. Following the landing of the second spacecraft the first lander was placed in a reduced mode of operation. Certain monitoring, such as meteorology, was continued through the direct link with Earth, but the relay to the orbiter was suspended. Operation of the Viking 2 lander continued for two months. During that period all instruments performed successfully.

The landers and orbiters were powered down during the period of the Sun's intercession between Mars and the Earth from mid-November to

104

mid-December 1976. At that time a radio science experiment to test the general relativity theory was performed. This was done by determining the influence of the solar corona on the transmission from the spacecraft. Both pairs of orbiter/landers were used to measure the attenuation of the spacecraft signals by the Sun. The 42-minute round trip for light to travel between the Sun and Mars was determined to an accuracy of one ten-millionth of a second.

Orbiter experiments

Both the Viking 1 and Viking 2 orbiters came as close to the surface of Mars as 1,500 kilometers. In late September the engine was fired on Viking 2 to perform a maneuver that would increase its orbital inclination. This plane change resulted in an inclination of 75°, which permitted a considerable improvement in the spacecraft's view of the polar regions. The summer solstice began in the northern hemisphere in early July, and therefore the Viking 2 orbiter was able to view the changing polar events through the seasons during which the polar hood and the seasonal polar cap are formed.

The cameras on board the orbiters provided the primary data for the final selection of the landing sites. The Chryse area (latitude 20° N, longitude 40–50° W) was thoroughly mapped by means of the mosaics of several thousand photographs. The Chryse basin was found to be a low region into which several ancient rivers empty. While there was no evidence of an ancient ocean, the general region is flat. The source and sink of fluid that created this region is still disputed. The Utopia site of Viking 2, selected primarily because of its northern latitude, is a volcanic terrain covered by a mantling that appears to have been deposited from more northerly regions. It was anticipated that large sand dunes would be found in this region, but these were not seen in the lander pictures.

Panorama of Martian surface (above) taken by camera in the Viking 1 lander reveals a landscape of sand dunes and large rocks. The two low hills in the center on the horizon may be part of the rim of a crater. The nearest of the two large rocks is 3 meters (10 feet) in diameter and 8 meters (25 feet) from the spacecraft. The orange-red color of the surface materials of Mars is shown in a Viking 1 photograph (opposite page). The reddish hue of the sky is probably due to scattering and reflection of the reddish sediment suspended in the lower atmosphere.

(Photos) Courtesy, NASA

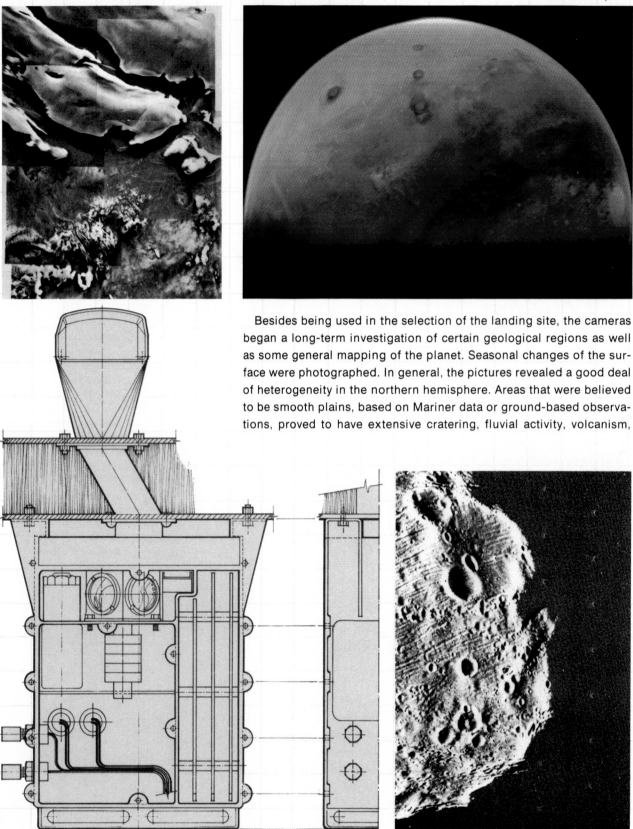

(Photos) Courtesy, NASA

Besides being used in the selection of the landing site, the cameras began a long-term investigation of certain geological regions as well as some general mapping of the planet. Seasonal changes of the surface were photographed. In general, the pictures revealed a good deal of heterogeneity in the northern hemisphere. Areas that were believed to be smooth plains, based on Mariner data or ground-based observations, proved to have extensive cratering, fluvial activity, volcanism,

X-ray fluorescence spectrometer

(Photos) Courtesy, NASA

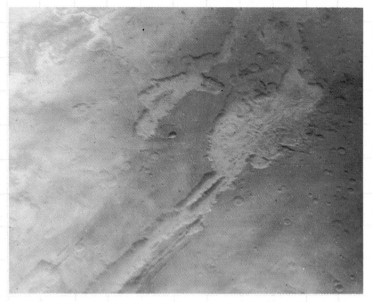

erosion, and possibly some glaciation. Large regions exhibited catastrophic flooding but had left no evidence of sedimentary basins. Most
of the surface appeared to be old. The crater density ranged from about
one-tenth to the same as that on the Moon, and the presence of numerous small craters on Mars suggested that wind erosion played a minor
role in their formation. Diffuse morning clouds, wave clouds associated
with surface features, and discrete equatorial clouds were observed.
The polar regions revealed vast areas of layered deposits, sand dunes,
and areas free of ice, suggesting a complex climatic history.

An infrared spectrometer mounted on the scan platform of each orbiter was used to detect water vapor in the Martian atmosphere. This
scanning device was used to measure the latitudinal variations and
diurnal variations in the amount of water vapor and, by operating over
a complete Martian year, was designed to be able to measure the seasonal changes as well. At the time of the first measurements, the southern hemisphere, which was at the onset of winter, had little water vapor
in the atmosphere (0–0.3 precipitable microns). By contrast, the northern hemisphere showed a significant amount of water (up to 75 microns
at latitude 70–80° N). The north polar region revealed a slight drop
in water-vapor abundance. There was also a strong diurnal repetitive
cycle in certain regions, peaking out in the local mid-afternoon.
Based upon the abundance of water vapor in the polar region, a lower
limit can be put on the atmospheric temperature in excess of −68° C
(−90° F). This indicates that the permanent polar cap consists of water
ice, confirmed by an infrared radiometer investigation.

An infrared radiometer measuring thermal emission of the surface
and atmosphere was mounted with the cameras and spectrometer, all
three instruments overlapping the same viewing area. The atmospheric
temperature above 20 kilometers varied from −108° C (−162° F) near
dawn to −88° C (−126° F) at 2:15 PM local time. This variation was

*North polar ice cap of Mars (opposite
page, top left) is shown in
photomosaic of television pictures
from the Viking 2 orbiter. Also
photographed by the orbiter, from a
distance of 880 kilometers (545 miles),
was Phobos, the inner satellite of
Mars (opposite page, bottom). Mars
from a distance of 560,000 kilometers
(348,000 miles) is rendered in color
(opposite page, top right) by
combining three separate pictures
taken from Viking 1 through color
filters. The large surface features are
volcanoes. Above left, three separate
pictures through red, green, and
violet filters were taken of Mariner
Valley on Mars by the Viking 1 orbiter
at an altitude of 31,000 kilometers
(19,000 miles) and were computer-
processed and combined to produce
the color photograph. Above is a color
mosaic of the Mariner Valley based on
15 photographs taken through
color filters by the Viking 1 orbiter.*

powered collector head

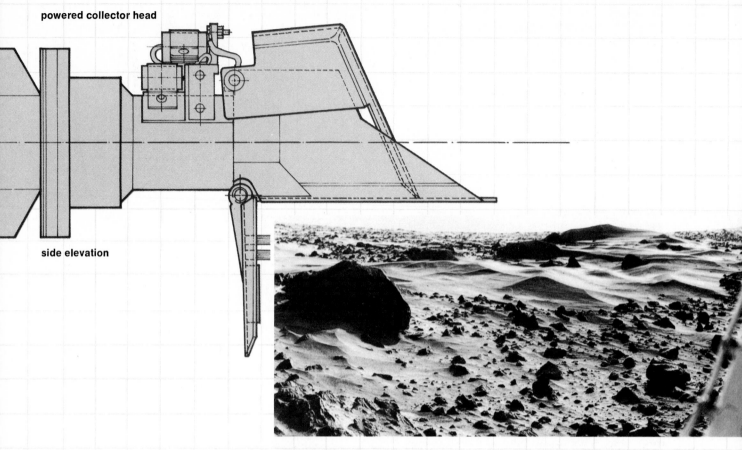

side elevation

Dune field on Mars (right) was photographed from the Viking 1 lander. The picture, which spans 100°, reveals a landscape similar to that of many deserts on the Earth. Cutting through its center is the lander's meteorology boom. Opposite top, the surface sampler of Viking 1 is seen at rest near fine-grained material and rocks of various types. Rocks with vesicles (small cavities) were found near both landing sites (opposite center). The collector head of the surface sampler of Viking 1 (opposite bottom) contains Martian soil that will be analyzed by the gas chromatograph mass spectrometer for the presence of organic molecules.

believed to be initiated at the lower levels. The temperature of the surface was found to be highly variable, the annual variation becoming modulated closer to the equator. The daily temperature range measured at the landing site of Viking 1 was about −90° C (−130° F) to −8° C (18° F). Diurnal variation decreasing with depth, a calculation was made for the soil samples collected from under the rock, and the temperature there was about −43° C (−45° F).

Lander experiments

During their descent the landers measured the physical structure and chemical composition of the Martian atmosphere. The atmospheric pressure and temperature were recorded, and a density profile was calculated yielding a mean molecular weight of 43.34. The entry of Viking 1 in the afternoon and of Viking 2 in the morning revealed a diurnal difference in temperature near the surface consistent with the infrared radiometer data. The upper atmosphere was found to consist mainly of carbon dioxide with small amounts of nitrogen, argon, carbon monoxide, oxygen, atomic oxygen, and nitric oxide. The ratio of the isotopes of carbon and oxygen to one another is similar to that on the Earth, but the ratio of nitrogen-15 to nitrogen-14 is higher, suggesting that Mars once had a denser atmosphere. This denser atmosphere could account for the evidence of ancient rivers seen in the photographs. (The pressure of 7.6 millibars cannot support liquid water.) The

108

(Photos) Courtesy, NASA

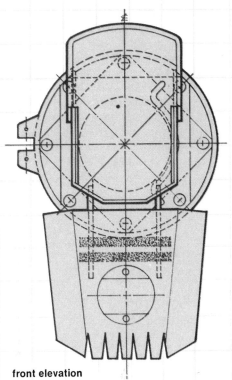

front elevation

ionosphere was also measured to determine the nature of the charged particles there. These data will be used in developing models to reconstruct the atmosphere and its history.

Hundreds of photographs were taken at each of the landing areas. Both sites were dominated by a variety of rocks lying among fine-grained material. Chryse and Utopia are similar in some ways and different in others. Both areas revealed a bright red color for the surface and a pink sky. The Chryse site contained drifts of fine-grained sediment that appeared in the lee of large boulders. The shape of the drifts and the layering indicate that there had been extensive periods of erosion and deposition. Chemical weathering of the rocks was also apparent. Rocks with vesicles (small cavities) and those that were fine-grained and smooth were found at both sites. Some rocks appeared to be fairly angular, possibly due to wind action.

The Utopia site is cut by a trough believed to be part of a larger polygonal pattern seen from orbit. In light of the significant difference between the two sites as seen from orbit, it is striking how similar they are at the ground level. This may be due to the fact that the large-scale features seen from above reflect the ancient processes, while the local planetwide weathering is contemporary.

The cameras were used to determine certain physical and magnetic properties of the Martian soil. Pictures helped to determine its bulk density, particle size, angle of internal friction, cohesion, adhesion, and

Courtesy, NASA

The Sun sets over Chryse Planitia. A camera on the Viking 1 lander began scanning the scene from the left about four minutes after the Sun had dipped below the horizon and continued for ten minutes, over a range of 120° from left to right. The color variation from blue to red is caused by a combination of scattering and absorption of sunlight by atmospheric particles.

penetration resistance. Small permanent magnets on the sampler collected material which indicated that the surface contains a small percentage of magnetic material, very likely magnetite. This suggests that the rocks are not completely weathered and opens the question of the origin of the magnetic material.

A weather station to measure changes in pressure, temperature, wind speed, and direction began operating on each lander at touchdown. Generally, the weather at both sites was repetitive and mild, as expected for the season. The daily temperature varied from −83° to −33° C (−117° to −27° F). The atmospheric pressure at each site ranged from 7 to 8 millibars (compared with 1,013 millibars at sea level on the Earth). Pressures varied daily by about 0.3 millibars, but there was a steadily falling average pressure during the first 20 Sols on Mars by about 5% due to the condensation of carbon dioxide at the polar cap. The wind direction at each site went through a complete oscillation each day. Wind speeds averaged a few meters per second, the peak gust being only 19 meters per second. This was too small to raise the dust particles anticipated during the major storm seasons, when Mars is closest to the Sun.

The seismometer on the Viking 1 lander failed to be uncaged, but the Viking 2 seismometer functioned normally. In November it registered what might have been a Marsquake.

An X-ray fluorescence spectrometer was used to determine the elemental composition of samples at each of the sites. Both sites yielded strikingly similar analyses of the fine-particle material. Its composition is high in silicon and iron, with additional significant amounts of magnesium, aluminum, calcium, and sulfur. These findings suggested that the main components are SiO_2 (45%) and Fe_2O_3 (18%), with Al_2O_3

(5%), MgO (8%), CaO (5%), and SO_3 (8%) the next most abundant. This composition represents a mafic (rich in magnesium and iron) igneous parent rock and suggests an iron-rich clay with small amounts of magnesium sulfates and carbonates and iron oxides.

Two samples from each site were analyzed for organic material using volatilization and pyrolysis and detection by gas chromatography-mass spectrometry. The sensitivity of the methods reached to the level of parts per billion, and no organic compounds were detected to that level. The absence of organics was somewhat surprising considering the likelihood of carbonaceous chondrites reaching the Mars surface from space or the possibility of new syntheses on the planet. Explanations of this absence involving dilution of organic material in the regolith (mantle rock) and destruction of it by ultraviolet radiation or oxidation seemed plausible. Gas chromatography-mass spectrometry was also used to measure the Martian atmosphere; it is ideally suited to measure isotopic ratios. Based on measurements in the atmosphere of neon, argon, xenon, and krypton and their isotopic abundances, it appeared that a history of outgassing from Mars would emerge.

Three experiments provided a direct test for life on Mars. They revealed a surface that was surprisingly active chemically, one that is very likely oxidizing in nature. All the experiments yielded results, but they were subject to wide interpretation. As of early 1977 no conclusions had been reached concerning the existence of life on Mars.

The communication and radar systems on the landers were used to perform certain experiments. The locations of the landers were determined by tracking telemetry. Some dielectric properties of the planet's surface were measured, suggesting a pumicelike texture.

Future activity

The landers and orbiters of Viking 1 and Viking 2 were scheduled to remain in operation in 1977 and 1978. During that time several experiments were to be completed. Additional surface samples would be collected by each lander for further chemical and biological analyses. Pictures were to be taken from the surface and from orbit (several tens of thousands would be taken by the orbiters). The seasonal events would be followed by the orbiting vehicles as well as by the meteorological, photographic, and atmospheric analysis instruments on the landers. The long-term sensing by the seismometer was considered extremely important, and the sampler arms of the landers were to be used extensively for investigations of the physical and magnetic properties of the surface material.

Among the first activities was to be the lowering of the Viking 2 orbiter so that it would come as close to the surface as 800 kilometers; this was to be done to improve the resolution of the cameras. Concomitant with this was to be a change in the inclination of the Viking 2 orbiter by another 5° (to 80°) so as to improve the viewing of the polar events.

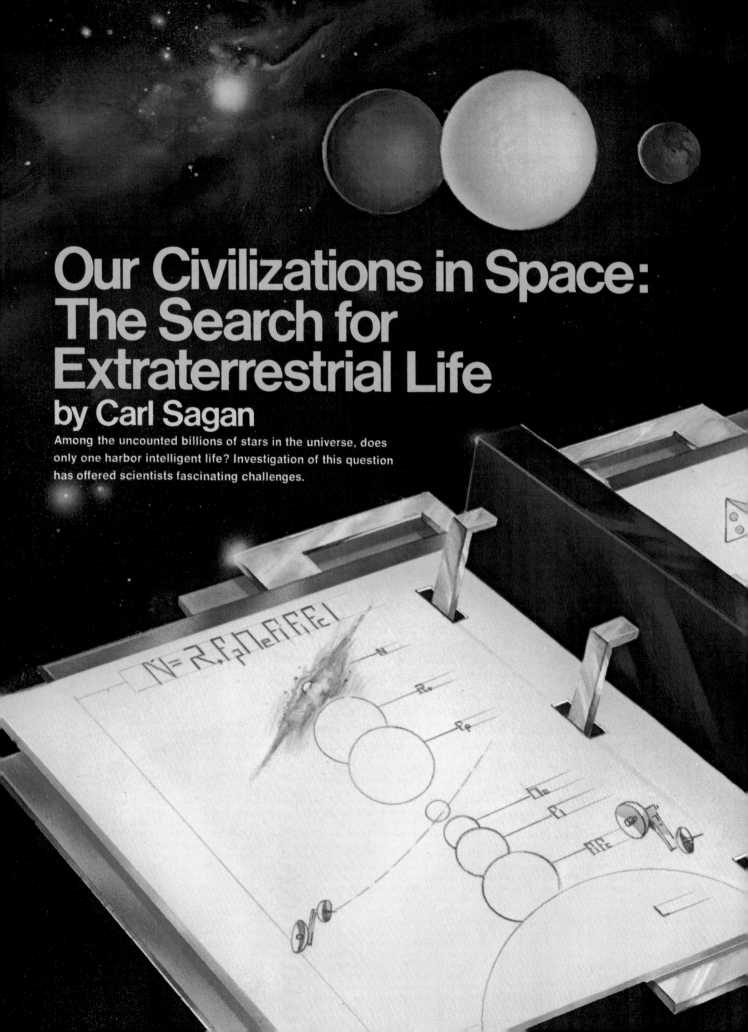

Our Civilizations in Space: The Search for Extraterrestrial Life

by Carl Sagan

Among the uncounted billions of stars in the universe, does only one harbor intelligent life? Investigation of this question has offered scientists fascinating challenges.

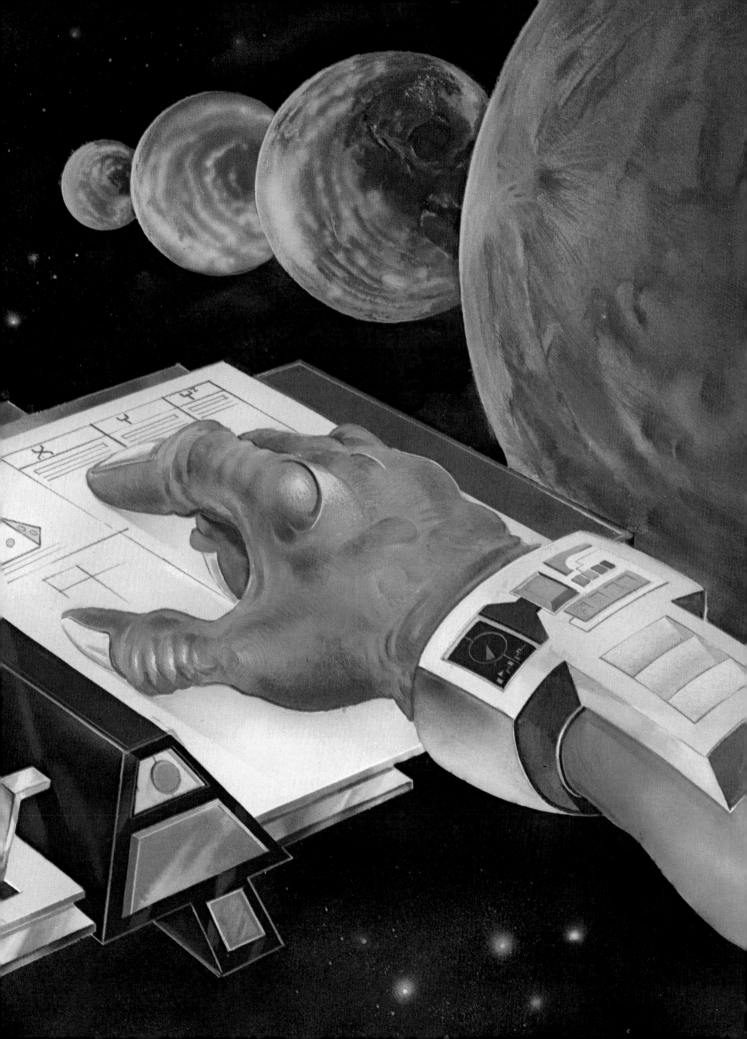

(Overleaf) If weighing the possibilities of intelligent life on other planets is assumed to be a uniquely human endeavor, then Earth's radio telescopes are searching in vain for a message from the skies. For an extraterrestrial civilization to be intentionally seeking radio contact, its scientists quite probably laid theoretical groundwork comparable to that of the astronomers of Earth.

In earlier times man commonly believed that his planet, the Earth, was the seat of mortal intelligence, about which all of creation seemed to revolve in homage. Some early thinkers, however, were bold enough to suggest that life might not be unique to Earth; as the Epicurean philosopher Metrodorus wrote, "To consider the Earth the only populated world in infinite space is as absurd as to assert that in an entire field sown with millet, only one grain will grow." After the Renaissance, fashions of belief in the existence of extraterrestrial intelligence fluctuated widely, but by the early 20th century most informed opinion once again held that the chances of finding intelligent life beyond the Earth were insignificant. But impressive advances in science and technology of the past few decades have allowed a new approach to the subject.

Estimating the chances

The probability of advanced technical civilizations arising in our Galaxy — presumably the only ones whose existence can be ascertained using methods currently available — depends upon a consideration of several uncertain parameters. In 1960 U.S. astrophysicist Frank Drake approached this problem with the following equation, which is often called the Green Bank formula: $N = R_* f_p n_e f_l f_i f_c L$. The letter N is the unknown quantity, the number of extant technical civilizations in the Galaxy; R_* is the average rate of star formation over the lifetime of the Galaxy; f_p is the fraction of stars with planetary systems; n_e is the mean number of planets per star that are ecologically suitable for the origin and evolution of life; f_l is the fraction of such planets on which life does arise; f_i is the fraction of such planets on which intelligent life evolves; f_c is the fraction of such planets on which a technical civilization develops; and L is the mean lifetime of a technical civilization.

Of all these factors, only the first can be determined easily from astronomical and astrophysical knowledge. Approximately 2×10^{11} stars comprise the Galaxy, whose age is about 10^{10} years; hence, R_* is about 10 per year. Developing meaningful values for the remaining parameters, however, is a much less secure enterprise.

Observational evidence on the existence of planets of other stars is still quite spotty. The only method so far capable of detecting a planet like Jupiter orbiting a nearby star is the gravitational perturbation technique, in which the dark companion planet is detected through its gravitational tugs on its primary star, whose motion through space can be observed from the Earth over the course of decades. The nearest single star amenable to such a method is Barnard's star, a cold, red sun some six light-years from the Earth. After a period of debate, two groups of scientists who extensively analyzed the motion of Barnard's star — one at Allegheny Observatory of the University of Pittsburgh, Pennsylvania, and the other at Sproul Observatory of Swarthmore (Pennsylvania) College — concluded that a gravitational perturbation exists, indicative of at least one and possibly more Jupiter-type planets in orbit. But the observations and their interpretation are difficult, and the two groups still do not agree on all questions of detail. The

CARL SAGAN *is David Duncan Professor of Astronomy and Space Sciences and Director, Laboratory for Planetary Studies, Cornell University, Ithaca, New York.*

Paintings by Ron Villani

observational situation is expected to be improved greatly by the construction of special astrometric telescopes on the Earth's surface and especially through the use of large optical telescopes in space, removed from atmospheric distortion.

On the theoretical side, virtually all successful models of the origin of the Sun's planetary system predict that solar systems will be a frequent, if not invariable, accompaniment to the origin of other stars. Although again the available data are sparser than might be wished, the existing evidence is consistent with the notion of abundant planetary systems among the 250 billion stars that make up the Galaxy, or a large fractional value for f_p.

The parameter n_e depends upon the distribution of the distances of planets from their primary and upon any tendency for such distances to vary systematically with the luminosity of the primary. But considering the adaptability of life and the vigor of natural selection, the product $f_p n_e$ is often assigned a value very near 1.

Evolution of life and intelligence

The paleontological record makes clear that life on Earth originated in the first few hundred million years of the planet's history, suggesting that such an event is not remarkably unlikely. Beginning in the early 1950s laboratory experiments that duplicated the chemical conditions of the primitive Earth have produced amino and hydroxy acids, nucleotide bases, porphyrins, and a variety of sugars; that is, nearly all the essential molecular building blocks of life. These readily occurring syntheses do not require peculiarly terrestrial conditions; indeed, they require a mixture of the most abundant gases — i.e., water, hydrogen, methane, and ammonia — in planetary atmospheres to be expected anywhere in the universe and any energy source capable of breaking chemical bonds, be it heat, ultraviolet light, or electrical discharge.

The case for an abundant cosmic organic chemistry has been further strengthened by two groups of recent scientific findings. One was the discovery of a wide variety of organic molecules, including amino acids, in meteorites, which originate from the airless and waterless asteroids. The other was the detection, through radio-astronomical microwave spectroscopy, of an entirely unexpected variety and abundance of simple organic molecules in the extremely inhospitable environment of interstellar space. Drifting through the Galaxy in enormous quantities are aldehydes, nitriles, cyanoacetylene, and other molecular building blocks that have been strongly implicated in prebiological organic chemistry on the primitive Earth. It is by no means clear that interstellar organic molecules contributed directly to the origin of life on such planets as the Earth; the surfaces of these planets were probably molten during their formation, thereby dissociating any weakly bonded organic molecules that fell during planetary formation. But the discovery of abundant organic molecules in interstellar space and in meteorites demonstrates how commonplace, efficient, and widely distributed are the earliest chemical steps that on Earth led to the

(Overleaf) Factors in a technical civilization's consideration of extraterrestrial life include gathering observational evidence for the existence of other solar systems, experimenting on the origin of life, understanding the evolution of intelligent beings, and estimating the lifetime of a civilization that is able to destroy itself.

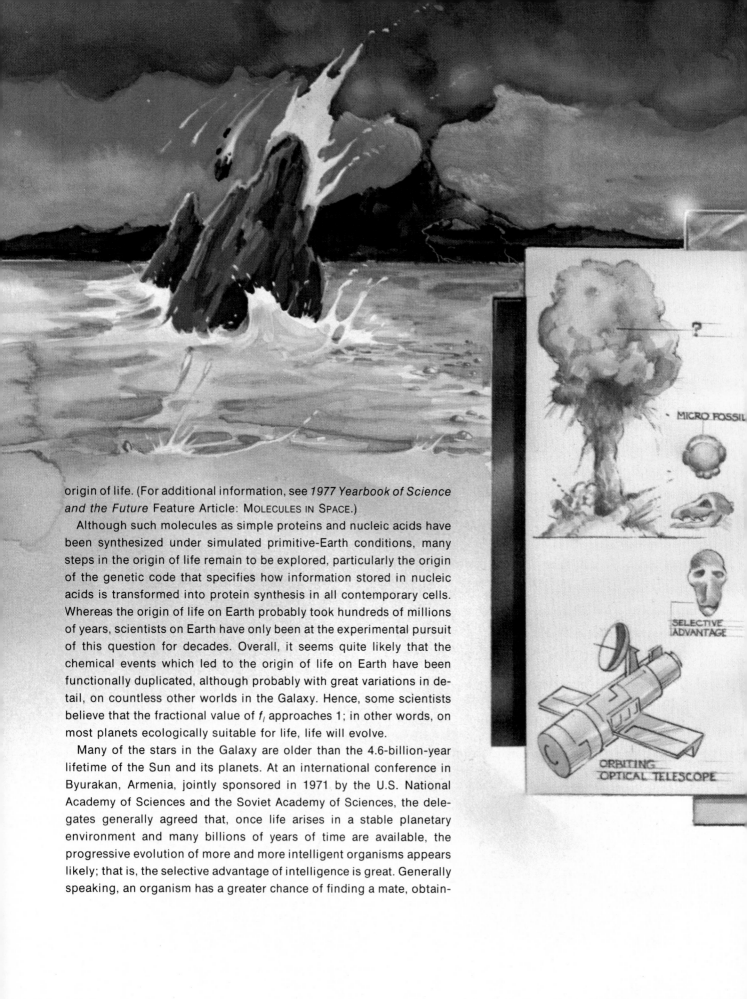

origin of life. (For additional information, see *1977 Yearbook of Science and the Future* Feature Article: Molecules in Space.)

Although such molecules as simple proteins and nucleic acids have been synthesized under simulated primitive-Earth conditions, many steps in the origin of life remain to be explored, particularly the origin of the genetic code that specifies how information stored in nucleic acids is transformed into protein synthesis in all contemporary cells. Whereas the origin of life on Earth probably took hundreds of millions of years, scientists on Earth have only been at the experimental pursuit of this question for decades. Overall, it seems quite likely that the chemical events which led to the origin of life on Earth have been functionally duplicated, although probably with great variations in detail, on countless other worlds in the Galaxy. Hence, some scientists believe that the fractional value of f_l approaches 1; in other words, on most planets ecologically suitable for life, life will evolve.

Many of the stars in the Galaxy are older than the 4.6-billion-year lifetime of the Sun and its planets. At an international conference in Byurakan, Armenia, jointly sponsored in 1971 by the U.S. National Academy of Sciences and the Soviet Academy of Sciences, the delegates generally agreed that, once life arises in a stable planetary environment and many billions of years of time are available, the progressive evolution of more and more intelligent organisms appears likely; that is, the selective advantage of intelligence is great. Generally speaking, an organism has a greater chance of finding a mate, obtain-

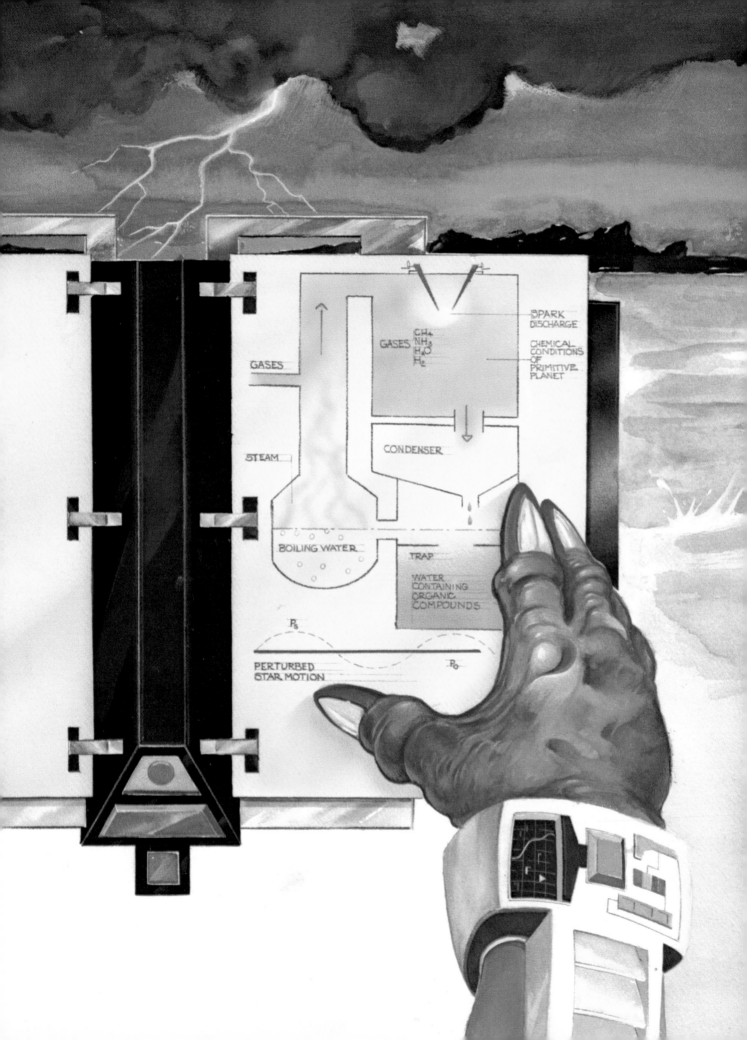

ing food, or avoiding a predator if it is smart than if it is stupid. This line of reasoning argues for a fairly large value for f_i.

Technical civilizations

The terms intelligent life and technical civilization are not synonymous. Although a progressive evolution of intelligence on Earth is quite clear in the paleontological record, extensive use of tools and the development of a technical civilization have occurred only very recently relative to the historical pageant of life. This suggests that technical civilizations may not be an inevitable consequence of the evolution of life elsewhere, although again the selective advantages of technical civilizations seem so great—at least until the capability for self-destruction is achieved—that they could be widespread in the Galaxy as well. Some evolutionary biologists, therefore, are inclined to assign the product $f_i f_c$ a fairly conservative value of $1/100$.

Of greatest uncertainty is L, the final parameter, representing the lifetime of a technical civilization. No such civilization exists for man to study except his own, for which the value of L is not yet determined. Given the definition of a technical civilization as one capable of interstellar communication, the one on Earth is only decades old. If technical civilizations cannot avoid rapid self-destruction, then L may be quite small, perhaps 10 years; such a value, together with the other parameter values assigned above, yields an N quite close to 1, from which it may be concluded that man is alone. But if technical civilizations tend to avoid self-destruction, their lifetimes may be extremely long. Then such considerations suggest the existence of as many as one million technical civilizations in the Galaxy—most of them substantially more advanced than mankind, who by definition has just achieved that status.

Given the existence of one million technical civilizations randomly distributed throughout the Galaxy—and the generally accepted notion that listening for radio signals is the most feasible means of detection—some hundreds of thousands of stars must be examined before there is even a fair chance of receiving a signal from the nearest technical civilization, assuming it is intentionally beaming messages in the general direction of the Sun. But any such numerical estimates, particularly because they depend on a guess for the average lifetime of a technical civilization, are extremely uncertain. Such calculations, however, do render plausible the contention that 20th-century man may have the capability to detect extraterrestrial intelligence.

Relevant technology

One indication of the present level of relevant technical capability on the planet Earth is the Viking mission to Mars. Viking, a brilliant technological success, represents the first serious attempt to search for microbial (and larger) forms of life on another planet. While a plethora of fundamental scientific information has been returned about the atmosphere, surface, and interior of the planet, its moons, and its ancient history (suggesting, incidentally, conditions much more favorable to the origin of life than many had thought), the results of the microbiology experiments currently are ambiguous. Although it seems clear that organic molecules are being synthesized at a low rate on the Martian surface, there is no unambiguous evidence for contemporary biology. Viking is a pioneering attempt to search for life on another planet, but because it has examined at first hand only one ten-millionth of the Martian surface, and because its experiments could only sample a small fraction of the possible biological environments on the planet, further work will be necessary to settle the question of life on Mars. But when such work is completed, it will certainly influence estimates of the likelihood of civilizations on planets of other stars. Likewise, space-vehicle investigation of Jupiter, Saturn, Saturn's moon Titan, and other objects in the solar system thought to contain prebiological organic matter are bound to shed light on the question. (*See* Feature Article: THE VIKING MISSION TO MARS.)

Perhaps the most impressive development within the last decade or two, one that makes experimental searches for extraterrestrial intelligence reasonable propositions, is the great advance in radio astronomy. The largest existing single radio telescope on Earth is the 305-meter-aperture Arecibo Observatory in Puerto Rico, a national facility operated by Cornell University for the U.S. National Science Foundation. For purposes of illustration, assume that mankind expects to receive a message from another civilization no more advanced than itself (the most modest assumption possible for this problem). If that civilization beamed a message from equipment identical to Arecibo, the maximum distance over which it could be detected with equipment on Earth is in the thousands of light-years; a spherical volume of space with such a radius encompasses hundreds of millions of stars. But, in fact, in the whole history of mankind only hundreds—not hundreds of millions—of stars have been examined for this purpose by sensitive radio telescopes. A serious coordinated long-term effort by a number of radio telescopes, including perhaps some built especially for the purpose, is required to perform a significant investigation of this problem. There are many stars to examine, about a dozen frequencies that should appear natural or obvious to both transmitting and receiving civilizations, and several other technical aspects of the transmission for which all bets must be covered. (For a detailed account of the instruments and techniques of radio astronomy, see *1977 Yearbook of Science and the Future* Feature Article: RADIO TELESCOPES.)

Past and present efforts

In 1960, using a 26-meter-aperture radio telescope at the U.S. National Radio Astronomy Observatory in Green Bank, West Virginia, Drake pioneered the concept of radio search with Project Ozma, a modest study of two nearby stars for several hundred hours over a three-month period. The frequency selected for examination was 1,420 megahertz (MHz; millions of cycles per second), the prominent 21-centimeter spectral line of neutral atomic hydrogen, the most abundant element in the universe. The results were negative.

Since then there have been a number of other searches, some of which were still in progress as of mid-1977. In 1968 V. S. Troitsky of the Gorky N. I. Lobachevsky State University in the Soviet Union examined 12 nearby stars at wavelengths of 21 and 30 centimeters. The initial phases of Project Ozma II, a search of the 21-centimeter line conducted from late 1972 through mid-1975 by Patrick Palmer of the University of Chicago and Ben Zuckerman of the University of Maryland, used two larger antennas at Green Bank and specialized equipment that could detect signals in any of several hundred narrow segments, or channels, of the broader 21-centimeter bandwidth. About 660 promising, mostly Sun-like stars within 80 light-years of the Earth were monitored six to seven times each, four minutes at a stretch. In neither project was any evidence found of intelligent life.

The most recent efforts include several small-scale searches in various countries as well as some ambitious proposals for the future. At the Algonquin Radio Observatory in Ontario, Alan H. Bridle of Queen's University, Kingston, Ontario, and P. A. Feldman of the National Research Council, Downsview, Ontario, are engaged in observing nearly 300 stars at 22.2 gigahertz (GHz; billions of cycles per second), a frequency at which water molecules absorb and reemit energy and another logical choice for an extraterrestrial civilization, at least for one that regards water as of crucial importance for life.

In the Soviet Union two separate systems are in use to look for pulses of radio emission received simultaneously by widely separated stations. One network of stations is operated by the Gorky Radiophysical Institute, the other by the Institute for Cosmic Research of the Soviet Academy of Sciences in Moscow. The latter network at one time stretched from Kamchatka in extreme eastern Siberia to a radio telescope aboard an oceangoing vessel in the equatorial Atlantic. These systems do not resolve individual stars but examine the entire sky at once. A search for signals from large sectors of the sky is also being carried out by Robert S. Dixon and colleagues at Ohio State University using a system of small antennas with a synthesized aperture equivalent to a 175-foot dish.

At Arecibo Observatory, Drake and Carl Sagan of Cornell University, Ithaca, New York, are conducting one of the largest of the searches, seeking signals not only from nearby stars but also from distant galaxies. Such an approach assumes that the transmission power of extremely advanced civilizations in other galaxies would more than compensate for the attenuation of their signals over intergalactic distances, and one of its main advantages is that an entire galaxy of billions of stars can be observed in a single session. By early 1977 the system had examined several nearby stars, from which a signal only 1/1,000 the power of Arecibo could be detected, and four nearby galaxies totaling a trillion stars, from which a signal equivalent in power to hundreds of millions of Arecibos would be required for detection.

The effort at Arecibo entails observations at four different frequencies: 1,420 MHz; 1,667 MHz, a spectral line of the hydroxyl, or OH, radical; 2,380 MHz, Arecibo's radar frequency for which radio noise inherent in the instrumentation is low; and 1,652 MHz. The attraction of this last frequency for interstellar broadcasting is based on the existence of a band of microwave frequencies within which total interference from space and from the Earth's atmosphere is minimal for a ground-based receiving system. This band is roughly bracketed by the frequencies closely associated with constituents of the water molecule — the 1,420-MHz hydrogen line and the 1,667-MHz hydroxyl line — and consequently has been dubbed the "water hole." Although an extraterrestrial broadcaster might select any of a multitude of channels within this band, the center of mass of the water molecule "naturally" defines a frequency of 1,652 MHz, offering at the very least a point at which to begin listening.

To date all of these programs have yielded negative results, although virtually every group has had occasional entertaining surprises. The Soviet group, for example, obtained an unambiguous detection of an extraterrestrial radio signal of intelligent origin; but the signal was almost certainly from an Earth satellite, probably a U.S. military reconnaissance satellite. Arecibo's observations of the galaxy Leo I detected what seemed to be an intelligent signal coming from six different locales in the sky; unfortunately it proved to be terrestrial emanations that were picked up by the sidelobes of the antenna.

It has been suggested in recent years that radio and other astronomical observations already in hand may in retrospect prove to be signals of extraterrestrial intelligence. For example, in late 1975 astronomers from the Owens Valley Observatory of the California Institute of Technology reported their detection and resolution of an extremely compact radio source at the very center of our Galaxy. This source, which appears to be no larger than the size of the solar system and possibly even much smaller, radiates a signal that varies with time. Also at the center of the Galaxy have been discovered very bright infrared sources of large dimensions, but at ordinary room temperature.

The physical conditions at the dense centers of galaxies are unfamiliar. There may be frequent collisions among stars and massive black holes. Violent explosive events are known to exist in the centers of other galaxies, and the largest explosive events in the universe, the quasars, may be simply the most energetic examples of explosions within galactic nuclei. Hence the compact radio and infrared sources at the center of our Galaxy may have perfectly natural explanations. The hypothesis that they are signals from an advanced civilization must be a hypothesis of last resort, to be considered seriously only when all other alternatives fail. But it is important to bear in mind that there is a wide range of astrophysical phenomena that are at best incompletely understood and that may ultimately prove to be the manifestations of astroengineering or signaling activity of extremely advanced extraterrestrial civilizations.

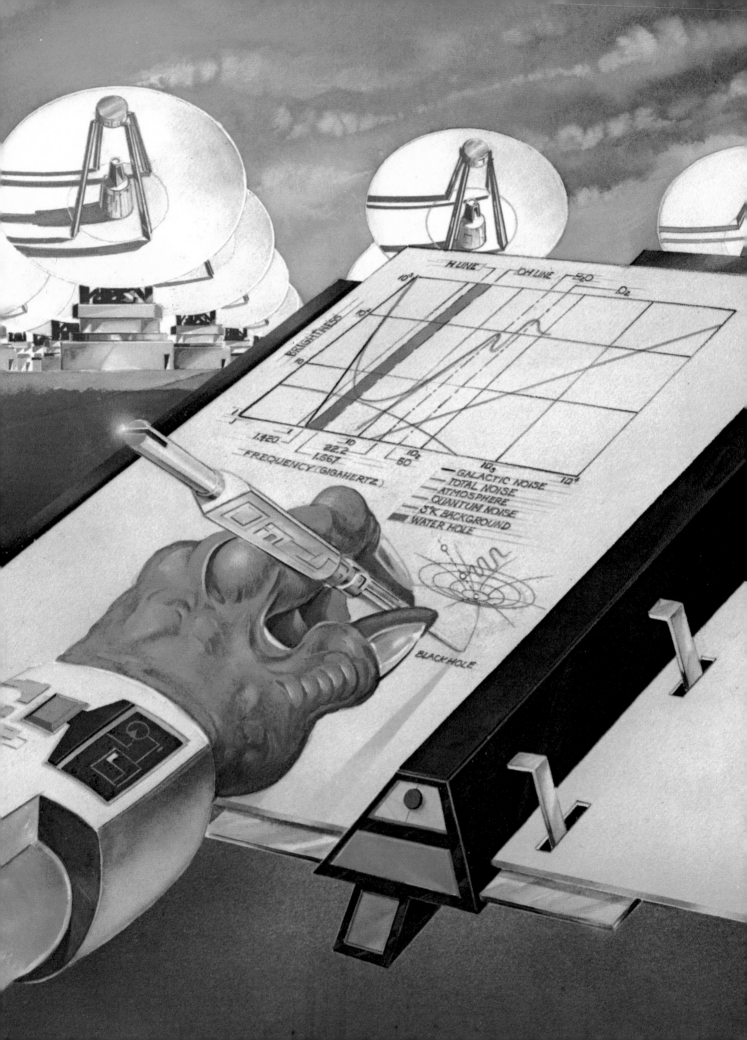

Future prospects

For several years coordination efforts at national levels in both the U.S. and the Soviet Union have devoted considerable attention to the direction of future research programs. Particular scrutiny has been given to collection systems with improved signal-gathering power, better frequency resolution, and swifter and more discriminating signal-processing techniques. In the U.S. an Interstellar Communications Study Group, sponsored by the National Aeronautics and Space Administration, has been examining several concepts for advanced radio telescopes. One proposal, termed Project Cyclops, envisions a vast array of 1,000 or more individual, steerable antennas, each 100 meters in diameter, with a collective aperture perhaps 100 times that of Arecibo. Another possibility is that of a single collector in orbit around the Earth or an array of antennas on the far side of the Moon. The most cost-effective scheme, however, is the use of existing radio telescopes with receivers of improved sensitivity in a dedicated long-term search. Of importance to all of these systems is the necessity for developing a computer-assisted multichannel signal analyzer that can process as many as one million frequency channels simultaneously. Such equipment could allow observation in many directions at the same time by selective synthesis of its received signals and would be capable of discerning complex messages sent on multiple channels.

Recently announced proposals from the Soviet Academy of Sciences have stressed the value of a smooth, systematic, and prolonged search utilizing existing equipment as much as possible. These plans call for a 15-year examination of the entire frequency spectrum between 1 and 100 GHz in three distinct surveys: one of local stars, a second of galaxies, and another of the entire sky. Some specialized equipment such as Earth- and Moon-orbiting observatories and a 2.5–3-meter, Earth-based infrared telescope was mentioned, as well as part-time use of the RATAN-600, a powerful 576-meter ring-shaped radio telescope recently completed in the Caucasus Mountains.

Contact: mistake or blessing?

In 1976 newspapers reported a letter written by British radio astronomer and Nobel laureate Sir Martin Ryle to the International Astronomical Union, urging that mankind not broadcast radio messages to other stars lest hostile civilizations, receiving such signals, mount punitive expeditions to Earth. Perhaps there is a kind of immunological system among galactic civilizations, poised to wipe out at a sufficiently early stage any potential competitors at the moment that they announce their existence. Or perhaps the fact that man can seriously consider such a possibility indicates how far civilization on Earth is from being ready for admission to an intercommunicating federation of galactic communities.

To date, radio telescopes have not been used to transmit intelligible messages to any nearby star. In 1974, in connection with the upgrading of the reflecting surface of Arecibo's antenna, a three-minute message

Any consideration of interstellar communication by radio waves—be it a single contemporary terrestrial radio telescope, the proposed antenna array of Project Cyclops, or the signaling activity of an extremely advanced civilization influencing the fates of entire stars—involves an assessment of the frequencies that should appear natural or obvious to transmitting and receiving civilizations alike. The radio spectrum of the sky as seen from the planet of another race of intelligent creatures, especially ones who regard water as critical for life, may share common points of interest with the sky spectrum as seen from Earth. To such a civilization the 1,420-MHz hydrogen line and the 1,667-MHz hydroxyl line would indicate likely frequencies for communication. These points of reference also might serve to define a band of frequencies between them—the "water hole"—for which the total radio noise from space and from a planetary atmosphere rich in oxygen and water vapor is relatively small for a receiving system on the ground.

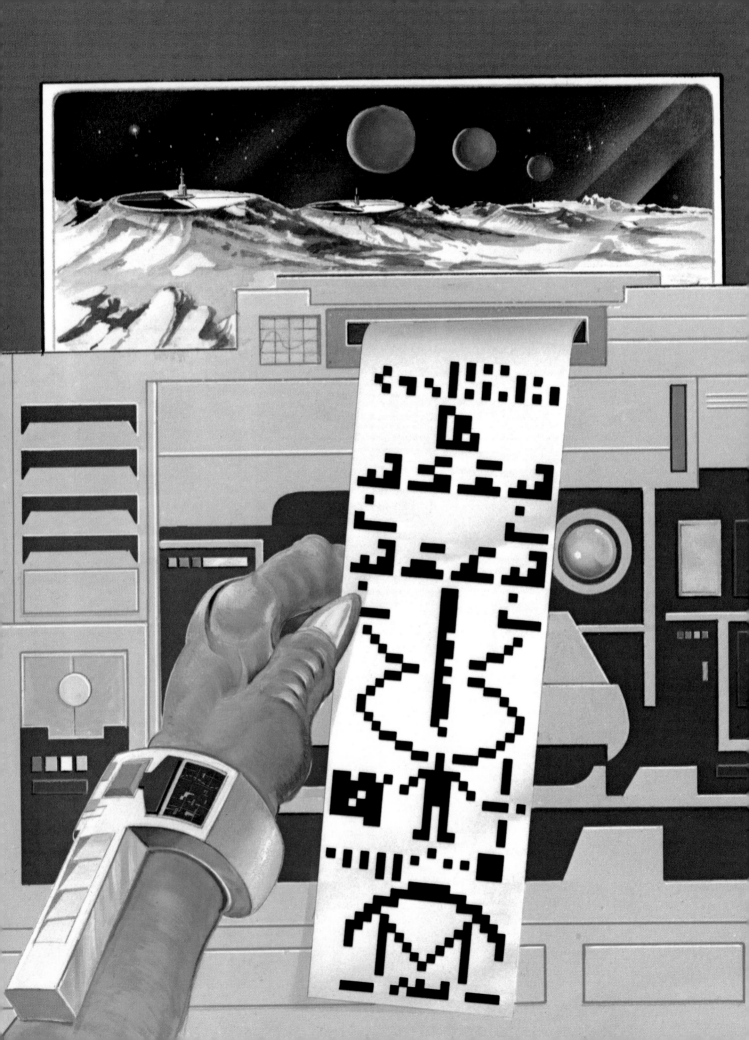

describing the DNA molecule, Earth's population, the solar system, and the physical appearance of man and the Arecibo telescope was beamed to M13, the Great Cluster in the constellation Hercules. If this was a mistake, the message's transit time of 24,000 years will afford mankind considerable time to develop its defenses.

These speculations aside, military and astronomical radar and commercial television do represent continuous intense indicators of the existence and the position of man's technical civilization and have been broadcasting such information for decades. This is a possibly sobering fact, considering the content of most broadcast entertainment, but the circumstance is too late to undo; there is no way to retrieve these radio signals expanding outward from the Earth at the speed of light. If those signals are received by extraterrestrial listeners, mankind will have to trust to the tolerance of the recipients, or else to the quality of an occasional worthwhile television program.

In contrast to Ryle's somewhat somber view of the possible motives of galactic civilizations, a number of astronomers think it plausible that the radio signals from extraterrestrial intelligences will contain an astonishingly rich array of readily decodable information on the physical sciences, technology, the history and biology of very different civilizations, and possibly even some advice for avoiding the more common forms of self-destruction. It seems likely that our civilization on Earth is one minor variety of an extremely diverse set of galactic societies. The receipt of a message from an extraterrestrial civilization would in the deepest sense deprovincialize mankind. The first attempts to detect such civilizations are under way and it seems likely that a worldwide investigation of the problem will be mustered in the coming years.

FOR ADDITIONAL READING

Carl Sagan, *The Cosmic Connection* (Doubleday, 1973).

Carl Sagan (ed.), *Communication with Extraterrestrial Intelligence* (MIT Press, 1973).

Carl Sagan and I. S. Shklovskii, *Intelligent Life in the Universe* (Dell, 1966).

Twenty-four thousand years in the future, an array of antennas on a moon of a planet in the star cluster M13 may detect the brief signal that was beamed into space from Arecibo Observatory in 1974. Decoded from binary notation into pictures, the message counts to ten, provides atomic numbers for several elements, and then uses this base to give information on the structure of DNA. Pictorial representations are given of the DNA double helix, our solar system, the human body, and the Arecibo telescope. Both the average height of a human and the diameter of the telescope are shown in units of 12.6 centimeters, the wavelength used to transmit the message.

The Flight of Birds
by R. McNeill Alexander

Wind tunnels and other research methods are helping
scientists determine the physiological mechanisms that allow
birds and certain other vertebrates to fly.

Nearly all species of birds can fly, and so can all bats. The extinct pterosaurs were reptiles with long wings, and they also could probably fly. There are other vertebrates that glide, such as the flying squirrels of North America and Asia and the short-winged flying lizards (*Draco*) of Southeast Asia, but none of them glides very well. This article deals only with birds, bats, and pterosaurs.

Flying birds and bats impress us with the agility of their movements. We can admire them and we can record their movements on film, but how can we study the physiology of an animal that is moving rapidly through the air? A solution that has been adopted in recent experiments is to have the air moving and the animal stationary. This requires a wind tunnel (figure 1). A huge electric fan sucks air in at the left and blows it out at the right, in a jet 1 meter in diameter traveling at up to 20 meters per second (45 miles per hour). The tunnel is designed so that the air in the jet flows as smoothly and evenly as possible, despite its speed. The bird flies or glides in the jet, in the position shown. It is trained to keep stationary, neither gaining ground nor dropping back. Its situation is then equivalent to that of a bird flying at the speed of the jet in still air. The tunnel can be adjusted so that the jet is horizontal, or tilted to simulate uphill or downhill flight.

Some ingenuity is needed to persuade the bird or bat to fly in the right place. Colin Pennycuick of Bristol University (England) used inducements of food. To train pigeons, he fixed a teaspoon bowl in the center of the tunnel opening and rolled maple peas down a tube into it. The birds could get the peas only by flying in the right place. To train fruit bats he used a device that dispensed squashed bananas.

Gliding ability

There are three main types of flight: forward flapping, hovering, and gliding. Wind tunnels have been used to find out how well birds and bats can glide and to compare their performance with that of man-made gliders. With the wind speed fixed and a trained animal flying in the jet, the angle of tilt is varied. When the jet is horizontal, the bird must flap its wings to keep itself airborne. If the jet is tilted sufficiently, simulating downhill flight, the bird can hold its wings motionless and glide. Because gliding requires less energy than flapping flight, a bird will generally glide if it can. By varying the angle of tilt, the experimenter can discover the minimum angle at which gliding is possible, at a given speed.

Results from such experiments are shown in figure 2. The sinking speed is the rate at which the animal or aircraft would lose height if it were gliding in still air. The gliding animals are compared to a medium-performance glider (wingspan 17 meters) and to a model glider (wingspan 1.1 meters). For each glider (man-made or animal), there is a minimum airspeed below which gliding is impossible. This speed is generally higher for large aircraft than for small ones because large aircraft have smaller ratios of wing area to weight; if all the linear dimensions of an aircraft are doubled, the wing area is increased by a

R. McNEILL ALEXANDER is Professor of Zoology and Head of the Department of Pure and Applied Zoology at the University of Leeds, England.

(Overleaf) Photograph by Rod Borland — Bruce Coleman Inc. Illustrations by Jean Helmer

128

Adapted from "A Wind-Tunnel Study of Gliding Flight in the Pigeon *Columba livia*," by C. J. Pennycuick, *Journal of Experimental Biology*, vol. 49, pp.509–526 (1968)

Figure 1. A wind tunnel is used to study the physiology of birds in flight. A fan (a) sucks in air through an intake filter (b) composed of wire mesh. A ring of stator vanes (c) and a three-inch thickness of metal honeycomb (d) remove swirl from the air current. A screen (e) is placed at the upstream end of an octagonal-shaped contraction (f), creating a steady, even airflow. The bird is trained to remain stationary in the airflow, either in a flapping or a gliding configuration. The tunnel is pivoted about a horizontal axis (g) and can be tilted by hydraulic jacks to various degrees above horizontal. At the bottom are wing configurations of a pigeon gliding in a wind tunnel at airspeeds of 8.6 meters per second (left), 12.4 meters per second (center), and 22.1 meters per second (right).

(Top and bottom right) M. Philip Kahl—Black Star; (bottom left) Marvin Newman—Woodfin Camp

factor of four but the weight rises by a factor of eight. For any glider there is an airspeed a little above the minimum at which the sinking speed is least. Higher airspeeds are possible only at the expense of an increase in sinking speed.

Of the birds tested in the wind tunnel the vulture was a small one. The bat was a large fruit bat. Both of them, and the falcon, were fairly similar in size to the model glider. They could glide over a similar range of airspeeds, and their sinking speeds were only a little greater than that of the model. This performance is not at all discreditable; the model was designed only for gliding, but the animals are also capable of other

130

Adapted from R. McN. Alexander, *The Chordates*, ©1975 Cambridge University Press, London

Hope Alexander—Woodfin Camp

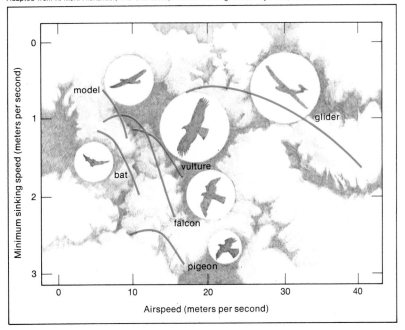

activities such as feeding and flapping flight. The performance of pigeons, however, was poor.

A bird gliding in still air must lose height. If the air is rising, however, the bird may be able to maintain its height or even to rise. Rising air can be found over cliffs and hillsides where the wind is deflected upward. It can also be found in thermals, which consist of warm air rising from hot ground. It is not unusual to find air rising in thermals at speeds of more than four meters per second. Glider pilots and many birds seek out thermals to keep themselves airborne for long periods, a technique known as soaring.

Conditions for soaring are excellent over the East African plains, especially during the dry season. Vultures, storks, and pelicans are common there and use soaring rather than flapping flight as their normal method of travel. Pennycuick found out how much they depended on soaring by following them in a motorized glider. One of his most remarkable observations concerned Rüppell's griffon vulture. This is the largest of the East African species with a mass of about 8 kilograms (17.5 pounds) and a wingspan of 2.4 meters. It nests on cliffs in the Gol Mountains, east of the Serengeti National Park, and feeds on the carcasses of antelopes and zebras. When the herds of game are far from the cliffs, it has to travel long distances to collect food for itself and its nestlings.

Pennycuick encountered a Rüppell's griffon at 2 PM one afternoon, about 75 kilometers (45 miles) from the Gol cliffs. A swelling at the base of the neck showed that its crop was full, indicating that it must have fed recently. It had probably eaten about 40 kilometers farther from the cliffs, where the main herds of wildebeest were that day. Pennycuick followed the bird, which soared all the way to the Gol cliffs and arrived

Opposite page, gliding configurations are compared for a Rüppell's griffon vulture (top), a glider (bottom left), and an African spoonbill (bottom right). Figure 2 (left) shows the minimum sinking speeds at various airspeeds for a glider with a wingspan of 17 meters (56 feet), a vulture, a falcon, a pigeon, a bat, and a model glider with a wingspan of 1.1 meters (3.6 feet). Above, kittiwakes soar off cliffs of Alaska's Sledge Island.

lift

drag

flapping

lift

drag

lift

drag

gliding

lift

drag

lift

drag

hovering

Figure 3. The aerodynamic force on a bird's wings during gliding, flapping, and hovering flight is divided into two components. The drag acts backward along the direction of motion, and the lift acts at right angles to it.

there at 3:40 PM. Five times it stopped to circle in thermals and gain height, but it covered the final 32 kilometers in a straight glide. Soaring, thus, can be an effective means of travel, and quite a rapid one. Storks migrating between Europe and Africa seem to cover most of the distance by thermal soaring.

Flight mechanisms

Figure 3 shows the aerodynamic force on the wings separated into two components. One of the two, a force called drag, acts backward along the direction of motion, and the other, called lift, acts at right angles to the direction of motion. Wings are shaped so that, when they are held at a suitable angle, tilted slightly from the direction of motion, the lift is much greater than the drag. Drag acts on the fuselage of an airplane or the body of a bird as well as on the wings, but nearly all the lift acts on the wings.

When an aircraft is gliding at constant velocity, the lift and drag on the wings and the drag on the fuselage together balance its weight. In level flight, the lift balances the weight and thrust is needed from the propellers or jet engines to balance the drag. Flying animals have to flap their wings so that they serve also as propellers.

Different animals flap their wings in different ways. The wing action is also different for fast and slow flight. As an example of flying technique, one can examine the movements of a long-eared bat flying slowly. Ulla Norberg of the University of Göteborg (Sweden) made the bat fly in a long cage. She fired three cameras simultaneously to get

132

Photos, courtesy, Ulla M. Norberg, University of Göteborg, Sweden

each of the sets of photographs. In the downstroke the wings move forward and down with their surfaces more or less horizontal. In the upstroke they rise with their surfaces almost vertical. In the downstroke the lift and drag on the wings act upward, counteracting the bat's weight. In the upstroke they act forward, counteracting the drag on the body. The wings function like the wings of an airplane in the downstroke and like the propeller in the upstroke.

In hovering flight, the animal's body remains stationary and the wings have to act like the rotor of a helicopter. They cannot, of course, revolve like a rotor but are flapped backward and forward. Different hovering animals use different techniques. The hovering diagram in figure 3 is based on films of hummingbirds hovering in front of flowers to drink nectar. The wings beat very rapidly, 15 to 50 times per second. The body is kept vertical, and the wings beat horizontally. The upper surfaces of the wings are uppermost in the forward stroke, but the wings turn upside down for the backward return stroke. The lift acts upward on the wings, both in the forward stroke and in the backward stroke.

Energy cost of flight

Birds and bats gliding in still air sink at a rate of 1 to 3 meters per second. This means that they lose potential energy at rates between 10 and 30 watts per kilogram of body mass. In order to fly on a level course, therefore, they would need to do aerodynamic work at the rate of 10 to 30 watts per kilogram. Their muscles work at an efficiency of only 20%, and so they would have to use up food energy at the rate of 50 to 150 watts per kilogram.

This prediction was tested in remarkable experiments by Vance Tucker of Duke University, Durham, North Carolina. He fitted birds with transparent masks connected by thin plastic tubing to oxygen analysis equipment. Air is drawn out of the tube into the analyzing equipment and is replaced by air seeping in around the back of the mask. Thus the bird has a good supply of fresh air, but all the air it breathes out is taken for analysis. The rate at which it uses oxygen is measured, and the rate at which it uses food energy can be calculated. Budgerigars flying in a wind tunnel used 120–200 watts per kilogram, depending on the speed at which they were flying. Laughing gulls used 60–70 watts per kilogram, and fruit bats used 50–70 watts per kilogram.

Long-eared bat flying horizontally is photographed from three directions simultaneously: from the front, from the side, and from below. The beginning of the upstroke is at the top and of the downstroke below.

Hovering uses energy faster than forward flight. Measurements have been made of the oxygen consumption of hummingbirds, hovering in a closed container while drinking sugar solution from a bottle. They used about 230 watts per kilogram.

These power consumptions, both for hovering and for forward flight, are high. They are far higher than mammals use in running. It seems fair to compare budgerigars with kangaroo rats, which are about the same size. The maximum rate at which kangaroo rats use oxygen indicates a power consumption of only 80 watts per kilogram.

Flapping flight uses much energy, but it is fast. A kangaroo rat using 80 watts per kilogram travels at only 0.5 meters per second. A

Photos, M. Philip Kahl—Black Star

White pelican (above) demonstrates upstroke during flapping flight. Hummingbird (below) can hover for long periods of time.

budgerigar uses 120–200 watts per kilogram but travels at 6 to 13 meters per second. Thus, a given amount of energy takes the bird much farther than the mammal. It is because they can travel long distances for relatively small energy costs that birds can make long migrations across areas where they can find no food. Birds migrating across the Sahara must travel 1,400 kilometers (870 miles) without a meal. They start the journey with a huge store of fat that makes up 25–50% of their body mass. This is their fuel store, and little of it is left when they arrive at the other side of the desert. Budgerigars live in Australia and so they never make this particular journey, but it can be calculated from the wind tunnel measurements that if they did they would need a fat store amounting to 34% of their initial mass.

Soaring is an even more economical method of travel than flapping flight. The oxygen consumption of gulls gliding in a wind tunnel was measured by the same method as was used for flapping flight. It showed that the gulls used only about 15 watts per kilogram. The storks that migrate by soaring between northern Europe and Africa must travel extremely economically.

Size limits

Hovering requires more power than other modes of flight, and it can be shown by aerodynamic considerations that the power needed, per unit body mass, is even greater for large birds than for small ones. Hummingbirds can hover more or less indefinitely; there is a record of one hovering continuously in a laboratory for 35 minutes. But the largest hummingbirds weigh only 20 grams (0.7 ounce), and larger birds can hover only for short periods. Pigeons (about 500 grams) can hover for a second or so, and birds larger than that cannot hover at all.

Small birds generally take off by jumping into the air, hovering,

Anthony Mercieca/National Audubon Society—Photo Researchers

134

Photos, M. J. Griffith/National Audubon Society—Photo Researchers

and then gathering speed. Birds too large to hover cannot do this. Birds of prey often take off by diving from a high perch. Vultures and albatrosses take off from the ground by running like a taxiing airplane until they are moving fast enough for their wings to lift them. Swans gather speed by running on the surface of water. The larger the bird the higher the speed needed for takeoff because the ratio of wing area to body mass is smaller in large birds.

The largest birds, such as the ostrich and the emperor penguin, have lost the ability to fly. They are so big that they could not take off even if they had well-developed wings and wing muscles. The largest modern flying bird is possibly the Kori bustard, which weighs up to at least 12 kilograms. It lives on the East African plains, spending most of its time on the ground. When chased, it runs. It needs a long run to take off and will not take off at all unless it is hotly pursued. It never flies far and can be caught by chasing because it becomes exhausted after taking off a few times.

The wingspan of the Kori bustard is about 2.5 meters. Large albatrosses are lighter but have larger wingspans, about 3.4 meters. The extinct pterosaur *Pteranodon* had far bigger wings, with a span of about 7 meters. This extraordinary animal lived in the Cretaceous Period and so was a contemporary of the later dinosaurs. Could it have flown? It seems certain that it must have done so for it appears to have been singularly ill-fitted for life on land.

Though the wings of *Pteranodon* were big, its body was quite small. It has been estimated that its mass was about 17 kilograms, a little more than a large Kori bustard. But its ratio of wing area to body mass was much larger than that of a Kori bustard, and so it had a lower takeoff speed, probably about eight meters per second. There is clear evidence that *Pteranodon* lived by the sea, and it could probably have

White pelican, above, completes downstroke (left) and glides (right). Kori bustard (below) may be the largest present-day flying bird.

Frederick Ayer—Photo Researchers

135

Black-backed gull (below) flies over mountains near the coast of Norway. A swallow-tailed gull (opposite page, top) begins flight by jumping from the edge of a cliff, while the greater flamingo (center) and mute swan (bottom) launch themselves into the air by running along the surface of a body of water.

taken off simply by spreading its wings and facing into a moderate sea breeze. Alternatively, it could have launched itself from a cliff top. It probably spent much of its time soaring in wind deflected upward by cliffs or by waves.

Pteranodon was astonishingly large, but a few bones have recently been found in Texas from a pterosaur that must have been even larger. The principal find was a humerus (an upper arm bone). In pterosaurs the humerus is relatively short, for most of the wing is supported by a hugely elongated finger. The length of the humerus is only a small fraction of the wingspan, and it is difficult to estimate the size of the animal from the humerus alone. It cannot be assumed that the proportions of the giant pterosaur were the same as those of smaller species known from more complete skeletons. Indeed, they were almost certainly different; careful measurement of other pterosaurs shows quite a regular relationship between proportions and size. A calculation that took this into account led to the amazing conclusion that the giant pterosaur had a wingspan of 15.5 meters.

Flying high

There is considerable evidence of birds flying more than 6,000 meters (20,000 feet) above sea level. Radar echoes believed to come from

Frank Siteman—Stock, Boston

Photos, Bruce Coleman Inc., (center and bottom)
M. Philip Kahl

migrating birds are regularly detected from such heights, though most migrating birds fly much lower. An aircraft was struck by an object at 6,400 meters and when it landed, mallard duck feathers were found stuck in the dent. Climbers have seen choughs flying at 8,000 meters, near the summit of Mt. Everest.

At 6,000 meters, air pressure is only 45% of the pressure at sea level. Because of this, birds have to fly 1.5 times as fast in order to have their wings support them, and the power needed for flight is 1.5 times as great as at sea level. The flight muscles of birds are well able to deliver this extra power; birds flying fast or uphill at normal pressures may use 1.5 or more times the minimum power needed for flight. It is remarkable, however, that the lungs and blood system can supply the muscles with the oxygen they need at such high altitude. At 6,000 meters men can barely survive and can manage only a few minutes of strenuous activity.

Tucker compared the behavior of sparrows and mice at simulated high altitudes. He put both in a hyperbaric chamber and reduced the pressure to 45% of normal atmospheric pressure and the temperature to 5° C (41° F). The mice lay still on their bellies most of the time, and could just crawl. Their oxygen consumption fell to half of normal, and their body temperature fell 10° C. The sparrows on the other hand, were alert and active. They breathed faster and more deeply than at normal pressure, and their oxygen consumption was actually a little above normal. Their body temperature fell only 2° C.

Why are birds so much better able to cope with high altitudes than mammals? Their lungs are not particularly large, but they are built to an entirely different design from mammal lungs. They contain fine tubes (capillaries) through which air passes and through the walls of which gas exchange takes place. Their hearts are large and so can circulate blood fast; the heart represents 1.5% of the body mass of a sparrow but only 0.5% of the mass of a mouse. These advantages are needed even for flight at sea level but are particularly necessary at high altitudes. Even with them, only some birds can fly really high. Budgerigars were tested in a wind tunnel in a hyperbaric chamber, with the pressure reduced to simulate an altitude of 6,000 meters. They flew well if they were supplied with oxygen through face masks, but without extra oxygen they could fly for only a few seconds.

How it began

Birds, bats, and pterosaurs must have evolved from animals that could not fly. How did this happen? It is only in the case of the birds that scientists have found a fossil intermediate between the modern flying vertebrates and their flightless ancestors that may help to answer the question. This fossil is *Archaeopteryx*, which lived in the Jurassic Period, at the time of the early dinosaurs. Only three reasonably complete specimens and a few isolated feathers have been found, all in the same district in Germany. They are beautifully preserved in an exceptionally suitable stone, the Solenhofen Limestone, which had so fine a

137

The ancient flying reptile Pteranodon, *with a wingspan of 7 meters (23 feet), probably launched itself into flight from a cliff top and soared in wind deflected upward by cliffs or by waves.*

grain that it was quarried to obtain lithographic stones for printers. Clear impressions of the larger feathers can be seen in the stone. They seem to have been closely similar to the feathers of modern birds.

Archaeopteryx must have looked a little like a magpie. It was about the same size and had a long tail. Having feathers and wings, it was clearly a bird. It was a bird, however, that showed clear evidence of having evolved from reptiles. The long tail was not just a fan of feathers, like the tails of modern birds, but instead had a vertebral column that extended along most of its length. Thus, it must have been like a lizard tail fringed with feathers. The hand had three long, separate fingers and was quite unlike the highly modified hand that supports the primary wing feathers of modern birds. The brain was much smaller than in modern birds of similar size though much larger than in reptiles of the same size. There was no beak; instead, *Archaeopteryx* had a snout like that of a lizard, with teeth in the jaws. These teeth were not simply attached to the jaws as in lizards but were set in sockets like the teeth of crocodiles and dinosaurs. This and other details of the skull indicate that *Archaeopteryx* had evolved from the thecodonts, the extinct group of reptiles from which crocodiles, dinosaurs, and pterosaurs also evolved.

The main wing feathers were arranged in the same way as in modern birds, but there has been some dispute as to whether they enabled *Archaeopteryx* to fly. The wing area is fairly easy to estimate from the

Courtesy, American Museum of Natural History, New York

fossils, but it is much more difficult to judge the body mass. Different scientists have claimed that *Archaeopteryx* could or could not fly, according to their estimates of its mass. There seems to have been no keel on the breastbone like the keel that separates the muscles of the left and right wings in modern birds. Some scientists have argued from this that the wing muscles must have been too small for flight, but others have pointed out that bats fly perfectly well with only a small keel.

Whether *Archaeopteryx* could fly or not, there must at some stage have been an ancestral bird with wings too small to fly. This seems inevitable, since evolution generally progresses by small steps. Why did wings start evolving if, in the initial stages, they were of no use for flight?

John Ostrom of Yale University believes that *Archaeopteryx* had very limited powers of flight. He recently made an ingenious suggestion as to why its wings evolved. He pointed out that *Archaeopteryx* must have evolved from thecodonts that ran around bipedally, on their hind legs. He suggested that these thecodonts became warm-blooded as an adaptation to an active running life and that they evolved feathers as heat insulation. Furthermore, Ostrom suggested that *Archaeopteryx* was a predominantly ground-living animal that captured large insects and other small prey. The wing feathers evolved so that the arms could be used to form a fence encircling the prey while *Archaeopteryx* prepared to seize it in mouth or hand.

Archaeopteryx, a flying animal that lived at the time of the early dinosaurs, is an intermediate between modern birds and their flightless ancestors. The artist's conception at the left, based on the fossil skeleton above, shows a creature that is a bird by virtue of its feathers and wings but that also reveals its kinship with reptiles by its snout and teeth, vertebral column in the tail, and clawed digits in the wings.

139

The Role of Zoos in Wildlife Conservation

by Gunter Voss

Once maintained as symbols of prestige and power or as public spectacles, the world's zoos have since become an integral part of efforts to protect endangered animals from extinction.

Père David's deer, Przewalski's horse, the European bison, the Hawaiian goose, the Laysan teal, and the Arabian oryx are all species doomed to extinction but for their preservation in zoological parks. Breeding secure populations in the 1970s, they argue strongly in defense of conservation efforts of the world's zoos. Zoo officials proclaim through park brochures that "many species of wildlife have found a protected future, a haven of survival, in zoos in the heart of metropolitan centers." And they often use the phrase "in the interests of conservation" when defending budgetary requirements for animal purchases. Nevertheless, within recent years doubts have arisen about the integrity of some zoos' concern for wildlife protection and have made the very concept of the zoo a target of critical scrutiny. As a college student once inquired of a zoo professional after hearing his lecture on the role of the zoo in conservation: "If you are so concerned with wild animal survival, why do you not leave the animals in nature? Why do you have them trapped to bring them to zoos in the first place?"

Tom McHugh—Photo Researchers

Peter B. Kaplan—Photo Researchers

With their natural habitats devastated by man's activities, the Hawaiian goose and Przewalski's horse have survived only in the confines of zoological parks and wildlife trusts.

Particularly questionable has been the laudability of conservation claims by zoos that strive to prosper even at the expense of the truth. To cite an actual circumstance, a North American zoo once featured a single male specimen of a wild-dog variety of mammal in a cage that bore a sign regarding the zoo's red wolf conservation project. The red wolf, *Canis rufus*, is listed as being in grave danger of extinction in the official compilation on threatened forms of wildlife issued by the International Union for Conservation of Nature and Natural Resources, Survival Service Commission, Morges, Switzerland. The compilation states that the remaining population of not more than 150 animals is restricted to southeastern Texas, the Mississippi Valley of northern Louisiana, and prairie marsh in southwestern Louisiana; its reported occurrences in eastern Oklahoma and the Ozark region of Arkansas would require further field research before such reports could be accepted as fact. However, when questioned, the animal's keeper acknowledged that it had been acquired from Wyoming, a state that does not border on any of those mentioned in the compilation. In truth, the red wolf cage held a Wyoming coyote, not rare by any yardstick.

The above situation, it must be stressed, is not typical; most zoo labels that mention conservation are well researched and express genuine concern. Nor is the question of the college student a particularly difficult one to answer; it is simply one formulated with a great deal of emotion and very little knowledge of the facts. Yet these examples serve to illustrate the bewildering array of information, misinformation, and emotion that comes into play whenever the issue of zoos and conservation is explored. There is no easy formula for arriving at objective conclusions. At the heart of the matter lie two complex issues: wildlife consumption by man and the definition of a good zoo.

Industry, medicine, and hunting

Consumption by man, by far the greatest threat to wildlife survival, is a complicated subject involving both necessity and great waste. When

GUNTER VOSS *is Director Emeritus, Toronto Zoological Park.*

(Overleaf) W. Schmidt—Peter Arnold

142

(Top) Francisco Erize—Bruce Coleman Inc.; (bottom) Gene Daniels—Black Star

carried to its extreme, it results in the destruction of habitat and the irreversible disappearance of species.

There are many reasons for wildlife consumption. The slaughter of whales, crocodilians, fur animals, and the great wild cats is carried out for fast commercial gains, with little if any concern for the future. Sportsmen object to it being called hunting, and rightly so because it is slaughter. To illustrate the immensity of this type of enterprise, in 1964 the country of Peru alone exported nearly 250,000 skins and hides; in other words, in just one country an animal was killed for its skin every two minutes, day and night, year-round. To quote William G. Conway, general director of the New York Zoological Park: "It's nauseating to remember that this kill, oftentimes associated with slow, agonizing death in snares, is carried out largely to adorn the girl who needs nothing."

Certain forms of wildlife, primarily monkeys and apes, are consumed by medical and pharmaceutical agencies at a staggering rate. During the peak years of polio vaccine production, for example, the United States alone imported 223,000 primates in 1958, 190,000 in 1959, and 221,000 in 1960. Of all rhesus monkeys imported into the U.S. for research, 83% are killed within a year. Only 57% of rhesus monkeys born in breeding colonies of biomedical research centers are raised to six months of age.

Hunting also takes its toll of wildlife. During the 1974 waterfowl-hunting season in Canada, for instance, more than 4,250,000 wild ducks and geese were killed. This count does not include numerous coots, more than 220,000 woodcocks and snipes, and 7,000 sandhill cranes. In the U.S. more than 60 million birds and mammals are killed by hunters each year. Nevertheless, such enormous annual harvests of wildlife represent the managed cropping of a renewable resource that can be repeated without damage year after year.

One aspect of hunting for which sportsmen have been attacked is trophy hunting. Some geneticists have pointed out that hunters who remove choice male specimens, the carriers of the finest trophies, from a wild population to decorate their homes with horns, tusks, and antlers consequently are removing the mature carriers of the finest gene combinations; if continued, such practices would lead to genetic decline and degeneration. In defense of the sportsman it could be argued that carriers of the largest trophies are animals beyond their sexual prime; their genetic information would already have been secured in a generation of offspring. Furthermore, the females of these species are also carriers of genetic codes.

Living trophies and exotic pets

If modern zoos can be traced to the bear moats of European medieval cities, then historically zoological parks owe their existence to man's desire for keeping living trophies. In the 19th century, when nature seemed bountiful enough to be undamageable, zoos served as depositories for collectors, much the same as did museums. The

Père David's deer (top) of China and the Arabian oryx, two other species rescued from extinction by zoo conservation efforts, would thrive again in the wild were they to be provided with well-protected nature reserves.

143

(Top left) Jonathan T. Wright—Bruce Coleman Inc.; (top and bottom right) M. Stouffer—Animals Animals;
(bottom left) Matt Herron—Black Star

Unregulated hunting of the great cats, deer and other ungulates, whales, and fur animals for commercial gains or for impressive trophies takes an immense toll of wildlife.

excitement connected with the scientific description of new species of plants and animals matched the spirit of the era. What better cause was there than acquiring scientific knowledge? How long the animal survived in captivity mattered little. The breeding of wild animals was at best a by-product, and certainly not a major objective. A remnant of this attitude lingers on in some zoos, although less in the interest of science than for the sake of higher attendance. These zoos, which might better be called menageries, maintain that they must offer visitors and the governments on whom they depend for financial support a colorful variety of species, the less common the better. Considering the present peril of much of the animal world, however, better arguments should prevail.

As an outgrowth of man's obsession with trophies, a modern trend in the keeping of living trophies has emerged. On the island of St. Vincent in the Windward Islands chain of the Lesser Antilles, the attractive St. Vincent parrot is featured in a mural within the arrival hall of the

144

Kent Reno—Jeroboam

airport. This parrot exists only on St. Vincent and export is prohibited for its protection. The birds surviving in the wild live in a shrinking habitat, on mountaintops retaining the tropical rain forest, which is being felled at ever higher elevations to make room for banana and citrus-fruit plantations. Halfway around the world at about the same latitude lie the Philippines, where the magnificent monkey-eating eagle is native to the forested parts of Luzon and Mindanao. Less than 50 pairs are thought to exist at large. Several years ago the International Union of Directors of Zoological Gardens resolved not to purchase monkey-eating eagles so that the incentive of collecting live birds for sale to zoos would be removed.

Yet, despite protection, numbers of St. Vincent parrots and of monkey-eating eagles continue to decline. One reason is the ongoing reduction of suitable habitat; another, often overlooked cause is man's vanity. People of influence and financial means have come to look upon the possession of a live St. Vincent parrot, on St. Vincent, or a live monkey-eating eagle, in the Philippines, as a status symbol. They do so in full knowledge of the birds' rarity, indeed because of it. This practice is live trophy keeping at its worst, and it may be more widespread than has ever been publicized.

The motivation is quite similar for people in industrialized nations who demand to have exotic pets. Contrary to the keeping and care of dogs, cats, and horses, humane regulations pertaining to exotic pets do not exist, and controls of the pet industry are inadequate. Regardless of the country, pet stores invariably keep such animals as primates confined to pitifully small and woefully inadequate quarters, as if this were a sales device to arouse the customers' sympathy. Exotic pets require conditions for their physical and social well-being that most pet owners cannot provide. The volume of wildlife channeled through the pet trade toward destruction out of ignorance remains enormous.

Many zoo officials are acutely aware of the seriousness of this unfortunate situation. To cite one indication, the delegates to a recent North American Zoo and Aquarium Convention voted strongly to condemn the keeping of exotic pets. Yet to some extent it is the zoo professional who helps to keep pet trade channels open. A zoo director once related how to his amazement he had discovered a rare specimen in a local pet store, a species of reptile that had not been seen on reputable importers' price lists for many years. "But there it was," he said. "Naturally I bought it for my zoo." In the last analysis this individual ought to have decided to let the rare animal die on the pet dealer's hands. This might at least have served to discourage such commercial trade.

Measured against the wild fur and leather industries, the medical and pharmaceutical requirements, hunting, live trophy keeping, and the pet trade, the demands by good zoological gardens on wildlife resources are very small, although not negligible. Zoo requirements over the years undoubtedly have had an influence on wild animal populations that probably never were very numerous. The siamang, orangutan, maned wolf, fennec, snow leopard, clouded leopard, cock of the rock,

Dwindling forests in the Philippines and the practice of live trophy keeping are contributing to the extinction of the monkey-eating eagle.

Tom McHugh—Photo Researchers

Mankind is ultimately the cause of wildlife habitat destruction on a vast scale. Conservation-minded zoos and trusts must occasionally intercede to provide animals with their last chance for survival, albeit captive survival in an artificially created environment.

hyacinthine macaw, wattled crane, hooded crane, shoebill, and rock-fowl could be examples of species significantly depleted in the wild by zoo acquisitions. On the other hand, it is a historical fact that on several occasions zoo professionals agreed to ban the acquisition of threatened forms of wildlife even before governmental or conservation bodies imposed such restraints.

Dwindling nature

Nature untouched by man can barely be found anywhere on the Earth. Projected from growth rates for the mid-1970s, the human population is expected to double in Asia in 35 years and in Africa and South America in about 25 years. Man's population increase is ultimately the cause of habitat destruction on an unimaginably grand scale. Every additional developed acre must be subtracted from wildlife habitat. The loss of habitats is the most severe threat to wild organisms because it means starvation, crowding, flight, fear, and certain death. Some change in habitat is inevitable; it is a basis of evolution. It must be man's concern, however, that a sufficiently rich and varied habitat is saved to provide both the matrix for man's commercial needs and for a diverse, intricate web of ecology in which biological change and evolution can continue.

Whether he admits it or not, man himself is part of this web of life. Therefore, if only for self-preservation, man is obliged to allow nature to replicate itself. Ideally, this is accomplished by setting aside nature reserves or wilderness areas—national, state, and provincial parks that are ecologically independent. Yet few, if any, actually are; some in fact are being threatened by their very popularity. Conservation has been defined as the planned management and wise use of nature's resources. Thus conservation is a way of life for all people. For some, the stake is financial; for others, the reward is health and recreation. In spite of a stirring toward ecological awareness in recent years, conser-

(Top) D. & R. Sullivan—Bruce Coleman Inc.; (center) Russ Kinne—Photo Researchers; (bottom) Tom McHugh—Photo Researchers

vation programs are still full of inner contradictions. Hence, with the best of intentions wilderness areas are set aside and then "improved" until no wilderness remains.

The good zoo

Man's population growth and land devastation cannot be expected to come to a quick halt. As an all too frequent consequence, the right conditions for wild animal populations to thrive and propagate no longer exist. It is at this stage that capture and captive breeding must be used as a last resort to save the species from extinction. Conservation authorities have neither the facilities nor the expertise; they need good zoological gardens to carry out the task. Breeding-oriented zoological gardens (and, on the botanical side, propagation-oriented botanical gardens) fill this need provided they are managed with a conscious and consistent orientation toward conservation and a sound understanding of biology. These are the good zoos, not fundamentally different from nature reserves.

The college student who asked why zoos capture animals did not understand that, in the race against vast destruction of natural habitat, good zoos must occasionally step in to provide the one remaining chance for survival, albeit captive survival. If they do this in consultation with international conservation bodies, notably the International Union for Conservation of Nature, they play a positive role no one else can play and thus repay to nature the debt that zoo history may have accumulated. Zoos are not equipped to save such animals as the blue whale and Steller's albatross, which require vast and specialized environments; however, the list of endangered wildlife species that could thrive in the care of good zoos is very substantial.

The zoo as specialist

What needs to be understood first is that the old-fashioned collector of "a fine variety of animals" runs a menagerie. By contrast, the operator of a good zoo tends to reduce the number of animal species in the collection. Frankfurt Zoo in West Germany and the New York Zoological Park did so, and possibly others, while making their exhibits more natural and meaningful. The net result was excellent. More sophisticated visitors came, acknowledging the good zoo's claim to being an institution of culture; more animals bred and raised their young naturally, converting the zoo from a consumer to a producer of animals.

The need for specialization was understood by some even before World War I, as the following account demonstrates. A large, strange-looking deer, named Père David's deer after the first white man to have described it, apparently originated from forests in northern China. By the latter half of the 19th century, Père David's deer existed nowhere but in the Imperial Gardens near Peking, except for a few that had been sent to zoological parks in England, France, and Germany. When it became known in Europe that floodwaters had caused parts of the garden walls to collapse and that many deer of the emperor's herd had

Over the years zoo demands on wildlife resources have had a small though significant effect on populations of such species as (top to bottom) the snow leopard, the fennec, and the orangutan, whose numbers were probably never very great.

(Top) Bill Brooks—Bruce Coleman Inc.; (center) Norman Tomalin—Bruce Coleman Inc.; (bottom) Charles E. Schmidt —Bruce Coleman Inc.

perished, the duke of Bedford offered to make available his estate, Woburn Abbey, if zoos would send their specimens to England.

The directors of the major European zoos knew well that Père David's deer were a rarity and unavailable in the traders' market at any price. Yet, conscious of conservation, they responded positively—and none too soon. In the unrest of the Boxer Rebellion of 1900, all Père David's deer from the Imperial Gardens were destroyed. Although reduced to a total of only 16 living deer at Woburn Abbey at that time, plus one or two at Peking Zoo, the species recovered. It can presently be observed at Woburn Abbey and in numerous zoological parks to which offspring were sent and where breeding continues. If the Chinese government were to provide a well-guarded nature reserve in the original haunts of the deer, several good zoos would most likely contribute animals from their own herds.

Such a restocking of nature did take place when the Pheasant Trust of Great Witchingham in England sent Swinhoe's pheasants to Taiwan for release in nature following revelations that the wild population had dwindled to critically low numbers but that the government had assured protection. Likewise, the Wildfowl Trust, of which the renowned British conservationist Sir Peter Scott is honorary director, was the source for reintroduction of the néné, or Hawaiian goose, to Hawaii. Presently this same trust is engaged in a breeding study of the white-winged wood duck, *Cairina scutulata*, with an aim to its repopulation of parts of the unspoiled primary rain forest of northeastern India, Thailand, or Malaysia.

Roland Lindemann's Game Farm in the Catskill Mountains of New York specializes in exotic hoofed animals, and his breeding success story with wild stock is unmatched. In charge of lemurs, leaf-eating monkeys, and apes at Cologne Zoo in West Germany, Uta Hick and her team of workers have achieved outstanding longevity and breeding results, especially of rare prosimians from Madagascar. Among many more examples of success through specialization are the white-eared pheasants of the Jersey Wildlife Preservation Trust in England and of Zoopark Berlin in East Berlin, the rare northern deer at Zoopark Berlin, the primates at Inuyama Monkey Center in Japan, and the kangaroos and antelopes at Oklahoma City Zoo. Others include the coscoroba swans and antelopes at San Antonio Zoo in Texas and the edentates at Lincoln Park Zoo in Chicago.

The Zoological Society of London operates Regent's Park Zoo in the city and Whipsnade Park in Bedfordshire. The Regent's Park Zoo maintains an enormous variety of species, Whipsnade comparatively few. Relative to the total of species in the collection, Whipsnade is faring far better as a center for reproduction and successful raising of captive wildlife. Australian wallabies and Chinese water deer produce dozens of young every year, and cheetah breeding at Whipsnade has become a specialty.

Consistent with specialization, a good zoo should provide its animals with suitable, biologically correct facilities and its visitors with meaningful exhibits that emphasize conservation. Bernhard Grzimek, former director of the Frankfurt Zoo, pointed out correctly that wild animals in good zoos help their brethren at large in three ways: (1) By reproducing, they maintain a viable gene pool for eventual reintroduction into nature. (2) They allow observational research supplemental to field studies, the results of which may be useful when protective measures in the animals' home range are contemplated. (3) The viewer of animals in captivity is more likely to develop an empathy for wildlife than if he had seen them on television or in a museum showcase; thus he is more likely to become active in conservation issues than if he had never been touched by the eyes of a living creature.

Alternatives

In criticizing zoological parks, people with a sincere concern for wildlife have suggested that conservation-oriented information centers selling books and field guides, offering lectures, and showing wildlife films would be superior to zoos. But zoo officials hold that it is the live animal that attracts large crowds, and that it is the crowds, not a handful of enthusiasts, who need to learn about nature. In addition, neither book nor film can bring out the deep-felt empathy with a living creature that zoos can evoke.

There are also people critical of cage confinement, in which bars appear reminiscent of prison cells. Further, examples of inhumane

Restricting cages and dismal surroundings (opposite page) are no longer considered in plans for new zoological parks. Modern designs emphasize natural settings, enhance animal comfort and health, and promote visitor interest. Where space permits, such as at Woburn Abbey in England (below), small herds of mixed species may roam freely over acres of natural landscape.

Bradley Smith—Animals Animals

Marvin Newman—Woodfin Camp & Associates

The lushness of tropical foliage is exploited to best advantage in realistic exhibits at São Paulo Zoo in Brazil.

crowding in transportation are cited. To deal with the latter issue first, many large animals travel best, suffering the least injury, when placed in rather narrow crates. This is not inhumane treatment but in the best interest of all: animal, shipper, and receiver. Nevertheless, overcrowding, especially of small birds and reptiles, in shipping containers has on occasion led to massive losses. Zoo professionals and the International Air Transport Association have jointly worked out a manual specifying acceptable crate types, sizes, and occupancy. Most major airlines adhere to these standards. Certain loopholes still exist, but work is being done to eliminate them.

But what about the barred cage? Following the example of major museums, leaders among zoo professionals have created exhibit sections for their respective zoos. Designers employed in these departments no longer even consider barred cages. Improved models of exhibits are tested and remodeled to satisfy such concerns as the animals' comfort, safety, and health; the reduction of boredom and of stress; the keeper's safety and ease of operation; and the aesthetic pleasure and learning experience of the visitor. Where zoo exhibits do not meet these ideal standards, quite probably the zoo budget is too small. In exceptional cases, there may be other less justifiable explanations, such as a reluctance to break with tradition or a stamp-collector's attitude prevalent among the zoo's officials.

150

Finally there are thoughtful people who advocate the keeping of common animal species exclusively. This way the endangered and the rare kinds would be left in nature. Although this proposal is based on good intentions, it does not acknowledge the grave dangers looming in nature—slaughter for quick gains, poaching, and habitat destruction. Facts have proven that in many cases removal from nature and transfer into the hands of concerned keepers is the only course open to meet the threat of extinction. If Père David's deer had not been acquired by European zoos at the end of the 19th century, the species would be extinct. It is possible that certain pheasants from Southeast Asia presently occur nowhere but in the collections of some zoos and hobbyists. And had it not been for the breeding of the white-tailed gnu by farmers in South Africa and zoological gardens, this striking antelope would no longer exist.

The last wild European bison, or wisent, was shot in Poland on Feb. 9, 1921. Fortunately zoological gardens had the species in their collections. An energetic and multilingual mammalogist in Hamburg, Germany, the late Erna Mohr, established a studbook of the wisent; traveled, photographed, and published wisent material; ensured that zoos exchanged specimens; and resisted political pressures aimed at crossbreeding with the American bison. As a result of these efforts wild-roaming wisent herds have been reestablished in Eastern Europe from zoo stock. The government of Poland proudly and efficiently protects the species in its extensive Bialowieza National Park, a wild forest once hunted by the tsars.

Robert L. Zentmaier—Photo Researchers

Meaningful, well-designed exhibits such as those at Regent's Park Zoo in London involve both animal and visitor in conservation issues.

Photos, Kenneth W. Fink—Bruce Coleman Inc.

Great apes frolic in large, moat-protected grottoes at San Diego Zoo in California.

Fitness for survival

Wisents, carefully selected and released into the original haunts of the species, learned quickly to avoid wolf and man. Would all other zoo animals be equally fit for survival in the wild? Raised and bred in protected environments, would not their instincts degenerate? Zoo professionals are correct when they emphasize the perfect suitability for survival in the wild of reintroduced, zoo-bred wisent, Swinhoe's pheasant, Hawaiian goose, and others, and there is confidence that Przewalski's horse would do well again in Mongolia, Père David's deer in China, maned sheep in the Atlas Mountains, and white oryx in southern Arabia. Nevertheless, it would be unscientific to generalize that all zoo creatures have retained their fitness for successful reintroduction. In fact some research results indicate otherwise.

Probably among the most difficult orders of animals to be reintroduced into nature are the primates and the carnivores, which normally undergo a long course of training from skilled parents before they can fend for themselves. In carnivores, reduced fear of man may lead to their becoming a problem. However, careful work with birds of prey has indicated ways by which predators can be conditioned to succeed in natural environments.

New directions

In spite of the generally gloomy world economic situation of recent years, some zoological parks have been created as or transformed into theaters of conservation education. Visitors to these places bring away with them the main theme of ecology, man's dependency on nature for his own survival.

Antwerp Zoo in Belgium, for example, established a breeding-oriented park away from the city at quiet Planckendael, where one can admire giant eland, pudu, red-breasted geese, wisent, and many other

152

rarities. At Whipsnade space is plentiful and propagation is emphasized; the visitor enjoys large herds of creatures in enormous paddocks or at large in the park. The San Diego Zoological Society opened a wild animal park at San Pasqual, Calif., and in the few years of its existence there have been spectacular breeding results with gorillas, waterfowl, and hoofed animals. Frankfurt Zoo has begun construction of a more spacious sister institution.

Conservation centers not open to the public have been established, or are in the process of being developed, at several locations in the U.S. using potential breeder animals pooled from various owners. Pooling of live animals from different zoological gardens has already been accomplished successfully with Galápagos tortoises at Honolulu Zoo, with St. Vincent parrots at Houston, Texas, and with monkey-eating eagles internationally. Four zoos pooled St. Vincent parrots, and through this effort one chick was raised. But the pooling of captive monkey-eating eagles may have come too late to save the species.

Some zoological parks reach out far to demonstrate their role as centers of conservation and conservation education. The New York Zoological Society has sponsored innumerable conservation-oriented projects and research undertakings, among them the renowned field research of Roger Payne on whale communication and migration and of George Schaller on mountain gorillas, predators of the plains in East Africa, tigers and deer in India, and snow leopards in Asia. The Frankfurt Zoological Society's involvement in conservation projects includes support for the Charles Darwin Research Station workers on the Galápagos Islands, funds for rehabilitating orangutans to the forests of Sumatra, a campaign against the slaughter of migratory birds in Italy, support for the preservation of wetlands in Europe and for the protection of eagles' nests, and the purchase of the island of Lubondo in Africa's Lake Victoria for game release and protection. Antwerp Zoo sponsors and protects a marsh in Belgium and the Chicago Zoological Society supports a wombat reserve in Australia.

The better zoological parks are showing themselves equal to good museums in their impact as cultural centers. Wise and scientifically trained zoo professionals take seriously many suggested alternatives to zoo tradition and challenges from concerned lay people. They also strive for improvement within the profession; self-policing actions, minimum standards for membership and for accreditation, and even expulsion of members not adhering to minimum requirements have been applied in national zoo and aquarium organizations on both sides of the Atlantic. Through stimulating exhibits, brochures, lectures, labels, and audiovisual means, increasing numbers of zoos are attempting to convey to their millions of patrons what a great tragedy is the loss of a species and its way of life to all living things. William Beebe, former curator of birds at the Bronx Zoo in New York City, expressed this idea most poetically: "When the last individual of a race of living things breathes no more, another heaven and another earth must pass before such a one can be again."

Pooling of captive Galápagos tortoises from several zoos resulted in a successful breeding program at Honolulu Zoo.

Miguel Castro—Photo Researchers

Once More Into the Loch
by George R. Zug

Equipped with all the resources that modern science
and technology could provide, a team of investigators
once again probed Loch Ness for the fabled
"Monster" within. But, as before, Nessie proved elusive.

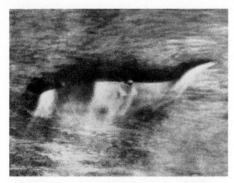

Photographs of objects in Loch Ness include those by (top) Hugh Gray in 1933, (center) Col. R. K. Wilson in 1934, and (bottom) Lachlan Stuart in 1951.

GEORGE R. ZUG *is Curator, Division of Reptiles and Amphibians, at the National Museum of Natural History of the Smithsonian Institution, Washington, D.C.*

Illustrations by Victor Hubbard

In 1933 a Scottish newspaper, the *Inverness Courier*, published a short report on the sighting by Mr. and Mrs. John Mackay of a large animal in Loch Ness, a large nearby lake. This sort of report was not uncommon, but this time it attracted the attention of the London and, eventually, the world press. At first, the news stories were accurate and serious, but they did not remain so for long.

London's *Daily Mail* launched an expedition to the loch in December 1933. The leader, M. A. Wetherell, was a big-game hunter and member of the Royal Zoological Society. He was assisted by a photographer and a journalist. Shortly after their arrival at the loch they made what they believed to be a startling discovery, the footprints of a monster. Wetherell stated that these round footprints were definitely made by a large, amphibious creature that "can breathe like a hippopotamus or crocodile with just one nostril out of the water." He announced that he would stake his reputation on the authenticity of the footprints. His reputation was to suffer. When casts of the footprints were examined by British Museum zoologists, they were discovered to match closely the right hind foot of a hippopotamus. It was later found that these footprints matched exactly the stuffed hippopotamus hind foot umbrella stand in the home of a Loch Ness resident. As a result of this practical joke any report of a large animal in Loch Ness would henceforth be subjected to ridicule.

Throughout the years, however, other sightings have occurred. The most frequent observation is a hump or overturned boatlike object slowly rising two to four feet above the lake's surface, accompanied by a splashing or surging of water. The object either remains stationary for a brief time and submerges or moves off at anywhere from five to ten knots, creating a large wake, and then submerges. Infrequently, a hump or a pair of humps is accompanied by a thin necklike object extending above the loch's surface. Those individuals who claim to have been close to the neck report a short snouted "head" that has no distinct separation from the neck, with a face that is somewhat horselike, bull-like, or eellike.

The reports of monster sightings are highly consistent in general details but often quite different in specifics. Surprisingly, they also match the water-bull or water-horse legends that are common in and around Loch Ness and other Scottish lochs. It is the consistency of these reports and the reliability of the observers that have led many people to become believers in the existence of Loch Ness monsters. Of course, there are an equal number of others who believe the opposite. They believe the observers are either lying, victims of a hoax or optical illusion, or drunk. Certainly some of the observations are optical illusions or misinterpretations of common objects such as diving birds, floating logs, or standing waves created by wakes of ships rebounding off the shores of the loch. It does seem unlikely, however, that all observations are misinterpretations or mass illusions, and it is on this basis that many individuals and groups of individuals have begun to investigate the Loch Ness phenomenon.

156

Adapted from Roy P. Mackal, *The Monsters of Loch Ness* © 1976, The Swallow Press Inc., Chicago

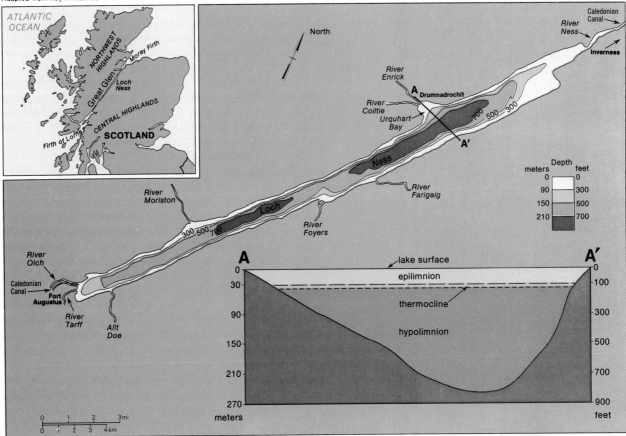

The Loch Ness Investigation Bureau, formerly the Loch Ness Phenomena Investigation Bureau, is such a group. Its volunteers have manned observation towers scattered around the loch since the early 1960s. Their objective has been to document surface sightings of the monsters either by still or motion-picture photography. Despite sophisticated camera equipment they have been only partially successful, obtaining only a few photographs of humplike objects or humplike objects with associated thin, necklike structures. They have also interviewed observers of the Loch Ness phenomenon, thereby documenting sightings and weeding out those obvious cases of misidentification.

Since the late 1960s the surface watchers have been joined by searchers using sonar, hydrophones, underwater cameras, submersible craft, and other specialized gear. Sonar has yielded the most frequent and consistent results of large objects that dive or surface rapidly, travel in a straight or complex path, and rapidly alter speed and direction. As interesting as these results may be, they have had little appeal to the news media. But the underwater photographs by the Academy of Applied Science of Boston stimulated the extensive news coverage of the past year and, more fortunately, added credibility to the existence of a population of large aquatic animals in Loch Ness.

The Academy photographs were obtained in 1972 and 1975 from an underwater time-lapse camera suspended about 40 feet below the

Loch Ness, a freshwater lake more than 20 miles long by 1 mile wide, lies in the Highlands of northern Scotland. Biologically, it is classified as oligotrophic, or "little nourishment," because the lower layer of cold water, the hypolimnion (diagram), never becomes completely depleted of oxygen. Below the 100-foot-deep epilimnion the water cools rapidly through the 30-foot thermocline. A–A' indicates the location of the fixed sonar screen experiments of the late 1960s and early 1970s.

Based on the evidence of photographs and other sightings, various species of
mammals, reptiles, and fish have been proposed as likely candidates for the Loch
Ness monster. On land in the foreground is a giant sea otter. Behind it on land is
one variety of plesiosaur, a marine reptile considered extinct for 65 million years.
In the foreground in the water are two giant eels, while in the far background is an
elasmosaur, a long-necked plesiosaur. Between them is a giant sea turtle.

NYT Pictures/Paul Hosefros

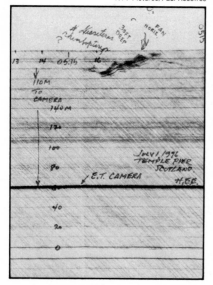

Photos, Syndication International—Photo Trends

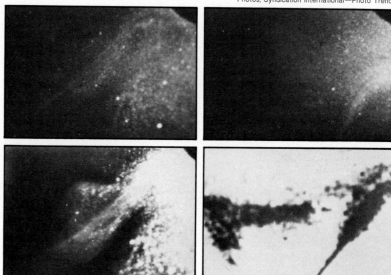

Sonar recorder printout for July 1, 1976 (left), reveals a fan-shaped image caused by an unidentified disturbance at a depth of 30 feet in the loch. Arrow at the bottom of the scan points to the position of the underwater camera. At the top right are two film frames from an underwater camera that were exposed at the same time objects were recorded by sonar in August 1972. Below each is the same frame after being computer-enhanced.

loch's surface in Urquhart Bay. In 1972 the Academy had a sonar aimed into the middle of the bay and the camera suspended in its beam. Late one night while watching the sonar chart, Academy observers saw a school of fish rapidly leave the sonar beam and be replaced by a much larger object. This object was soon joined by a second large object. The objects were within the beam for several minutes, long enough to be photographed if they had passed through the camera's field when it had fired its strobe. When the film frames, exposed at the same time the objects were recorded by sonar, were examined, no clear images could be discerned, certainly nothing that could be identified as a large aquatic animal or part of its body. One frame was computer-enhanced to sharpen the contrast of the amorphous image. This technique showed a flipperlike structure. Two other frames were similarly treated; one yielded another flipperlike structure, and the other a pair of objects that remain difficult to interpret.

The Academy tried for more underwater photographs in 1973 and 1974 with no success. Luck was with them again in 1975, when they obtained several more photographs on the time-lapse camera, which was being used as a backup system for the more sophisticated sonar-triggered camera. The two most interesting photographs presumably show a closeup of a head and a front view of the forepart of the body and neck of Nessie.

Natural history of Loch Ness

Loch Ness is the northernmost freshwater lake in the string of lochs extending northeast from the Firth of Lorn on the west coast of Scotland to the Moray Firth on the east. These lochs lie along the Great Glen fault, which divides the Scottish Highlands into the North and the Northwest Highlands and the Central and Southwest Highlands. Geologically, these lochs are old, having had their origin in the Devonian Period (approximately 350 million years ago) with the major movement

Photos, courtesy, Academy of Applied Science, Boston—Photo Trends

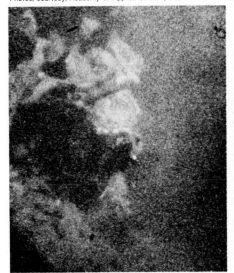 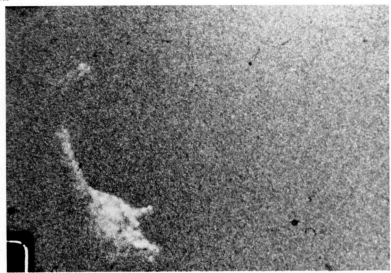

of the fault. Biologically, the lochs are young, having been scoured clean and deepened by the great ice sheets of the Pleistocene.

The last ice sheet receded about 10,000 years ago, and the lochs began to fill with water and life. Loch Ness filled first with salt water, for the weight of the ice sheet had depressed the land into the sea. As the land slowly rebounded, Loch Ness changed from an arm of the sea to a completely freshwater lake connected to the sea by the short (about six miles) River Ness. Loch Ness is the largest freshwater lake in Scotland and stands at a mean elevation of about 50 feet above sea level. It is a long, narrow lake, nearly 23 miles in length with a maximum width of 2 miles and an average width of somewhat less than a mile. The banks are steep and rapidly drop to a 100-foot depth or deeper. Most of the loch's bottom lies at 300 or more feet (mean depth 433 feet) with two large basins greater than 700 feet. Recent sonar data suggest that the maximum depth may exceed 900 feet. These data also show no evidence of subterranean connections to the sea.

The loch is fed by eight main rivers and more than twenty small streams. As the rivers and streams pass through boggy areas, they pick up and carry large amounts of organic materials to the loch. Many of these peat particles remain in suspension, giving the water a dark color, a slightly acid composition, and a low light penetration. Those particles that precipitate join with mineral sediments to create a fluid and mucky bottom. Apparently in many areas of the loch floor there is no clear demarcation between the bottom and the water, but rather a gradual increase in the density of the particles until a solid bottom is obtained. This transition between water and true bottom may occupy several feet and, thus, effectively hide anything falling or resting on the bottom of the lake.

The water of Loch Ness is cold, but it never freezes. During the summer the surface water may reach a temperature of 58° F (14.5° C). With increasing depth, the water cools gradually through the first

Images at a depth of approximately 35 feet in Loch Ness are revealed in photographs taken in June 1975 by a team from the Academy of Applied Science of Boston.

161

Loch Ness (center) is flanked by examples of the fanciful and scientific attitudes concerning the monster. At the top above is Winifred Carey, who claims to have seen the monster 15 times. Below is a sign warning against the monster and a painting of it on a research building.

Among the scientists working at Loch Ness were Tim Dinsdale (top), who headed a surface surveillance team. A sonar scanner is lowered into the loch (center), and a printout of its findings is read (bottom).

Adapted from Academy of Applied Science drawings by
Robert H. Rines in *The Monsters of Loch Ness* © 1976,
The Swallow Press Inc., Chicago

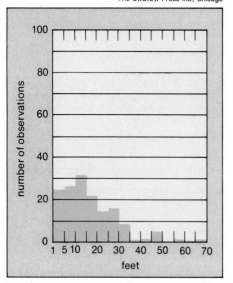

A frequency distribution in which the number of observations made from 1962 to 1971 is plotted against the length of the observed object (above) reveals the largest number between 10 and 15 feet. Below, expedition leader Robert Rines (right) and photo analyst Charles Wyckoff prepare the underwater camera rig for operation in June 1976.

NYT Pictures/John Hosefros

hundred feet (epilimnion) and then rapidly through a 30-foot thermocline until it reaches 42° F (5.5° C). Below this level (hypolimnion), the water remains at that temperature. During the winter the latent heat of the large water mass and the cool, although not cold (mean January air temperature is 38° F), winter temperatures allow the entire water mass to fall to 42° but not much lower.

This temperature stratification, the narrow, linear shape of the loch, and the direction of the prevailing winds produce opposing currents within the loch. The general direction of flow is northeast with the water flowing out the River Ness to the North Sea. This flow is continual and of a relatively slow speed. Northeast or southwest winds create surface waves while they are blowing, and seiches or internal surges develop when they have stopped. The continual pressure of the wind drives the water to the opposite end of the loch from which it is blowing, thereby tilting the surface. As the wind slows or stops, the water slides back into place with a slow rocking movement along the long axis of the loch. The surface movement is not great, but the waves of the thermocline are 15–20 feet high. This movement is not visible on the surface of the loch, and the current created is slow (about one foot per second).

The waters of Loch Ness are well oxygenated from the surface to the bottom. The surface water is fully saturated with oxygen, and the bottom water still possesses a 70% oxygen saturation. The coolness of the water, in addition to having a high oxygen load capacity, reduces the rate of decay and thereby prevents oxygen depletion even with a slow water turnover or circulation. The slow rate of decay and the great depth of Loch Ness are the two factors that prevent corpses, monster or otherwise, from bobbing to the surface. Slow decay prevents a rapid buildup of gases in the body cavity, and the gases that do form are compressed by the great water pressure; therefore, a carcass never becomes buoyant enough to rise.

With its high oxygen content, Loch Ness could be a biologically productive lake, but its high peat content precludes this. Both the low light penetration and acidity act to retard or prevent the growth of a planktonic or submergent vegetation. The acidity binds calcium carbonate and other minerals in the water, thus preventing their use by plants. The low light penetration restricts plant growth to the upper 20 feet or so of the loch. The steep banks of the loch and heavy wind action reduce the amount of shore vegetation that can survive in the lake. The zooplankton is similarly reduced owing to the low density of phytoplankton. This in turn should result in low fish populations, but that seems to be false. Resident fish populations are probably not great, but the migration of eels and salmon through the loch significantly boosts its overall productivity. Fish censuses have led to estimates that 100,-000 tons of salmon (adults and juveniles) pass through the loch each year. This figure seems high, but even if it is reduced by a factor of ten and then added to the resident eel, trout, and char populations, it provides an abundance of fish sufficient to support a small quantity of large, fish-eating animals.

Recently some biologists, using mathematical models developed for fisheries research, estimated that Loch Ness could support populations that ranged from between 10 large monsters (1,500 kilograms or 1.5 tons each) to 150 small ones (100 kilograms or 0.1 ton each). Their only assumptions, generally considered as reasonable ones, were that the monsters eat fish and that Loch Ness has a low productivity of plant nutrients.

Nessiteras rhombopteryx

The identity of these large creatures in Loch Ness remains a mystery. The evidence is still too incomplete and somewhat contradictory. Nonetheless, this has not prevented speculation. The guesses of the monster advocates encompass a wide range of aquatic animals: plesiosaurs, long-necked seals, giant annelid worms, giant eels, and embolomere amphibians. The antimonster advocates suggest that the Loch Ness phenomena may represent floating mats of vegetation, large logs, clusters of gas bubbles, otters, common seals, or sturgeon. No matter what the animals are, if they are new to science they have a name, *Nessiteras rhombopteryx*. This name, which they received in December 1975, is based on the photographs by scientist Robert Rines of flipperlike structures. The name is derived from Ness for Loch Ness and the Greek *teras* for wonder or marvel, *rhombos* for diamond shape, and *pteryx* for fin—the "Ness wonder with diamond-shaped fin."

It is easier to say what *Nessiteras* is not than what it is. Yet such disclaimers are also likely to err, owing to the limited evidence. To begin on a positive note, the Loch Ness monster is a population of animals and not a singular entity. No single animal could have a life span to encompass the centuries of sightings. Furthermore, observers report multiple individuals and different sized individuals. The sonar data also have shown multiple individuals. The majority of the data indicates that the adult size is about 25 feet long with a maximum diameter of 6 feet, which, without knowing the exact body shape, would suggest a body weight of 1,800 to 3,200 pounds.

The population would contain 10 to 12 adult individuals at the maximum body weight and 18 to 20 at the lower weight. In such small populations, the life span of an individual once it reaches maturity is long; to speculate for Nessie, 50 years would not be unreasonable. The annual recruitment rate would be very low, probably less than one individual per year. The animals probably take several years to attain reproductive maturity. Mortality would be highest at birth or hatching and gradually decrease with increasing size and maturity.

The external features are of little help in deciphering Nessie's identity. The overall body shape is assumed to be plesiosaurlike with a thin neck and tail abruptly joining a robust, spheroidal body; however, a fat-bodied eel shape cannot be excluded. The reports of dorsal crests on the neck and posterior part of body and tail imply the presence of fins, although this remains an uncertainty. Of the head, only its brevity, indistinct union with the neck, and wide mouth are constant features.

Adapted from Academy of Applied Science drawings by Robert H. Rines in *The Monsters of Loch Ness* © 1976, The Swallow Press Inc., Chicago

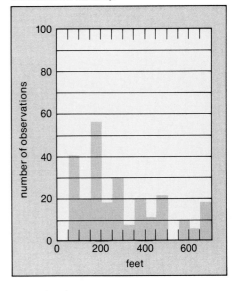

A frequency distribution comparing the number of observations of an object with the depth of the loch at the observation point (above), made from 1962 to 1971, shows the largest number between 150–200 feet. John Mills, below, tends the control console for the underwater closed-circuit television system.

NYT Pictures/Paul Hosefros

Adapted from Academy of Applied Science drawings by
Robert H. Rines in *The Monsters of Loch Ness* © 1976,
The Swallow Press Inc., Chicago

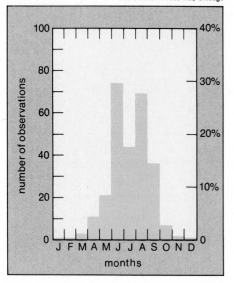

*According to data collected from 1962
to 1971, the number of observations
of an object in the loch was largest in
June and August. Below, Charles
Wyckoff (left) and Robert Rines (right)
lower the underwater camera rig.*

NYT Pictures/John Hosefros

The eyes are variously reported as large, small, slitlike, or invisible. The head may be smooth or bear assorted projections. Overall, the external features do not seem to match any known species and, in particular, provide little to no information on the class of animals to which *Nessiteras* may belong.

Nessie cannot be an invertebrate, at least not if the several land sightings are of the same creatures as the loch surface sightings. A giant worm or giant mollusk would be unable to support such a large body mass, let alone move it on land. They possess hydraulic skeletons and depend upon their buoyancy in water to maintain their body form and ability to move. On land, a soft-bodied invertebrate would be flattened by its own weight.

Many of Nessie's characteristics are shared with amphibians. One factor, however, eliminates amphibians as a likely choice. All living and extinct amphibians are freshwater animals, and only a few species can tolerate brief exposures to brackish water. Since Loch Ness and all connecting lochs and streams were buried beneath an ice sheet until 10,000 years ago, Nessie's ancestors must have been marine creatures and, thus, could not be amphibians.

Nessiteras as the last survivor of the plesiosaurs is the favorite of many advocates. Unfortunately, it seems unlikely, even though some of the physiological arguments against the creatures being reptiles have fallen in the last few years. It is now known, for example, that one large aquatic reptile, the leatherback sea turtle, can maintain an elevated body temperature in cold water and that the green sea turtle can and does hibernate underwater. If they are physiologically so adapted, another reptilian species could possess similar adaptations. But two major points continue to argue against the plesiosaur theory. Plesiosaurs appear to have been like turtles in that they had to come ashore to lay their eggs. Neither the activity of the Ness creatures nor the northern Scotland climate can support this mode of reproduction. The fossil record indicates that the plesiosaur became extinct in the Late Cretaceous. Although other supposedly extinct animals have reappeared later, the plesiosaur niche has been filled by whales and seals, thereby affirming their demise.

The reproductive habits of seals also argue against *Nessiteras* being a long-necked seal. All seals give birth to their young on land. Seals are air breathers, and neither the diving profiles nor the frequency of surfacing provides strong evidence for assuming that the Loch Ness creatures breathe air.

The sharks and the bony fishes are the only remaining vertebrate classes that have not been eliminated as contenders. Both are diverse groups with a myriad of adaptations that encompass the characteristics reported for Nessie. Perhaps Nessie is a rare but known species rather than a new and exotic species.

Even if Loch Ness creatures are finally identified, the enigmatic monster problem will remain, for monster sightings have not been confined to the Scottish lochs. Such sightings have been reported along the coast of Scotland and in large coastal lakes from Ireland through the Soviet Union, in North America, and in the Southern Hemisphere from Argentina to Australia. The Bierman-Zarzynski Expedition, an organization resembling the Loch Ness Investigational Bureau, recently began an investigation of a monster said to inhabit Lake Champlain in the northeastern U.S. Therefore, no matter what the outcome is at Loch Ness the adventurers and curiosity seekers will continue to have monsters to discover.

The modern search

The modern search for Nessie began in 1960 with the first attempt to observe and track the creatures under water rather than wait passively for their infrequent, brief, and partial exposures on the surface. Since assorted vessels passing through Loch Ness had recorded large motile objects on their echo-locating gear, the 1960 expedition, from Oxford and Cambridge universities, carried a sonar unit. The scientists were more successful in their surface sightings than with sonar contacts, yet their preliminary sonar survey demonstrated the value of sonar investigations. Subsequent sonar surveys in the early 1960s were also unsuccessful or inconclusive, but beginning in 1968 with the use of much improved sonar units several research teams had positive contacts with large creatures.

The surveys have been performed in two ways. In the sonar gate or screen method, the sonar is anchored on the shore and the beam is projected straight out into the lake perpendicular to the shoreline. The beam forms a cone of sensitivity across the entire loch from the bottom to the top. Any object moving up or down the loch will pass through this sonar cone or screen and be recorded on the sonar. The second method, the mobile search, begins with the sonar mounted on a boat. The boat follows prearranged search patterns until an object is located and then follows the object. With either method it is desirable to obtain a permanent record of the sonar data. In those sonar units that display their data on an oscilloscope, a time-lapse camera is aimed at the screen and a picture is taken at regular intervals. Other sonar units possess strip-chart recorders, and the sonar data are etched directly onto a continuously moving paper tape.

The advantages of searching for Nessie with sonar are many. Foremost, the search is entirely under water where the creatures live. Movement patterns and speeds can be determined; for example, the diving profiles were obtained from sonar data. The size and a very rough estimate of shape can be determined. The major disadvantage of sonar is that it provides little information with which to identify the creatures.

The research division of the Loch Ness Investigation Bureau, under the direction of Roy Mackal, began in 1968 to diversify the search. The researchers decided on three main approaches: obtaining a biopsy of Nessie, monitoring the sounds in the loch, and photographing under water by means of baited shutter releases. The biopsy method was initiated first. Small biopsy devices were attached to the head of

Adapted from Academy of Applied Science drawings by Robert H. Rines in *The Monsters of Loch Ness* © 1976, The Swallow Press Inc., Chicago

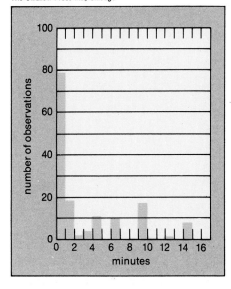

The duration of about one-third of the observations of an object in the loch from 1962 to 1971 (above) was less than one minute. Below, a diver surfaces after inspecting the underwater equipment of the 1976 expedition.

NYT Pictures/John Hosefros

167

crossbow arrows and harpoons and were designed to penetrate only a couple of inches into the creature's skin and remove 2–3 grams (0.7–1 ounce) of tissue. The plan was to shoot them at the animal's hump as it surfaced. A harpoon was also mounted on a minisub in 1969 in an attempt to stalk the creatures under water. As of late 1976 no biopsy had been collected.

The baited underwater cameras were failures. The first problem was that the cameras would fire as they were lowered or rocked by water currents. This was solved, but the bait failed to attract the animals. The acoustic monitoring by hydrophones suspended at different locations and levels in the water was only slightly more successful. A number of different sounds were recorded, and as of late 1976 several remained unidentified. The most intriguing one was a regularly spaced series of knocklike sounds that would stop as motorboats approached the area.

Attempts to stalk the monsters with minisubs also failed. In 1969 two minisubs were used in exploration surveys, and both found that the high peat content greatly restricted visibility. During the first submergence of one sub, visibility was so poor that the operator could not see where he was going and ran the craft into the bottom. Even when a large creature was sighted on the sonar, the maximum speed of the sub was insufficient to get close to it.

The most interesting results were obtained with the Edgerton underwater camera-strobe system. A 16-mm time-lapse camera was mounted in a waterproof case and synchronized to open its shutter as the strobe fired. In 1972 the camera and the strobe were mounted side by side. With the camera so close to the light source the peat particles reflected so much light back into the camera that the images were fogged, and the film had to be computer-enhanced to reveal the images of flipperlike structures. During subsequent years the strobe and camera were attached to the opposite ends of a supportive rig four feet long. The clarity of the 1975 pictures shows the effectiveness of this separation.

With the success of the simple Edgerton arrangement, the Academy of Applied Science decided to try a more sophisticated camera setup in 1975. A camera, strobe, and sonar transducer were attached to a single supportive frame that was anchored to the bottom of the loch in 80 feet of water. All three were aimed diagonally upward in the same plane. The sonar was a trigger mechanism, and its signals were read by a minicomputer. If the signal indicated that an object with a 4–5-foot diameter at a distance of less than 40 feet was crossing through the sonar beam, the computer would fire the camera and strobe until the object left the field. Although a few sequences of pictures were taken, nothing appeared on film. Either the passing objects stirred up clouds of silt or silt settled on the camera lens while the camera rigging was being anchored.

The accomplishments of the 1975 investigation led to a better equipped and organized investigation in the summer of 1976. The primary goal remained to obtain clear and detailed photographs of the creatures in order to identify them. To this end, the photographic setup was greatly enlarged. Two submersible rigs were suspended in the water facing one another. One rig held strobe lights, a television camera, Polaroid camera, and stereo cameras; the other had a strobe, time-lapse camera, and tungsten lamps for the television camera. The time-lapse camera functioned as in past years, snapping pictures independently. The other camera required a round-the-clock monitoring of the television. If something showed on the screen, the monitor would activate the other camera. In spite of extensive pre-expedition testing, the sophisticated equipment suffered many malfunctions.

The search for Nessie extended beyond the photographic unit. One team used sonar to map the bottom topography of the lake and to search for skeletal remains. If such remains are located, they will be retrieved by divers or a grappling device. Recovery of bone would permit an identification of the creatures. Although no bones had been definitely detected by early 1977, the sonar team did find stone circles similar to Stonehenge on the bottom of the lake and several unidentified objects that the team believed deserved further investigation. Another team used a high-resolution infrared instrument to scan the surface of the loch in an effort to determine whether the creatures surface more frequently and less obtrusively than they do in the commonly reported sighting.

FOR ADDITIONAL READING

Peter Costello, *In Search of Lake Monsters,* (Coward, McCann & Geoghegan, 1974).

F. Fraser Darling and J. Morton Boyd, *The Highlands and Islands*, The New Naturalist: A Survey of British Natural History (Collins, 1964).

Tim Dinsdale, *Monster Hunt* (Acropolis Books Ltd., 1972).

Roy P. Mackal, *The Monsters of Loch Ness* (The Swallow Press Inc., 1976).

Robert H. Rines, Charles W. Wyckoff, Harold E. Edgerton, and Martin Klein, "Search for the Loch Ness Monster," *Technology Review* (March/April 1976, pp. 25–40).

Peter Scott and Robert Rines, "Naming the Loch Ness Monster," *Nature* (Dec. 11, 1975, pp. 466–468).

Nicholas Witchell, *The Loch Ness Story* (Penguin Books Ltd., 1975).

The Limits to Computation

by Ronald L. Graham and Michael R. Garey

Even with the help of modern computers, mathematicians often fail to find adequate solutions to many complex problems of practical significance. Recently, several important breakthroughs have been achieved.

Craig

Computation time is shown for various time complexity functions and for several values of size n for a problem instance. See text on p. 180.

Writers of science fiction are fond of imagining colossal, anthropomorphic supercomputers, capable of solving almost instantly any problem posed to them. These fantastic machines are in many ways natural extrapolations of the digital computers of the 1970s, which already have become the most sophisticated tools ever devised by mankind. As one views the rapid progress in computer technology and the wide variety of tasks currently performed using computers, it seems reasonable that supercomputers will someday become reality and that there is in fact no limit to the complexity of problems that eventually will be solvable by computers.

More than 40 years ago, however, British logician Alan Turing demonstrated conclusively the existence of fundamental limitations on what can be done using computers. His discoveries laid the groundwork for what is known as the theory of computational complexity. This theory seeks to quantify the amount of time and other resources required to solve problems on computers and has been the subject of particularly intense research activity during the last ten years. Quite recently a number of startling new results have been obtained.

Computer algorithms

The theory of computational complexity studies the properties of general step-by-step problem-solving methods called algorithms. A great many algorithms are familiar tools of computation, although that term might not be used in referring to them. For instance, many people have learned (and probably forgotten) an algorithm for determining the square root of any given number. Also well known are algorithms for computing baseball batting averages, for determining the area of any given triangle, for finding the greatest common divisor of two given numbers, and for summing arbitrary lists of arbitrarily large numbers.

These examples indicate the very general capabilities possessed by algorithms. They are intended to solve not just one single occurrence of a problem but every occurrence of that problem, even though each occurrence may involve different values of the problem parameters. For this reason it will be convenient to think of a problem as a rather general entity, consisting of certain parameters whose values are left unspecified and a prescription of what is to be constructed or computed from those parameters once they have been specified. An instance of a problem is obtained by assigning actual values to all the parameters. For example, one such problem is that of arranging an arbitrary list of English words into alphabetical order. The parameter left unspecified is the list of words, so an instance of this problem would be obtained by giving a specific list, such as the first 100 words of this article.

An algorithm for a given problem must be capable of solving any instance of that problem. In order that others may use it or that it be executed on a computer, every step must be specified completely and in sufficient detail that there never will be any ambiguity about what to do next. Before going on, it may be instructive to consider how an

RONALD L. GRAHAM is Head, Discrete Mathematics Department, and **MICHAEL R. GAREY** is a Member of the Technical Staff, Mathematics Research Center, Bell Laboratories, Murray Hill, New Jersey.

Illustrations by John Craig

	size n					
complexity		10	20	30	40	50	60
	n^2	0.0001 second	0.0004 second	0.0009 second	0.0016 second	0.0025 second	0.0036 second
	n^3	0.001 second	0.008 second	0.027 second	0.064 second	0.125 second	0.216 second
	n^5	0.1 second	3.2 seconds	24.3 seconds	1.7 minutes	5.2 minutes	13 minutes
	2^n	0.001 second	1 second	17.9 minutes	12.7 days	35.7 years	366 centuries
	3^n	0.059 second	58 minutes	6.5 years	3,855 centuries	2×10^8 centuries	1.3×10^{13} centuries

algorithm for alphabetizing a list of words could be so specified. Most natural languages have built-in ambiguities that make such specificity difficult, although people with common backgrounds often will agree on what is meant. The usual way of specifying an algorithm, in such detail that it can be executed on a computer, is to express it as a computer program written in a precise computer language. The input to such a computer program is used to describe the particular instance to be solved.

Instead of thinking in terms of any single existing computer, mathematicians have found it useful to introduce an abstract model of a computer, called a Turing machine. This model is conceptually simple, yet broad enough to reflect accurately the behavior of any existing or planned computer. Thus the Turing machine provides a common framework for mathematicians' investigations into the properties of algorithms. For the purposes of this article, however, it will not be necessary to define a Turing machine in rigorous detail. It will suffice simply to think in terms of any standard computer, and the following discussions will not depend on any special capabilities possessed by one computer but not another.

An alphabetizing algorithm

One simple algorithm for alphabetizing an arbitrary list of words can be described as follows. Assume that the positions in the list are numbered from 1 through m in order, in which m is the total number of words on the list. The algorithm will scan repeatedly through the list, interchanging adjacent words whenever they are not in alphabetical order, until the whole list has been alphabetized. To do this, it uses two auxiliary variables. The first, called POINTER, will always be the number of the next position on the list to be examined. The second, called CHANGE, will always be the number of interchanges made so far in the current scan of the list.

step 1: Set POINTER to position 1 and set CHANGE to 0.

step 2: Compare the two words in list positions POINTER and POINTER + 1 to find the leftmost place in which they differ. If the word in position POINTER + 1 has the alphabetically earlier letter in this place (no letter or "blank" is considered earlier than "a"), then interchange the positions of the two words and add 1 to CHANGE.

step 3: Increase POINTER by 1. If POINTER is less than m, return to *step 2* to continue this scan of the list.

step 4: (Reaching this step implies that POINTER equals m, so the algorithm is at the end of the list.) If CHANGE is 0, the list is now in alphabetical order. If CHANGE is larger than 0, however, return to *step 1* to begin another scan of the list.

Undecidable problems

In 1936 Turing proved the existence of a class of problems, called undecidable problems, which are so difficult that no algorithm for solving them can ever be devised. This astounding discovery, which ranks among the most profound intellectual achievements of the 20th century, is especially significant because computers seem to embody all the logical and computational capabilities imaginable. Thus, whatever instruments man may ever have at his disposal, the undecidable problems are destined to remain forever beyond his computational reach.

Turing showed specifically that one particular problem, called the Halting Problem, is undecidable. The Halting Problem is that of deciding, given an arbitrary computer program and an arbitrary input for that program, whether or not the program will eventually stop when given that input. An algorithm for this problem would have obvious uses, for example, in "debugging" computer programs and in avoiding embarrassing computer-budget overruns.

The proof that such an algorithm can never be given proceeds by assuming the existence of a program P* that actually can solve the Halting Problem; i.e., one that can determine for any given problem P and specified input I whether or not P will halt when applied to I. Suppose one's attention is now restricted to those programs P that themselves answer questions about programs, so that the inputs I to which they are applied are actually descriptions of other programs. In such situations P* can be used to decide whether or not a given program P of this type will halt when applied to a description of P itself. Suppose P* were so structured that, whenever it decides that P halts, it prints "P halts" indefinitely, without stopping; otherwise, it simply prints "P does not halt" and stops. Next consider what P* will do when asked to decide about *itself*. It either will continue printing "P* halts" indefinitely, without ever halting, or will print "P* does not halt" and then halt. Hence, whatever the program decides about itself, it obviously will contradict that decision by the manner in which it prints its answer. Because only one assumption was made—that a program for solving the Halting Problem existed—and because that assumption leads to a contradiction, it must be admitted that no such program can exist. The Halting Problem is undecidable.

In the years since Turing's initial discovery, many other problems from a variety of mathematical realms have been shown to be undecidable. One of the most picturesque is known as the Tiling Problem. In the Tiling Problem, one is given a finite variety of equal-sized square tiles. Each tile has each of its four edges colored with a specific color and is given a fixed orientation, with its edges running horizontally and vertically. It is assumed that one can obtain as many copies of each kind of tile as are needed. These can be put together, like dominoes, to form various configurations. In doing this, it is required that abutting edges of adjacent tiles be of the same color and that no tile be rotated from its initial orientation. The question to be decided is whether or not the given tiles can be used to form increasingly large, completely filled-in,

In this variation of the Tiling Problem, copies of 19 tiles are used to form arbitrarily large, completely filled-in, square configurations with the requirement that the purple, white, and blue tile be used at least once; other conditions described in text also hold. Depicted is a portion of a solid tiling that appears indefinitely extensible in all directions. Yet proving this property seems beyond the scope of present-day mathematics.

square configurations. If such tilings are possible, the given set of tile varieties is said to be solvable.

Notice that there is an effective, though possibly lengthy, method for demonstrating that a given set of tiles is *not* solvable. For if it is not solvable, then there must exist a square of some size, say 1,000 by 1,000 tiles, that cannot be formed. Thus, if one considers each size square in turn, in order of increasing size, and examines all possible ways of forming a square of that size with the given set of tiles, one will eventually discover some size that cannot possibly be formed. However, if the set of tiles *is* solvable, this procedure will never demonstrate this fact conclusively because it will never terminate.

How then could it ever be shown that a set is solvable? One approach is as follows. Suppose one were able to form a particular square configuration R, say of size *r* by *r*, in such a way that both horizontal boundaries had the same pattern of colors and that both vertical boundaries had the same pattern of colors. Then it is easy to see that any square could be formed with side length a multiple of *r* simply by placing together copies of R. Of course, every other size square occurs as a portion of one of these squares, so this method would show that the given set of tiles is solvable.

If every solvable set of tiles could be used to form some such configuration R, then one would have an algorithm for the Tiling Problem. First, all possible 2-by-2 squares could be formed from the tiles, then all the 3-by-3 squares, then all the 4-by-4 squares, and so on. Eventually one of two things would happen. If the set of tiles is solvable, one should eventually find a square, R, having the desired repeated color patterns. If the set is not solvable, one should find some size square for which no tiling is possible. In either case, the procedure will eventually terminate. However, it turns out that there exist solvable sets of tiles that cannot be used to form any square with such repeated color patterns. The first such set, constructed by Robert Berger of Harvard University in 1964, contained more than 20,000 types of tiles. It played a major role in his proof that the Tiling Problem is undecidable, completing a line of attack initiated some years earlier by the logician Hao Wang. Very recently Raphael Robinson of the University of California at Berkeley and Roger Penrose of the University of Oxford succeeded in reducing the number of needed tile varieties to only 24.

Of course, the existence of these sets of tiles alone is not enough to prove the undecidability of the Tiling Problem. They only show that the approach proposed above cannot give an algorithm. The main portion of Berger's proof shows that the computation of any computer program can be simulated exactly by an appropriately chosen set of tiles. In particular, to each computer program and each input to that program there corresponds a set of tiles that is solvable if and only if the program will eventually stop when given that input. This implies that any algorithm for solving the Tiling Problem could also be used to solve the Halting Problem. But because the Halting Problem has been proved undecidable, it follows that the Tiling Problem also is undecidable.

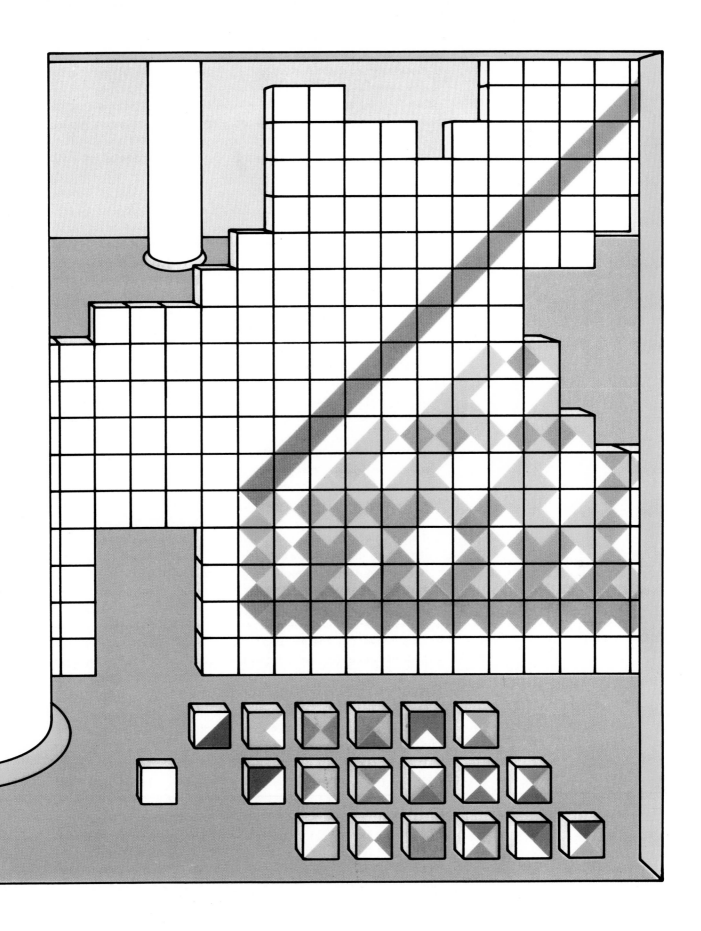

An instance of the Traveling Salesman Problem is shown for 22 U.S. state capitals. A salesman begins at his home city, visits the other cities, and returns home, traveling the least total distance in the process. The route traced in red has a total length of 8,119 miles. The shortest route, however, has a total length of 8,117 miles. The reader is invited to find it.

Decidable problems that are hard

Undecidable problems like the Halting Problem and the Tiling Problem are beyond the capabilities of any computer because no algorithm for solving them can exist, even in principle. However, there is another sense in which a problem can be too hard. This second sense applies to those problems for which algorithms can be specified, the so-called decidable problems. A decidable problem can be hard because, even though algorithms exist for its solution, none of them can possibly operate in a reasonable amount of time. This is somewhat akin to the problem of automatic weather prediction; a computer program for predicting one day's weather from that of the preceding day would not be very useful if it required more than 24 hours to do it. Similarly, an algorithm for solving instances of a problem of current interest might not be useful if it required many years of computer time. Thus, it is not enough that an algorithm exists to solve a particular problem; it is important that a suitably fast algorithm exists.

Consideration of what is meant by "suitably fast" forms the main thrust of the theory of computational complexity; namely, analyzing the amount of time required by algorithms for solving particular problems. Since there often are many different ways to solve a given problem, such analyses are important for comparing different algorithms as well as for determining beforehand whether an algorithm is fast enough to be used in practice.

Of course there is not just a single length of time associated with an algorithm, but rather a whole collection of execution times, one for each instance of the problem. The time required by an algorithm is really a mathematical function, one that gives for each problem instance the amount of time needed by the algorithm to solve that instance. This function is usually quite complicated and not particularly amenable to mathematical analysis. For some purposes, it is more convenient to express computation time as a function of the "size" of an instance. The size of a problem instance is defined to be the number of symbols needed to describe that instance. For example, the size of a list of words to be alphabetized would be the sum of the letter counts of all the words on the list. The function that gives for each size the largest amount of time required by the algorithm to solve any problem instance of that size is called the time complexity function for the algorithm. It is usually possible to determine this function, or a close approximation to it, by a mathematical analysis of the algorithm.

An important distinction between algorithms can be based on the rate at which the values of their time complexity functions grow with problem instances of increasing size. This distinction essentially partitions algorithms into two classes, although all algorithms are not necessarily one type or the other. The first class includes those for which the time complexity function grows only at a moderate rate, whereas the second includes those for which this function grows explosively. In defining these classes precisely the variable n can be used to denote the size of a problem instance. The first class, called

178

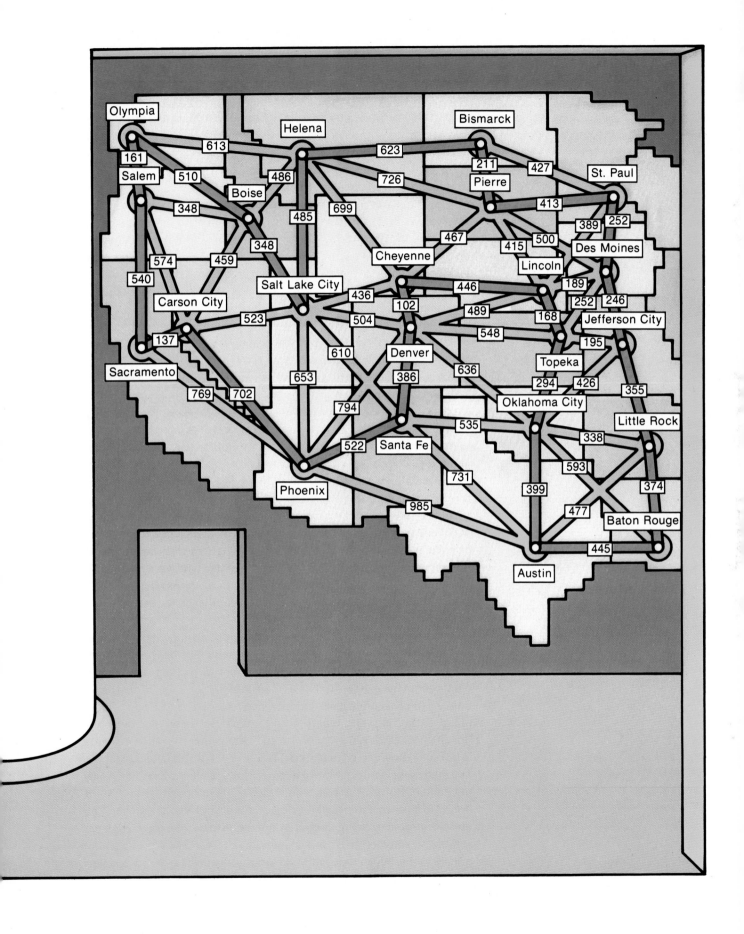

In one example of the Bin Packing Problem, four trucks, each with a capacity of 10,000 pounds, can be used to deliver the loads depicted. In fact, with an additional 1,800 pounds, four trucks will still suffice. Again, the reader is invited to determine how such a task can be accomplished.

polynomial algorithms, consists of those algorithms for which the time complexity function grows no faster than n to some constant power, such as n^2, n^5, or n^{10}. Notice here that the size n does not appear in the exponent. The second class, called exponential algorithms, consists of those for which the time complexity function grows as fast as some constant to the power n, such as 2^n, 3^n, or 7^n. Here the size n does appear in the exponent.

Perhaps the easiest way to see why this distinction is important is by examining some examples. The table on page 173 illustrates the computation time for various time complexity functions of each type and for various values of the size n for a problem instance. The first three functions, n^2, n^3, and n^5, are time complexity functions for typical polynomial algorithms; the last two functions, 2^n and 3^n, are time complexity functions for typical exponential algorithms. Each is to be interpreted as giving the time in microseconds required by that particular algorithm for solving an instance of size n.

The immense difference between the growth rates of computation time for the two types of algorithms is quite striking. All five algorithms require comparable amounts of time for instances of size 10, but as n grows they diverge rapidly, and the polynomial algorithms become far superior. In general, the growth rate for exponential algorithms is so explosive that they are not reasonable to use for solving problem instances of even moderately large size. For these reasons it is important to find polynomial algorithms for solving problems. A decidable problem for which it is impossible to give a polynomial algorithm is said to be intractable, because even with future computers there is little hope for the solution of large-sized instances of such a problem.

What is known about the existence of intractable problems? It is only within the past few years that researchers in mathematics and computer science have succeeded in proving that any of the classical decidable problems are intractable. The first results of this type were obtained in 1972 by Albert Meyer and Larry Stockmeyer of the Massachusetts Institute of Technology. Subsequent work has lengthened the list of intractable problems.

One of the most easily described examples of an intractable problem deals with what is called Presburger Arithmetic. Basically, Presburger Arithmetic involves a simple, logical system for writing down statements about the integers 0, 1, 2, 3, ... The statements are formed using only the logical connectives (and, or, not), quantifiers ([for all x], [there is a y such that]), and plus ($+$) and equals ($=$) signs. For example, [for all x] [for all y] $(x + y = y + x)$ is such a statement. Another example is [for all x] [there is a y such that] $(x + x = y + y + 1)$. Notice that the first statement is true; it merely expresses the familiar commutative law of addition. However, the second statement is not true, because $x + x$ is always an even number while $y + y + 1$ is always an odd number. The decision problem for Presburger Arithmetic is to decide, given any such statement, whether or not the statement is true.

In 1930 the Polish logician M. Presburger showed that the decision

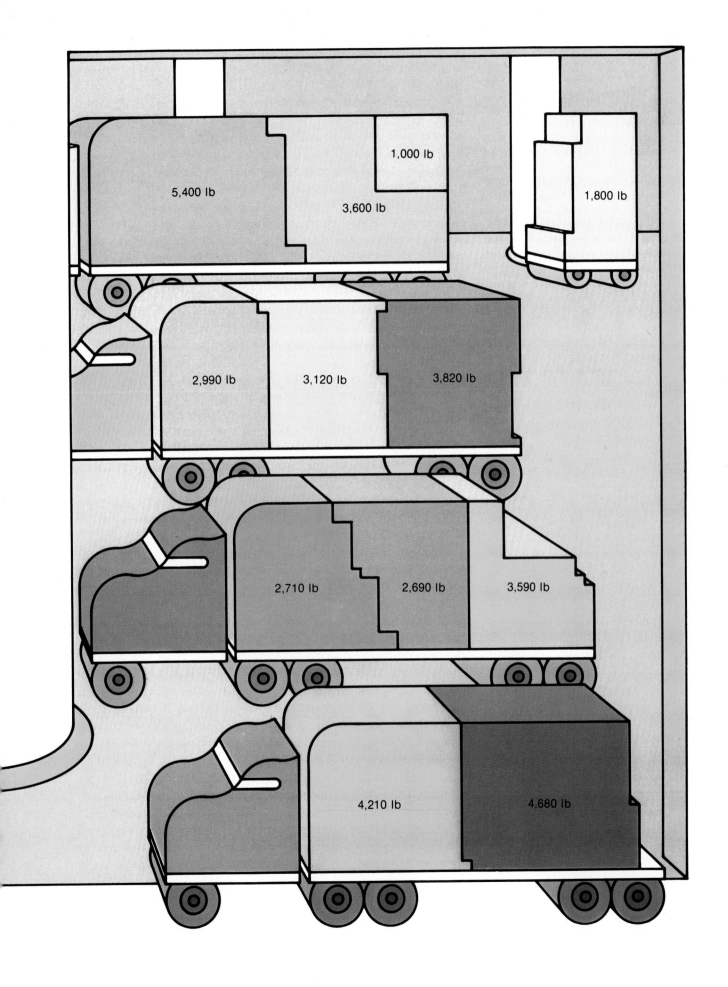

The Minimum Network Problem has as its objective the connection of a given set of points with a network having the shortest possible total length. Shown at the top of the facing page are three connecting networks for the corners of a square. The left one, using no junction points, has a total length of 3. The center one, with one junction point (a), has a total length of $2\sqrt{2}$, or 2.828.... The right network, with two junction points (a and b), has a total length of $(4/\sqrt{3}) + \frac{1}{2}$, or 2.808..., and is the shortest possible connecting network for this situation. The network shown in the lower figure connects 11 oil-consuming and oil-producing locations in the U.S. It employs five additional junction points and is the shortest possible connecting network for these locations. Without junction points the network would be 5% longer.

problem for Presburger Arithmetic is decidable. He gave an explicit algorithm that will always eventually determine whether or not any given statement of the above type is true. This was a major contribution, for it was by no means obvious beforehand that such an algorithm would exist. Unfortunately Presburger did not give a polynomial algorithm and subsequent efforts to improve upon his method met with little success.

However, in 1974 Michael Fischer of MIT and Michael Rabin of the Hebrew University, Jerusalem, showed that the decision problem for Presburger Arithmetic is intractable. In fact, they showed something even stronger. They proved the existence of a number c such that, for any algorithm that solves the decision problem for Presburger Arithmetic and for all sufficiently large numbers n, there are statements with no more than n symbols that cause the algorithm to take more than $2^{2^{cn}}$ steps. This "superexponential" function grows much more rapidly than even the exponential functions discussed above. Such results certainly help to explain the lack of success in devising computer programs that would automatically prove theorems in mathematics.

A perplexing class of problems

The subject of intractable problems remains one of the most active fields of research in contemporary mathematics and computer science. Many individual problems still have not been classified as to whether or not they are intractable; neither polynomial algorithms nor proofs of intractability are known for them. One particular collection of such problems has been singled out for special attention, both because of the practical importance of the problems in the collection and because of the intriguing way in which they are all related. These are known as NP-complete problems.

The class of NP-complete problems first arose during 1971 in the work of Stephen Cook of the University of Toronto, Ontario. While investigating the capabilities of hypothetical "nondeterministic" computers (the symbol NP in NP-complete stands for nondeterministic polynomial time), he succeeded in showing that several unclassified problems were equivalent in the sense that a polynomial algorithm for any one of them could be used to build a polynomial algorithm for each of the others. Thus either all of them are intractable or else none of them is. Subsequently, Richard Karp of the University of California at Berkeley and others showed that many additional problems, some of which had been studied for years in other contexts, were similarly equivalent to the problems of Cook. All such equivalent problems are called NP-complete problems.

This remarkable equivalence of so many different problems reduces a multitude of classification questions to one single question. Are all the NP-complete problems intractable or can they all be solved with polynomial algorithms? Little progress has been made in answering this perplexing question. However, based on many years of unsuccessful attempts to find polynomial algorithms for individual problems in

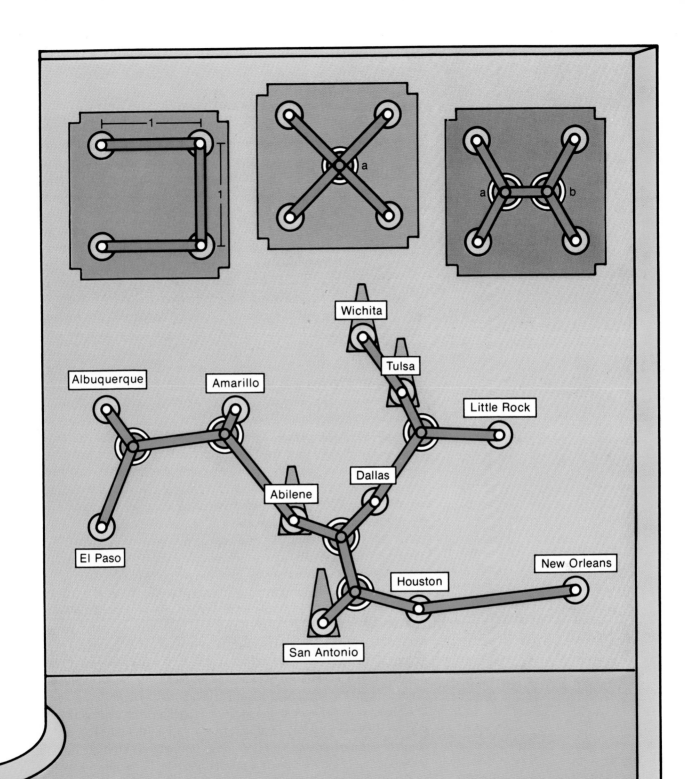

this class, the intuition of most mathematicians is that all NP-complete problems are indeed intractable. Demonstration that a problem belongs to the class of NP-complete problems is widely accepted as a demonstration of its intractability.

Several typical examples can be used to illustrate the wide variety of problems currently known to be NP-complete. One example is known as the Traveling Salesman's Problem. In this problem a salesman is given a list of cities and a road map telling him the shortest route between each pair of cities. The salesman would like to begin at his home city, visit all the other cities, and return to his home city, traveling the least total distance in the process. The problem of finding this shortest route has recently been shown to be an NP-complete problem. The only algorithms known for solving it consider essentially all possible routes and compare them to find the best, a hopeless proposition for general instances involving even as few as 30 cities.

A different type of NP-complete problem, called the Bin Packing Problem, can be described as follows. One is given a list of items to be delivered—say, by truck—from one fixed location to another. Each item has a certain weight and the truck has some maximum total weight it can hold. The objective is to determine which items should be taken together on each trip so as to minimize the total number of trips needed for delivery of the items. For example, if the weights of the items are 4,500, 4,250, 3,500, 2,500, 2,250, and 2,000 pounds and the truck capacity is 10,000 pounds, then two trips would be sufficient. In the first trip the truck can carry the items weighing 4,500, 3,500, and 2,000 pounds and in the second trip it can carry the rest. However, if the truck can hold only 9,500 pounds then three trips would be required, even though the total weight of the items is only 19,000 pounds.

The Bin Packing Problem can appear in a variety of guises; *e.g.*, cutting up the minimum number of standard-length boards to produce pieces having prescribed lengths or scheduling a list of television commercials of various lengths into the smallest possible number of station breaks. Instances of this problem that involve many different items can be extremely difficult, and again no method short of considering essentially all possibilities is known always to work.

The last illustration is called the Minimum Network Problem. In this problem one is given a set of locations representing, for example, oil-producing sites in an oil field or branch locations of a large corporation. The object is to connect all the locations together with a network having the shortest possible total length (so that all the oil can reach a common refinery or shipping port, or so that all the corporate branch locations can communicate on a private-line telephone network). What makes this problem difficult is that junction points are allowed in the network if they can help decrease the total length. For example, if four oil wells are located at the four corners of a square one mile on a side, it is easy to envision a network of pipelines with a total length of three miles connecting them. This is not the shortest network, however. The shortest network requires two junction points and has a total length of

184

$(4/\sqrt{3}) + \frac{1}{2} = 2.808\ldots$ miles. The difficulty of determining in general precisely where to place these junctions for large sets of locations is what makes the Minimum Network Problem NP-complete.

Because of the considerable differences among the preceding problems, it is by no means obvious that they are actually equivalent; *i.e.*, that any polynomial algorithm to solve one of them (if it existed) could always be used to obtain polynomial algorithms for solving the others. In fact, the proofs that they are indeed equivalent are long and complicated. Techniques for proving such equivalences are constantly being developed and improved, and a substantial amount of theory is emerging that deals just with NP-complete problems. The examples presented are intended to indicate the great diversity of NP-complete problems and how remarkable it is that they can be shown to be computationally equivalent.

Future directions

The field of computational complexity is still relatively young, and many questions remain to be answered. One of these has already been discussed, that of determining whether or not the NP-complete problems are all intractable. More generally there is a real need to assemble a collection of analytical tools for determining precisely the inherent complexity of problems. Efforts are proceeding in this direction, but progress is slow.

One direction in which substantial gains *are* being made is that of coping with the complexity of intractable problems that arise in practical applications. Many of these problems are optimization problems, which require one to find the best (cheapest, smallest, shortest, and so on) among all "feasible" solutions. The intractability of such problems often can be avoided by no longer requiring the best solution, but by merely asking for a good solution. For some intractable problems simple algorithms have been discovered that are guaranteed always to find feasible solutions coming within a fixed small percentage of the best solution. In these cases the tradeoffs between the time required to find a solution and the quality of that solution are important. Also under way is research into the possibility of devising simple algorithms capable of finding good solutions "on the average." It is anticipated that the next few years will see substantial progress on these fronts.

Nature's Nuclear Reactor
by George A. Cowan

Two billion years before mankind existed to contemplate the feasibility of nuclear fission, nature already had performed the definitive experiment.

In September 1972, almost 30 years after construction of the first man-made fission reactor at the University of Chicago, scientists of the French Commissariat à l'Énergie Atomique (CEA) announced discovery of a long-dormant fission reactor in the Gabon republic on the western equatorial coast of Africa. It is the first and, to date, the only known example of such a reactor in nature. It underwent a sustained nuclear fission reaction during the accretion of a rich deposit of uranium 1.8 billion years ago and operated at a very low power level, 10–100 kilowatts, over a period of several hundred thousand years. During this time it generated 10,000–15,000 megawatt-years of energy, enough to satisfy the needs of a major metropolis for a few years. It was nearly intact when it was uncovered in 1970 in an open-pit uranium mine called Oklo.

The French investigation

Between 1970 and early 1972 a considerable part of the exposed reactor ore at Oklo was mined, concentrated to a claylike uranate material called yellow cake, and shipped to France as normal uranium. There it was converted to an insoluble fluoride and then to uranium hexafluoride, a gaseous compound used as feed material for the diffusion plant at Pierrelatte. There, as at Oak Ridge, Tennessee, the highly fissionable uranium-235 (^{235}U) isotope, which comprises only a little more than 0.7% of the atoms in the natural element, is enriched to 3% abundance for use in fission reactors or to much higher concentrations for fabrication into nuclear weapons.

In the spring of 1972 analysts in the mass-spectroscopy analytical laboratory at Pierrelatte prepared a fresh uranium standard, using "natural" uranium that contained some Oklo material. When compared with earlier standards, the new standard was found to contain slightly less than the expected amount of ^{235}U. The discrepancy was very small, only 4 parts in 1,000, but the method of analysis is extremely precise and a difference of this size had never before been observed, even in uranium from the Moon.

At first it seemed reasonable to assume that the standard had been contaminated with uranium depleted in ^{235}U, the residue from diffusion

GEORGE A. COWAN is Leader of the Chemistry and Nuclear Chemistry Division, Los Alamos Scientific Laboratory.

Illustrations by John Draves

186

William Maeck

(Overleaf) between 1970 and 1972 the Oklo mine in Gabon yielded uranium ore that subsequently was found to have served as fuel for the first and, to date, the only known example of a natural fission reactor.

plant operations. But further analyses demonstrated that the depletion also existed in uranium hexafluoride produced at the chemical plant. The supply chain was traced backward, finally reaching the mills that supplied the yellow cake. One of the suppliers was the Mounana mill in Gabon, which processed ore from two mines in the vicinity of Franceville, Mounana, and Oklo. A systematic analysis of uranate samples taken from its various shipments to France showed that some of these shipments were depleted in ^{235}U.

Mill records revealed that the depletion occurred only when ore from the Oklo mine was being processed and that the greater the uranium concentration in the ore, the greater was the depletion. It was established that the effect had first appeared at the mill in 1970 and was present in 700 tons of uranium that had been shipped to France over the intervening two years. A net deficiency of 200 kilograms of ^{235}U existed in the affected concentrate. Although it is generally believed that natural uranium contains 0.7202% ^{235}U with a spread of no more than 1 part in 1,000, the affected Oklo uranium received in France was depleted in ^{235}U by nearly 30 parts in 1,000 to an average value of 0.69%. The discrepancy initially observed at Pierrelatte was almost a factor of ten smaller because the Oklo material had been mixed with a great deal of normal uranium during later processing.

During the initial survey of the Oklo ore body several years earlier, core samples had been taken on a closely spaced grid and analyzed for uranium. These cores were analyzed again to determine the ratio of ^{235}U to ^{238}U, the abundant isotope of uranium. Although most of the uranium was found to be entirely normal, one sample from a drill hole and two separate rock fragments contained uranium that was very slightly depleted in ^{235}U. In another sample, part of a rich uranium seam in a core from a region then being mined, the element contained 0.44% ^{235}U, only 60% of the natural abundance!

Thus the principal source of the depleted uranium was identified. It was a relatively small, highly localized region of very rich ore in a thick, roughly lens-shaped pocket. But the mystery was greater than ever. Although each element in the periodic table has its own chemistry and can be more or less readily separated from other elements, isotopes of the same element differ very little in chemical and physical behavior and their separation is enormously more difficult. There was no obvious natural process that could take place on a large scale to produce the observed 40% depletion.

A number of tentative hypotheses were advanced, among them the suggestion that somehow the ^{235}U had been destroyed by fission. The products of fission include a broad distribution of more than 30 elements ranging in atomic mass from less than 80 to more than 160. Analyses were undertaken for some of the rare-earth elements on the heavy end of the fission-product distribution; it was assumed that these elements were relatively immobile and might still be present. As soon as the results became available, the mystery was dispelled. Not only were these fission products present in the affected ore in large quanti-

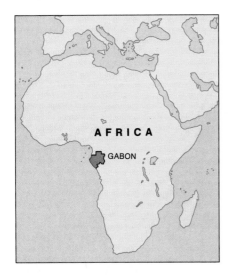

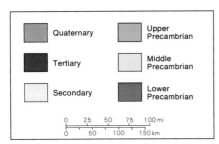

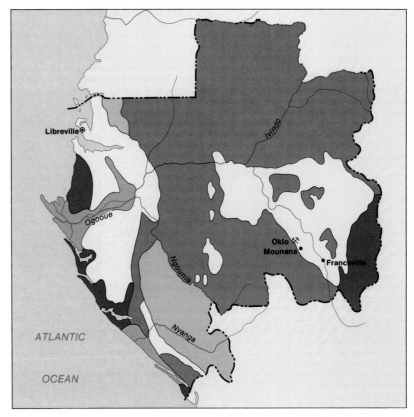

ties but they were virtually absent from the unaffected ore. Even more significantly, the isotopic ratios within individual elements corresponded closely to their known yields in fission and were not at all similar to the ratios observed in the natural elements. It was clear that the ^{235}U was depleted because it had served as the fuel in a reactor.

Except for an extremely low equilibrium level of products from the spontaneous fission of ^{238}U, none of the residual fission-product elements in the ore was radioactive. Fission products are unstable when created and decay in times ranging from minutes to millions of years. At each stage in the decay process, the radioactive nucleus emits a negative beta particle (an electron) during the transformation of a neutron into a proton. The residual nucleus is a new element with the same mass but containing one more proton. Several such transitions are commonly required before stability is reached. The longest-lived radioactive species have half-lives, the time in which 50% of the nuclei decay, of about ten million years. The absence of any significant fission-product activity in the affected ore meant that much more than ten million years had passed since the reactor had last operated. It was a natural "fossil," unrelated to any source arising from contemporary, man-made reactor technology.

Roger Naudet of the CEA was appointed late in 1972 to manage Project Franceville, the name given to the expanded French investigation. He and some colleagues went to Gabon to find and sample the

The Oklo mine rests in terrain predominantly of Precambrian age, i.e., older than about 600 million years. To account for the absolute number of fissions that were calculated to have occurred in core samples taken from the reactor zones, it was necessary to assume that the reactor had operated nearly two billion years ago, when uranium ore contained five times as much ^{235}U as it does presently. Through independent isotope-dating measurements, the age of the host rock also was found to be about two billion years.

189

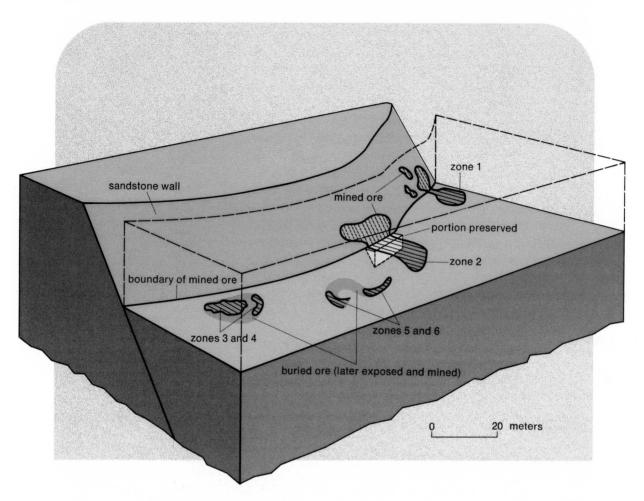

zone 1

sandstone wall

mined ore

portion preserved

boundary of mined ore

zone 2

zones 3 and 4

zones 5 and 6

buried ore (later exposed and mined)

0   20 meters

Of the six reactor zones initially detected at Oklo, portions of zones 1 and 2 had been mined when the reactor was discovered; their boundaries, therefore, are not known with certainty. Zones 3 through 6 had not yet been exposed, and their configurations were determined from core samples. Subsequent examination revealed that zones 3 and 4 were tortuously connected, as were zones 5 and 6, thus reducing the number of distinctly separate zones to four. As mining operations resumed following the investigation, a portion of zone 2 was preserved by pinning it to the face of the adjacent sandstone wall.

reactor zone. Their exploration, begun in March 1973, quickly succeeded in locating not only the zone in question but also several more immediately adjoining reactor zones, some of them still unexposed. These were highly irregular in shape but, in an idealized approximation, may be thought of as slabs tilted to a 45° angle, 1 meter thick and 10–20 meters on a side. Because of their proximity, they may be considered a single reactor.

Information from the new samples produced fresh surprises. One sample showed a ^{235}U abundance of 0.3%! Also, when the relative abundances of the various fission products in a given sample were plotted on a yield curve, they were found to correspond reasonably well to the known abundances for ^{235}U fission induced by slow (thermal) neutrons. It was increasingly clear that despite the age of the deposit and its complex geological history, more than half of the fission-product elements had been largely retained in the reactor zone. This remarkable stability of the reactor as a whole made it possible to calculate the absolute number of fissions in a given sample and compare the results with the depletion of ^{235}U. When this was done, it was evident that much more ^{235}U had fissioned than exists in present-day ore.

Part of the explanation lay in the fact that ^{235}U was once more abun-

190

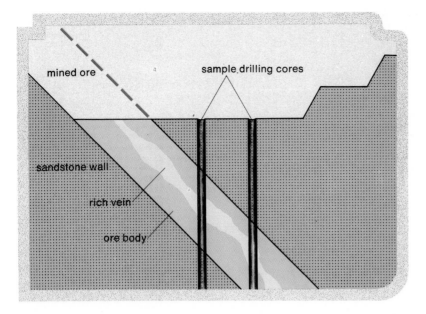

Shown at left in generalized cross section, the main body of uranium ore at Oklo can be envisioned as a large slab tilted to a 45° angle and resting against the face of a sloping sandstone wall. Within a rich vein running through this body lay the reactor zones, each roughly 1 meter thick and 10–20 meters on a side.

dant in uranium than it is today. The isotope has a half-life of 700 million years, or only 15% of the age of the Earth. To account for the number of fissions, it was necessary to assume that the reactor had operated nearly two billion years ago when the ore contained five times as much ^{235}U. The principal isotope of uranium, ^{238}U, decays with a half-life of 4.5 billion years and was initially 30% more abundant in the ore. As a result, the isotopic abundance of ^{235}U at that time was 3%, the same as in the enriched fuel elements used in man-made, water-moderated power reactors. The age of the host rocks was found by isotopic dating measurements to be almost two billion years. It was concluded that the reactor began to operate at the same time or soon after these rocks were formed.

Despite this explanation, however, there remained unresolved a difference between the observed depletion of ^{235}U and a considerably higher value calculated from a comparison of the amounts of certain reactor products present in the ore samples. In other words, more fission products were present than could be explained from a knowledge of the amount of ^{235}U initially present and the amount remaining. This difference was shown to be due largely to the capture of neutrons by the abundant isotope ^{238}U, which is quickly transformed by radioactive decay to the plutonium isotope ^{239}Pu. Some of the plutonium, which is very fissionable, is destroyed by neutrons but, at Oklo, most of it decayed by alpha particle emission with a half-life of 24,400 years to ^{235}U, augmenting the amount already present. The additional fuel made in this way replaced about half of the fuel destroyed by fission.

Requirements for a fission reactor

A fission reactor is supported by neutrons that are emitted in the process of fission and then almost immediately reabsorbed to produce more fission. This recycling of neutrons is called a neutron chain

191

Adapted from Frejacques *et al,* International Atomic Energy Agency SM-204/24, "The Oklo Phenomenon" Proceedings

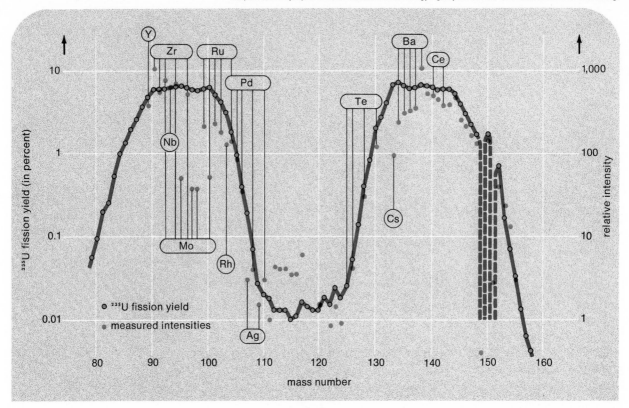

To examine the hypothesis that the depletion in ²³⁵U from Oklo was a result of fission, a team of French investigators examined Oklo ore for fission products. Not only were such isotopes found to be present in large quantities, but also their ratios—and particularly the isotopic ratios within individual elements—corresponded closely with known ²³⁵U fission yields.

The curve shown above depicts expected yields (in percent) of fission products plotted against their atomic masses. Superimposed on this curve are actual measured relative concentrations (shown as relative intensities) of fission-product isotopes contained in a sample of Oklo ore, as derived from mass-spectrometer data.

This close correspondence made clear the fact that ²³⁵U at Oklo had undergone a natural chain reaction.

reaction. Each fission produces an average of 2.5 neutrons. If at least one of these neutrons, 40% of the total, is absorbed by a uranium nucleus to produce another fission, the reaction is self-sustaining. The remaining neutrons can be absorbed in other isotopes or escape entirely from the reactor zone.

In order for a natural reactor to meet this requirement, a number of essential conditions must be satisfied. The most important of these involves the ratio of easily fissionable ^{235}U to less fissionable ^{238}U. It is true that reactors can be built with natural uranium if it is dissolved in or moderated with "heavy" water in which deuterium, the hydrogen isotope with an atomic mass of two, slows the fast neutrons emitted in fission and thereby helps retain them within the reactor. Alternatively, the uranium can be distributed in a lattice of spheres or fuel rods of a certain size embedded in a suitable moderator of water, beryllium oxide, or carbon. But in nature the first design is essentially impossible and the other designs are very unlikely. The most likely natural reactor assembly would be a massive seam or lens of very rich uranium ore containing an optimum amount of uniformly distributed normal or "light" water moderator and very little additional neutron-absorbing impurities. Under these conditions the minimum abundance of ^{235}U in an essentially "infinite" mass of uranium must be 1% to sustain a chain reaction. This means that no natural reactor is likely to have operated more recently than 400 million years ago.

A second necessary condition is that the uranium must be present in high concentration, certainly more than 10% by weight. If it is not, the

192

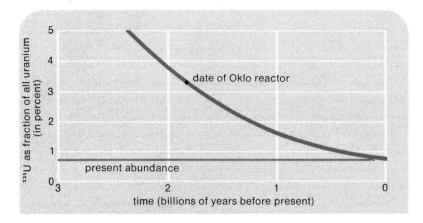

Uranium-235 decays about six times more rapidly than ^{238}U; consequently, since the formation of the Earth 4.6 billion years ago, the abundance of ^{235}U as a fraction of all uranium has decreased from about 25% to its present value of 0.7202%. When the Oklo reactor began to operate 1.8 billion years ago, the abundance of ^{235}U was about 3%.

other elements present absorb too many neutrons, reducing the share absorbed by ^{235}U to less than the necessary 40%.

A closely related third condition is that the reactor zone must be larger than the average distance a neutron travels between its point of origin and its point of reabsorption. Otherwise too many neutrons escape. Both the size and concentration constraints relax as the age of the reactor increases. However, very rich uranium deposits of age greater than two billion years have not yet been found and do not seem to occur in nature. At this limit in age, uranium of 10% average concentration and seams of ore greater than 0.5 meters thick may be taken as minimum conditions.

A fourth condition is that the reactor must contain a suitable moderator that degrades fast, energetic fission neutrons to velocities where they are readily absorbed in ^{235}U. Although deuterium is better because it absorbs fewer neutrons, normal hydrogen in water is almost ideal as a moderator. The amount of water in a consolidated sedimentary ore is generally sufficient. A highly porous, saturated sediment would contain too much. Water that is considerably in excess of the optimum amount can shut off the reaction by absorbing too many neutrons.

A fifth condition for a natural reactor is that the uranium ore must not contain significant amounts of isotopes that strongly absorb slow neutrons. Such isotopes are called poisons. For example, less than 0.1% boron by weight or 1% lithium contain enough of the poisonous isotopes boron-10 and lithium-6 to make a chain reaction impossible. Some other elements that are particularly effective in this respect are cadmium and the rare earths.

These conditions vary in magnitude and importance over the lifetime of the reactor. In the short term the power level of the reactor is probably determined by variations in the amount of water present. If energy is produced at a rate higher than its dissipation to the outside, water will boil away until the undermoderated condition produces a sufficient decrease in the power level. This effect keeps the power level low, around 10–100 kilowatts, just sufficient to simmer water.

Over the long term the dominant factors are the concentration of ^{235}U and the accumulation of fission-product poisons, particularly the rare earths. The combination of ^{235}U depletion by fission, the

193

Fission of a ^{235}U nucleus is induced by absorption of a slow, or thermal, neutron, which excites the nucleus into a deformed, unstable configuration. As fission occurs, the dividing nucleus emits gamma rays and a few energetic neutrons (2.5 average). For a chain reaction to be self-sustaining, at least 40% of these neutrons must induce fission in other ^{235}U nuclei; the remainder can be absorbed by other elements or can escape from the reactor zone. Hence, as one requirement for its operation, a natural nuclear reactor must contain a suitable moderator, such as water, that degrades energetic neutrons to velocities at which they are readily captured in ^{235}U. Another condition is that the reactor zone be sufficiently large to prevent the escape of too many neutrons. Further, the uranium ore must not contain significant amounts of impurities, such as boron-10, which would "poison" the chain reaction by readily absorbing slow neutrons.

increasing burden of fission products and, finally, termination of the ore-formation process that would have brought in fresh ^{235}U must eventually stop the chain reaction.

The duration of the reaction at Oklo has been estimated in two ways. Simple heat-transfer calculations were used to estimate the power level. The total energy divided by the power is the duration. Estimated in this way, it is of the order of half a million years. The second calculation involves an estimate of the amount of fission in plutonium, based on a careful analysis of the relative yields of fission products. Although a large amount of plutonium was made in the reactor, its contribution to fission was only a few percent of the total. This means that most of it must have decayed to ^{235}U. Therefore, the power level, which determines the rate of burnup, must have been low. Pursued quantitatively, this argument also results in an estimated duration of about half a million years for the Oklo reactor.

Other fossil reactors

The fact that Precambrian uranium contained enough ^{235}U to support a natural chain reaction was pointed out many years ago by isotope geologists. In 1953 George W. Wetherill of the University of California at Los Angeles and Mark G. Inghram of the University of Chicago mentioned this possibility. In 1956 Paul K. Kuroda of the University of Arkansas quantitatively calculated some of the requirements for natural reactors and concluded that they were distinctly possible in Precambrian times. But these suggestions did not stimulate widespread interest. The Sun and stars serve as ever-present examples of natural thermonuclear reactors, but there is no known example of a neutron-sustained fission reactor in the Galaxy. Before Oklo the notion that one might have existed on Earth seemed farfetched. Now, given the evidence from Oklo and some recent information concerning the probable genesis of uranium-ore deposits, such reactors appear to have been almost inevitable. Probably natural reactors did not occur frequently but it seems unlikely that the discovery at Oklo will remain unique.

A systematic search is now under way for other examples of natural reactors. The participants are scientists from government agencies and mineral exploration companies in a number of countries. This interest can be justified in a number of ways and the principal motivation may be different in each case. The most general one is best described as scientific, the desire to achieve a reasonably complete understanding of natural reactor processes—how they start up, the various modes of control and their relative roles, depths of burial and associated operating temperatures, retention or loss of reactor products, the way in which reactors eventually shut down, and the geological conditions that can give rise to such reactors and then preserve them for nearly half the life of the Earth. Much has been learned or surmised concerning these questions with respect to the Oklo phenomenon but it is not clear whether the postulated processes will prove to have a general relevance, applicable to somewhat different geophysical and

194

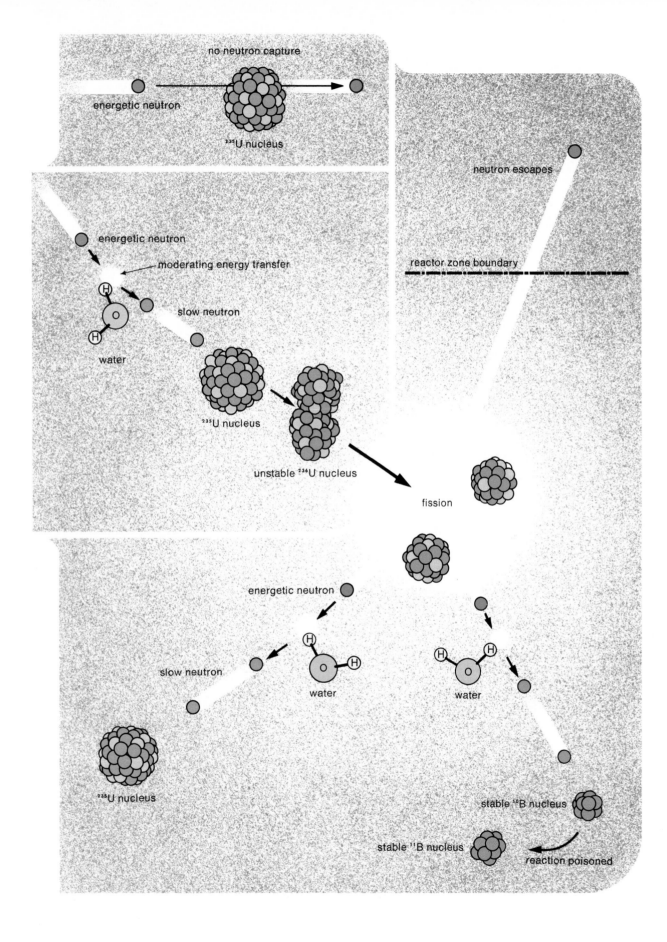

no neutron capture

energetic neutron

²³⁵U nucleus

neutron escapes

reactor zone boundary

energetic neutron

moderating energy transfer

H

O

H

slow neutron

water

²³⁵U nucleus

unstable ²³⁶U nucleus

fission

energetic neutron

H

O

H

slow neutron

water

H

O

H

water

²³⁵U nucleus

stable ¹⁰B nucleus

stable ¹¹B nucleus

reaction poisoned

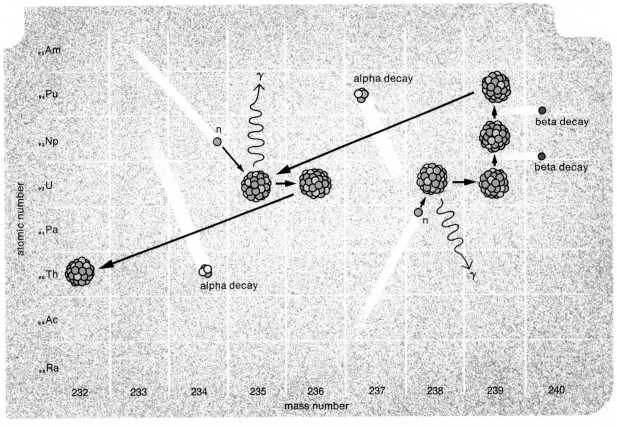

Although most ^{235}U nuclei that capture neutrons go on to fission, about 15% retain the neutron and dissipate their excitation energy as gamma rays. Being unstable, these newly formed ^{236}U nuclei decay by emission of an alpha particle (two protons and two neutrons) to thorium-232. Also affecting the nature and rate of a chain reaction is the fact that ^{238}U captures neutrons readily; in so doing, it is transformed to ^{239}U, which through beta decay (the transformation of a neutron into a proton with the emission of a beta particle, or electron) becomes radioactive plutonium-239. Although ^{239}Pu can be destroyed by neutron-induced fission, in a slow chain reaction such as occurred at Oklo most of it decays by alpha emission to ^{235}U, augmenting the amount of that isotope already present. In fact, analysis of Oklo samples indicated that additional fuel made in this way replaced about half the original ^{235}U destroyed by fission.

geochemical environments, or whether Oklo will remain a special case with little or no predictive value.

Migration of reactor products

These general considerations are closely related to practical and applied problems. As an example, the observation that many of the reactor products have remained in place is clearly relevant to the problem of reactor-waste storage. A frequently proposed solution for the ultimate disposal of man-made radioactive waste is storage in stable geologic formations. The stability of such storage must be assured for hundreds of thousands of years. It is difficult or impossible to reliably extrapolate laboratory data on this time scale. Thus, particular attention has been paid to the Oklo data as a source of experimental information. (For an assessment of waste-storage problems, *see* Feature Article: NUCLEAR WASTE DISPOSAL.)

What has been observed is that two alkali metals, rubidium and cesium, and two alkaline earths, strontium and barium, have been almost completely replaced by an influx of natural material from the host rocks. This behavior is to be expected from the known chemistry of these elements. Other elements that were apparently quite mobile are molybdenum, cadmium, and iodine and the rare gases, krypton and xenon. The other fission products were mostly retained, although some were partly redistributed within the reactor. These include zirconium,

196

niobium, technetium, ruthenium, palladium, silver, tellurium, cerium, neodymium, samarium, and gadolinium. Only one-third of the lead, the stable end product of the decay chains of ^{235}U and ^{238}U, was retained in the reactor. Bismuth, the end product of the decay of neptunium-237 and ^{241}Pu, was immobile as was thorium, the end product of the decay of ^{236}U and ^{240}Pu. Plutonium appears to have remained completely immobile. Because it has by now completely decayed to ^{235}U, the evidence for its stability is the absence of excess ^{235}U not only outside the reactor zone but also outside the grains of uraninite in which the plutonium was made during reactor operation.

On the whole the relative stability at Oklo of most of the potentially bothersome reactor products is reassuring with respect to the problem of geologic storage of radioactive wastes. But, as indicated earlier, it is difficult to identify the important requirements for choosing a long-term storage site on the basis of what has been learned from one reactor. Similar information from at least a few natural reactors located in somewhat different geochemical environments will be immensely valuable in this regard.

Exploration for rich uranium deposits

In such regions as the Northern Territory in Australia where Precambrian deposits of uranium have been found, it is possible that undiscovered fossil reactors of rich uranium exist. If so, the dispersion of mobile fission products through the soil in the vicinity of these deposits may serve as a guide to their location. A particularly promising example is ruthenium (Ru), which although very rare in the Earth's crust is an abundant fission product. Of the order of 5% of the ^{99}Ru that was made in Oklo migrated away as technetium-99, an intermediate product in the mass-99 decay chain with a half-life of 213,000 years. If this were uniformly mixed in one cubic mile of soil, it should produce a quantitatively measurable change in the isotopic abundance of ^{99}Ru in the natural ruthenium background. Thus, the region in the vicinity of fossil reactors may contain traces of this rare, somewhat mobile element.

Small perturbations may also exist in the ratio of ^{235}U to ^{238}U if a fossil reactor has been wholly or partially dispersed into a neighboring host rock. Dispersion may come about, for example, as the result of mountain building or volcanic activity. The dispersed material may then reappear in ore deposits of a later age overlying the original Precambrian host rocks. Depending on the age of the reactor, the ^{235}U may be depleted, remain unaffected, or actually become slightly enriched. Despite the fact that the probability of dispersion increases with age, it seems less likely that a reactor one billion years in age will be found than one two billion years in age, simply because the lower ^{235}U content of the younger deposit would require that it be richer, thicker, and purer than the earlier reactor. However, if such a young reactor did indeed exist, its higher ^{238}U content would absorb a larger fraction of the available neutrons. This effect could more than replace the ^{235}U consumed by fission, becoming in effect a breeder of fissile material.

William Maeck

Marked with stakes and string where core samples were drilled, the surviving portion of reactor zone 2 rested just below the floor of the Oklo mine when the reactor was discovered in 1972. Above and behind zone 2 the ore body continues, with regions of oxidized uranium showing as yellow patches on the rock.

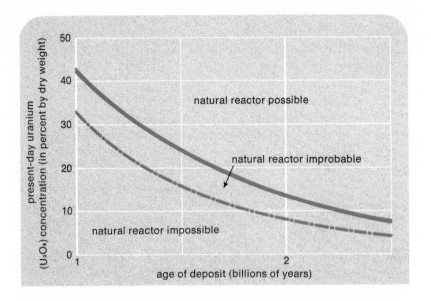

Another necessary condition for a natural reactor is that the uranium be present in relatively high concentration, so that other elements present do not reduce the share of neutrons captured by ²³⁵U to less than the necessary 40%. As can be seen in the set of curves above, concentration constraints relax as the age of the reactor increases. However, very rich uranium deposits greater than two billion years in age probably do not occur in nature. At this age limit, uranium of 10% average concentration by weight seems to be a minimum requirement.

Very small decreases in ²³⁵U have been measured in uranium from the Colorado Plateau. A set of highly precise mass-spectrometric analyses showed that the ²³⁵U in these samples is depleted 0.03% relative to the average in uranium from elsewhere in the world. Such a small effect might conceivably arise from minute differences in the chemical behavior of the uranium isotopes as they moved into the sandstone ores in which they are found. However, it may also have been due to reactor-depleted uranium somehow dispersed upward from the Precambrian rocks that underlie the Colorado Plateau. In this respect it is interesting to observe that the known deficiency of ²³⁵U in the Oklo deposit is about equal to the deficiency of ²³⁵U in Colorado Plateau uranium if the observed 0.03% deficit in ²³⁵U exists in the entire known reserves of the Colorado Plateau. At present, insufficient data exist to choose between the two hypotheses.

In addition, although the very rich uranium deposits of the African republic of Zaire have been exhausted and relatively few highly precise measurements of their isotopic abundance ratios are available, the existing data suggest that they were slightly enriched in ²³⁵U (0.03% relative). Their age, 600 million–900 million years, indicates that if reactors had existed in these deposits, the ²³⁵U would have remained constant or actually increased.

Formation of natural reactors

An examination of the formation of natural reactors is really a study of the birth of rich uranium deposits in Precambrian times. The frequency of discovery of such deposits in recent years has led to an increasing realization that nearly all of the world's known uranium deposits are located in or are very close to Precambrian formations. All of the richest extensive deposits are Precambrian. A number of hypotheses have been advanced to account for this striking association and the subject remains controversial. One plausible view is that three major modes of uranium concentration have existed in geological times. One of these modes operated prior to two billion years ago, the others afterward.

The first mode was essentially mechanical. Grains of insoluble uraninite, partially oxidized uranium, were eroded from crystalline rocks and washed downstream. Because of their high density they accumulated in stream sediments and formed placer deposits similar to those of gold, thorium oxide, and the heavy rare earths. But two billion years ago blue-green algae began to proliferate, producing free oxygen in quantity for the first time in the Earth's history. In this new environment the uranium grains were no longer stable but were transformed to soluble compounds in a higher oxidation state. Wherever the uranium in stream sediments was exposed to oxygen, it became dissolved in water and was washed downstream.

The advent of oxygen marked the beginning of the second mode of concentration, which has continued to operate over the past two billion years to mobilize uranium. During the earliest part of this period, the process led to the formation of extensive deposits of more highly concentrated ore. Until the existing, suddenly unstable reservoirs of placer deposits were exhausted, a one-time pulse of mobilized uranium moved steadily toward new resting places, probably swampy river deltas where decaying organic ooze produced a reducing environment and reprecipitated the uranium into sediments.

Many geologists argue that each uranium deposit has a source in nearby, contemporary rocks. But it is conceivable that nearly the entire pool of concentrated uranium was created more than two billion years ago, initially in placer deposits, and has not been greatly augmented since that period. The available uranium has merely been recycled.

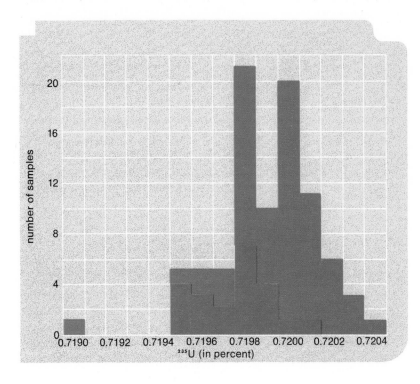

Analysis of the abundance of ^{235}U in 88 samples of uranium ore from various parts of the world shows perturbations in distribution. The peak at 0.7200% represents ores taken primarily from Australia, Canada, and Europe, whereas the anomalous peak at 0.7198% represents ores from the Colorado Plateau in the U.S. The fraction of these ores that were mined in New Mexico (plotted separately) suggests that ^{235}U from the Colorado Plateau is slightly depleted relative to the average concentration from elsewhere in the world. One possible explanation assigns this discrepancy to reactor-depleted uranium that was somehow dispersed upward from Precambrian rocks that lie below the Colorado Plateau.

Many of the rich pockets of uranium capable of supporting neutron chain reactions were formed within traps created by folding of the sedimentary ore formations during crustal upheavals that occurred after the first oxidation-reduction cycle. This is the third and youngest mode of uranium concentration. Occasionally there have been additional periods of dispersion and reconcentration, but it seems reasonably certain that the major rich ore-forming period ended over a billion years ago. Once the initial reservoir of enriched sediments in the river beds was exhausted, the oxidation-reduction cycle was unlikely to produce new uranium deposits of sufficient concentration to rank with the Precambrian bonanzas.

Dispersion of natural reactors

The dispersion of a reactor may be more complicated than the dispersion of the original ore deposit. Physical destruction, usually by erosion of a surface deposit, is the simplest and, probably, commonest case. Much more complicated is chemical destruction, which involves the chemistry and relative mobility of the 30-odd reactor-product elements, each of them a special case. When exposed to oxidizing surface waters, particularly in the presence of carbonates or dissolved carbon dioxide, uranium is one of the more mobile elements. Thus, the major part of a uranium ore deposit that has contained a nuclear reactor may be geochemically dispersed by interaction with near-surface water but still leave behind a pocket of the more immobile elements, such as zirconium, niobium, ruthenium, rhodium, palladium, silver, the rare earths, bismuth, and thorium.

The processes that operate to disperse ores have not been generally considered as carefully as those that control ore formation. However, such processes are central to the question of the long-term storage of reactor products in geological formations. Study of the remnants of partially dispersed reactors, if any exist, will probably contribute as much to an understanding of this problem as will study of intact reactors. Selection of samples that can lead to the positive identification of a partially dispersed reactor undoubtedly will be extremely difficult. The occurrence of slightly depleted uranium ore over a broad area suggests the possible existence of distinctive ore residues of the immobile reactor products in the same region. Exploratory field geologists may recognize the distinctive elemental pattern when they encounter such immobile residues and provide samples for isotopic analyses.

The search for intact natural reactors

A large fraction of the natural reactors that might have survived intact may be deeply buried under later sediments and will be sought only when new exploratory techniques for deeply buried uranium are developed. As suggested earlier, these techniques may include a search for mobile products so rare that they can be recognized in the surrounding environment.

Currently it is necessary to limit a search to those recognized, rich uranium deposits that offer a chance of meeting the criteria for nuclear reactor sites. Even in this limited context, the problem is not a simple one. In regions that are actively being mined, the ores are constantly assayed for uranium content but almost never for isotopic abundances. Isotopic ratios are usually measured for the first time only in uranium delivered to gaseous diffusion plants as uranium hexafluoride. At this point any depleted uranium is likely to have been mixed with large amounts of unaffected material. Thus the perturbation may be so small that it passes without special notice. The circumstances that led to the discovery of the isotope anomaly at Pierrelatte were almost accidental and cannot be expected to form a reliable basis for identification of natural reactors in the future.

A much more satisfactory procedure is to select promising individual samples of uranium ore on the basis of purity of the ore, concentration of the uranium, and age, thickness, and extent of the deposit. Considerable reliance must be placed on access to drill cores that are obtained during a survey of the extent of the ore deposit. However, even when cores have been taken on a very closely spaced grid—for example, every 100 square meters of area—the probability of intersecting a reactor with a cross section of 30 square meters is only one in four.

A second desirable source of samples is the ore exposed during actual mining, provided that the field geologist calls attention to the regions of highest concentration as they are uncovered. Sampling was undertaken in this way at Oklo after the Pierrelatte discovery. Because suspension of mining operations in the vicinity of the reactor may be requested immediately upon its discovery, the reluctance of an operating company to invite such a troublesome and possibly expensive consequence could severely handicap any search for natural reactors that relies on this technique.

A third source of samples comprises the mills that make yellow cake. Frequent analysis of batches of product from the mills in Precambrian areas may be the most practical technique for finding new reactors.

A fourth source of samples can be found in the collections of geology museums. However, documentation of the source of given specimen with respect to the previously enumerated criteria is likely to be very poor and will produce large numbers of uninteresting samples. Furthermore, the source has usually been mined out and is unavailable for further study.

Despite the fact that no wholly satisfactory method exists for finding natural reactors with a reasonable expenditure of effort, it is probably safe to predict that more reactors eventually will be identified. Whether or not this proves to be true in the future, the Oklo discovery has provided a new and fascinating approach to the study of geologic phenomena. The highly interdisciplinary character of the continuing investigation is one of the most novel and potentially valuable features of the program. But apart from the promise of practical benefits, the discovery at Oklo offers a particularly dramatic reminder of the ingenuity of nature and the endless variety of its surprises.

Nuclear Waste Disposal
by H. M. Parker

Unlike household garbage, radioactive wastes from atomic power plants cannot be merely discarded and forgotten. Expected increases in the number of nuclear reactors by AD 2000 demand secure methods of waste storage.

The production of electricity from coal, gas, or nuclear fission is accomplished identically after each of these sources of energy is used to generate heat. Before that stage two important differences distinguish nuclear power from its counterparts. On the favorable side, the fission of one gram of uranium-235, which is the fissionable content of 140 grams of natural uranium, provides as much energy as the burning of three tons of coal or 700 gallons of fuel oil. On the unfavorable side, the fission process generates life-threatening fission products whose radioactivity exceeds that of any sources previously known and whose toxicity may persist for thousands of years. A modern nuclear reactor contains radioactivity that is equivalent to about 2,000 tons of radium, which is several million times the amount of this element in commerce.

Fuel for nuclear power originates as uranium ore. Radioactive itself, this material contains other radioactive elements that must be removed prior to its use as fuel. In fact, all stages of the nuclear fuel cycle — from milling ore to reprocessing spent fuel — may generate some undesirable radioactive components. It is during the intense magnification of radioactivity in the reactor, however, that the major high-level radioactive wastes are produced. Until their decay, these wastes must be segregated from the biosphere to the greatest extent possible.

In weighing the hazards of radioactive waste, the main concern of society is not the possibility of massive radiation injury. That result is much less likely from accidents in waste storage than from a catastrophic accident to a nuclear reactor, a case that has been extensively analyzed. More relevant is the potential for small quantities of radioactive substances to escape into the air or water sources and eventually enter the body. There is no question that radioactivity can produce cancer and genetic mutations in man, although the degree of harm that can arise from low levels of exposure is still uncertain. Inadequate processing, storage, transport, or disposal can disperse radioactivity

John Marmaras—Woodfin Camp

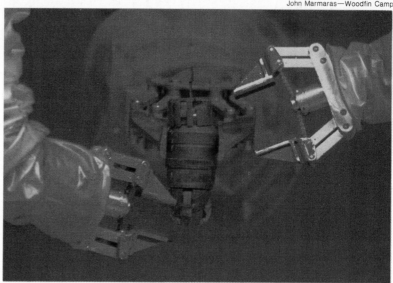

(Overleaf) Suspended 30 feet aloft, a crash-shielded model of a shipping cask for radioactive material awaits testing within a drop tower at the U.S. Oak Ridge National Laboratory. Manipulators (above) operated by remote control from behind special radiation-protective glass are often used to transport radioactive matter within the confines of a single room or chamber.

H. M. PARKER is President, HMP Associates Inc., Richland, Washington.

(Overleaf) Photograph courtesy, Union Carbide Corporation, Nuclear Division, Oak Ridge National Laboratory.
Illustrations by Dave Beckes

into the environment. The biological consequences of such events must be predicted through a chain of prudent assumptions.

To assess future problems of commercial waste management from a nuclear economy, one must use past experience in handling radioactive wastes. For the United States that experience lies in its 30-year-old nuclear weapons program. Recently the comprehensiveness of that country's existing or proposed waste-management systems has come under increasingly severe public and technical scrutiny, with considerable justification. In 1973 reported leakages of high-level liquid wastes from short-term storage tanks of the Hanford Works, a federal plutonium production plant near Richland, Washington, did not inspire public confidence. Progressive addition of nuclides to the list of significant hazards has deflated claims of scientific omniscience; tritium was first recognized as a fission product in 1959, iodine-129 as a very long-lived biological hazard only about a decade ago, and carbon-14 as a product of impure uranium oxide fuels a few years later. In addition, several years of apparent vacillation by the U.S. government in the choice of a long-term underground repository or retrievable surface storage facility has not helped.

Nevertheless, over the past 30 years control of nuclear wastes has become more effective than control of such age-old chemical wastes as mercury and arsenic. The allocation of another 30 years to develop more secure methods, such as a well-tested geological repository, is not unreasonable. However, public concern demands that such time be used decisively in the pursuit of excellence, with no unreasonable burden left to future generations.

Composition and classification of radioactive wastes

The most significant radioactive wastes from the nuclear program arise through two separate mechanisms. The principal one is the neutron-induced fission process that occurs in uranium-235 and in a few other

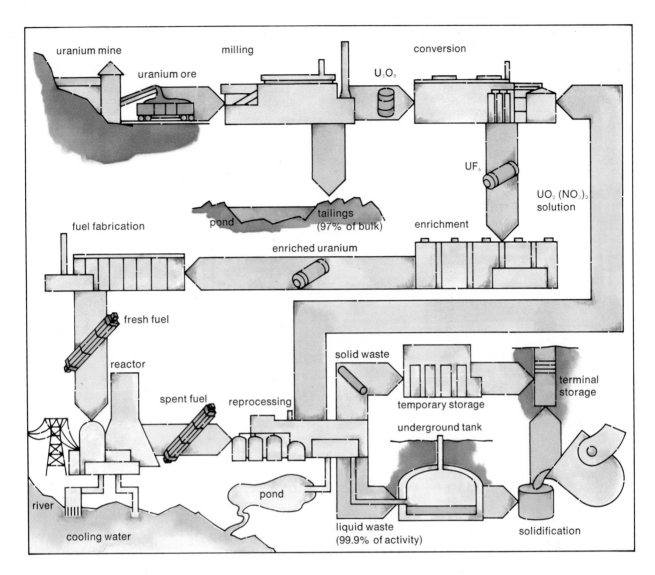

The following labels appear within the figure:

uranium mine

milling

conversion

uranium ore

U_3O_8

fuel fabrication

pond

tailings (97% of bulk)

UF_6

$UO_2(NO_3)_2$ solution

enrichment

enriched uranium

fresh fuel

reactor

solid waste

terminal storage

spent fuel

reprocessing

temporary storage

underground tank

river

pond

cooling water

liquid waste (99.9% of activity)

solidification

fissionable materials. In the course of liberating heat to generate power and neutrons to sustain the fission process, fissioning uranium nuclei divide into pairs of smaller nuclei called fission products. The species so created are regular elements of the periodic table but with unstable nuclear configurations. In their search for stability, they decay into other nuclear species, often several times in rapid sequence, emitting electrons, or beta (β) rays, and frequently energetic photons called gamma (γ) rays. This decay provides the intense radioactivity of the fission products and causes the chemical composition of fission-product wastes to change continually with time.

The second mechanism involved in waste production is the modification of the nuclear identity of fuel and fission products by direct neutron absorption. Characterized by a chain of successive absorptions and nuclear decays, this process is especially important in the creation of transuranic species from unspent uranium fuel. Many transuranic nuclides emit energetic helium nuclei, or alpha (α) particles, and are

All stages of the nuclear fuel cycle may generate radioactive wastes. Whereas milling of uranium ore produces 97% of waste bulk, more than 99% of the potentially hazardous activity of nuclear wastes is contained in liquid waste produced during reprocessing of spent fuel. Bulky and unwieldy, it is liquid waste that creates the majority of immediate storage problems.

Table I. Significant Radioactive Nuclides

nuclide and half-life	principal emissions	source	manner of release	biological significance
tritium (hydrogen-3), 12.3 years	β	fission product and neutron activation of heavy water	isotopically mixed with ordinary water in liquid wastes and in vapor released to the atmosphere	incorporation in water enables it to pervade all life forms including genetic material
carbon-14, 5,730 years	β	neutron-absorption product	carried in liquid wastes	only recently recognized as a significant hazard; long half-life and high biological activity
krypton-85, 10.7 years	β and γ	noble gas fission product	into the atmosphere	worldwide distribution; hazard to skin; intake from the lungs to blood and fatty substances
strontium-90, 29 years; cesium-137, 30.1 years	both β emitters; cesium-137 also a γ emitter	fission products	carried in liquid wastes	strontium is a chemical analog of calcium and has a strong affinity for bone, decays to strongly radioactive yttrium-90; cesium, a potassium analog, is broadly distributed and retained in soft tissue*
technetium-99, 213,000 years	β	fission product	carried in liquid wastes	very long half-life; migrates easily through soil sediments
ruthenium-103, 39.6 days; ruthenium-106, 369 days	both are β emitters; ruthenium-103 also a γ emitter	fission products	escape into atmosphere from stacks of fuel-reprocessing plants; carried in liquid wastes	short half-lives preclude long-range problems; ruthenium-106 decays to a short-lived β emitter
iodine-129, 15.9 million years; iodine-131, 8 days	β and γ	fission products	escape into atmosphere from stacks of fuel-reprocessing plants	nuclides deposit on vegetation, transfer to milk through cattle; affinity for thyroid gland; long half-life of iodine-129 allows steady accumulation in the environment; iodine-131 is a key consideration in accidental releases
plutonium-239, 24,400 years; also plutonium-238, 87.8 years, and other isotopes	α	neutron-absorption product	carried in liquid wastes; when used in oxide form as a nuclear fuel, it tends to escape confinement as a fine dust	affinity for bone; dust retained in lungs and lymph nodes; demonstrated proclivity to produce cancer in animals; undoubtedly carcinogenic in man, although no case has yet been demonstrated
transuranic nuclides, including neptunium, americium, curium, and higher elements (including plutonium, described separately above); several species have very long half-lives	α, β	neutron-absorption products and decay products of higher transuranic nuclides	carried in liquid wastes	may show a radioactive toxicity similar to that of plutonium; these nuclides are members of the actinide series and are often identified by this more inclusive term, which also encompasses some relatively innocuous members

*Note: taken together, radioactive strontium and cesium nuclides generate a considerable fraction of the heat of high-level wastes during the first decades; their relatively long half-lives, high abundance, and biological compatibility materially influence waste-management policies.

regarded collectively as biologically dangerous. They also decay into other alpha emitters, thus prolonging the hazard.

Through a similar process of neutron absorption, called neutron activation, various normally stable elements present in the reactor as fuel cladding, moderators, control elements, coolants, and impurities can be rendered radioactive. For the most part, these activated materials are less significant and often not as persistent as fission products. Nitrogen in air coolant, for instance, is activated to a powerful gamma emitter, fortunately of very short life. Argon in air coolant gives argon-41, whose rate of production may set limits on safe reactor operation. Irradiation of cladding material often leads to the production of cobalt-60, with a significant five-year half-life. The hydrogen isotope deuterium (hydrogen-2), a constituent of the heavy water used as a neutron moderator, is activated to tritium (hydrogen-3), an unstable isotope with a half-life of about 12 years. Other activation products have much longer, troublesome half-lives: for example, carbon-14 (half-life, 5,730 years) and nickel-59 (half-life, 80,000 years). Important characteristics of several species of radioactive nuclides found in nuclear wastes are delineated in table I.

Although it is possible to consider the composition of radioactive waste in terms of elemental mass abundance, it is often the case that rapidly decaying nuclides will have negligible mass in proportion to their activity. In addition, mass abundance depends upon many variables, including the kind of fuel used and the length of time the fuel is allowed to fission and cool. Hence it is usually of more interest to discuss waste composition in terms of its activity. Activity is the rate of disintegration of a radioactive species; it is usually expressed in curies (Ci), with 1 Ci = 3.7×10^{10} disintegrations per second. (The becquerel, or Bq, equivalent to 1 disintegration per second, is not yet in common use.) For example, for uranium fuel allowed to fission for 33,000 megawatt-days in a pressurized water reactor and cooled 30 days, the ten most active nuclides account approximately equally for 76% of the total activity. By contrast, after ten years of cooling, the four most active nuclides are responsible for 90% of the total activity. Per metric ton of nuclear fuel, the total activity as a function of cooling time will decrease from a maximum of 138 megacuries (MCi) at the time of discharge from the reactor to 10.8 MCi after 30 days of cooling, to 2.2 MCi after 1 year, and to 0.04 MCi after 100 years.

Both mass abundance and activity, however, are only secondary indices of the hazards of radioactive wastes. One needs to estimate the radiation dose to people and other life forms for any given release. Complete specification of the hazard over the lifetime of nuclear wastes is difficult or speculative. For wastes that present themselves through water sources, one method of specification is through the use of a toxicity index, defined as $\log_{10}$ of the volume of water (in cubic meters) that is required to dilute the wastes to conventionally accepted maximum permissible concentrations. A useful simplification, it nevertheless ignores all the problems of transfers through the ecological web

Courtesy, Nuclear Fuel Services, Inc.

Cask-encased element of spent nuclear fuel is lowered into an unloading pool. The fuel element is then removed and transferred underwater to an adjoining storage pool to await reprocessing.

and the obvious fact that widespread contamination at such concentrations would be unacceptable.

More than 99% of the total activity of nuclear waste is first encountered in liquid form, remaining as a by-product after spent nuclear fuel is chemically dissolved and all reusable fuel and fission products are reclaimed. Bulky and unwieldy, liquid creates storage problems that require immediate attention. Liquid wastes are commonly categorized by level of activity as low, medium or intermediate, or high, but agreement on the activity ranges of each has never been achieved. In the U.S., high-level wastes are practically defined as those arising from the first cycle of solvent extraction during fuel reprocessing or equivalent. Each site tends to have its own terms, which may be source-oriented or treatment-oriented, and only secondarily related to waste activity or relative hazard.

At the Hanford Works, for example, the limits arbitrarily and consistently have been: low level, below 5×10^{-5} microcuries/milliliter (μCi/ml); intermediate level, 5×10^{-5} to 10^2 μCi/ml; high level, above 10^2 μCi/ml. The International Atomic Energy Agency (IAEA), by comparison, offers six categories ranging from a throw-away level for wastes with activities below 10^{-6} μCi/ml to a level requiring long-term storage with cooling for wastes with activities above 10^4 μCi/ml. These categories are not consistently used, nor are three similarly conceived ones for gaseous wastes. However, four categories of solid wastes have formed the basis for orderly transportation regulations in many countries. As applied to storage, arbitrary terminology is customary.

The Hanford Works: a study in short-term storage

Built during World War II, the Hanford Works was the original complex of fuel fabrication plant, nuclear reactors, and chemical separations plants for the production of plutonium through the irradiation of uranium-238. It occupies 570 square miles adjacent to the Columbia River in a region of southeastern Washington that experiences an average annual rainfall of 6.5 inches. Its separations plants and waste-storage facilities were built near the center of the reservation on a plateau that offers 200–300 feet of dry sediments above the water table.

During chemical processing, noble-gas fission products are released into the air along with radioactive iodine nuclides, some ruthenium, and some entrained fission products and actinides. All except the noble gases, however, are retained with high efficiency on chemical absorbers and filters. The main liquid wastes generated during processing are stored in large underground tanks.

A total of 152 large underground storage tanks exist at Hanford for high-level radioactive wastes. The older tanks are of single-wall carbon steel and concrete. Currently, all high-heat liquid waste is stored only in newer double-wall tanks; low-heat waste and the salt cake from a waste-solidification program are stored in older single-wall tanks. The tanks are in four sizes: 55,000 gallons, 500,000 gallons, 750,000 gallons, and 1,000,000 gallons.

Lowell J. Georgia—Photo Researchers, Inc.

Since the Hanford plant was built, 20 confirmed tank leaks have occurred, all of which have been from single-wall tanks. Each of the leaks has been assigned to one of four causes: corrosion of carbon-steel tank liners, cracking or mechanical failure of the steel liner, thermal expansion due to local overheating, or buckling due to other causes. These tank leaks have varied in size from very small, *i.e.*, about 1,500 gallons, to 115,000 gallons for the notorious leak that occurred in 1973. Total volume from the 20 leaks is 464,000 gallons. Current government policy for these wastes requires their solidification to salt cake, which will continue to be held in the tanks. Although the probable release from this condition is very low, such storage will not be as secure as solidification to a high-quality glass.

As the remaining liquid waste is converted to salt cake, additional tank leaks are expected. In the future, an increasing fraction of liquid waste will be stored in double-wall tanks, where a leak in the inner tank can be detected and corrective action taken without escape of liquid from the outer tank to the ground. Detection systems currently under development have the objective of locating a leak before it exceeds 1,500 gallons. These systems plus the use of double-wall tanks should virtually guarantee that a leak as large as 115,000 gallons will not occur again under normal operations.

None of the leakage from underground tanks at Hanford has been proved a hazard to the groundwater located some 200–300 feet below the surface. Essentially all of it has remained fixed in sediments beneath or adjacent to the tanks and is expected to remain in this status, short of almost cataclysmic changes in climate or hydrology.

The effectiveness of this retention was determined incidentally from monitoring the movement of deliberately released intermediate-level wastes. These wastes contained about 40,000 Ci of cesium-137, about one-fifth to one-sixth the activity of the eventual accidental leaks. An independent review by the U.S. National Academy of Sciences (NAS) in

Houses built to gauge the effects of radiation from uranium ore tailings are studied by scientists at Colorado State University. Presently hundreds of millions of tons of tailings from uranium mills stand in outdoor mounds in the western U.S.

209

1966 looked unfavorably on these releases, and they have since been reduced by a factor of 1,000.

When the planned releases of large volumes of intermediate-level wastes were made, extensive programs were mounted to study the consequences. For all short-term and medium-term purposes, the results of the studies were favorable. Dry sediments below a disposal point were found to absorb liquids like a sponge and hold them in place as effectively as a tank. Such sites now hold 5.3×10^7 gallons containing 60,000 Ci of active wastes. This method of disposal, called the specific retention method, is no longer approved.

Additionally, it was found that larger volumes would essentially saturate the sediments and proceed downward to the water table. The soil columns were found to function as ion-exchange media, releasing elements already in the soil while retaining in their place most of the active materials, usually quite close to the point of entrance. Each radioactive element has a characteristic retention curve—sometimes more than one for different chemical forms. By chance, most of the more mobile forms are short-lived. Hence, it would have been possible to permit such disposal until the significant nuclides just approached the water table. At one stage in the history of these releases, a prescribed level of actual contamination of the groundwater was permitted before changing disposal points, a poor policy.

The best studied case of this type occurred between 1952 and 1956 when 40 million gallons of waste containing about 750,000 Ci of mixed fission products including strontium-90 and cesium-137 were released into underground timbered cribs. Disposal was stopped when instruments in test wells indicated strontium and cesium at accepted concentrations 18 meters above the water table. In 1966 advanced monitoring instrumentation determined that downward movement of the liquid and of its activity was greater than expected. The groundwater became locally contaminated with strontium-90, as well as with ruthenium, technetium, and tritium.

Despite the indisputable failure of waste management to avoid contamination, the episode was not as serious as it appeared. Subsequent testing established that more than 99.9% of the dangerous activity of strontium and cesium would continue to be retained within 15 meters of the cribs. Moreover, it would be an oversimplification to expect all waste constituents to migrate with equal swiftness through saturated sediments to the Columbia River. Over the past 20 years it has become increasingly clear that some constituents—e.g., tritium, ruthenium, and technetium—do move rather freely through the ground. In fact, these have been used as tracers to follow movement of the contaminated groundwater. According to present estimates, travel time for such highly mobile species could be as low as 15–30 years, and, indeed, tritium has already been detected in the banks of the river as far as 11 miles from the release point. For strontium, cesium, and other slow-moving nuclides, however, travel time is calculated to be in excess of 1,000 years. In addition, analytic and computer models of water-table

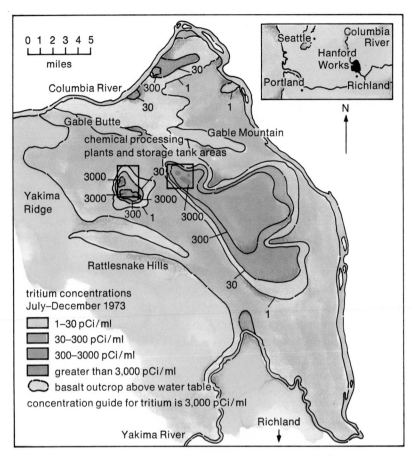

Scale:
0 1 2 3 4 5
miles

Columbia River

Seattle •
Portland •
Columbia River
Hanford Works
Richland •

N ↑

30
300
30
1
1

Gable Butte
chemical processing
plants and storage tank areas
Gable Mountain

3000
3000
300
30
3000
3000
1
300

Yakima Ridge

Rattlesnake Hills

30

1

tritium concentrations
July–December 1973

1–30 pCi/ml
30–300 pCi/ml
300–3000 pCi/ml
greater than 3,000 pCi/ml
basalt outcrop above water table
concentration guide for tritium is 3,000 pCi/ml

Richland

Yakima River

contours have indicated that by the middle of the 21st century travel time to the river can be doubled by a concerted reduction of further liquid input to the ground.

A separate case at the Hanford Works precipitated yet another round of controversy over disposal practices. The release of relatively large amounts of plutonium wastes, variously estimated at 25–70 kilograms, into a single crib led to public fears that the material could become sufficiently concentrated to undergo a spontaneous chain reaction. Although this eventuality was shown to be scientifically unfounded, the main mass of plutonium at the site was ordered removed. This situation would not arise in commercial reprocessing.

In retrospect, the leaks at the Hanford plant and the use of its unique dry sediments for waste retention probably did significant damage to its overall waste-management image. Molded by such lessons of experience, the future of waste management at Hanford has been projected to include the following guidelines: (1) High-level wastes will continue to be evaporated to salt cakes stored in the large tanks; whether they should later be converted to a less leachable solid for shipment to a federal repository or basalt-cavern burial at Hanford is undecided. (2) Intermediate-level wastes will not be released until they have been treated to reduce their activity to releasable amounts. (3) Solid wastes will be controlled with emphasis on careful packaging and

Studies over the past 20 years have made it clear that certain of the more short-lived components of liquid wastes, particularly tritium, ruthenium, and technetium, migrate rapidly through saturated sediments. Monitoring of test wells at the Hanford Works during the latter half of 1973 revealed a pattern of widespread groundwater contamination with tritium from liquid wastes that had been intentionally released to the ground. Tritium was also detected in the banks of the Columbia River as far as 11 miles from the release point.

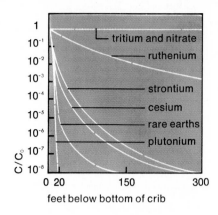

feet below bottom of crib

Extensive investigations at the Hanford Works established that soil below its underground liquid-waste storage cribs functions as ion-exchange media, releasing elements already in the soil while retaining most of the active wastes. Shown above are retention curves for several radioactive species monitored during their downward migration through typical Hanford sediments; C/C_0 is the ratio of nuclide concentration at a given depth to its initial concentration. Fortunately most of the activity of the more hazardous, long-lived species is effectively trapped within 15 meters of the cribs.

isolation against leaching. (4) Such controversial situations as the relatively large accumulation and storage of plutonium wastes at one location will be corrected.

The Savannah River Plant: a comparative study

The Savannah River Plant (SRP) is the second of the major plutonium production centers in the U.S. First operated in 1953, it is a complex of nuclear reactors and separation plants in a reservation occupying 300 square miles in western South Carolina.

From the viewpoint of waste management, three important characteristics differentiate the SRP from the Hanford Works. First, its later start permitted evaluation of Hanford experience. Du Pont & Co., responsible for the SRP, had the advantage of having designed, built, and operated the Hanford facilities. Second, in contrast to the graphite moderators used in the production reactors at Hanford, heavy water is employed for the purpose at the SRP. For this and other reasons, tritium is a more significant waste nuclide at the SRP than elsewhere. Third, climate and groundwater conditions are strikingly different from those prevailing at Hanford. Safety margins for retention of wastes in dry sediments do not exist at the Savannah plant.

High-level liquid wastes are retained at the SRP's reprocessing plants in large carbon-steel tanks that have progressive improvements in design over earlier Hanford models. The first design was essentially a cup-and-saucer arrangement in which any leakage from the tank could be held in the saucer. Newer versions are complete double-walled tanks with internal cooling coils and a central column that greatly stiffens the entire structure.

The reprocessing of highly radioactive wastes involves storage and settling of sludge in one tank, leaving predominantly radiocesium in the remaining liquid, or supernate; transfer to a sludge collection tank; concentration of the liquid in an evaporator; and accumulation of salt in a salt storage tank. The active materials produced in the first cycle of solvent extraction are termed high-activity wastes, to use SRP terminology. Later-cycle wastes are called low-activity wastes, but these are what might normally be called intermediate wastes. These too must be stored, evaporated, and reduced to salt cake. The primary difference between the two types is that the latter do not require continuous cooling and can be handled in simpler tanks.

Tanks at the Savannah River Plant range in volume from 750,000 gallons to 1,300,000 gallons with a total capacity of 30 million gallons, currently about two-thirds occupied. Leakage (about 1% of the amount at Hanford) has been encountered in the tanks with no serious consequences to date. The newer tanks, short of some unforeseen catastrophic mode of destruction, should have high integrity for several decades. There now seems to be a greater chance of accidental spilling during transfer or by overfilling than by tank leakage. Nevertheless, despite the reduced mobility of sludges and salt cakes compared with liquids, storage cannot be accepted as final at this location.

Table II. U.S. Commercial Wastes in AD 2000 (based on a 500-Gw installed nuclear capacity)				
	annual addition		accumulated to AD 2000	
waste type	volume x 10³ cu m	activity MCi	volume x 10³ cu m	activity MCi
ore tailings (mining and milling)	19,000	0.2	260,000	3
nontransuranic wastes (miscellaneous low-level wastes: 90% from reactors, 10% from rest of cycle)	200	1	2,000	3
low-level transuranic wastes (emissions: α greater than 10^{-9} Ci/g, low β, γ)	6	5	60	40
intermediate-level transuranic wastes (emissions: α greater than 10^{-9} Ci/g, high γ)	2	1	22	5
high-level solidified waste (in glass or ceramics)	0.4	1,100	2.5	6,700
noble gases (particularly krypton-85)	in cylinders	60	—	440
iodine (iodine-129 from stacks)	0.01	0.0003	100	30
tritiated water (from coolant activation)	60	0.3	660	2
tritium (fission product)	0.1	4	1	30
carbon-14 (from nitrogen-14 in fuels)	—	0.005	—	0.05
cladding wastes	0.5	50	4	200

Current expectation is that the material will eventually be solidified and transferred to a federal repository, if the necessary technological and political decisions can be made. The Savannah River Plant staff have long considered a method of storing the wastes some 1,500 feet below the SRP site in bedrock. This concept has been independently examined by a committee of the NAS, which concluded that the project may be feasible but only after extensive exploratory work. Between 350 and 1,000 feet below the site lies the Tuscaloosa aquifer, a main water resource for the region. It seems unlikely that convincing proof of continued safety of the aquifer over geologic time can be developed.

Meanwhile, the stored wastes are causing no radiation exposure except to SRP staff involved in the processing and transfer. Unavoidable processing releases to the atmosphere and to plant streams are also causing some exposure, but comparable with local variations in natural background radiation.

Courtesy, Southern California Edison Company

Technicians work to remove spent fuel elements from reactor core at the San Onofre Nuclear Generating Station in California. About one-third of the reactor's 157 fuel assemblies are replaced during refueling every 16 months.

Terminal storage

Until recently, major projections of waste accumulation in the U.S. assumed an installed nuclear power of 1,200 Gw by AD 2000. In mid-1975 this figure was revised downward to 850 Gw, and the current best guess is taken to be 500 Gw. Precision in the power forecast is not needed, however, because the choice of reactor and fuel types materially alters waste composition. Estimated volumes of wastes are also speculative, being based upon the expectation of improving management practices. Hence, any forecast of the magnitude of the waste problem, such as depicted in table II, cannot be accepted as final.

The ore tailings shown in the table are expected to be returned in bulk to disused mines. They release small amounts of radon-222, a noble gas whose decay products include polonium-218 and polonium-214, both strong alpha emitters with a preference for deposition in the human lung. Currently more than a hundred million tons of tailings from uranium mills stand in outdoor mounds in the western U.S.

Miscellaneous low-level beta- and gamma-emitting wastes are generated throughout the nuclear fuel cycle and will probably be buried in surface pits. Tritiated water arising from reactor operations is also expected to be sent to disposal sites. All other waste types in the table must be afforded high-level storage.

Conventional high-level wastes may require separation from the biosphere for at least a million years. Retention of liquids or relatively immobile sludges for such times is out of the question. Their reduction to insoluble solids has been studied for nearly 20 years and, as was mentioned above, satisfactory methods, such as incorporation in special glass compounds, now exist. One key question is how and where to store these solids.

In the U.S., where the responsibility for long-term disposition of commercial wastes has been inherited by the Energy Research and Development Administration (ERDA) from the defunct Atomic Energy Commission (AEC), federal regulation requires solidification by the waste producer within five years and transfer to a federal repository within ten years. Yet, as of 1977, this repository does not exist, and proposals for it have not progressed beyond the review stage.

As originally conceived, the federal repository was to have been a salt mine, as recommended to the AEC by the NAS in 1957. In 1970 the AEC proposed a demonstration salt-mine facility near Lyons, Kansas. Specific review of the proposal, however, revealed several preexisting man-made flaws in the integrity of the site; among the worst was the distinct possibility of the destructive intrusion of water from mining operations in the vicinity.

The AEC then proposed a temporizing method of retrievable surface storage. In one suggested version, solidified wastes would be sealed in large steel canisters, which in turn would be placed in concrete cylinders and erected on barren land. The need for extensive surveillance and the vulnerability of the stored wastes to war, sabotage, neglect, and natural disasters are obvious and have overshadowed

214

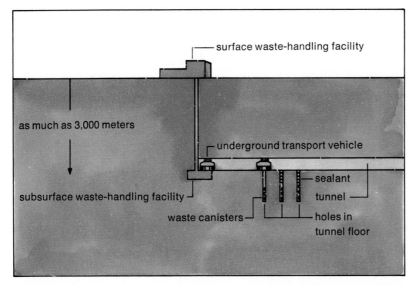

surface waste-handling facility

as much as 3,000 meters

underground transport vehicle

subsurface waste-handling facility

sealant

tunnel

waste canisters

holes in tunnel floor

Depicted are several concepts for geological disposal of nuclear wastes (top to bottom): solid waste emplacement in a mined cavity, similar to operations in progress at the Asse mine in West Germany; three plans for seabed disposal that exploit aspects of plate tectonics and rapid coverage characteristics of undersea regions with high sedimentation rates; and three plans for disposal on or below polar ice sheets.

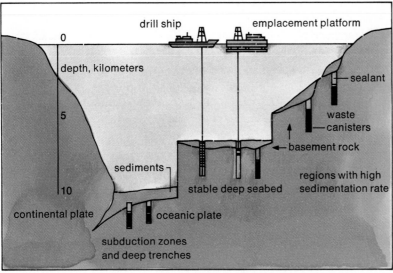

drill ship

emplacement platform

0

depth, kilometers

sealant

waste canisters

5

basement rock

sediments

regions with high sedimentation rate

10

stable deep seabed

continental plate

oceanic plate

subduction zones and deep trenches

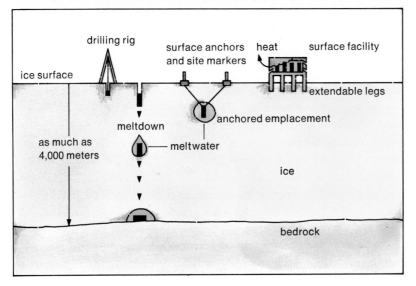

drilling rig

surface anchors and site markers

heat

surface facility

ice surface

extendable legs

meltdown

anchored emplacement

as much as 4,000 meters

meltwater

ice

bedrock

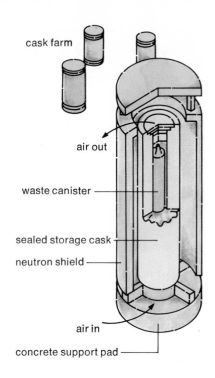

cask farm

air out

waste canister

sealed storage cask

neutron shield

air in

concrete support pad

One method of temporary surface storage, the sealed storage cask concept, involves placement of solidified wastes in large steel canisters, which in turn would be encased in concrete cylinders and erected on barren land.

technical issues for the present. Such a scheme of retrievable storage is sensible if new technological developments related to ultimate disposal are anticipated.

The most recent proposal has been to pursue the study of geological disposal in salt beds of southeastern New Mexico, in shales, and in crystalline rocks such as granite in the hope that acceptable repositories may be developed in various parts of the country. This plan arose from a preliminary study of alternatives that included ten geological concepts, three concepts each for disposal in ice sheets and seabeds, three options for disposal in space, and three transmutation concepts. Given the reservation that analysis projected over a million or more years obviously cannot be verified experimentally, the study yielded several conclusions. (1) Full examination of any of the concepts may require 15–30 years. (2) The estimated cost of the most attractive methods will not hinder the development of commercial nuclear power. (3) Several geological concepts offer a low risk of serious environmental impact; *i.e.*, those offering retrievability, solidification before arrival at the disposal site, and storage without the involvement of melting rock by fission heat. (4) By comparison, all other proposed methods of storage are decidedly less secure.

Projection into space, at best feasible only for selected wastes, requires consideration of the possibility of an aborted mission, in which case the ability of the waste container to survive the incident intact must be guaranteed. Concepts for disposal in polar ice sheets, in which high-activity wastes would be allowed to melt into the ice of their own accord, possess some advantages for nuclides with relatively short half-lives, on the order of 700 years. The persistence of the transuranic nuclides and certain fission products, however, could allow them to outlive the estimated life expectancy of the ice sheet itself. In addition, the Antarctic currently is kept free of nuclear wastes by international treaty. With regard to disposal in the sea, only placement in prepared holes in the stable deep seabed is likely to be further pursued, and that only within a framework of international cooperation.

Transmutation concepts involve bombardment of wastes with neutrons to convert persistent nuclides to forms that are less toxic or of shorter half-life, or both. An objective would be to produce a waste that would not require absolute retention for more than about 1,000 years, thus diminishing one objection that million-year storage goes beyond the life span of civilizations. However, this method, as well as the extraterrestrial concepts, requires complex partitioning of the active wastes. It is quite possible that unavoidable releases at that step would exceed probable releases from sound geological disposal. (Even for untransmuted wastes, the necessity for secure million-year storage may be an overstatement; calculations have shown that the most active wastes would decay to the equivalent of a bed of uranium ore in several thousand years.)

The formulation of waste-disposal policies, practices, and goals in all nations that use nuclear reactors has been broadly similar. The princi-

216

pal practical differences lie in the aggressiveness with which improved methods have been installed. In France, for example, encasement of milder wastes in bitumen, far superior to incorporation in concrete, has been highly developed. As of late 1976, progress of a vitrification plant in southern France for the solidification of wastes was gratifying. Wastes and molten glass were to be mixed together, poured into stainless-steel containers, and temporarily stored in air-cooled underground concrete vaults. The United Kingdom, which has had excellent experience with liquid storage in stainless-steel tanks, is planning an industrial-scale vitrification plant for the mid-1980s. Canada has delayed its waste-management issues by not reprocessing fuel, choosing instead to retain fission wastes within spent fuel pieces. Japan, with limited land resources, looks favorably toward ocean dumping or shipment of its wastes to another country.

West Germany is the first nation to store low-level and intermediate-level solids in a salt mine. The Asse mine, near Braunschweig, is a former commercial salt and potash mine with 145 underground "rooms" or excavated caverns, each averaging 24,000 cubic meters. The rooms occupy galleries between 490 and 800 meters below ground. Dry waste is stored in drums at the lower levels with the intention to seal off a filled cavern with salt. Intermediate-level waste occupies a shielded cavern at the 490-meter level. Experiments conducted to study the heat and stress burdens of high-level solids were expected to lead to demonstration storage of quarter-million-curie glass blocks before 1980. German work on four methods involving solidification in glass ceramics was advancing in parallel.

It is truly difficult for the concerned citizen to reach a balanced judgment on the prospects for responsible waste management. There are advocates of nuclear power, and advocates of nuclear moratorium. One side considers that all the basic problems have been solved, and the other points to a nearly endless catalog of uncertainties, which range from arguments stressing the radiological hazard of the transuranium elements, risks of sabotage, diversion to illicit nuclear weapons, and the effects of geological changes to concerns about the lifetimes of civilizations and the risk of intrusion into forgotten disposal sites.

The most intense radioactivity of nuclear wastes is lost in a thousand years—a quite feasible span for a federal repository. Environmental damage from radioactive releases thus far has been quite small. If control methods continue to improve, it seems likely that results will continue to be good, although not necessarily perfect.

One course is clear. Waste-management research must have the attention and funding that it has received only belatedly in the last decade. Waste management can and must be upgraded and maintained at a high level throughout the nuclear age. It can, in fact, become the model for the way a responsible nation should handle hundreds of other carcinogenic and mutagenic substances upon whose beneficial qualities it also depends.

Courtesy, Gesellschaft für Strahlen-und Umweltforschung, Munich

View through protective lead-glass window into a storage chamber of the West German repository at the Asse mine reveals a pile of iron-banded drums of dry nuclear waste. Above the chamber and connected to it by vertical shafts is a control room from which drums of waste are lowered to their final location under surveillance of a closed-circuit TV system.

Plate Tectonics: Past, Present, and Future

by Robert S. Dietz

Only in the last decade have scientists begun to perceive the true nature of the Earth's surface—an interlocking mosaic of rocky plates whose restless activity underlies many geological phenomena.

Over the past decade the Earth sciences have witnessed the emergence of one of the most practical and thoroughly unifying developments in the history of science. Whereas classical structural geology was formerly concerned with uplift, subsidence, and time, a new concept called plate tectonics has added a fourth dimension; now great horizontal shifts of thousands of kilometers dominate descriptions of the mechanisms of crustal deformation. The concept of plate tectonics holds that the lithosphere, or outermost layer of the Earth's surface, is divided into about seven major rigid spherical caps or plates 100 kilometers (60 miles) thick. These ride on a weak, soft, partially melted layer of rock called the asthenosphere, or upper mantle. Except for the Pacific and India-Australia plates, each of the other five major plates is named for the particular continent embedded within it as a passive passenger. Accordingly, there also is a North America, South America, Eurasia, Africa, and Antarctica plate. Additionally, there are several smaller subplates (e.g., the Nazca, Cocos, and Caribbean plates) and some microplates.

Norman O. Tomalin—Bruce Coleman Inc.

(Overleaf) Solidified lava formation, Galápagos Islands, Ecuador.

Plates and junctures

The ideal plate can be visualized as rectangular, although no such plate exists — perhaps because the Earth is not flat but spherical. Along one edge is a subduction zone, usually marked by an oceanic trench, where the cold lithospheric plate dives steeply into the Earth's mantle, reaching a depth of 700 kilometers before it is fully resorbed. Along the edge opposite the subduction zone is a mid-oceanic ridge, or pull-apart zone. As its axial rift opens, the gap is quickly filled by an inflow of liquid basalt and quasi-solid mantle rock, which solidifies to form new ocean crust. The two other antithetical edges, connecting the ridges to the trenches, are boundaries called transform faults where crust is neither created nor consumed. The term transform has been applied because these faults are not absorbed by a plastically yielding crust; instead they maintain their sharp displacement until they blend or transform into either trenches or ridges. The boundaries of the interlocking plates never end but transform into other types of boundaries, eventually encircling the world in a closed mosaic network.

Three types of boundaries between contiguous plates are possible: (1) divergent junctures where new basaltic crust is created; (2) shear junctures, the transform faults at which plates slip laterally past one another; and (3) convergent junctures, the trenches at which two plates overlap, with one plate diving beneath the other and being consumed. It is presumed that the amount of subduction just equals the amount of plate growth by accretion so that the Earth grows neither larger nor smaller. In addition, the subducting plate is not fully digestible by the mantle; certain components (magmas) rise to the surface, intruding along the leading edge of the overriding plate. If the subduction zone is oceanic, as most are, this material forms trench-associated island arcs (for example, the Indonesian archipelago and the islands of Japan and the Philippines) that eventually may be carried to and become part of the continental margins. Because of their buoyancy, the continents are not subducted; embedded in the surface of denser lithospheric plates, they survive forever as the ocean basins grow and collapse in a ponderous accordionlike cycle.

The junctures of plate boundaries are termed triple junctions because invariably three boundaries meet. It is probably not trivial that there are no quadruple or quintuple junctions on Earth, but the reason for this is not clear. It has been shown that 17 types of triple junctions are possible, depending upon the types of boundaries meeting at the nexus, although not every type exists on Earth. Velocity-vector analyses have revealed that these have either stable or unstable angular geometries depending on whether they can maintain these geometries as they evolve.

Evolution of the concept

Plate tectonics is an integration of several early theories of structural geology including continental drift and seafloor spreading. The controversial notion that continents had been drifting like rafts across the

ROBERT S. DIETZ is Professor of Earth and Planetary Sciences at Washington University, St. Louis, Missouri.

George Holton—Photo Researchers

Earth's surface for hundreds of millions of years after the breakup of a single great landmass, Pangaea, was first formulated more than 50 years ago by the German meteorologist Alfred Wegener and extended by subsequent investigators. There was considerable evidence for drift, such as the appearance of a fit between the west coast of Africa and the east coast of South America, but this was regarded by Wegener's opponents as "soft" data, on a par with Italy looking like a boot. Nevertheless, as scientifically unsound as it seemed to be, the suggestion that continents somehow do move continued to haunt the earth sciences until it drew new life from two lines of "hard" data.

The first of these made use of an earlier proposal that the magnetic field of the Earth undergoes periodic reversal. In the early 1960s it was observed from airborne magnetometer surveys that the seafloor appeared to be paved with zebra-stripe patterns of rock of alternating magnetic polarity that ran parallel to the mid-oceanic ridges. These anomalies suggested that, as liquid basalt welled up from the asthenosphere into the axial cracks of the ridges and solidified, it took on the prevailing polarity of the Earth's field; from this evidence came the inescapable conclusion that new ocean floor was being created as the mid-oceanic rift zones spread apart. The anomaly patterns also provided vectorized measurement of the exact amount of seafloor spreading and in fact are analogous to rings by which the age and growth of a tree may be measured. The second line of convincing evidence came from the World-Wide Standardized Seismograph Network, which was

Steaming lava from a new volcano inundates the stark landscape on the Icelandic island of Heimaey. The Reykjanes ridge, a divergent plate juncture, is exposed on land at Iceland, whose volcanic nature is further enhanced by the existence of an ascending plume of magma, or hot spot, from the asthenosphere.

221

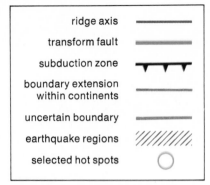

ridge axis

transform fault

subduction zone

boundary extension
within continents

uncertain boundary

earthquake regions

selected hot spots

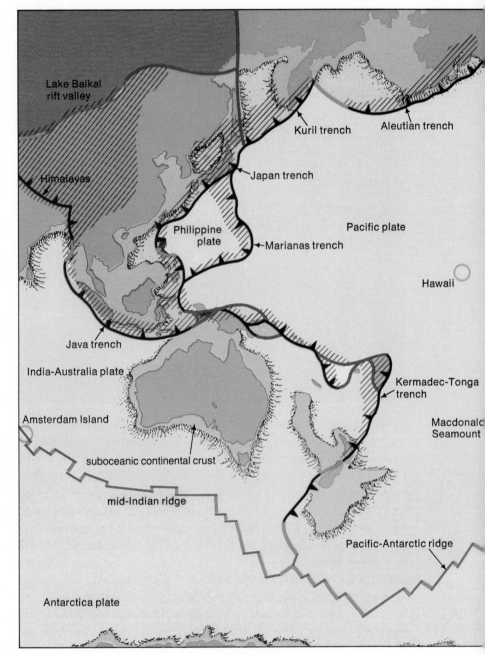

Lake Baikal
rift valley

Himalayas

Kuril trench

Aleutian trench

Japan trench

Philippine
plate

Marianas trench

Pacific plate

Hawaii

Java trench

India-Australia plate

Amsterdam Island

suboceanic continental crust

mid-Indian ridge

Antarctica plate

Kermadec-Tonga
trench

Macdonald
Seamount

Pacific-Antarctic ridge

The Earth's outermost layer, or lithosphere, comprises a mosaic of rigid plates 100 kilometers thick in constant relative motion. Three types of boundaries between plates are possible: divergent junctures where new seafloor is being created along mid-oceanic ridges; convergent junctures where plates overlap, with one plate being subducted; and shear junctures where plates slide past one another along transform faults. With few exceptions the earthquakes of the world are distributed along narrow zones that outline the plate boundaries. Hot spots, or plumes of lava that remain stationary beneath the plates, have been shown responsible for many volcanic island chains.

established initially in 1960 to monitor clandestine atomic-bomb detonations. By providing the first precise information on locations of earthquake epicenters, this net revealed that the earthquakes of the world are not randomly distributed but with relatively few exceptions form narrow zones of seismic activity that actually outline the boundaries of lithospheric plates.

It is reasonable to wonder why geologists were slow in discovering the plate-tectonic Earth. First, nearly all of the evidence is hidden beneath the sea—beyond knowing until the advent of marine geology in the years following World War II. The plate boundaries, which are

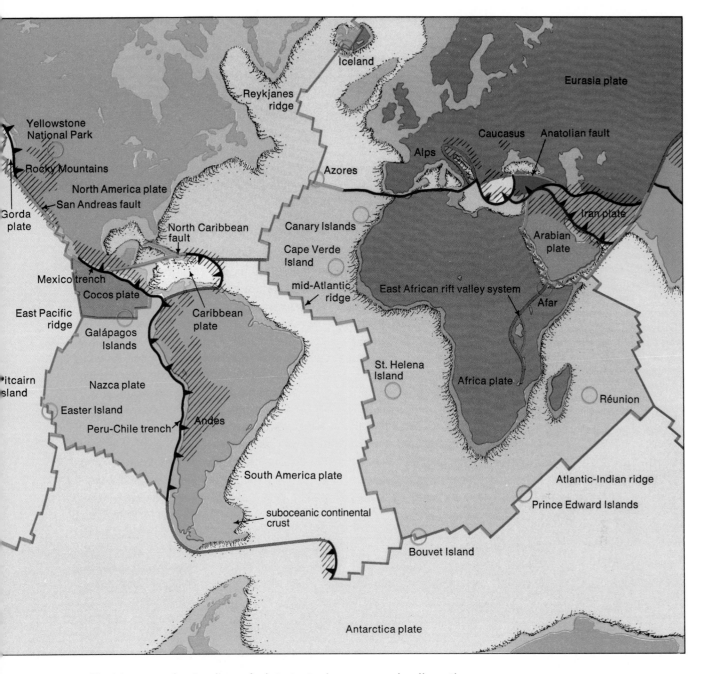

Yellowstone
National Park

Rocky Mountains

North America plate

San Andreas fault

Gorda
plate

Mexico trench

Cocos plate

East Pacific
ridge

Galápagos
Islands

Pitcairn
Island

Nazca plate

Easter Island

Peru-Chile trench

Andes

North Caribbean
fault

Caribbean
plate

South America plate

suboceanic continental
crust

Iceland

Reykjanes
ridge

Azores

Canary Islands

Cape Verde
Island

mid-Atlantic
ridge

St. Helena
Island

Bouvet Island

Eurasia plate

Caucasus

Anatolian fault

Alps

Iran plate

Arabian
plate

East African rift valley system

Afar

Africa plate

Réunion

Atlantic-Indian ridge

Prince Edward Islands

Antarctica plate

critical to an understanding of plate tectonics, are nearly all on the
ocean floor. With the exception of continent-to-continent collision
zones such as the Himalayan arc, subduction zones are wholly submarine. The mid-oceanic ridge is exposed on land only at Iceland and even
there it is anomalous, being "overprinted" by an ascending plume of
magma, or hot spot, rising from the Earth's mantle. The principal transform faults found on land are the San Andreas fault of California, the
Alpine fault of New Zealand, and some segments along the Alpine-
Himalayan collision front. The Afar triangle in Ethiopia is the only triple
junction visible on the Earth's surface.

223

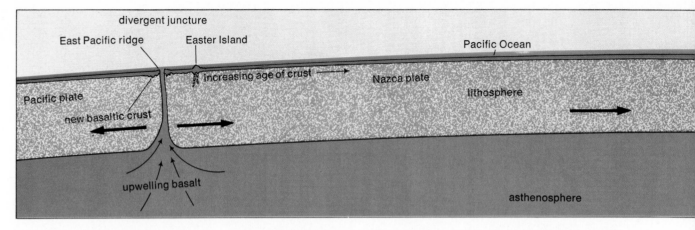

divergent juncture

East Pacific ridge   Easter Island   Pacific Ocean

increasing age of crust   Nazca plate

Pacific plate   lithosphere

new basaltic crust

upwelling basalt

asthenosphere

Cross section through the eastern Pacific (above) near latitude 27° S depicts birth of new ocean floor along the East Pacific ridge and subduction of the Nazca plate below the South America plate. Diverging Pacific and Nazca plates create a gap that is filled by an inflow of liquid basalt from the asthenosphere. As the Nazca plate dives into the asthenosphere and is consumed, certain low-density components rise through the overriding plate to build the Andes mountain chain.

Second, geologists had not suspected that the Earth was unique tectonically among planets. Its surface proved to be neither fixed like that of the Moon, Mercury, or Mars nor convecting like the gases of Jupiter. Instead, its carapace consists of a mosaic of plates in relative motion, which converge, pull apart, or shear past one another. Although this motion is almost undetectable in human terms, being only about as fast as one's fingernails grow, it is immensely important geologically. The rate of drift is about an order of magnitude greater than mountain growth or continental erosion. The following example will serve to compare the rates of subsidence and drift for a geological feature. Drilling in the Bahama platform off Florida revealed that it is composed of shallow-water coral-reef limestones to a depth of at least six kilometers. Apparently this extensive plateau has been sinking slowly by this amount over the past 150 million years, since the mid-

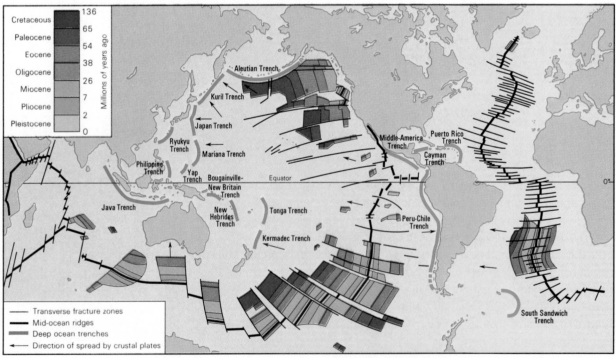

Courtesy, *Fortune* Magazine, "The Secret of the Spreading Ocean Floors," February 1969, by Max Gschwind based on the work of Bruce C. Heezen and Marie Tharp

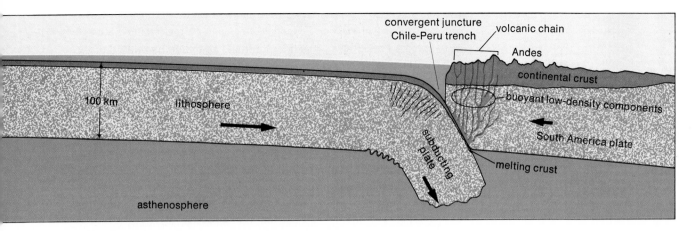

labels: convergent juncture Chile-Peru trench, volcanic chain, Andes, continental crust, buoyant low-density components, South America plate, melting crust, subducting plate, 100 km, lithosphere, asthenosphere

Jurassic, a remarkable record of subsidence. Yet over the same period the Bahamas have drifted some 6,000 kilometers from their former position, which was near Ascension Island in the South Atlantic. Hence, the horizontal drift of this island chain has exceeded its subsidence rate by a factor of 1,000.

Driving forces and hot spots

A principal gap in plate tectonics is a definitive understanding of the forces that drive crustal plates over the face of the Earth. With some logic it can be argued that plate tectonics necessarily will remain only a hypothesis until the driving mechanism is explained. Some geophysicists have suggested extraterrestrial forces, such as tidal drag, but these ideas generally have gained little favor. Somewhat similarly, convection cells in the mantle, at least those of the toroidal type, which classically had been invoked to explain continental drift, now appear to be nonexistent.

Recent findings support the view that the plates are being dragged down into the subduction zones by their oldest edges, which are cold and hence heavy. Lithospheric plates are born hot at mid-oceanic ridges but cool as they move away from this zone of accretion; complete cooling requires at least 100 million years. Moreover, as these cold lithospheric slabs descend into the trenches, increasing pressure induces certain polymorphic transformations in rocks and minerals. These changes take place more readily at low temperatures and hence enhance the weight of the cold slabs. Such transformations include the change of basalt into the dense metamorphic rock called eclogite and that of the common mineral olivine into denser phases that have structures akin to rutile or spinel. An apt analogy can be drawn that compares a lithospheric plate to a wet towel floating on the surface of a swimming pool. If small weights are added to one end of the towel, they will initiate "subduction" along this margin.

Although this dragging down of the crustal plates seems valid, it cannot be the entire story and a variety of forces must interplay. It is evident, for example, that all plates drift even though some, like the North America and Antarctica plates, are not being subducted along

Ages of various regions of the seafloor (opposite page, bottom) and precise measurements of seafloor spreading have been derived from analysis of magnetic anomaly patterns found in oceanic crust. Red-hot lava (below) from Hawaii's Kilauea Volcano solidifies underwater to form characteristic sacklike "pillow" structures. Indicative of submarine emplacement of molten rock, pillow lavas have been observed by deep-diving expeditions in the axial rifts of mid-oceanic ridges.

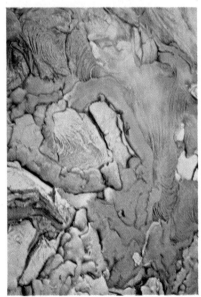

Richard W. Grigg

225

any margin. Also, plates that contain embedded continents appear to drift more slowly than such oceanic plates as the great Pacific plate and its associated subplates. This characteristic seems to be related to the fact that the lithosphere is both older and colder beneath the continents and hence thicker.

Formerly, geologists generally supposed that the formation of pockets of molten rock took place near the surface of the Earth. Modern discoveries, however, have assigned the sources of magma to ever-increasing depths, sometimes as deep as several hundred kilometers. One extravagant claim even ascribes the source of Oregon josephinite, a native nickel-iron mineral somewhat similar to that found in meteorites, to the mantle-core boundary about 3,000 kilometers below the Earth's surface. Although this explanation seems to be highly dubious, petrologists now identify the so-called hot spots, of which more than 100 have been identified, with deep mantle sources.

Hot spots are plumes of lavas that rise through the mantle like the ascending shafts of air beneath scattered cumulus clouds. The Earth's mantle bears certain similarities to the ocean, in which areas of upwelling occupy only about 1% of the sea surface while a slow, equalizing subsidence of water occurs everywhere else. The mantle appears to be the only shell of the Earth that is fixed, or essentially so, relative to the axis of rotation. The movement of the lithosphere over hot spots leaves trails of extinct volcanoes that record the drift of the plates.

It is likely that hot spots also play some role in driving plates because they seem to be present along mid-oceanic ridges and triple junctions. Possibly they control the locus of initial rifting by imposing a region of weakness on the lithosphere. Perhaps also the outward flowage of viscous rock from the center of the hot spot creates a drag force on the lithosphere that tends to drive the plates away from the ascending plume of magma. It is worth noting, however, that the Earth's paramount hot spot—the Hawaiian plume, which created the Hawaiian Islands and Emperor Seamount Chain—has not resulted in the disruption of the Pacific plate. The island of Hawaii is presently the world's most abundant source of lava; it is followed by Iceland, the Azores, and the Galápagos Islands. The last-named three all occur along rift boundaries or triple junctions.

Old and new plates

In the scenario of plate tectonics, old plates disappear by subduction into trenches as new plates presumably form to replace them. The Pacific is currently a collapsing ocean, the Atlantic is an opening one, and the Indian Ocean shows features of both processes. A sharp bend of the magnetic anomaly patterns (the Great Magnetic Bight) in the northeastern Pacific has been interpreted in relation to a former triple junction and, in turn, to the Kula plate, which has entirely disappeared by sliding into the Aleutian trench. There are also other plates in the Pacific of which only remnants presently remain, such as the Gorda plate off northern California and Oregon.

Transform faulting along the San Andreas in California (top left) displaces the course of streams crossing the fault line. The retreat of glacier ice from a section of New Zealand's Alpine fault recently exposed another conspicuous example of shearing between crustal plates (top right). Ertale Volcano (bottom left) smolders in the Danakil Depression of Ethiopia. Formerly part of the rifting floor of the Red Sea, the Danakil became landlocked several thousand years ago and its waters evaporated, leaving a landscape strewn with volcanic cones, parched salt deposits, and geysers of sulfurous brine (right).

Russ Kinne—Photo Researchers
G. R. Roberts, Nelson, N.Z.

Victor Englebert

Victor Englebert

(Top) Jack Couffer—Bruce Coleman Inc.; (bottom) G. R. Roberts, Nelson, N.Z.

Werner Stoy—Bruce Coleman Inc.

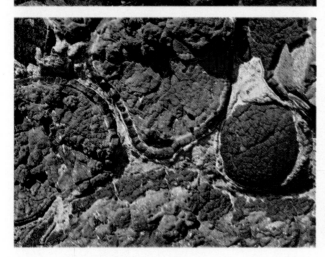

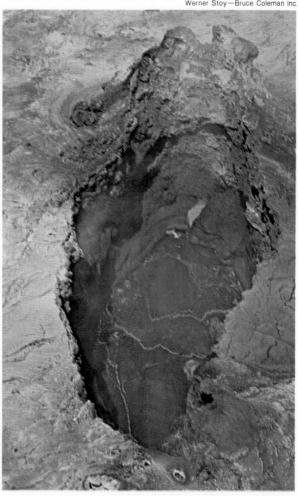

Bizarre lava formations on the Galápagos island of Fernandina (top left) and fiery craters on Hawaii (right) attest to the volcanic origins of these islands. Among the world's most abundant sources of lava, the Galápagos and Hawaiian chains are being created by the passage of oceanic plates over stationary hot spots. Off New Zealand's South Island lie stretches of submarine pillow lava (above), evidence of the region's association with lithospheric plate margins. Straddling the boundary between colliding plates, New Zealand's land masses ride the tops of two abutting blocks of continental crust.

If the plate-tectonic Earth is in a steady state, as seems philosophically most satisfying, either new plates must form or a major reorganization of the drift vectors of existing plates must occur from time to time. A bend in the Hawaiian-Emperor Seamount Chain near Milwaukee Seamount to the northwest of Midway Island, for example, apparently reflects a change in the absolute motion of the Pacific plate about 40 million years ago from a formerly northward drift to a presently northwestward drift. Even though the Pacific plate has its own system of trenches, this alteration of its drift motion may have affected other plates of the world system.

Earth scientists do not know how new plates form and can only make an educated guess. The plates are born from molten rock and cool with time; thus it seems likely that the older segments of plates, far from the mid-oceanic ridges, are slightly denser than the underlying asthenosphere. Because of this density inversion the plate may tend to break along some line of weakness and sink into the upper mantle along the ruptured edge. This process in turn requires the plate to pull apart elsewhere, creating a rift into which new ocean crust upwells. The Red Sea appears to be an example of the modern birth of such a new

228

Adapted from "Plate Tectonics Comes of Age" by Tom Alexander, illustrations by Richard Edes Harrison and Antonio Petruccelli, *Smithsonian* magazine, January 1975, p. 39

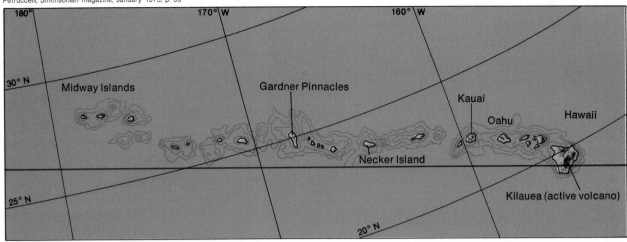

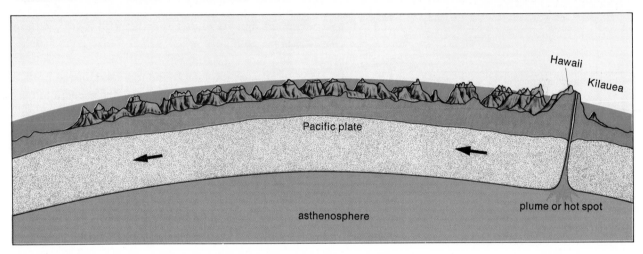

ocean basin. Filling the gap created by diverging lithospheric slabs requires flowage of the asthenosphere toward the gap and hence against the direction of drift. The drag forces so created along the bases of the sliding slabs oppose drift motion, creating a sort of "contravection" rather than a convection. If this scheme is correct, it is the trenches that actively consume plates and contribute to their motions, whereas the mid-oceanic ridges are but the passive consequences.

Collision of continents must also have major repercussions, because owing to their buoyancy they cannot be subducted into trenches. Modern examples are the collision of Africa with Europe and of India with the underbelly of Asia. The former event, which may have commenced about 30 million years ago, lifted part of the leading edge of the overriding Eurasia plate to form the Alps and appears to have rendered the Africa plate relatively stationary since that time. The latter event, which probably occurred about the same time, threw up the Himalayan rampart as India underthrust Asia. This is the only mountain front in the world as high as the continental slopes that offset the continents of the world from the ocean basins. A segment of continental crust as large as the subcontinent of India itself seems to have underridden Asia and

Island chains are formed when lava from stationary hot spots drives upward through the slowly drifting lithosphere to emerge as active volcanoes. The Hawaiian Islands, Midway, and the string of islands and seamounts between them can be interpreted as tracks left by the northwestward movement of the Pacific plate over the Hawaiian plume, the Earth's most active hot spot. Millions of years in the future, this process may form a new volcanic island to the east of Hawaii.

229

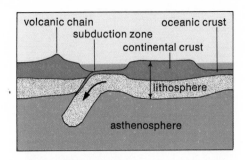

volcanic chain / oceanic crust
subduction zone
continental crust
lithosphere
asthenosphere

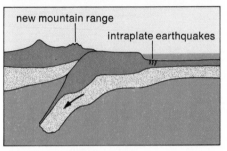

new mountain range
intraplate earthquakes

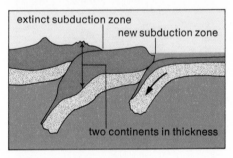

extinct subduction zone
new subduction zone
two continents in thickness

J. Seidensticker—Bruce Coleman Inc.

slid along the base of that continent. As a consequence the Tibetan Plateau apparently is two continents thick, a concept that has been supported by seismic evidence. A line of intraplate earthquake epicenters has been detected in the southeastern Indian Ocean. To account for them it has been suggested that they delineate the eventual locus of a new subduction zone. The India-Australia plate, partially stymied by the Himalayan impact, is attempting to create a new trench to relieve the crustal stress.

A succession of Pangaeas

That continents have drifted for the past 200 million years has now been well established. Yet it also has become apparent that the breakup and dispersion of the universal continent of Pangaea almost certainly was not a unique occurrence—only the most recent one. The "fossil compasses" that were frozen into solidifying basalts record apparent positions of the Earth's poles that are quite unlike those of today. To have produced such apparent changes, when in fact the rotational poles actually remained fixed, large horizontal shifts of the lithosphere must have occurred during at least the last 2.7 billion years of the Earth's 4.6-billion-year history. The continents must have coalesced into earlier Pangaeas and dispersed several times over the vast sweep of geologic time. An average modern drift rate of 6.6 centimeters per year would be sufficient to move a continent entirely around the Earth's 40,000-kilometer circumference since the dawn of the Cambrian Period, about 600 million years ago. Therefore, the universal continent that covered two-fifths of the globe at the end of the Paleozoic could easily have been Pangaea Three or Pangaea Four. Nevertheless, continents seem to have maintained a certain identity throughout these cycles, perhaps by closing and then reopening along the same sutures. Such a sequence is observed in the mid-Paleozoic closing and Triassic reopening of the North Atlantic Ocean along much the same suture line, although fragments of the African and North American continents were exchanged in the process.

There is some reason to suppose that in the earliest aeons of the Archean the Earth was not plate tectonic but had a crust that was rigid and fixed like those of Mars, Mercury, and the Moon. The fixity of the Martian crust apparently has permitted underlying hot spots to build huge volcanoes to heights much greater than those on Earth. The exposed mountain roots of Earth's Archean terranes, which occupy the nuclei of most of the continents, show a structural style unlike those of later aeons. For example, geologists cannot find within these foldbelts any geosutures where mantle rock was squeezed up by the collision of ancient drifting continents. More detailed studies are needed, however, before an accurate picture of the early history of the Earth's crust can be constructed.

In a world which seems quite asymmetrical it is interesting to note that the continents cover almost exactly 40% of the Earth's surface, or about 200 million square kilometers overall. This is correct when continents are measured down to their true boundary, the 2,000-meter isobath, rather than to the waterline. The ocean covers 71% of the Earth but, owing to the broad continental shelves, this figure is not a measure of the true area of the ocean basins. Noteworthy, too, is that when the most recent Pangaea commenced splitting apart it broke into two supercontinents of almost equal size, Gondwana and Laurasia, each of which covered an area of 100 million square kilometers. This event may have been purely fortuitous; currently there is no rational explanation.

It may seem strange that, after dispersing, the continents once again can suture up into a single Pangaea. But the Earth is a sphere and such conjoining is inherent in the game plan of plate tectonics. Consider, for example, the future of the Earth 100 million years hence. Projecting modern drift vectors, the Pacific Ocean will entirely collapse as the Pacific plate is subducted. The New World will suture up to Australasia and Asia while the Atlantic widens to become the universal ocean, or Panthalassa. Only Antarctica will remain as an isolated island continent because the boundaries of the plate on which it rides consist entirely of spreading ridges and transform faults; there is no trench to beckon it. New trenches can only be created in ocean basins and, once they form, they tend to migrate toward a continental margin, eventually becoming marginal of a continental block like the Peru-Chile trench of today. There is an important caveat, however, for any projected scheme of crustal movement: the birth of a new trench can markedly alter the chain of events. A new subduction zone within the Atlantic Ocean, for example, would abruptly transform it into a closing ocean basin.

Practical applications

In providing scientists with a new perspective in understanding the causes and mechanisms of large-scale crustal movements, the plate tectonic model of the Earth has given man a potentially powerful tool for the prediction of earthquakes and perhaps ultimately for their control. In 1976 the U.S. Geological Survey was embarked on a program mainly to study the San Andreas fault of California, although the level of funding for the project seemed hardly commensurate with its importance. It is known that the part of California to the east of the San Andreas fault on the North America plate inexorably slips about six meters per century relative to the part that lies to the west on the Pacific plate. Such a slippage, if it occurs all at once, is sufficient to generate a great earthquake such as that which produced the 1906 San Francisco disaster. The best information about this amount of offset comes not from measurements directly across this shear zone but from the determination of spreading rates along the mid-oceanic ridges of the Atlantic and Pacific oceans; thus, plate-tectonic considerations at distant sites, rather than precise surveys in California, provide the better data concerning shifting along the San Andreas.

The Guatemala earthquake of February 1976 occurred in conformance with expectations of plate tectonics. Of course, it was not predicted and hardly could have been because this Central American

Extensive inland mountain ranges like the Himalayas (opposite page, bottom) seem to have been created from the collision of two large segments of continental crust (top). Because of its buoyancy, the underriding segment of such a collision is eventually stymied, and to relieve mounting stresses, a new subduction zone may be produced elsewhere along thinner oceanic crust.

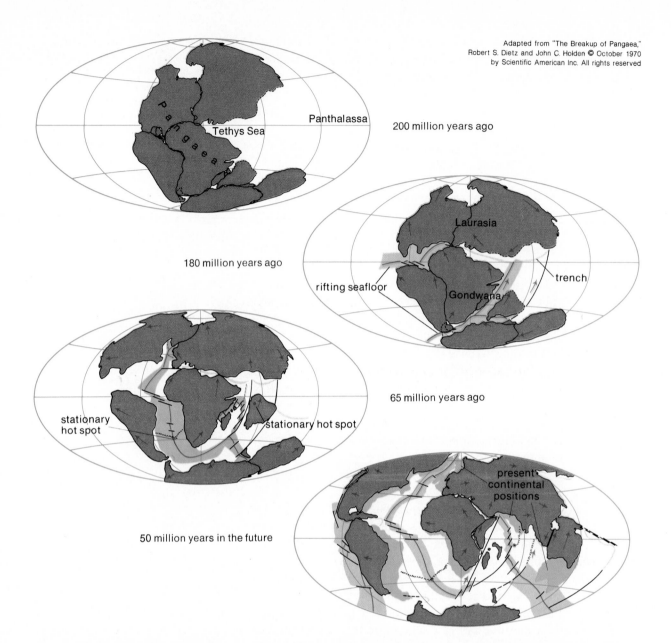

Adapted from "The Breakup of Pangaea,"
Robert S. Dietz and John C. Holden © October 1970
by Scientific American Inc. All rights reserved

Panthalassa

Tethys Sea

Pangaea

200 million years ago

180 million years ago

Laurasia

rifting seafloor

Gondwana

trench

65 million years ago

stationary hot spot

stationary hot spot

present continental positions

50 million years in the future

Based on best computer fits using the 1,000-fathom isobath to establish continental boundaries, the universal landmass Pangaea may have had the configuration depicted at top. Rifting and subduction contributed to the separation of landmasses that define modern continental locations. The world 50 million years in the future is expected to see further widening of the Atlantic and Indian oceans, shrinking of the Pacific, and significant changes in continental shapes and positions.

region was not instrumented with an appropriate array of sensors. Nevertheless, the quake did occur along the North Caribbean transform fault, which is the plate boundary between the Caribbean and the North America plates. Because North America is known to be drifting west-ward with respect to the Caribbean plate, one should expect a left lateral shear; that is, an observer standing on either side of the fault would observe the far side to move to the left. Studies following the quake determined that this kind of motion indeed had taken place. However, this plate boundary consists of two parallel faults running through Guatemala, and it was the one thought to be the more inactive that yielded. This earthquake may have provided another demonstra-tion that faults locked for long periods of time are more dangerous than those that relieve their stress by creeping.

232

In July 1976 northeastern China to the east of Peking was severely shaken by an earthquake that caused extensive damage and great loss of life. The Chinese were thought to have developed advanced techniques of earthquake prediction, yet apparently they had little inkling of this disaster. The China quake is an example of an intraplate earthquake, one that remains difficult to interpret in terms of plate tectonics. Geologists suppose that the thick continental plates act like a strong epidermis over the active mantle so that the epicenters on continents only indirectly reflect shearing activity within the upper mantle. The United States is not free of such intraplate earthquakes; probably its greatest, the earthquake at New Madrid, Missouri, occurred in the midcontinent region near St. Louis in the early 19th century.

Although it is true that random search, intuition, and luck often have yielded more success in finding ores than has the scientific approach, it would be laughable, for instance, to look for gold in the basaltic terrain of the Hawaiian Islands or Iceland. Plate tectonics is providing man with a more discerning view of the Earth and, in turn, with the knowledge of where to look for metals, nonmetals, and energy resources. For example, it is known that the Atlantic Ocean was once closed and, within the bounds of certain geologic constraints, the New World and the Old World can be joined in a jigsaw fit. The suture is not perfect, however, and even the best computerized fits show residual areas of misfit—overlaps and underlaps of one continent with respect to the other. In the search for petroleum, the overlaps are especially interesting because they may indicate the presence of ancient deltaic accumulations or giant salt deposits laid down just after the initial breakup. Such sedimentary piles create conditions favorable to the accumulation and preservation of petroleum.

It has become increasingly apparent that plate tectonics can be extremely useful in mineral exploration. Recently it was pointed out that most of the world's copper porphyry deposits are distributed along ancient or modern subduction zones. They appear to have been formed by the same process of incomplete lithospheric absorption that gives rise to volcanic island arcs, a concept that explains the presence of large sulfide deposits on such islands as those of Japan and the Philippines. The emplacement of copper porphyry deposits of the southwestern U.S. and of the Andes are likewise related to the descent of lithospheric plates along continental margins.

Other base-metal deposits have been shown to originate from activity along mid-oceanic ridges. Deep-sea drilling into the oceanic crust and dredging near active rifts have recovered metallic sulfides, minute veins of pure copper, and large specimens of almost pure manganese oxide, indicating that hydrothermal processes have been concentrating metals from the upwelling magma. Some land deposits whose origin had long been enigmatic were shown to have been created by this process. The historic copper ore mines of Cyprus lie within a massif that is believed to be a slab of ocean crust formed by seafloor spreading and subsequently thrust upward to its present position. The Red Sea,

M. P. Kahl—Bruce Coleman Inc.

Descent of lithospheric plates along continental margins often gives rise to coastal mountain ranges. The Argentinian Andes are apparently a product of such subduction along the Peru-Chile trench of South America.

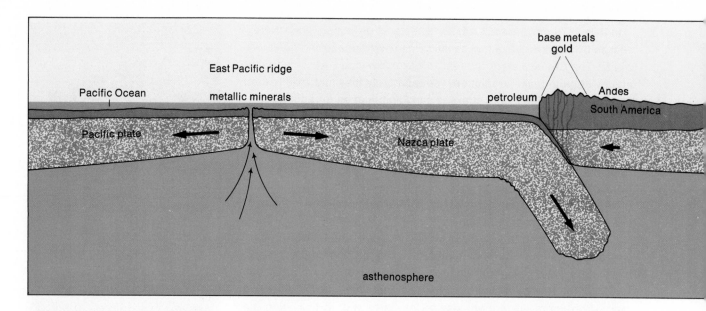

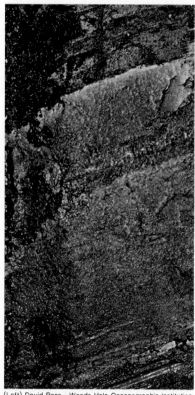

(Left) David Ross—Woods Hole Oceanographic Institution; (right) courtesy, NASA

which represents the birth of a divergent juncture between the Africa and Eurasia plates, overlies the richest submarine metal sulfide deposits known. Quite clearly the presence of deep hot brine pools underlain by metal-rich sediments far beneath the Red Sea can be traced to hydrothermal solutions associated with magma injections along the newly formed divergent juncture and the rise of these solutions through thick salt beds.

234

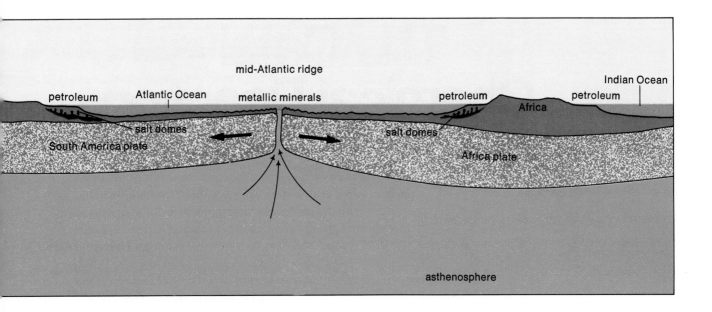

The birth of an ocean is graphically portrayed in a Gemini 11 photograph (opposite page, bottom right) taken from 400 miles in space. Creation of a new divergent juncture has driven the Arabian Peninsula, at right, from the African continent on the left, widening the Red Sea, at the top, and the Gulf of Aden. A sample of metal-rich mud from a mile beneath the floor of the Red Sea (bottom left) reveals iron minerals (blue-grey and red-brown layers) and sulfides of lead, copper, zinc, gold, and silver (off-white zone near top). The significance of plate tectonics to mineral exploration is shown above in a cross section of the Earth near the Tropic of Capricorn. Metal deposits in the seafloor have been found to originate during activity along mid-oceanic ridges. They come to be distributed as well along ancient and modern subduction zones, as metallic minerals from the melting subducted plate rise through the leading edge of the overriding plate. Salt deposits or deltaic accumulations laid down along the edges of continental margins create conditions favorable to the formation and preservation of petroleum.

A continuing revolution

By any measure, plate tectonics is a healthy and burgeoning concept. Together with the exploration of the terrestrial planets, it is at the forefront of present-day excitement in the earth sciences. It has come to be regarded as the proper model for global tectonics — the way the Earth really works. The acceptance of this new paradigm was quite abrupt and involved remarkably little cogent dissent. In fact, opposition has been overwhelmed by the weight of new supporting evidence. In the words of geologist Kenneth Deffeyes of Princeton University: "Ninety-nine percent of the profession [of geology] has had to admit that they were wrong, including a great many who were in print saying that continental drift could not possibly happen. Everything has got to be rewritten."

FOR ADDITIONAL READING

N. Calder, *The Restless Earth* (Viking Press, 1972).

A. Cox (ed.), *Plate Tectonics and Geomagnetic Reversals* (W. H. Freeman, 1973).

W. Glen, *Continental Drift and Plate Tectonics* (Merrill, 1975).

A. Hallam, *A Revolution in the Earth Sciences* (Clarendon, 1973).

U. B. Marvin, *Continental Drift* (Smithsonian Institution Press, 1973).

S. W. Matthews, "This Changing Earth," *National Geographic* (January 1973, pp. 1–37).

W. Sullivan, *Continents in Motion* (McGraw-Hill, 1974).

J. T. Wilson (compiler), *Continents Adrift, Readings from Scientific American* (W. H. Freeman, 1972).

P. J. Wyllie, *The Way the Earth Works: An Introduction to the New Global Geology and Its Revolutionary Development* (John Wiley and Sons, 1976).

235

The Catalysis of Chemical Reactions
by Vladimir Haensel

Scientists have not yet fully explained the ability of catalysts to accelerate chemical reactions without themselves being consumed. Nevertheless, during the past 200 years these substances have become indispensable agents in research and industry.

One of the most important characteristics of a chemical reaction is the speed at which the atoms or molecules participating in the reaction interact. Many reactions proceed very slowly at room temperature. It is well known, however, that raising the temperature of the system will increase the rate of reaction, and for many processes this simple technique has served well.

Consider a container filled with a gas such as oxygen. As reflected by the temperature of the gas, the molecules within the container will exhibit a range of momenta, some moving about more rapidly than others and colliding more frequently with other molecules. The distribution of these velocities is described by an equation known as the Maxwell-Boltzmann distribution law, which can be represented graphically by a probability curve that relates relative numbers of molecules to their velocities. For example, at very low temperatures, less than 5% of the molecules have velocities greater than twice the most probable value, and less than 0.05% have velocities greater than three times the most probable value, indicating a rather narrow range of distribution. When the temperature is raised, the average velocity is increased and the range of velocities is expanded as a greater number of molecules are provided with a higher kinetic energy.

To undergo a specific reaction, molecules require a certain minimum energy, called the activation energy. As temperature is increased, more and more molecules attain this required level of energy and can undergo reaction. Unfortunately, for many reactions simply supplying the activation energy can be of serious detriment to the desired outcome, producing effects that outweigh the merit of the technique. For instance, in addition to accelerating the formation of a specific product, elevated temperatures may shift the equilibrium of the reaction in the direction of the original reactants. Heat may also accelerate the rate of other possible reactions that remove one or more reactants from the system before the desired product can be formed. For such reasons chemists have sought alternate methods for speeding up reactions, ones that avoid this "brute force" approach.

VLADIMIR HAENSEL is Vice-President for Science and Technology, UOP Inc., Des Plaines, Illinois.

Photographs, courtesy, UOP, Inc. Illustrations by John Draves

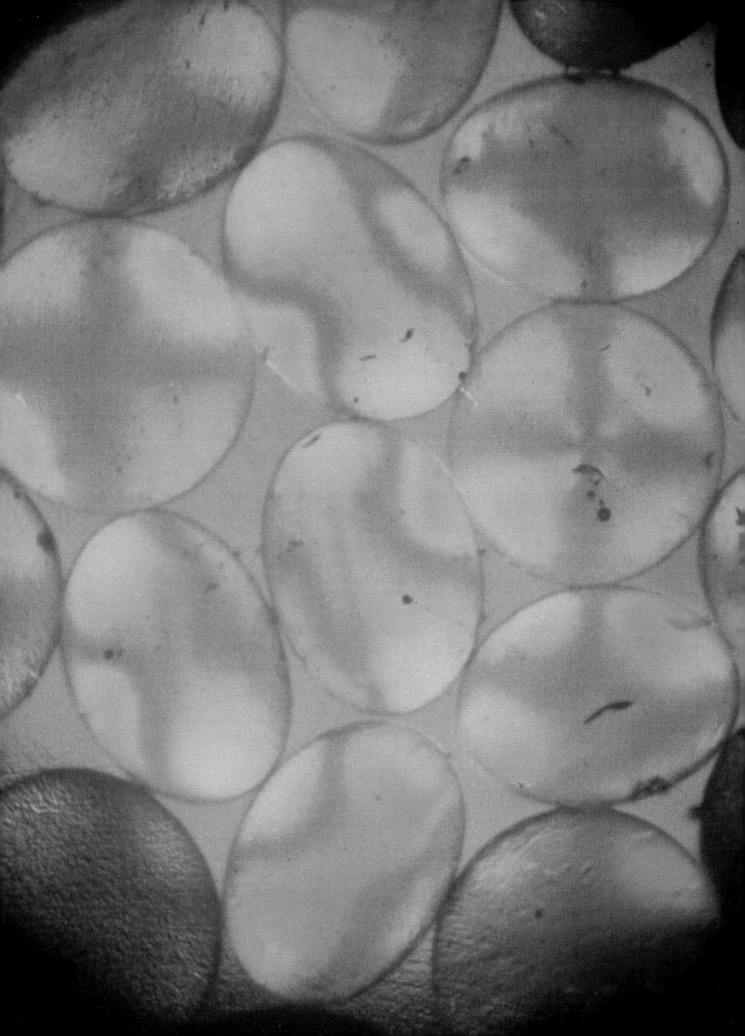

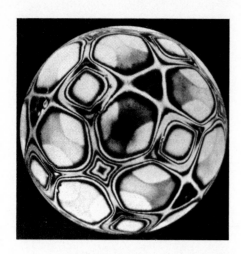

(Overleaf) Preformed particles of catalyst substrate viewed under polarized light exhibit internal irregularities. Above, magnified 5,000 times, is the topography of a cleaved catalyst surface.

One way to circumvent these problems would be to find a means of lowering the necessary activation energy, thus increasing the fraction of molecules that could react at a given temperature. In general, the substances termed catalysts perform exactly this function, and they do so without being consumed in the reaction. By analogy one can compare the catalyst to a vaulting pole. Without the pole an athlete can clear a height of 7½ feet. With it he can leap more than 18 feet. Yet the pole remains virtually unchanged after the jump and can be used many times. Another attribute of the catalyst can be illustrated by continuing the analogy. If the athlete's sole objective is to reach a height of 18 feet, but not necessarily in one jump, he can use a ladder. In this case relatively little difficulty is involved, because one step at a time is taken and only one small segment of energy need be on hand for each step. Similarly, if a chemical reaction can be broken into a number of steps, then a relatively large fraction of the reactants will have the required lower energy. By combining temporarily with the reactant, the catalyst provides for such intermediate stages. A carefully chosen catalyst can also do much to minimize the effects of competitive reactions by selecting specific ones from among those that can occur. Although this selectivity is not perfect, it is usually very high.

Historical contributions

Although the earliest uses of catalytic substances are lost in antiquity, the name catalysis and its definition are known to have been coined by the Swedish chemist Jöns Jacob Berzelius in 1835. Berzelius theorized that catalysis "involved the development of a force of affinity coming from the catalyst and having an effect on the chemical activity of the reagents." His reason for such an explanation was based on what he called "notable discoveries," such as that of the German investigator Johann Wolfgang Döbereiner. In 1823 Döbereiner found that a stream of hydrogen mixed with air would ignite on contact with a spongy, porous form of platinum, and he employed this effect in an ingenious invention that replaced the tinderbox for lighting lamps and candles. Among early applications of catalysis to industry was a process for the manufacture of sulfuric acid patented by Peregrine Phillips, a British chemist, who in 1831 observed that sulfur dioxide could be oxidized in air using a platinum catalyst.

The years that followed Berzelius saw many brilliant investigators, scientists who understood chemistry and had a certain intuitive feeling about catalysis. Albeit in what appears to be rather empirical manner, people like Fritz Haber (ammonia synthesis), V. N. Ipatieff (petroleum-refining processes), Franz Fischer and Hans Tropsch (conversion of carbon monoxide and hydrogen into gasoline and alcohols), and Karl Ziegler and Giulio Natta (polymerization of propylene) laid the groundwork for modern industrial catalysis. Paralleling their accomplishments were the theoretical contributions of such men as Paul Emmett, the dean of catalytic chemistry in the U.S., and Sir Hugh Taylor, the originator of the concept of active centers, which pinpointed Berzelius' concept of a hundred years earlier. It has been through such contributions, which combined the theoretical with the intuitive and the practical, that catalysis has achieved a major role in the U.S. economy of the 1970s, participating directly or indirectly in the production of goods worth more than $100 billion per year. Important examples are the catalysis-oriented petroleum and petrochemical industry, the large participation of catalytic chemistry in the rubber, plastic, and fertilizer industries, and, most recently, its application in pollution-control devices for automotive and industrial use.

Heterogeneous catalysis

Catalytic processes are often classified in terms of the phases, or states of matter, in which the participants exist as they undergo reaction. Reactions in which the catalyst and reactants are present in different phases are known as heterogeneous reactions. As the nature of the situation might imply, these processes require the participation of phase boundaries, or surfaces, in the catalytic act.

Despite the recognized importance of surfaces and the development of highly sophisticated tools to probe these regions, the events that attend heterogeneous processes are not yet clearly understood. In general, solid catalysts of high activity usually have a large surface-to-mass ratio, ranging from a few square meters per gram to as much as 1,000 square meters per gram. Thus it is not unusual for a few grams of a catalyst to have the surface area of a football field, about 4,000 square meters. This enormous surface is a result of the presence of numerous, extremely small pores within the catalyst structure. Each pore, which may range in size from a few angstroms to about 1,000 angstroms (1 angstrom = 10^{-8} centimeter), is surrounded by a wall; hence the more pores, the more surface area. As can be expected, pore size has a substantial effect upon the catalytic reaction. Some molecules are too large to enter the smallest pores and, in that case, such pores are ineffective. In other situations, where B is a catalytically formed product in a sequential reaction A→B→C, large pores are preferred to allow product B to leave the catalyst before forming product C. Similarly, when the reactants are liquid, diffusion through the catalyst is very slow; in this instance a relatively low surface area with large pores is both sufficient and desirable.

The nature of the catalytic surface may be examined by considering a solid particle. Its surface area can be increased by breaking it into smaller pieces. The electronic structure of newly exposed surfaces will show the imperfections of the break in the form of surface energy states that remain more or less tightly bound to the bulk. It is these irregularities that provide the reactants with some of the intermediate energy steps needed to achieve the activation energy. Thus, the more surface that can be developed, the greater is the chance for creating surface imperfections. Surface alone, however, is not sufficient for catalysis; compressed sawdust or finely divided sugar, for example, are not known catalysts.

Electron micrograph of the surface of a high-activity catalyst provides some concept of the enormous area such materials make available to reactant species.

239

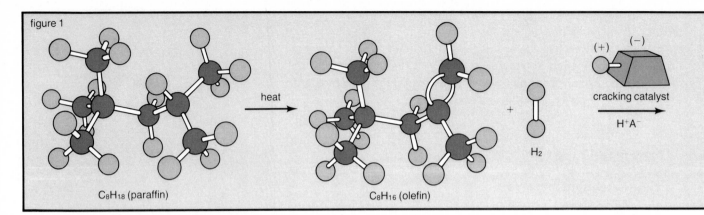

figure 1

heat

C_8H_{18} (paraffin) ⟶ C_8H_{16} (olefin) + H_2

$(+)$ $(-)$
cracking catalyst
H^+A^-

High working temperatures and high catalytic activity allow cracking of petroleum-derived paraffins through reactions similar to that schematically depicted. See text.

To illustrate the surface effect, one can compare the catalytic activity of platinum in three different forms: platinum foil; precipitated, finely divided platinum (platinum black); and platinum deposited or dispersed on a support material having a large surface area, such as silica, alumina, or activated carbon. On the basis of metal content relative to catalytic activity, platinum foil is the poorest catalyst, platinum black is intermediate, and supported platinum is better than foil by many orders of magnitude. Thus, one can improve a catalyst by finely dividing it or, better yet, by depositing it as a very thin layer or as small clusters on a high-surface support. Not all high-surface supports are alike. Indeed there are great differences among them, and in many instances it is the existence of bonds between the deposited or dispersed material and the support that accounts for increased catalytic activity, stability, and selectivity.

One of the widely accepted methods of preparing catalysts involves precipitation and mixing of a number of components in the wet state, followed by drying and calcining in air at relatively high temperature, perhaps 500–700° C (930–1300° F). Depending upon ultimate use, the drying step may be followed by reduction in hydrogen at elevated temperatures. Proper compositing of components has been found to lead to catalysts of exceptional activity, even though each component alone has relatively low activity. For example, in the conversion (cracking) of higher boiling fractions of crude oil into gasoline, silica (SiO_2) is a very poor catalyst; by itself alumina (Al_2O_3) is also poor. Yet properly prepared composites of silica and alumina are extremely active catalysts for this conversion. It must be stressed that these are not mechanical mixtures but rather are a chemically interacted species of silicic acid and aluminum hydroxide.

As postulated by Charles L. Thomas of Universal Oil Products Co., both silicic acid and aluminum hydroxide are polymeric materials having alternating silicon and oxygen or aluminum and oxygen bonds in large molecules. However, because silicon is tetravalent (Si^{4+}) and aluminum is trivalent (Al^{3+}), when the two species are composited the introduction of a trivalent aluminum atom into a tetravalent silicon structure creates a valence deficiency, which is relieved by an extra

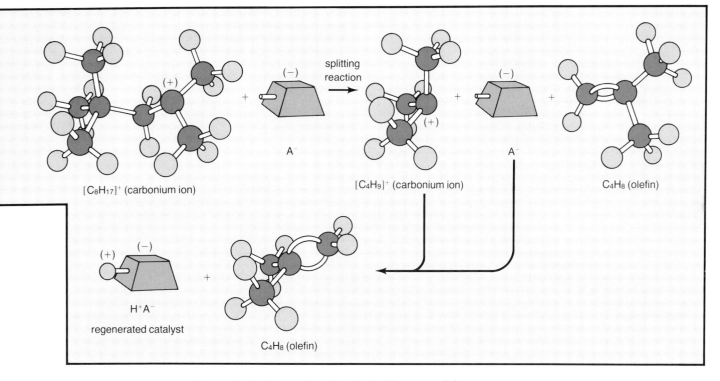

$[C_8H_{17}]^+$ (carbonium ion)

$[C_4H_9]^+$ (carbonium ion)

C_4H_8 (olefin)

H$^+$A$^-$

regenerated catalyst

C_4H_8 (olefin)

splitting reaction

positive charge in the form of a hydrogen ion (proton). Thus, a solid acid is formed that is orders of magnitude stronger than either silicic acid or aluminum hydroxide. In fact, the acidity of such a composite is greater than that of sulfuric acid.

In recent years the amorphous silica-alumina composite has been further composited with a crystalline silica-alumina of the molecular-sieve family to create even more stable and active cracking catalysts. A good relationship between the acidity function of the composite and its cracking activity has been established. Furthermore, the combination of high innate activity and high working temperature (about 500° C) makes these catalysts sufficiently active to participate in a series of complex hydrocarbon reactions (see figure 1). Initially, a thermal (noncatalyzed) reaction converts a paraffinic hydrocarbon to an olefin. The addition of the acid catalyst to the olefin produces a surface-associated ionic species (a carbonium ion) that subsequently undergoes a splitting reaction, releasing a molecular fragment. Finally the smaller carbonium ion returns a hydrogen ion to the catalyst, thereby regenerating it intact. This picture is somewhat alien to traditional chemistry, which interprets processes in terms of either clear-cut interactions between acids and bases or well-defined organic reactions in solution. In this case the acidic sites are the result of an upset in chemical structure and are not well defined, but they do react with those hydrocarbons that are sufficiently basic in character.

The surface of the silica-alumina catalyst can be further modified by deposition of a small amount of nickel, cobalt, platinum, palladium, or another of the Group VIII elements of the periodic table. For purposes

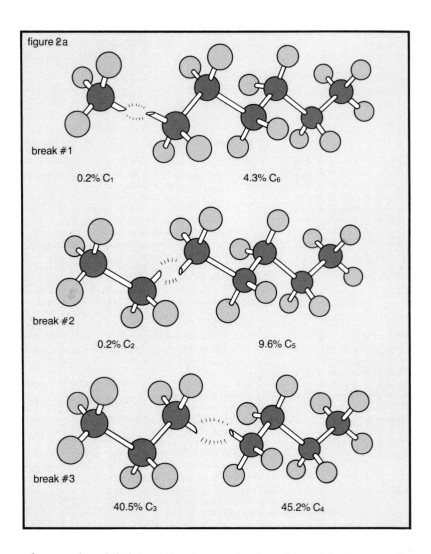

figure 2a

break #1

0.2% C₁   4.3% C₆

break #2

0.2% C₂   9.6% C₅

break #3

40.5% C₃   45.2% C₄

Cracking of normal, or straight-chain, heptane (C_7H_{16}) in the presence of hydrogen and a catalyst does not proceed by simple breaks; otherwise, equivalent amounts of each pair of fragments would be produced, rather than the experimentally derived percentages shown above. Instead (opposite page), hydrocarbon ions of the reactant and of the intermediates are postulated to interact on the catalytic surface, forming ions of yet higher molecular weight (step d). These larger species then undergo splitting reactions (step e) to produce the fragments observed. See text.

of comparison it is interesting to examine how this catalyst composite behaves toward a paraffin hydrocarbon, but in the presence of hydrogen and at an elevated pressure (50 atmospheres), and at a lower temperature (250° C). This modified composite can dehydrogenate paraffins to form olefins as well as catalyze the same sequence of reactions that was described for the silica-alumina catalyst alone; however, the products of the reaction are more saturated. The Group VIII metals facilitate the initiation and termination reactions by virtue of dehydrogenation and hydrogenation catalysis. The simple case of converting straight-chain heptane (C_7H_{16}) is illustrated in figure 2 a–b.

It is obvious that when splitting occurs (figure 2a), the resulting fragments do not come by a simple break; otherwise an equivalent amount of C_1 and C_6 as well as C_2 and C_5 would be formed. It is postulated that hydrocarbon ions of the reactant and of the intermediates migrate across the surface and interact to form ions of still higher molecular weight that cannot be released except by a splitting reaction (figure 2b). Thus, C_6 and C_5 are formed from C_7 and C_4 ionic interaction. The overall picture is what Robert L. Burwell of Northwestern University,

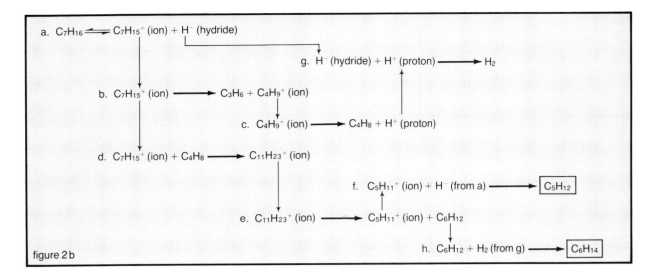

a. $C_7H_{16} \rightleftharpoons C_7H_{15}^+$ (ion) $+ H^-$ (hydride)

g. H^- (hydride) $+ H^+$ (proton) $\longrightarrow H_2$

b. $C_7H_{15}^+$ (ion) $\longrightarrow C_3H_6 + C_4H_9^+$ (ion)

c. $C_4H_9^+$ (ion) $\longrightarrow C_4H_8 + H^+$ (proton)

d. $C_7H_{15}^+$ (ion) $+ C_4H_8 \longrightarrow C_{11}H_{23}^+$ (ion)

f. $C_5H_{11}^+$ (ion) $+ H^-$ (from a) $\longrightarrow$ $\boxed{C_5H_{12}}$

e. $C_{11}H_{23}^+$ (ion) $\longrightarrow C_5H_{11}^+$ (ion) $+ C_6H_{12}$

h. $C_6H_{12} + H_2$ (from g) $\longrightarrow$ $\boxed{C_6H_{14}}$

figure 2b

Evanston, Illinois, calls an "organometallic zoo," an image that so aptly describes the situation on the surface of the catalyst.

Thus, as the reaction progresses, the heterogeneous catalytic process involves the migration of the various reaction intermediates from one site to another. A transformation frequently encountered in petroleum refining, nonane to trimethylbenzenes, may involve ten or more intermediates, which migrate from one type of site to another within a very short period of time. One may wonder about the distances over which such intermediates can migrate. Experiments by Paul B. Weisz of Mobil Research and Development Corp. on separation of sites by mechanical means have indicated that a separation of more than one or two millimeters causes a substantial reduction in activity. Because the size of the reacting molecule is of the order of 10–20 angstroms, the ratio of the distance traveled to molecular size is of the order of one million. Related to the size of a human being, this is equivalent to the distance of a thousand miles.

As pointed out above, the number of intermediates involved in a catalytic reaction can be quite large. If one considers that at every step there is an opportunity to form the wrong product instead of the desired product, one is amazed at the selectivity of catalytic reactions. A good illustration of this is the catalytic removal of a single methyl group from a branched paraffinic hydrocarbon in contact with hydrogen over a nickel catalyst at about 200° C. In figure 3, 2,2-dimethylbutane can lose one of its four methyl groups, and yet a specific one is removed to the exclusion of the others. In figure 4, 2,2,3-trimethylpentane can lose any of its five methyls, but again only a specific one is removed.

Structure and stability

The early and very elegant work of A. T. Gwathmey of the University of Virginia showed that "for many reactions the different crystal faces have markedly different activities. . . ." Most interesting was the observation that, when exposed to reactants at elevated temperatures, the

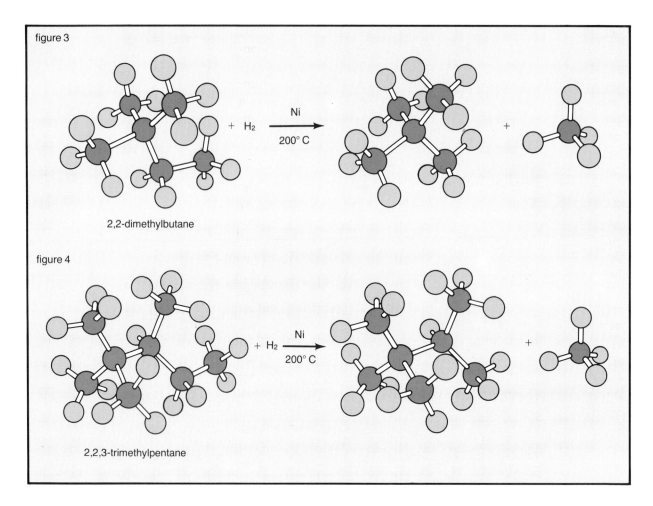

figure 3

2,2-dimethylbutane

figure 4

2,2,3-trimethylpentane

The selectivity of catalytic reactions is well illustrated by consideration of the catalytic removal of a single methyl group (−CH₃) from each of two branched paraffinic hydrocarbons in contact with hydrogen over a nickel catalyst at 200° C. In each case only a specific methyl group is targeted for removal. See text, p. 243.

different faces of a crystal undergo structural changes that are readily apparent to the eye. Thus, in catalysis metal mobility can occur commonly at temperatures far below the melting point of the metal. In fact, a term often applied in this regard is sintering, which is the result of metal migration and subsequent agglomeration into larger islands and crystals. When sintering occurs the catalyst usually loses activity. Supported catalysts, wherein the active ingredient is rather firmly fixed on structures of high surface area, are less prone to undergo sintering; many such catalysts will last for years of continuous operation.

When one considers that catalysts are often used at temperatures exceeding 500° C, it is incredible that they last as long as they do. For example, in the Platforming® process for the conversion of low-grade gasoline fractions into high-octane fuels, a catalyst is used that consists of minute amounts of platinum on an aluminum oxide support; the support also contains some chloride ions to enhance the necessary acidic function. It has been estimated that over the active life of the catalyst, each platinum atom converts on the average some 20 million molecules of gasoline.

This impressive durability emphasizes the often expressed notion of the catalyst's lack of change during the reaction. However, only so

244

much ruggedness can be built into the catalyst and catalyst poisoning is an important problem. There is, in fact, an analogy between environmental pollutants and substances that inhibit, or poison, catalysts. Human beings can tolerate some pollutants, usually in small concentrations, with some temporary discomfort. Other pollutants have a cumulative effect and cause irreversible damage to the organism. Concentration is an important factor; low concentrations of carbon monoxide can be tolerated, but higher concentrations are fatal. Likewise, a platinum catalyst can be incapacitated by sulfur, the extent of poisoning being related to concentration, but such poisoning is reversible. When arsenic is present, however, the platinum catalyst is permanently poisoned. Only when platinum catalysts were used for upgrading gasoline was it realized that some gasolines contain as much as 30 parts per billion of arsenic. The platinum plucked the arsenic compound out of the feedstock and died in the process.

The most severe test of ruggedness and resistance to poisoning has come about in a recent large-scale application of heterogeneous catalysis—the use of catalytic converters for the control of automotive emission. The major pollutants are carbon monoxide, hydrocarbons, and oxides of nitrogen. The manufacture of millions of catalytic converters and their essentially trouble-free performance represent a great achievement for catalyst technology, analytical techniques, and mechanical engineering. Whereas nearly all industrial catalytic operations are essentially continuous and uniform in character, automotive-exhaust converters must deal with large variations in exhaust-gas flow rate, temperature, and composition, which depend a great deal upon the individual driver. In addition, the catalyst must perform adequately for 50,000 miles and occupy very little space. It must not overheat, must offer little resistance to exhaust flow, and, of course, must be economical to manufacture and install.

The requirements imposed on a small catalyst package can be appreciated from the following illustration. If a car is driven for one hour and consumes about four gallons of fuel, its total exhaust effluent will be about 160 kilograms (350 pounds); it should be kept in mind that every kilogram of burned fuel consumes an additional 15 kilograms of air. At a temperature of 450° C this quantity of exhaust will occupy a volume of 325,000 liters (11,000 cubic feet), which is equivalent to the volume of a moderate-sized house. Thus, during one hour the catalyst must contact the equivalent of the volume of the house, converting carbon monoxide and hydrocarbons into carbon dioxide and water. At this rate the time for a single molecule to pass through the converter is less than 4/100 of a second.

In addition the catalyst must convert the oxides of nitrogen to molecular nitrogen. In this connection E. E. Weaver of Ford Motor Co. found that, when the catalyst receives a stoichiometric mixture (the exact amount of oxygen needed to convert all of the combustible substances in the exhaust), it will most effectively convert the oxides of nitrogen to molecular nitrogen. The most important feature of this total

245

Selected important catalytic processes		
catalyst	use	catalytic action
Fe-Al_2O_3-K_2O (heterogeneous)	ammonia synthesis	$N_2 + 3H_2 \rightarrow 2NH_3$
Pt (heterogeneous)	oxidation of ammonia (step in nitric acid production)	$4NH_3 + 5O_2 \rightarrow 4NO + 6H_2O$
NO (homogeneous) or Pt, V_2O_5 (heterogeneous)	production of sulfuric acid	$2SO_2 + O_2 \rightarrow 2SO_3$
Ni-Al_2O_3 (heterogeneous)	production of hydrogen	$CH_4 + H_2O \rightarrow CO + H_2$
Ni (heterogeneous)	hydrogenation of oils to fats	oleic acid + $H_2 \rightarrow$ stearic acid
$HCo(CO)_4$ (homogeneous)	hydroformylation of olefins to aldehydes (oxo process)	$RCH = CH_2 + CO + H_2 \rightarrow RCH_2CH_2CHO$
$PdCl_2$-HCl (homogeneous)	production of acetaldehyde by oxidation of ethylene	$CH_2 = CH_2 + O_2 \rightarrow CH_3CHO$
Hg salts (homogeneous or heterogeneous)	production of acetaldehyde by hydration of acetylene	$CH \equiv CH + H_2O \rightarrow CH_3CHO$
$TiCl_3$-$Al(C_2H_5)_3$ (heterogeneous)	polymerization of propylene to polypropylene	$nC_3H_6 \rightarrow (C_3H_6)_n$
ZnO, Cr_2O_3 (heterogeneous)	synthesis of methanol	$CO + 2H_2 \rightarrow CH_3OH$
Ag (heterogeneous)	manufacture of ethylene oxide	$C_2H_4 + \frac{1}{2} O_2 \rightarrow$ ethylene oxide
SiO_2-Al_2O_3 (heterogeneous)	petroleum cracking	$C_{12}H_{26} \rightarrow C_8H_{18} + C_4H_8$
$AlCl_3$ (heterogeneous)	petroleum isomerization	n-$C_6H_{14} \rightarrow CH_3C(CH_3)_2CH_2CH_3$
H_3PO_4 or H_2SO_4 (homogeneous)	petroleum alkylation	$C_4H_{10} + C_4H_8 \rightarrow C_8H_{18}$
invertase (enzyme)	production of invert sugar in confectionery manufacture	sucrose $\rightarrow$ D-fructose + D-glucose
cellulase (enzyme)	digestive aid; reduction of viscosity of vegetable gums; animal-feed manufacture	hydrolyzes cellulose
papain (enzyme)	meat tenderizer; digestive aid; beer chillproofing	hydrolyzes peptides, amides, and esters
rennin (enzyme)	curdling milk in cheese production	hydrolyzes peptides
glucose oxidase (enzyme)	egg desugaring; oxygen removal in food processing	oxidizes glucose to gluconic acid in presence of O_2
catalase (enzyme)	peroxide removal during food processing and industrial manufacturing	$2H_2O_2 \rightarrow 2H_2O + O_2$

assignment is that, although the initial concentration of these impurities is quite low, they must be reduced to the still lower concentration levels prescribed by federal pollution-control regulations. Here again one is amazed at the ability of the catalyst to accomplish this, particularly if one realizes that minute amounts of supported platinum and palladium are accomplishing the conversion in a short time.

With regard to catalytic poisoning, automotive-exhaust catalysts are poisoned by lead, and this is one of the reasons that no-lead fuels have been introduced. Accidental use of leaded fuel can be tolerated, however, and the catalyst will recover from this poison.

Homogeneous catalysis

One of the most rapidly expanding areas of catalysis is that of homogeneous catalysis, in which at least one of the reactants and the catalyst are present in the same phase, usually as a gas or liquid. Although many reactions catalyzed in heterogeneous catalysis are quite selective in character, homogeneously catalyzed reactions, in general, are even

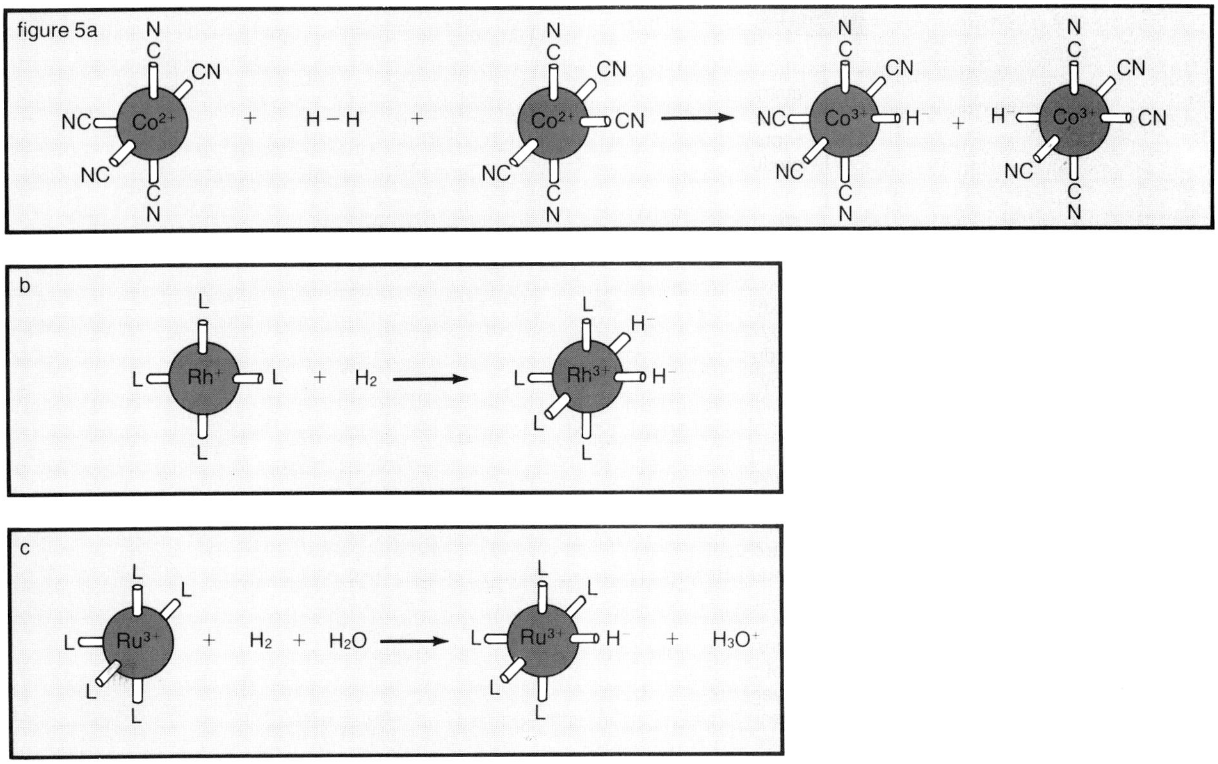

figure 5a

b

c

more selective and more specific in character. Homogeneous catalysis reactions are usually carried out under relatively mild conditions of temperature and pressure, factors that contribute to high reaction specificity. About 20 industrial applications of homogeneous catalysis are currently in use, despite the fact that in homogeneous catalysis the separation of reaction product and catalyst presents a problem not encountered in heterogeneous catalysis. In fact, this problem of separation has resulted in considerable work on attaching the catalyst to a surface without losing its desirable properties.

Among the most exciting advances in homogeneous catalysis in recent years is the ability to fix molecular nitrogen and make it form such compounds as ammonia. One reason for this interest is that plants fix nitrogen as part of the living cycle. A. E. Shilov of the U.S.S.R. and Joseph Chatt of Great Britain are among early workers in this field.

What is there about a homogeneous catalyst that allows it to promote the reaction of a nitrogen molecule? In the case of heterogeneous catalysts the role of surface irregularities as points of attachment was emphasized. In the case of homogeneous catalysis one must examine the molecular level for an "irregularity" or a "potential irregularity." Such requirements can be found in compounds possessing structural vacancies that will accommodate one or more reactants. As shown in the examples in figure 5, there are several different ways of activating or storing hydrogen in a more reactive form.

Another fascinating development in homogeneous catalysis is the synthesis of metal cluster complexes—*i.e.*, molecules containing

Ionic complexes of certain transition metals, which consist of positive metal ions coordinated to organic side groups called ligands (shown generalized as L), often possess catalytic properties; if soluble in liquids, they can act as homogeneous catalysts. The cobalt ion (Co^{2+}) in pentacyanocobalt (5a) serves to activate hydrogen because its "coordination sphere" has a vacant position that can hold a formally negative hydrogen, or hydride, ion (H^-). In the same manner the rhodium ion (Rh^+) can accommodate two negative hydrogen ions (5b). Dissolved in water, a complex of ruthenium (5c) splits a hydrogen molecule into a negative ion and a positive ion, the latter of which binds to a molecule of water as a proton. Such catalytic complexes are capable of adding hydrogen atoms to various unsaturated compounds and are useful polymerizing agents.

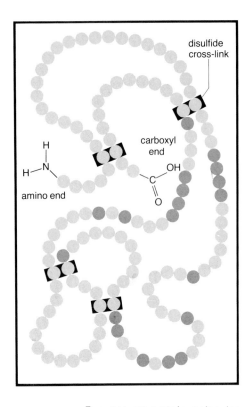

groups of adjacent metal atoms—and their application to catalysis. The work of Earl Muetterties at Cornell University, Ithaca, New York, is helping to bridge the gap between homogeneous and heterogeneous catalysis by utilizing the multiple sites present in metal cluster complexes for reactions that to date have not been attained using catalysts of single metal atoms. (For additional discussion of metal-cluster catalysis, *see* Year in Review: CHEMISTRY: *Inorganic chemistry*.)

Enzymatic catalysis

Another type of catalysis, the catalysis of the chemical reactions of living cells by means of enzymes, is the oldest of all, because without it life on Earth could not exist. The enzymes consist of some 100 to 1,000 amino acids, similar and different, bonded in various combinations as regulated by a genetic code. Cross-links between various amino acids within each enzyme allow the molecule to maintain a unique three-dimensional conformation, and it is this "irregularity" that gives the enzyme its catalytic activity and its specificity or selectivity. The specificity of enzymatic action has been likened to a key and lock combination, wherein only the exact combination of grooves and teeth on a key will open the lock; an inexact combination will most likely ruin the lock, while a widely different key will do nothing. By virtue of their conformation most of the known enzymes possess a cleft or indentation—the keyhole of the lock—that will accept for catalysis only compounds with very specific molecular structures. In fact it has been suggested that each biochemical process requires its own specific enzyme for catalysis.

As one can expect from systems made up of cross-linked chains, enzymes are delicate; acidity and temperature changes disrupt the conformation with subsequent loss of activity. As heterogeneous catalysts frequently contain promoters (which by themselves are inactive), some enzymes need "cofactors," which may be metal ions or organic molecules called coenzymes. Recent research has concentrated on ways to fortify or stabilize enzymes against adverse conditions; that is, to keep the large molecules from unfolding and losing catalytic activity. Some success has been achieved using special reagents capable of producing additional cross-links within the enzyme.

Beyond their basic function in catalyzing the chemical reactions of living cells, enzymes derived from microorganisms and plant and animal tissues are finding applications in many fields. Once primarily employed in the fermentation industry, they have since been put to such uses as the conversion of whey, a dairy-industry waste product, into food supplements; the transformation of cornstarch into sugar syrups; and the production of medicinal substances and food additives.

As was pointed out in the case of homogeneous catalysis, the problem of separating product and catalyst also exists for enzymatic processes. Much work is under way on enzyme-immobilization techniques, such as microencapsulation within polymer membranes, covalent attachment to chemically activated support material, and

Enzymes are protein molecules composed of as many as 20 different amino acids covalently bonded in chainlike sequences as directed by a genetic code. Sulfur-sulfur cross-links between amino acids at certain locations within the enzyme, as well as some additional, relatively weak interactions, help the molecule maintain a folded, three-dimensional configuration. By virtue of their configurations, most enzymes possess a cleft or indentation that will accept for catalysis only specific molecular structures, called substrates. The two-dimensional representation of egg-white lysozyme shown above comprises a chain of 129 amino acids linked at four places by disulfide bonds. The function of lysozyme is to split a particular complex sugar. The amino acids that line the cleft into which this sugar substrate fits are represented by the darker circles.

248

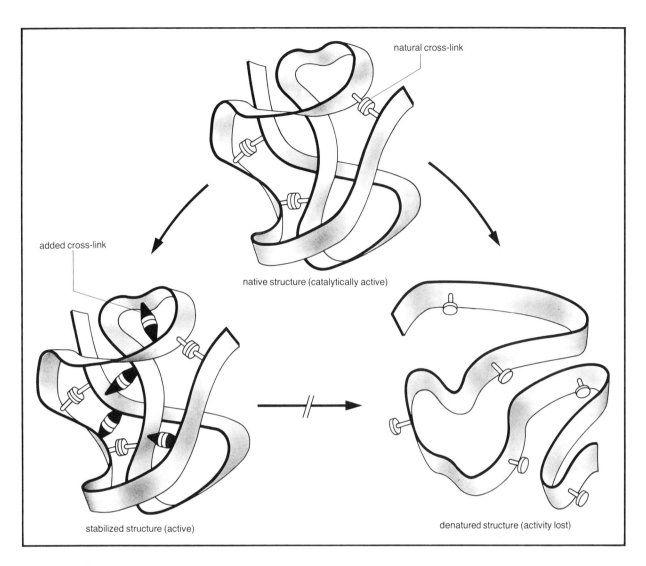

natural cross-link

added cross-link

native structure (catalytically active)

stabilized structure (active)

denatured structure (activity lost)

entrapment within materials that form cross-linked matrices in the presence of enzymes. Here again, similar to homogeneous and heterogeneous catalysis, these extra hooks and linkages must not interfere with the selectivity, efficiency, and longevity of the basic catalytic act.

The future

When Berzelius formulated his definition of catalysis he postulated an unknown force operating in such processes, a "new force of affinity." Commenting on that definition, the great German chemist Justus von Liebig wrote: "The assumption of this new force is detrimental to the progress of science, since it appears to satisfy the human spirit, and thus provides a limit to further research." That Liebig's concern was unfounded in this instance needs no further proof than a review of catalytic technology over the past 150 years, but, of course, in that scientist's day future progress in catalysis was beyond anyone's imagination. Catalysis will flourish as long as there are people who are curious about and fascinated by its many mysteries.

Catalytically active enzymes are delicate structures; temperatures and chemical conditions that differ from the enzymes' natural environment may denature, or disrupt, these structures with subsequent loss of activity. Research directed toward stabilizing native configurations against adverse conditions is a major undertaking of enzyme technology and has had some success in adding extra intramolecular cross-links to enzyme structures.

249

Science
Year in Review
Contents

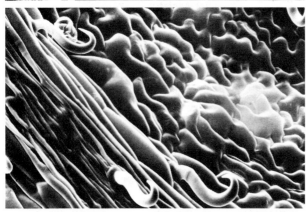

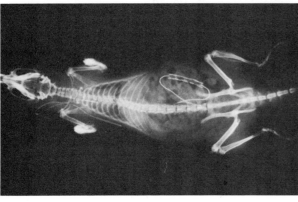

Contributors to the Science Year in Review

Joseph Ashbrook *Astronomy.* Editor, *Sky and Telescope,* Cambridge, Mass.

Fred Basolo *Chemistry: Inorganic chemistry.* Professor of Chemistry, Northwestern University, Evanston, Ill.

Louis J. Battan *Earth sciences: Atmospheric sciences.* Director, Institute of Atmospheric Physics, University of Arizona, Tucson.

Harold Borko *Information sciences: Information systems.* Professor, Graduate School of Library and Information Science, University of California, Los Angeles.

Robert E. Boyer *Earth sciences: Geology and geochemistry.* Professor of Geological Sciences and Education and Chairman of the Department of Geological Sciences, University of Texas at Austin.

D. Allan Bromley *Physics: Nuclear physics.* Henry Ford II Professor and Chairman, Department of Physics, Yale University, New Haven, Conn.

George F. Cahill, Jr. *Medical sciences: Diabetes research.* Professor of Medicine, Harvard University, Cambridge, Mass., and Director of Research, Joslin Diabetes Foundation, Inc., Boston, Mass.

Charles M. Cegielski *Chemistry: Applied chemistry.* Associate editor, *Encyclopaedia Britannica,* Yearbooks, Chicago, Ill.

F. C. Durant III *Information sciences: Satellite systems.* Assistant Director, National Air and Space Museum, Smithsonian Institution, Washington, D.C.

Robert G. Eagon *Life sciences: Microbiology.* Professor of Microbiology, University of Georgia, Athens.

Gerald Feinberg *Physics: High-energy physics.* Professor of Physics, Columbia University, New York, N.Y.

David R. Gaskell *Materials sciences: Metallurgy.* Associate Professor of Metallurgy, University of Pennsylvania, Philadelphia.

Robert Geddes *Architecture and civil engineering.* Dean of the School of Architecture and Urban Planning, Princeton University, Princeton, N.J.

Robert Haselkorn *Life sciences: Molecular biology.* F. L. Pritzker Professor and Chairman of the Department of Biophysics and Theoretical Biology, University of Chicago.

L. A. Heindl *Earth sciences: Hydrology.* Executive Secretary, U.S. National Committee on Scientific Hydrology, U.S. Geological Survey, Reston, Va.

Richard S. Johnston *Space exploration: Manned space flight.* Special Assistant to the Director, NASA Johnson Space Center, Houston, Texas.

John Patrick Jordan *Food and agriculture: Agriculture.* Director, Colorado State University Experiment Station, Fort Collins.

Lou Joseph *Medical sciences: Dentistry.* Manager of Media Relations, Bureau of Public Information, American Dental Association, Chicago, Ill.

C. Frederick Kittle *Medical sciences: General medicine.* Professor of Surgery and Director of the Section of Thoracic Surgery, Rush Medical College, Presbyterian-St. Luke's Medical Center, Chicago, Ill.

Mina W. Lamb *Food and agriculture: Nutrition.* Professor emeritus, Department of Food and Nutrition, Texas Tech University, Lubbock.

Howard J. Lewis *U.S. science policy.* Director, Office of Information, National Academy of Sciences.

Melvin H. Marx *Psychology.* Professor of Psychology, University of Missouri, Columbia.

Darryll Outka *Life sciences: Zoology.* Associate Professor of Biochemistry, Iowa State University, Ames.

Richard K. Pefley *Mechanical engineering.* Chairman, Department of Mechanical Engineering, University of Santa Clara, Calif.

Pertti J. Pelto *Anthropology.* Professor of Anthropology and Medicine, University of Connecticut, Storrs.

Froelich Rainey *Archaeology.* Director of the Museum Applied Science Center for Archaeology and Professor of Anthropology, University of Pennsylvania, Philadelphia.

Anthony Ralston *Information sciences: Computers.* Chairman and Professor, Department of Computer Science, State University of New York at Buffalo.

Arthur E. Reider *Medical sciences: Psychiatry.* Clinical Instructor in Psychiatry, Harvard University, Cambridge, Mass.

Arthur L. Robinson *Chemistry: Physical chemistry.* Research News Writer, *Science* magazine.

Mitchell R. Sharpe *Space exploration: Space probes.* Historian, Alabama Space and Rocket Center, Huntsville.

Benjamin Simon *Medical sciences: Psychiatry.* Consultant in Psychiatry and Neurology, Region I, U.S. Department of Health, Education, and Welfare and Clinical Assistant Professor of Psychiatry, Tufts University, Medford, Mass.

Albert J. Smith *Life sciences: Botany.* Associate Professor of Biology, Wheaton College, Wheaton, Ill.

Frank A. Smith *Transportation.* Senior Vice-President, Transportation Association of America, Washington, D.C.

J. F. Smithcors *Medical sciences: Veterinary medicine.* Editor, American Veterinary Publications, Santa Barbara, Calif.

William E. Spicer *Physics: Solid-state physics.* Professor of Electrical Engineering and Materials Science and Engineering, Stanford University, Stanford, Calif.

Lynn Arthur Steen *Mathematics.* Professor of Mathematics, St. Olaf College, Northfield, Minn.

Edward H. Sussenguth *Information sciences: Communications systems.* Director of Communications Systems Architecture, IBM Corp., Research Triangle Park, N.C.

Norman M. Tallan *Materials sciences: Ceramics.* Chief, Processing and High Temperature Materials Branch, Air Force Materials Laboratory, Dayton, Ohio.

Wayne Thatcher *Earth sciences: Geophysics.* Research Geophysicist, National Center for Earthquake Research, U.S. Geological Survey, Menlo Park, Calif.

David S. Watt *Chemistry: Organic chemistry.* Assistant Professor of Chemistry, University of Colorado, Boulder.

Kenneth E. F. Watt *Environment.* Professor of Zoology and Environmental Studies, and Research Systems Analyst in the Institute of Ecology, University of California, Davis.

James A. West *Energy.* Associate Assistant Administrator, International Energy Affairs, Federal Energy Administration, Washington, D.C.

Warren S. Wooster *Earth sciences: Oceanography.* Professor of Marine Studies and Fisheries, Institute for Marine Studies, University of Washington, Seattle.

Frederick Wooten *Optical engineering.* Professor of Applied Science, University of California, Davis.

Anthropology

The year could appropriately be regarded as the "Year of Margaret Mead," who celebrated her 75th birthday; it also marked a half century since she returned from her first notable field trip to Samoa. In honor of her 50 years of significant contributions to anthropology, the American Museum of Natural History established a research fund in her name. In her speech as retiring president of the American Association for the Advancement of Science, Mead focused on the contrasts and misunderstandings between scientific method in the "nonhuman" sciences and the techniques of "human science," arguing that:

> ... it is not by rejecting one or another but by appropriately combining the several methods evolved from these different types of search for knowledge that we are most likely in the long run to achieve a kind of scientific activity that is dominated neither by the arrogance of physical scientists nor by the arrogance of humanists who claim that the activities which concerned them cannot meaningfully be subjected to scientific inquiry.

Mead was also honored by the American Anthropological Association, which bestowed on her its Distinguished Service Award. The co-recipient of the award was Lita Osmundsen of the Wenner-Gren Foundation for Anthropological Research, for her years of service as director of that major supporting institution.

The year was also notable as the one in which two anthropologists shared the Nobel Prize for Physiology or Medicine. Baruch S. Blumberg of the University of Pennsylvania and D. Carleton Gajdusek of the National Institutes of Health, both medical anthropologists, were honored "for discoveries concerning new mechanisms for the origin and dissemination of infectious diseases."

Gajdusek, after years of research in New Guinea, was able to demonstrate that the mysterious wasting disease kuru, found among the cannibalistic Fore people of the highlands, is caused by a slow-growing virus. The illness was found to affect mainly women and young people of both sexes and was transmitted by the practice of eating human brains. Gajdusek's detective work on kuru involved a complex interweaving of biological and cultural data. The vital clue was that adult males in the Fore population did not suffer from the disease. Gajdusek learned from fieldwork that adult males do not engage in cannibalism because of a belief that it would stunt their growth.

Blumberg's recognition came because of his discovery of the "Australian antigen," a factor in type B viral hepatitis. Until recently, type B hepatitis was often transmitted inadvertently in blood transfusions, but Blumberg's discovery has made it possible to greatly reduce such transmissions by careful screening for contaminated blood.

Medical anthropology. The Nobel Prizes awarded to Blumberg and Gajdusek reflect a significant expansion of anthropological interest in medical and health sciences. In 1976 the Society for Medical Anthropology had over 1,500 members, and several new graduate programs in medical anthropology were announced. There was a rapid expansion of research in paleopathology, culture and community health, ethnic components in medical problems, sociocultural epidemiology, and nutritional anthropology. During 1976 the National Can-

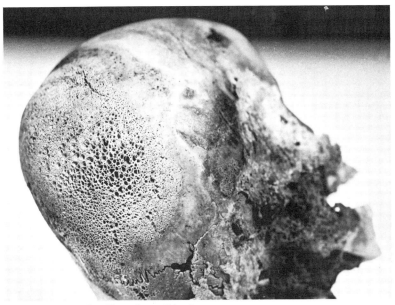

Sievelike porosity on the skull of a three-year-old American Indian child indicates porotic hyperostosis, a disorder believed to be caused by iron deficiency in the diet. The child lived in Arizona about 800 years ago.

Courtesy, M. Y. El-Najjar, Case Western Reserve University

cer Institute announced its interest in research on the relationship between nutritional factors and culture and different types of cancer. Recent heart and diabetes research also involved anthropological perspectives.

Research in paleopathology demonstrated some interesting interrelationships of nutritional data, pathology, and cultural materials. Mahmoud El-Najjar of Case Western Reserve University, Cleveland, Ohio, and colleagues reported studies of skeletal materials from prehistoric northeastern Arizona that show a significant incidence of porotic hyperostosis, a disorder possibly related to iron deficiencies in the diets of Indians living in the area nearly 800 years ago. For example, a well-preserved mummy of a child found in Canyon de Chelly showed large areas of spongy bone in the skull and growth-arrest lines that suggest nutritional problems and illness.

A large number of skeletal materials from the same region with similar porotic hyperostosis suggest that nutritional problems (and associated illness) were present. These studies may throw light on some puzzling cultural developments and movements of peoples in the region, including the abandonment, during the 13th century, of certain well-settled areas.

Sociobiology. Perhaps the most important intellectual controversy of recent years, for anthropologists as well as others, erupted around Harvard zoologist Edward O. Wilson's book *Sociobiology* (1975). Wilson's exploration of genetic factors in human behavior (*e.g.*, possible genetic inheritance of "altruistic behavior") was seen by some anthropologists "as an attempt to justify genetically the sexist, racist, and elitist status quo in human society." A motion to condemn sociobiology on those grounds was introduced in the 1976 annual meeting of the American Anthropological Association in Washington, D.C., but was overwhelmingly voted down.

The controversy centers on the question of the extent to which genetic factors play a role in human social behavior. For example, Wilson's somewhat tentative suggestions about genetic influence in human sexual division of labor (*e.g.*, male hunting activity and female food-gathering activity) were challenged by some anthropologists who pointed out that, in many human societies, the division of labor is much less pronounced (*e.g.*, where women participate in hunting or men in food gathering). Judging from the large number of papers on sociobiology presented at the 1976 annual meeting, there is a growing interest in studying the complex interactions between biological (including genetic) factors and the socially learned, cultural elements in human behavior.

Ecological anthropology. Related to the biocultural theme of recent research was the continued growth of ecological anthropology, marked by an intensified focus on the interrelationships between human groups and their environments. Napoleon Chagnon of Pennsylvania State University and his associates presented new materials about population dynamics and size of local communities among the warlike Yanomamo people of the Amazon Basin. Nancy Howell of Toronto and others were analyzing the marriage patterns and other demographic data from Bushmen groups in the Kalahari Desert of southern Africa. New evidence was presented in support of the hypothesis that preagricultural human communities maintained relatively stable populations through a variety of means, ranging from abortion and infanticide to contraceptive practices, including fertility-regulating botanical materials.

The growing anthropological focus on population and related ecological concerns is one of the points of strong contact between cultural/social anthropologists and archaeologists. A collection of studies on *Demographic Anthropology* (1976), edited by archaeologist Ezra Zubrow of Stanford University, includes analyses of contemporary populations, as well as estimates of population growth patterns from archaeological data in the Near East and the American Southwest. A study by Michael A. Jochim on *Hunter-Gatherer Subsistence and Settlement* (1976) draws on a variety of ethnographic data sources to describe relationships between composition of local groups, interactions of geographically contiguous groups, and fluctuations of food resources at an archaeological site in southwest Germany.

Whereas many ecological theorists have focused on population pressure as the major factor in producing and escalating warfare, a book by Andrew P. Vayda, *War in Ecological Perspective* (1976), which analyzes warfare among tribal groups in New Zealand, New Guinea, and Borneo, shows that a variety of ecological factors play a role. He finds, for example, that factors accounting for the persistence of warlike activities may be quite separate from the original causes of war.

Archaeology/prehistory. James A. Tuck and Robert J. McGhee reported on an archaic Indian burial mound in Labrador over 7,000 years old. The mound, which contained a juvenile human skeleton and various artifacts, is of special significance because such elaborate burials are generally found only among sedentary food-cultivating societies. The ancient Labrador people who left this grave site were hunter-gatherers.

In areas of Pre-Columbian civilizations researchers expanded their analysis of regional trade net-

Based on a photograph, courtesy of Ray T. Matheny, Brigham Young University

Based on a photograph taken in 1948 before the site was disturbed, drawing depicts canals, reservoirs, a civic center, and a moated fortress of the Maya Indians at Edzná, Campeche, Mexico. The letters indicate: (a) a civic/ceremonial center; (b) canal; (c) water reservoirs; (d) canal; and (e) moated fortress. The canals and reservoirs are dated about 150 BC. Light-colored patches represent agricultural plots of current inhabitants.

works, as well as continuing detailed study of ecological systems in prehistoric environments. Ray T. Matheny of Brigham Young University, Provo, Utah, and co-workers identified hydraulic systems that played a role in the development of lowland Mayan civilization at the site of Edzná in the western Yucatán Peninsula. In Peru researchers from the University of San Marcos excavated cave sites over 4,050 m above sea level in which they found evidence that specialized hunting of animals of the llama family began as early as 5500 BC and domestication of these animals began between 2500 and 1750 BC.

Richard E. Leakey reported a well-preserved skull from East Africa that is "almost identical" to the well-known Peking remains from China but is more than twice as old. Donald C. Johanson of Case Western Reserve University reported a new series of fossil remains in Ethiopia, including some hand bones and other materials that appear to be at least three million years old. (*See* Feature Article: ANTIQUITY OF MAN IN AFRICA.) Yale University anthropologist David Pilbeam reported significant new fossil evidence from Pakistan that sheds light on prehuman primate ancestors of eight million to ten million years ago. This possible ancestor of the genus *Homo*, labeled *Ramapithecus*, had been known only from a series of jaw fragments and teeth. Pilbeam's discoveries include, for the first time, parts of arms and thighbones as well as another complete lower jaw. (*See* Year in Review: ARCHAEOLOGY.)

State of the discipline. Responding to the continuing shortage of regular academic teaching positions, as well as the need for greater anthropological expertise in the formulation of public policy, the American Anthropological Association adopted a resolution authorizing creation of an organization for channeling research into useful applied areas. As a result, Anthropological Research Services was established as the organization for seeking contracts and grants in such areas as education, public health, and the preservation of natural resources. The organization was also empowered to seek financial support. It is expected that Anthropological Research Services will eventually develop into a major research institute.

Education continued to be a growth area for anthropological research. The National Institute of Education (NIE) awarded a contract to a group of North Carolina anthropologists for "field studies in urban desegregated schools." Anthropologists were also involved in a series of ethnographic field studies focusing on technical assistance in inner-city schools. Another contract from NIE involved anthropological research on parental participation in special education.

Despite severe cutbacks in some areas of publishing, a number of new periodicals and books appeared during the year. Three new periodicals in medical anthropology were announced. Other new publications included a series entitled *Working Papers in Culture and Communication*, published at

Temple University, Philadelphia; *Anthro-Tech: A Journal of Speculative Anthropology*, devoted to the study of technology and its effect on human culture; and a newsletter of the recently established Society on Anthropology and Humanism. Publication of the World Anthropology Series of books based on the papers presented in the IXth International Congress of Anthropological and Ethnological Sciences (Chicago, 1973) continued throughout 1976, with Sol Tax of the University of Chicago, the organizer of the congress, as general editor.

The current state of anthropology continued to reflect the tensions and the dynamic qualities of a profession that is an amalgam of biological science, social science, and humanistic study. Mead's speech at the annual meeting of the AAAS reflected the ongoing concern that differences in methodology and philosophy not lead to a breakdown of communications between the "hard sciences" and the "human sciences." Some of the important trends in anthropology during the year, especially in such areas as ecological research and medical anthropology, indicated the growth of new links between these two scholarly traditions.

—Pertti J. Pelto

Archaeology

The already critical conflict between industrial development and the preservation of the environment was impinging on the world of archaeological monuments. Most dramatic was the attempt by UNESCO to raise $15 million to save the Acropolis in Athens. Sulfur oxides from automotive and industrial pollution in the city combined with water vapor to form sulfuric acid, which was turning the Acropolis marble to gypsum, a powdery substance that was being worn away by rain, wind, and the hands and feet of millions of tourists. Some figures from the pediment of the Parthenon and the remaining caryatids of the Erechtheum were being removed and replaced by casts. Tourists were prohibited from walking inside the Parthenon, and wooden pathways were to be built limiting tourists to specific areas.

Elsewhere in Greece, plans to build a shipyard and cement plants at Pylos caused such a furor that the National Archaeological Council resigned en masse. In Egypt rising groundwater, perhaps due to the Aswan High Dam, was imperiling temples and tombs of the Luxor region. The most urgent problem was the Colossi of Memnon, the great 65-ft statues of Amenhotep III. In England the 750,000 tourists who visited Stonehenge each year were slowly rubbing away the ancient markings on the stones, and the British Department of the Environment proposed to erect a fence with an earthen bank and ditch to keep visitors 100 ft away. Corrosive pollutants from petrochemical plants were destroying the stones and colors of Venice. At Chartres, in France, dirt, pollutants, fungi, and algae were corroding the stained glass windows of the cathedral.

It was possible that modern chemistry, which causes part of the problem, might yet help to solve it. The French were using a new chemical to preserve and protect the stained glass windows of Chartres, and other chemicals had been developed

Statues of Amenhotep III, known as the Colossi of Memnon, near Luxor in southern Egypt, reveal damage to lower sections, caused by rising groundwater.

Keystone

© Biblical Archaeologist

Wide World

Clay tablets (left) found in Syria are covered with cuneiform script (above). They indicate that Ebla in Syria was the center of a great ancient empire.

to protect and preserve stone and mud-brick (adobe) structures. As yet, however, none had been produced that would penetrate the tough, fine-grained marble of the Acropolis sufficiently to protect it.

Africa. Following Mary Leakey's announcement in 1975 of a 3,750,000-year-old fossil of a primitive but truly human type, her son, Richard E. Leakey, and Donald C. Johanson described more recent discoveries of the same type in Kenya and Ethiopia. These later discoveries included skulls, hands, and thighbones with some remarkably advanced features, indicating that a more primitive form of true man must have been evolving toward this stage for perhaps a million years.

Leakey also reported a virtually complete skull of *Homo erectus*, best known as Peking Man but also known from other sites in Asia, Europe, and Africa. This was found in Kenya by Bernard Ngeneo and was dated at 1.5 million years old, a million years older than the estimated age of Peking Man. The new skull includes much of the face, making it possible to reconstruct the appearance of *Homo erectus* more accurately.

Johanson also reported the remains of what appears to be a family of ancient man in the Afar region of Ethiopia. He found more than 150 bones representing two children and from three to five adults. They date from 3 million to 3.5 million years ago and were true men. One hand pieced together is approximately the size of a modern man's hand and appears capable of as much dexterity.

Leakey and Johanson now see the tentative picture of human evolution as follows: from a group of apelike creatures living more than five million years ago arose a manlike creature. This line then divided into two types, true man with a larger brain and near-man (*Australopithecus*) with a smaller brain. Near-man, after splitting into a small and a large type, finally became extinct about one million years ago. *See also* Feature Article: ANTIQUITY OF MAN IN AFRICA.

Syria. Translations of the 15,000 clay tablets found in 1975 at Tell Mardikh (ancient Ebla) in Syria showed that Ebla was the center of a great empire, communicating with Mesopotamia and Egypt, and the original base of a major civilization—a discovery that could revolutionize the history of the ancient Near East. The tablets record that at one time the king employed 11,000 administrators and civil servants. There are also accounts of military campaigns, international treaties, details about Ebla's government-operated textile and metal industries, and hymns and incantations to hundreds of named gods. Among the literary and religious texts are references to creation and flood myths similar to those of the Sumerians and, later, Hebrews, who arrived in Palestine about 1,000 years after the tablets were written.

The breakthrough in translation came when Gio-

257

vanni Pettinato discovered, among the tablets unearthed by Paolo Matthiae of the University of Rome, vocabulary lists giving the Sumerian equivalent of words in this new and unknown language, now called Eblaite. Excavations so far completed had exposed a few rooms in one corner of a palace and some adjacent buildings, but the mound covers 140 ac and presumably much more of the city would be uncovered. Matthiae estimated that 10,-000 to 20,000 people lived and worked in the palace and that the kingdom had a population of 260,000. The site dates from about 4400 BC, but most of the tablets are from about 2300 BC.

Egypt. The discovery of a temple of the pharaoh Ikhnaton (Akhenaton; reigned 1379–1362 BC), known to history for his heretical conception of one god, Aton, was announced during the year by Donald B. Redford, director of the University Museum (University of Pennsylvania) team involved in the long-range Ikhnaton Temple Project. The site, in Thebes near Luxor in the Karnak Temple complex, was determined by the discovery of a long foundation wall and fragments of decorated relief, including one stone block identifying the structure as part of the temple Gem-Pa-Aton.

The chief significance of this find relates to the study of 40,000 distinctive stone building blocks, known as Talatat, that have been found over the past 100 years in various excavations at Karnak. Since 1966 the Ikhnaton Temple Project, utilizing a computer, individual photographs of the blocks, and a staff of young Egyptian archaeologists, has been matching up these stones into entire chains of scenes showing Ikhnaton and Nefertiti, his consort, paying tribute to the sun-god Aton. Some eight temples are represented by the Talatat, but no meaningful structures could be delineated. The foundations of Gem-Pa-Aton provide a ground plan on which to rebuild part of the temple complex.

Greece. A unique altar of burnt offerings from the early 5th century BC was discovered at the sanctuary of Artemis near the Homeric city of Hyampolis, just west of Atalanti in central Greece. The stone altar was intact, with all the votive offerings placed on it for the last sacrifice, some 2,400 years ago. A German team directed by Reiner Felsch had been working in the area for three years.

Another unique feature was the presence of two stone statues embedded in the altar with lead about the feet. The one intact figure, 11 cm tall, probably represents Apollo and is one of the best examples of Archaic Greek art. Among the many offerings were a painted clay cock, a clay mask probably representing Artemis, and many bronze rings. There was also a Phocaean silver coin dating from 457–446 BC.

China. A New China News Agency article on paleoanthropological research in China during the past 25 years contained references to numerous recent discoveries, including an "apeman" who lived 1.7 million years ago, about one million years earlier than the famous Peking Man of Chou-k'ou-tien. Reinterpreting past and recent finds of the "Upper Cave Man" (first discovered in a cave above that containing Peking Man) near Chou-k'ou-tien, the Chinese archaeologists concluded that he lived about 500,000 years ago, was a proto-Mongoloid type, and may be ancestral to the Chinese, American Indian, and Eskimo people. They pointed out that since few human fossils were found in China until recently, Western researchers erroneously assumed a gap of hundreds of thousands of years between Peking Man and Upper Cave Man and generally rejected a line of descent between Peking Man and modern man.

Relating to the historic period, a recent report disclosed the discovery of some 1,000 bamboo slips inscribed with the earliest known Chinese laws. They were found in one of 12 tombs in Yünmeng county in central China that were discovered by peasants digging a drainage ditch. Dating from the Ch'in dynasty (221–206 BC), they include laws, acts concerning farmland, judicial cases, a book on the "ways of officials," and specific cases showing how court trials were conducted.

Thailand. Pisit Charoenwongsa, co-director of the Thai Department of Fine Arts/University Museum (University of Pennsylvania) excavations in northeast Thailand, was preparing a paper giving a new time perspective to prehistoric archaeology in Southeast Asia, based on his work with Chester Gorman of the University Museum at the site of Ban Chiang. Until recently Southeast Asia had been seen by archaeologists as a "cul-de-sac," a "cultural backwater" where innovation took place only after Indian and Chinese cultural penetration in fairly recent times. However, following the discovery of early agriculture, pottery manufacture, and metal manufacture in the area, there has been a growing awareness of the probability that an innovative, indigenous, and very early bronze age originated there.

Materials excavated at Ban Chiang in 1974 and 1975, still in the process of study, represent seven time phases at the site, dating from the mid-4th millennium BC to the early 2nd millennium AD (based on a series of 18 carbon-14 dates and an equal number of thermoluminescence dates). Cast tin-bronze objects are found in the earliest level c. 3600 BC, and iron objects in the fourth level (1200–1600 BC). Evidence of domesticated rice and domesticated cattle and pigs also appears in the earliest level. Thus it might well turn out that

Southeast Asia was the center of development rather than a cul-de-sac. However, tin and copper deposits are known in southern China as well as in Thailand, Malaysia, and other regions in the area, and it remained uncertain whether bronze manufacture actually began in northeast Thailand.

Central America. An excavation at a site called Abaj Takalik near Retalhuleu, Guatemala, conducted by John A. Graham and Robert F. Heizer of the University of California at Berkeley, was of particular interest because, for the first time, extensive Olmec and Maya carved monuments (stelae) were found at the same site. The Olmec civilization, centering on the Gulf Coast of Mexico, was probably the oldest true civilization in America and certainly preceded the Maya by some centuries, although Olmec and Maya inscriptions are clearly related. More than 50 stelae were found at the site, and several of them were produced by the Olmec people. One, of the Maya type, gives a date of June 3, AD 126—which is 166 years older than a stela at Tikal that was previously the oldest known in the Maya area. Further, this highland site, like that at Kaminaljuyú in Guatemala City, substantiates the idea that Mayan civilization originated in the highlands rather than in the hot lowlands where the most famous sites are located.

North America. The age and the origin of the American Indians continued to be an unresolved argument among American archaeologists. For example, Paul S. Martin of the University of Arizona believed that technically skilled hunters first arrived in America via the Bering Strait about 12,000 years ago while Richard S. MacNeish claimed that small bands of unskilled hunters arrived, also via the Bering Strait, at least 40,000 years ago. The argument was intensified by a new dating process called racemization, developed by Jeffrey L. Bada, for dating bones. By means of this process, a human skeleton from a cliff near Del Mar in California was dated at 48,000 years old, and further dating led some to speculate that man may have been in America as long as 70,000 years ago.

One of the most expensive archaeological digs ever undertaken in America was directed to this basic controversy. The National Geographic Society and the U.S. National Park Service were investing $600,000 in an area around Dry Creek,

Carved monuments by the Maya (left) and Olmec (right) Indians were discovered in Guatemala. This was the first time that significant numbers of Mayan and Olmec monuments were found at the same site.

Photos by John A. Graham, © National Geographic Society

75 mi S of Fairbanks, Alaska, where Charles Holmes discovered an ancient site in 1973. William R. Powers and Russel D. Guthrie of the University of Alaska planned to search a 4,000-sq mi area for sites like that at Dry Creek, now dated to 11,000 years ago. Dry Creek lies in a narrow corridor that was ice-free during the glacial period and could have been a migration route for man and animals.

The trend among archaeologists toward attempting to answer contemporary social and political questions was exemplified by recent comments by the excavators of the vast Cahokia mound complex in southern Illinois. They spoke of it as the New York City of AD 1000 and thought their study could provide urban America with hints for survival. The site was believed to represent an Indian population of up to 40,000 persons. There is evidence of a highly organized society with a class structure, and the Cahokians traded as far east as the Atlantic, as far south as the Gulf of Mexico, and as far north as Lake Superior. The archaeologists in charge, including Melvin L. Fowler, James Anderson, and Charles J. Bareis, speculated that this great urban settlement broke down from within, through disintegration, disease, or a change of climate.

Techniques. The Applied Science Center for Archaeology (MASCA) at the University Museum (University of Pennsylvania) continued work on the "correction factor" for radiocarbon dating, in collaboration with the Laboratory of Tree-Ring Research at the University of Arizona. Part of this work included a search for buried bristlecone pine logs in California's White Mountains. Some years ago it was discovered that the amount of carbon-14 in the atmosphere has not remained constant as originally assumed, and that early radiocarbon dates are younger than the actual dates. The surest way to check and correct carbon-14 dates is to analyze tree rings from very ancient bristlecone pines, whose growth records can be traced down to the present. A correction factor has been worked out for the period from 5390 BC to AD 1950, but to reach further back in time one must find older logs.

It is no mean task to find such logs, which are buried deep in broad alluvial fans washed out from canyons in the White Mountains. To this end, Henry N. Michael of MASCA was carrying out experiments with a new instrument known as a soil-penetrating radar, developed by the Stanford Research Institute. An improved system employs telemetry to transmit the sensed data to a nearby vehicle equipped with a computer and display unit. The vehicle also contains a position-location device which plots the location of the radar traverses. Detected anomalies can thus be superimposed on a map or aerial photograph.

—Froelich Rainey

Architecture and civil engineering

Skyscrapers. In 1896, after designing the Wainwright Building in St. Louis, Mo., and the Guaranty Building in Buffalo, N.Y., Louis H. Sullivan wrote about the problems to be faced in the erection of tall office buildings. His article, "The Tall Office Building Artistically Considered," attacked the notion that office buildings be only "the joint product of the speculator, the engineer, the builder." Instead, Sullivan urged that architects face the fact that the tall office building was "a problem to be solved—a vital problem, pressing for a true solution."

Sullivan analyzed the design of the office building in terms of its structure, its rooms, its windows, its horizontal and vertical planning, and its relations with the street on the ground floor. He proposed a *form* that would, for the solution of the problem, be "a final, comprehensive formula." His works and his words were both brilliant. He demonstrated that the office building had three parts: first, the ground floor and lower floors, which give public access; second, the tiers of typical, general office lofts; and third, the attic or top floors with specific purposes and equipment. In Sullivan's words, "From this [analysis] results, naturally, spontaneously, unwittingly, a three-part division, not from any theory, symbol or fancied logic. And thus the design of the tall office building takes its place with all other architectural types."

Sullivan's three-part form appeared for a long time to be the conclusive solution, but recent work has seemed to reconsider, revise, or deny Sullivan's propositions. This new work is characterized by the following: (1) the exterior skin is entirely glass, minimizing the difference between window and wall; (2) the exterior surface consists of a metal grid of lines, from top to bottom, without any expression on the outside of the changing functions and uses inside; (3) the structural frame is completely covered by the exterior skin, and does not appear on the exterior as an element of the building; and (4) the towers are trapezoidal in mass and outline, like cut stones or prisms. Several recently built examples are described below.

The John Hancock Tower in Boston, Mass. (I. M. Pei & Partners, architects, engineers; James Ruderman, structural; Cosentini Associates, mechanical), is a 60-story office building located next to H. H. Richardson's Trinity Church (1877) and facing obliquely onto Copley Square. The floor plan and building mass are trapezoidal, angled sharply away from the square. The reflective glass facades give dramatic reflections of the surrounding buildings.

Courtesy, Philip Johnson and John Burgee, photo by Richard W. Payne   Courtesy, Kevin Roche, John Dinkeloo and Associates

Pennzoil Place in Houston, Texas (left), and One United Nations Plaza in New York City (right) are recently constructed skyscrapers characterized by a trapezoidal shape and by an exterior skin that completely covers the structural frame and minimizes the difference between window and wall.

One United Nations Plaza in New York City (Kevin Roche and John Dinkeloo, architects, engineers; Weiskopf & Pickworth, structural; Cosentini Associates, mechanical) is a combination of an office building and a hotel. The tower is 505 ft high, only 3 ft shorter than the UN Secretariat across the street. Offices comprise the lower 26 stories, with the hotel above. The 45° slantbacks of the exterior facade occur on the 12th and 28th floors. The skin consists of aluminum grid lines and green glass from top to bottom.

Pennzoil Place in Houston, Texas (Philip Johnson and John Burgee, architects, engineers; Ellisor, structural; I. A. Namen & Associates, mechanical), consists of twin 36-story towers, trapezoidal in floor plan, connected at lower levels by a sloping greenhouse roof that parallels the sloping roofs of the towers. The result is a dynamic geometric composition of prisms.

Despite their dramatic impact on the urban scene, these buildings raise Louis Sullivan's problem once again. Because they seem to minimize the expression of human uses, of social values and symbols, of the structural and mechanical engineering systems, they raise questions about their designs as well as the reconsideration of Sullivan's

formal proposition. Perhaps the problem, as Sullivan posed it, remains: "How shall we impart to this sterile pile, this crude, harsh, brutal agglomeration, this stark, staring exclamation of eternal strife, the graciousness of those higher forms of sensibility and culture that rest on the lower and fiercer passions? How shall we proclaim from the dizzy height of this strange, weird, modern housetop the peaceful evangel of sentiment, of beauty, the cult of a higher life?"

Groundscrapers. Sullivan believed "that it is of the very essence of every problem that it contains and suggests its own solution." He searched for "not an individual or special solution, but for a true normal type," and found justification for his quest in the great "types" of architectural history, such as the Greek temple and Gothic cathedral. In recent years, there has developed an international body of work that suggests the emergence of a Sullivanesque architectural-type solution in the design of new university buildings. These buildings serve the specific needs of a collegiate community, such as ease of access, flexibility and adaptability for change, the possibility of future extension, and provision for both private and public activities. As a result, the solutions have in common the follow-

261

Courtesy, Southern Illinois University at Carbondale

Faner Hall (the Humanities and Social Sciences Building), Southern Illinois University at Carbondale, connects campus circulation paths by means of broad, covered passages and arcades.

ing characteristics: (1) the buildings are composed of many parts that are systematically linked together, somewhat like a spine or a chain; (2) the composition of the building is determined by the pedestrian circulation routes, which serve as the skeleton of the building design; (3) the buildings are low to the ground, providing easy access for the users and increasing the likelihood of social interaction.

There are a number of historical precedents for the emergence of this type of building, including the plan for the University of Virginia (1817–26) by Thomas Jefferson and the competition plan for the Free University of Berlin by Candilis, Josic and Woods, architects (1963). In 1976 architectural journals in Italy and the United States presented the plans for two university buildings that carried forward these ideas, although for very different sites and institutions.

Faner Hall (the Humanities and Social Sciences Building) at Southern Illinois University (Geddes Brecher Qualls Cunningham, architects) is a 900-ft long, low building that ties campus circulation paths together with broad, covered passages, colonnades, and arcades. The structural and mechanical equipment modules create flexible, adaptable spaces for classrooms, seminars, meet-

ing rooms, and offices. The University of Calabria, Italy (Gregotti Associates, Architects), was planned to be a linear structure for teaching and research facilities along a central spine. Set along the side of a valley, bridging over the rolling ground, the spine connects with a main highway and a railroad station, somewhat like the growth and pattern of a new town.

Alvar Aalto (1898–1976). Among the characteristics of modern architecture have been the varied contributions within the international movement of individual architects, of regional influences, and of national characteristics. Finland's great architect, Alvar Aalto, reflected the cultural characteristics of his native land and a personal approach to the functional, social, and spiritual aspirations of architecture. Aalto ranks with Le Corbusier, Frank Lloyd Wright, Walter Gropius, Ludwig Mies van der Rohe, and Louis Kahn in the history of 20th-century architecture.

For more than 50 years, Aalto designed furniture, buildings, and urban districts. His work explored the nature of materials in an industrial civilization; for example, his furniture designs were based on new technologies for the molding of plywood. There was always a strong influence of the landscape on his buildings and cities; his buildings were carefully related to the natural surroundings, and often contained plants and gardens as part of their design. An outstanding example of these intentions in Aalto's work was the Town Hall at Säynätsalo, Finland, which used modest native materials, brick and wood, to create a complex group of building blocks around a courtyard landscape. But it is impossible to characterize Aalto's buildings in too simple a way; indeed, the richness and complexity of his work made him a powerful figure in the modern movement, challenging others to probe deeper into technology, materials, landscape, light, and space in architecture.

—Robert Geddes

Astronomy

Important achievements in astronomy during 1976–77 included the successful missions of Viking 1 and Viking 2 to Mars and the introduction into full service of the largest optical telescope in the world. In addition, significant new discoveries were made concerning the Sun, Uranus, minor planets, and X-ray sources.

Solar rotation. Astronomers long ago learned from sunspot and other observations that the Sun's rotation period is shortest, about 25 days, at the solar equator and increases steadily with latitude, being 27.5 days at 45° N or S and 30 days near the poles. But recently a year-to-year change in this pattern was found by Robert Howard, from work at the Hale Observatories. He reported that since 1967 the rotation rate at the equatorial regions has speeded up by 0.5%. The acceleration is greatest 10° to 15° on either side of the equator and tapers off gradually toward the poles.

This finding resulted from daily observations of the Sun's disk with the 150-ft solar tower telescope at Mount Wilson, Calif. At 24,000 different points on the disk, a spectral line of iron (wavelength 5250 Å [angstroms] in the green) was examined for Zeeman splitting, which is a measure of the local magnetic field, and for wavelength shift, which indicates line-of-sight motion, caused mainly by the Sun's axial rotation.

The changes in rotational velocity are presumably only skin deep, limited only to the photosphere or visible surface, for if they extended deep into the Sun they would require a prohibitively large expenditure of energy. Howard suggested that the velocity increase may be caused by the Sun's magnetic fields. He and V. Bumba argued that the magnetic field lines that emerge from the surface are linked to a subsurface source that rotates more rapidly. Thus, the field lines plow through the photosphere at a slightly higher speed than the glowing gases and in this way could serve as "paddles" to accelerate the surface. Howard's calculations showed that the amount of energy required by this process to achieve the observed effects is only about as much as is released by a large solar flare.

The Maunder minimum. A Colorado astronomer, John A. Eddy, collected information about a remarkable long-lasting disturbance of the solar-activity cycle for 70 years, from about 1645 to 1715. A British solar expert, E. W. Maunder, had noted in 1890 that during this interval practically no sunspots were seen. Eddy collected new evidence that solar activity virtually ceased during what he terms the "Maunder minimum." There was a conspicuous dearth of auroral displays, whose occurrence is known to be strongly correlated with solar activity. Furthermore, the extensive Japanese, Korean, and Chinese records of naked-eye sunspots show a lack of them during the 17th century.

Further indirect evidence is gained from recent measurements of radioactive carbon-14 in tree rings of known age. This isotope is formed in the atmosphere by the action of cosmic rays. When the

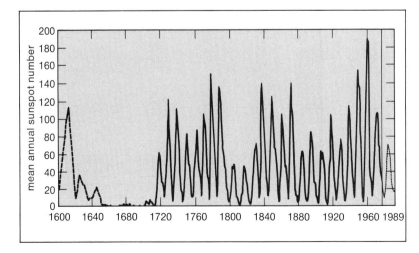

Graph of sunspot occurrences since 1600 strikingly reveals the "Maunder minimum," a period of very low activity from about 1645 to 1715.

(Photos) Tass—Sovfoto

The largest optical telescope in the world, the 6-meter (236-inch) reflector in the Soviet Union's new Astrophysical Observatory, is seen with glass in open (right) and closed (far right) positions.

Sun is active, its magnetic field is strong, preventing some cosmic rays from reaching the Earth. The anomalously high observed abundance of carbon-14 in 17th-century tree rings hence supports Eddy's contention that the Sun was nearly or quite inactive from 1645 to 1715. In addition, Eddy suggested that the familiar 11-year sunspot cycle may have begun for the first time at the close of the 70-year Maunder minimum.

Soviet 6-meter telescope. The largest optical telescope in the world went into full operation late in 1976. It is the 6-m (236-in) reflector at the U.S.S.R. Academy of Sciences' new Astrophysical Observatory in the northern Caucasus Mountains. The site is at an elevation of 2,100 m (6,888 ft), 41 km (25 mi) from the small town of Zelenchukskaya.

The design of the reflector is unique in that it is the first large optical telescope to be mounted, not as an equatorial but as a computer-controlled altazimuth. (Equatorial mounting consists of two axles at right angles to one another with one parallel to the Earth's axis of rotation.) This innovation was clearly a great success. The moving parts of the telescope weigh 800 metric tons, yet it could be driven with an accuracy of ± 0.3 sec of arc to track a star. The 6-m primary mirror of 24-m focal length is made of Pyrex. Although this mirror fulfilled expectations, it will eventually be replaced (perhaps in 1983) by a mirror made of a ceramic with a much lower coefficient of thermal expansion, which should provide even better imagery.

With the present mirror stars as faint as blue magnitude 24 could be photographed with exposures of 30 to 40 minutes. In red light the limit was

magnitude 23 to 23.5 for a 90-minute exposure. The telescope also had such accessories as a series of prime-focus spectrographs. According to the chief designer, B. K. Ioanisiani, the total cost of the instrument and associated equipment was about $36 million.

A British astronomer, Sir Bernard Lovell, who visited the 6-m telescope in late 1976, reported: "The instrument itself marks an historical epoch in the development of astronomy for two reasons, first because it is unlikely that a larger telescope will ever be constructed on Earth, and second because the success of the altazimuth mounting may lead to the abandonment of the polar axis design for any future large telescopes."

Vikings on Mars. The two Viking missions to Mars provided much new information about the planet. The Viking 1 spacecraft entered into orbit around Mars on June 19, 1976, and its instrumented lander set down safely on July 20 on the western slope of Chryse Planitia. This spot, a rock-strewn plain, was at longitude 47.94° W, latitude 22.84° N. Viking 2 began to orbit Mars on August 7 and sent down its lander on September 3 to a point in Utopia Planitia at longitude 225.71° W, latitude 47.97° N. Both of the orbiters and the landers were expected to function until late 1978. (For additional information on the mission, *see* Feature Article: THE VIKING MISSION TO MARS; Year in Review: SPACE EXPLORATION.)

An important result from the very sharp orbiter photographs is the clear existence of dry riverbeds and many signs of water erosion in the geologic past. While numerous channels had been photographed less distinctly by Mariner 9 in 1971–72, their nature was debatable. Large regions were seen to exhibit catastrophic flooding, but there was no evidence of sedimentary basins. The atmospheric pressure at the Martian surface (7.6 mb, compared with 1,013.25 mb at Earth's surface) is too low to permit the existence of liquid water.

The Martian atmosphere consists predominantly of carbon dioxide, with small amounts of molecular nitrogen, argon, carbon monoxide, molecular and atomic oxygen, and nitric oxide. The mass spectrometer aboard the Viking 2 lander measured traces of krypton and xenon. The abundance ratio of nitrogen-15 to nitrogen-14 is greater than on the Earth, suggesting that Mars once had a denser atmosphere.

The widely held view that the polar caps consist of frozen carbon dioxide was shown to need modification as the result of measurements taken by the second orbiter's atmospheric-water detector. This infrared sensor revealed over the north polar cap an amount of water vapor that would correspond to a liquid layer 0.06 to 0.07 mm deep. That much water vapor requires near-surface atmospheric temperatures of over 200 K (−73° C), which are too high for the survival of a frozen carbon-dioxide cap at Martian pressures. Therefore, the shrunken remnant of the north cap that was visible when those observations were made must consist primarily of water ice. The cap when at its greatest extent is known to be chiefly made up of carbon dioxide.

The amount of water vapor was greatest over latitudes 70°–80° N. Near the equator there was only about 0.005 mm of precipitable water, and none was detectable south of latitude 60° S. The Martian northern summer solstice had begun in early July.

After the orbital inclination of the Viking 2 orbiter was increased to 75° in late September, the entire north polar region of Mars could be viewed under favorable lighting through widely scattered clouds. Near the pole were revealed extensive layered deposits, largely covered with perennial ice. The pole was girdled by dune fields of some very dark material.

After touchdown, both landers made regular observations of barometric pressure, temperature, and wind speed and direction. The midsummer weather at both sites was mild by Martian standards. The daily temperature ranged from about 190–240 K (−83° to −33° C), with the peak about 3 PM local time. The pressure at each place was between 7 and 8 mb, with a steady drop totaling about 5% during the first 20 Martian days as carbon dioxide condensed at the very cold, growing south polar cap.

Both the Viking 1 and 2 landers used X-ray fluorescence spectrometers to analyze the composition of the Martian soil. Strikingly similar results showed large amounts of silicon and iron, and lesser amounts of magnesium, calcium, and sulfur. Alkaline metals are relatively scarce. The composition suggests an iron-rich clay. So close a match in composition at two sites on opposite sides of Mars makes it seem likely that its surface is less differentiated than the Earth's.

Valuable astronomical results were achieved from the radio tracking of the landers on Mars as

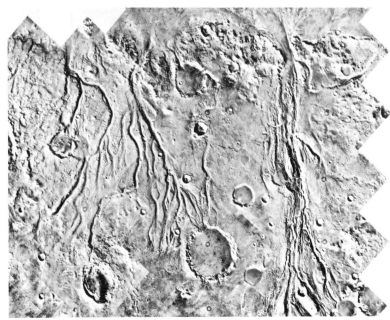

Photomosaic of surface of Mars consists of pictures taken by the Viking 1 orbiter. The channels suggest that a massive flood of waters once crossed this terrain. In several cases the channels cut through craters, but in others the craters are superimposed on the channels and are therefore of later origin than the flood.

Courtesy, NASA

the planet rotated. One outcome was the determination of accurate latitudes and longitudes of the lander sites. Also, the sidereal rotation period of Mars was determined as 24 hours 37 minutes 22.6628 (±0.0004) seconds, which is only 0.004 second shorter than the value from Earth-based observations adopted by *The American Ephemeris and Nautical Almanac*. The north celestial pole of Mars was located at right ascension 21 hours 9 minutes 22 seconds, declination +52° 43.3 minutes, by far the most accurate determination yet.

Although the question of whether life exists on Mars was not answered conclusively, the preliminary results from the three biology experiments carried by each lander tended toward the answer no. The gas chromatograph experiments of both Vikings tested Martian soil but found no light organic molecules at a sensitivity of one part per million and no heavy organic molecules at one part per billion.

The pyrolysis experiment was designed to test whether photosynthesis occurs in a soil sample under a light that simulated Martian sunlight. The labeled-release experiment was intended to ascertain if any component of Martian soil, such as a microorganism, would assimilate a nutrient solution. Both experiments yielded ambiguous results. The preliminary data could be interpreted either to support the hypothesis that life exists on Mars or to support the hypothesis that the soil contains a superoxide that reacts readily with water to yield oxygen. This might be a hyperoxidized state of iron or of some other heavy element. Many space scientists hypothesized that a photocatalytic reaction involving ultraviolet light (wavelengths as short as 1900 A are known to reach the Martian surface) converts the red iron oxide coating of Mars into a hyperoxidized state.

Minor planets and Uranus. Important new knowledge about the physical characteristics of the asteroids and of Uranus was rapidly amassed during the year, due mainly to the large-scale application of two new methods for measuring their diameters. Less than half a dozen minor planets are large enough or come close enough to the Earth to reveal disks in even large telescopes, and those disks are too tiny for reliable direct measurement.

The two new methods are both indirect. One, first used by David Allen, involves the measurement of the apparent brightness of an asteroid at both visible and infrared wavelengths. From these data, which define the amount of solar radiation reflected from the asteroid's surface relative to the amount absorbed and reemitted as heat, it is possible to calculate the diameter and albedo (reflectivity) of the body. In the second method observations of polarization and apparent brightness yield the diameter and albedo. By early 1977 these procedures had been applied to approximately 200 minor planets, mainly by astronomers working in Hawaii, Arizona, and Chile. The two methods agreed well with one another.

According to David Morrison's discussion, asteroid 1 Ceres is the largest of the minor planets with a diameter of 1,003 km (622 mi). It is followed by 2 Pallas with 608 km (377 mi); 4 Vesta, 538 km (334 mi); 10 Hygiea, 450 km (280 mi); and 31 Euphrosyne, 370 km (230 mi).

The most significant finding to emerge was that the great majority of minor planets can be divided into two sharply defined groups: very dark objects, called type C, that reflect only 2–5% of the sunlight incident on them; and lighter objects of type S, with albedos of about 15%. The C asteroids have reflection spectra resembling those of carbonaceous chondritic meteorites, while the spectra of the S

Comet West, one of the brightest comets in recent years, as photographed from the Massachusetts coast on March 8, 1976. In early March the comet shone as brightly as Jupiter.

Dennis di Cicco, *Sky and Telescope*

asteroids are like those of silicate-rich stony meteorites.

In the solar system the dark minor planets of type C greatly outnumber the more easily observable type S objects, after proper statistical allowance is made for selection. Moreover, as Morrison found, the proportion of dark asteroids increases as one moves farther from the Sun through the asteroid belt. At a distance of two astronomical units from the Sun. they are 50% of the total, but beyond three astronomical units the share rises to 95%. This means that the outer part of the belt probably contains a previously unsuspected large population of very faint minor planets.

The remarkable new asteroid 1976 UA, first photographed on Oct. 18, 1976, at Hale Observatories, has an orbital period of only 283.2 days, breaking the record set by 1976 AA with a 347-day period. On October 20 the asteroid passed only 720,000 mi from the Earth, appearing no brighter than magnitude 12.

A major discovery took place in March 1977 when Uranus occulted a star. This event provided evidence that Uranus, like Saturn, is encircled by rings. Probably five in number, the rings each appear to be only a few kilometers wide.

X-ray bursters and globular clusters. Two problems of great current interest to astronomers are why certain globular star clusters are strong X-ray sources and why some of those sources emit X-rays in brief, intense bursts. Systematic mapping of the X-ray sky began in 1970 with the Uhuru satellite, which in the next three years located about 150 X-ray sources. Since then satellites launched by the U.S., Great Britain, the Netherlands, and the Soviet Union have continued exploring the X-ray sky with increasingly sophisticated instruments. In particular, X-ray sources can be observed by them at wavelengths from 0.1 to 100 Å.

As of December 1976 astronomers had discovered six X-ray sources that coincided approximately in position with globular star clusters. All of these six are highly variable, which suggests that more of the approximately 130 globular clusters in our Galaxy may turn out to be X-ray sources.

Most theoreticians agree that a celestial X-ray source is a compact object (probably a neutron star or a black hole) that is drawing gas from its surroundings onto its surface. As it falls through the intensely strong gravitational field of the compact object, the gas gains kinetic energy which is converted into heat and radiated as X-rays.

Adopting this idea, John N. Bahcall and Jeremiah P. Ostriker suggested that the observed X-ray emission from a globular cluster may be caused by the infall of gas toward a massive black hole at the cluster center. Their calculations indicated a prob-

Courtesy, William Liller, Harvard University

Globular star cluster (center) in Scorpius is believed to house the source of the rapidly repetitive X-ray burster MXB 1730-335.

able mass of 100 to 1,000 Suns for such a black hole.

Some recent observations seemed to support this model. A massive black hole, though itself invisible, would by its presence cause a visible excess concentration of stars in its neighborhood. Edward B. Newell, working at the Australian National Observatory, looked for this excess light in the globular cluster Messier 15 (a well-established variable X-ray source). Their photoelectric scans of the cluster implied the existence of a tiny bright nucleus 3 sec of arc across. The Australian scientists estimated the invisible mass at the center of Messier 15 as 800 ($\pm$ 300) times that of the Sun. General relativity theory predicts that the gravitational collapse of so great a mass could produce a black hole.

The globular cluster X-ray sources described above are all more or less persistent sources. Dramatically different are the so-called X-ray bursters discovered by Melioranski and his team in Moscow with the Kosmos 428 satellite. A burst source that attracted general attention was the X-ray source 3U 1820-30, which coincides in position with the globular cluster NGC 6624 in Sagittarius. At intervals of several hours, this object emits an intense burst of X-rays, lasting usually less than 10 seconds. This burst source was discovered by Jonathan Grindlay's group with the Astronomical Netherlands Satellite, and more detailed observations were made by George W. Clark's team at the Massachusetts Institute of Technology, using the SAS-3 satellite.

Even more spectacular is the rapidly repetitive burster MXB 1730-335 in Scorpius found by Walter H. G. Lewin's team at the Massachusetts Institute of Technology a few months later. It emits sharp bursts of X-rays at intervals that vary from a few seconds to several minutes. The more intense an individual burst, the longer is the wait until the next burst. It is as if a reservoir of energy (or material to provide it) must build up to a fixed level and discharge; the larger the discharge, the longer it takes to build up for the next firing.

Photographing the location of MXB 1730-335 with the new 4-m telescope at Cerro Tololo, W. Liller discovered a faint star cluster. Later infrared observations showed it to be of the globular type, almost completely hidden by interstellar dust.

Lewin and his team discovered 12 more burst sources with SAS-3. A total of 25 are known to date. They are strung along the galactic equator and have a particularly high concentration near the galactic center.

The theoretical interpretation of X-ray bursters is still uncertain. At least two appear to be associated with globular clusters, but there are many for which no cluster is apparent. Their observed properties are difficult to satisfy by black-hole models such as were proposed. One possibility put forward by Fred Lamb and his associates is that the strong closed magnetic field of a neutron star dams up the infall of hot ionized gas, letting it descend to the surface only in spurts with each spurt producing a burst of X-rays.

—Joseph Ashbrook

Chemistry

Investigations of catalysis and catalytic agents, especially those of the homogeneous and enzymatic varieties, bore heavily on the direction of chemical research in recent months. The chemical activity of small clusters of metal atoms was found in many respects to resemble the surface chemistry of metal in bulk; important industrial processes that in the past had relied on heterogeneous catalysts and high energy expenditures were successfully duplicated in the laboratory under relatively mild conditions using organometallic reagents; and a number of complex molecules were synthesized catalytically in reactions designed to mimic enzyme-mediated processes found in nature. (For a broad overview of catalysts and catalytic processes, see Feature Article: THE CATALYSIS OF CHEMICAL REACTIONS.) Other highlights of the past

year included development of photochemical methods for harnessing solar energy, the growth of laser chemistry, and several new uses for the diverse capabilities of artificial membranes.

Inorganic chemistry

Research in inorganic chemistry during the past year dealt with several fundamental aspects of the field, including the syntheses and reactions of new compounds and the spectra, structures, and bonding of inorganic systems. The year was highlighted by the awarding of the 1976 Nobel Prize for Chemistry to an inorganic chemist for original research on borane compounds.

Metal clusters. Metal compounds generally contain only one metal atom or ion surrounded by other groups or ions. Some metal compounds, however, contain three or more metal atoms bonded together to form triangular or polyhedral arrays, and frequently the center position of such an array is vacant. The periphery is enveloped by other groups or ions, called ligands, which are bonded to the metal. Compounds of this type are known as metal clusters. Classical examples of such systems are the species $Mo_6Cl_8^{4+}$ and the

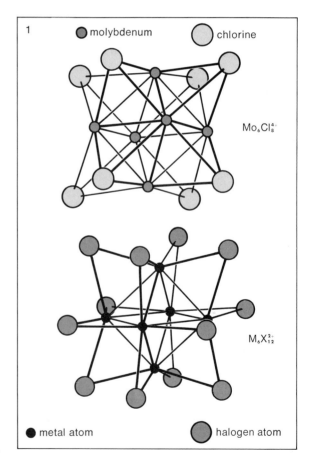

1

● molybdenum   ○ chlorine

$Mo_6Cl_8^{4+}$

$M_6X_{12}^{2+}$

● metal atom   ○ halogen atom

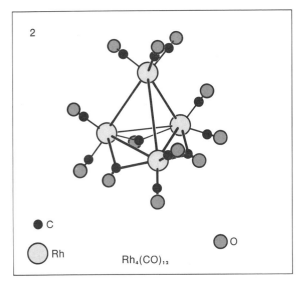

2

● C

◯ Rh

◯ O

$Rh_4(CO)_{12}$

$M_6X_{12}^{2+}$ (M = niobium, tantalum; X = chlorine, bromine) depicted in (1). Examples of more recent discovery include the compound $Rh_4(CO)_{12}$, shown in (2), and the ion $Co_6(CO)_{14}^{4-}$.

The last decade experienced a renewed interest in metal cluster compounds, in part due to the research efforts of F. Albert Cotton and co-workers, originally at the Massachusetts Institute of Technology, Cambridge, and later at Texas A. & M. University, College Station. This work focused attention on the nature of metal-metal bonding in these systems and provided X-ray data on the structure of several such compounds. Information as to bonding and structure was necessary in order to permit further progress in the field.

Recently Earl L. Muetterties and his associates at Cornell University, Ithaca, N.Y., decided to approach metal clusters as small pieces of metal and designed experiments in which these structures were expected to behave as metal surfaces. Metals and metal oxides in the solid state are extremely important heterogeneous catalysts for several commercial processes. Iron oxide, for example, is used as the catalyst for the Fischer-Tropsch synthesis of gasoline from coal, an important process in South Africa and one destined to find great use in a world growing critically short of natural petroleum. One of the difficulties with this process is that it is not selective, yielding mixtures of paraffins, olefins, and alcohols. The past 20 years experienced the great success of homogeneous

catalysis of various reactions to produce selectively controlled products; thus, it has long been considered possible to use metal clusters as homogeneous catalysts for the reduction of carbon monoxide, the Fischer-Tropsch reaction.

This breakthrough was achieved during the past year by Muetterties' research group, who demonstrated that $Os_3(CO)_{12}$ and $Ir_4(CO)_{12}$ in toluene solution catalyzed the hydrogen reduction of carbon monoxide to give methane according to the equation $3H_2 + CO \rightarrow CH_4 + H_2O$. These catalytic reactions were effected in sealed glass tubes at 140° C (285° F), at pressures of about two atmospheres, and under conditions of complete homogeneity of the reaction systems. It is not known for certain how the reaction proceeds, but one possibility is represented schematically in (3).

Only two metal atoms of the metal cluster are shown, and the reaction scheme suggests activation of carbon monoxide through the formation of a bond between its oxygen atom and an adjacent metal atom. This facilitates cleavage of the C—O bond, whereupon individual C and O atoms readily react with hydrogen to form methane and water, the desired products. The resulting free bonding sites on the metal atoms in turn readily accept more CO and the reaction cycle repeats. This capacity for regeneration and for the production of desired products via a low-energy reaction pathway constitutes the requirements of a catalyst.

The ultimate goal of the use of metal clusters as catalysts is to control the formation of products through selective changes in the metal, in groups attached to the metal, and in experimental conditions. For example, the reaction described above takes place in the solvent toluene, whereas in molten $NaCl \cdot 2AlCl_3$ the reaction generates ethane (C_2H_6) almost exclusively. Patents were issued to Union Carbide for use of $Rh_6(CO)_{16}$ as a catalyst in the conversion of CO and H_2 to methanol (CH_3OH), ethylene glycol ($HOCH_2CH_2OH$), and propylene glycol ($CH_3CHOHCH_2OH$). Ethylene glycol is used as antifreeze, as a solvent, and as a starting material for the manufacture of polyester fibers. These embryonic results were most encouraging in that they supported the view that it should be possible to modify metal-cluster catalysts to generate desired products from coal and water sources on a commercial scale.

It is worthy of note that investigations involving

3

$$-M-M- + 2CO \rightarrow \overset{\displaystyle OC}{\underset{\displaystyle |}{}} \overset{\displaystyle CO}{\underset{\displaystyle |}{}} \quad \overset{-CO}{\rightarrow} \quad \overset{C-O}{/ \ \backslash} \quad \rightarrow \quad \overset{C}{\underset{\displaystyle |}{}} \overset{O}{\underset{\displaystyle |}{}} \quad \overset{+H_2}{\rightarrow} \quad -M-M- + CH_4 + H_2O$$
$$-M-M- \qquad -M-M- \qquad -M-M-$$

Chemistry

homogeneous catalysis during the past year also contributed to the water-gas shift reaction $H_2O + CO \rightarrow H_2 + CO_2$. This reaction has been of great industrial importance for the past 40 years as a means for the production of hydrogen from water. The commercial process requires the use of a heterogeneous catalyst, either iron oxide or copper metal, and a temperature of about 300° C. Observations reported recently by Peter C. Ford and co-workers of the University of California at Santa Barbara revealed that $Ru_3(CO)_{12}$ added to an alkaline alcoholic solution could efficiently catalyze this reaction at 100° C. Independently, the research of Richard Eisenberg and his students at the University of Rochester, N.Y., showed that rhodium carbonyl iodide in glacial acetic acid also catalyzes the water-gas shift reaction. The mechanism of this reaction is not known, but it could proceed via the following reactions: $[RhI_2(CO)_2]^- + 2HI \rightarrow [RhI_4CO]^- + H_2 + CO$; $[RhI_4CO]^- + H_2O + 2CO \rightarrow [RhI_2(CO)_2]^- + 2HI + CO_2$. Note that the sum of the two reactions is equal to the water-gas shift reaction, which is as it should be for a catalytic process.

Photochemistry. Inorganic chemists have long known that many inorganic compounds, particularly metal complexes, are photosensitive. The past quarter century experienced a continual increase in research in inorganic photochemistry, which in the United States was due largely to the pioneering effort of Arthur W. Adamson at the University of Southern California. Metal complexes, such as $[Cr(NH_3)_5Cl]^{2+}$ in aqueous solution, were studied in considerable detail. First the types of photochemical reactions had to be established, and then the dependence of these reactions on the energy of the light radiation. These experimental results in turn were interpreted in terms of modern concepts of bonding and spectroscopy. Such worldwide research eventually provided a base for the fundamental understanding of photochemical reactions of inorganic compounds.

Building upon this foundation, some photochemists recently turned their attention to the important task of utilizing solar energy. One unique approach to the use of sunlight for the formation of hydrogen and oxygen from water was reported by David G. Whitten and his associates at the University of North Carolina. The process works by one of the most efficient mechanisms for converting light energy into chemical energy, i.e., photoinduced electron transfer, which fortunately is also one of the most extensively studied photochemical reactions of metal complexes—in particular the redox behavior of the tris(2,2'-bipyridine)ruthenium(II) ion $[Ru(bipy)_3]^{2+}$. In the excited state afforded by sunlight, the ruthenium complex should be able to reduce water to hydrogen. It does not, however,

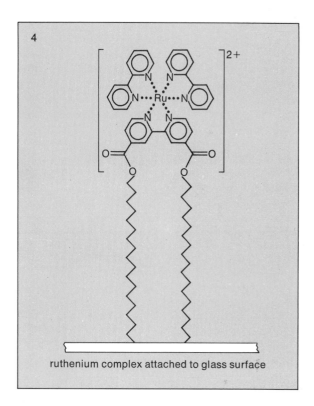
ruthenium complex attached to glass surface

because decay of the excited state is faster than the electron transfer needed for hydrogen production. This drawback was overcome by rendering the complex insoluble, which allowed electron transfer to take place more easily. For this purpose, the complex was modified as is shown in (4) and deposited in monolayer films on glass slides. Irradiation of the glass slides placed in water generated hydrogen and oxygen. The energetics of the process makes sense because the excited-state energy of the ruthenium complex is more than ample to provide the energy required to cleave water. Whether the process would be economically feasible, however, was not yet determined.

Another approach to the use of sunlight for the production of hydrogen and oxygen, developed in the laboratory of Mark S. Wrighton at the Massachusetts Institute of Technology, involves the photoassisted electrolysis of water by means of a photochemical cell. It had been known since 1839 that irradiation of an electrode in an electrochemical cell yields a photocurrent, and presumably such a device could be used to convert light energy into chemical energy in the form of storable fuel, such as hydrogen. Although metal electrodes do give photoelectric effects, semiconductor photoelectrodes were found to have the highest light efficiency for electron flow in the external circuit, a fact first reported a few years ago for the n-type photoelectrode of titanium dioxide (TiO_2). Since

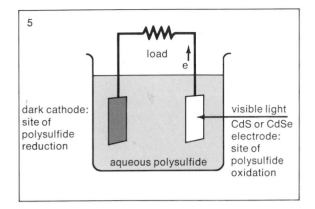

5

load

e

dark cathode:
site of
polysulfide
reduction

visible light
CdS or CdSe
electrode:
site of
polysulfide
oxidation

aqueous polysulfide

that time several other semiconductors have been used with modest success.

One serious drawback for the use of these systems in solar energy conversion was their limitation to ultraviolet light. Electrodes responsive to visible light were needed. It had been known that both *n*-type cadmium sulfide (CdS) and cadmium selenide (CdSe) electrodes have this desired property but that unfortunately they suffered from anodic dissolution when used as electrodes in photochemical cells. Recently in Wrighton's laboratory it was discovered that an electrolyte containing either sulfide or polysulfide in aqueous solution prevents the destruction of CdS and CdSe electrodes, thereby permitting the construction of the photochemical cell shown in (5). Because CdSe responds to about 50% of the Sun's light, it was estimated that for a CdSe-based cell about 2% of the insolation at the Earth's surface could be converted to electricity. Although these results were most encouraging, this beginning was a long way from the development of an economical device for the large-scale conversion of solar energy.

Borane chemistry. The 1976 Nobel Prize for Chemistry was awarded to William Nunn Lipscomb, Jr., of Harvard University for his original research on the structure and bonding of boron hydrides. (*See* Year in Review: SCIENTISTS OF THE YEAR.) His theoretical and experimental work on these compounds spans a period of more than 25 years, during which time the field of boron chemistry experienced dramatic growth, extending into such areas as high-energy fuels, organic syntheses, organometallic compounds, and polymer chemistry. Borane compounds (compounds of boron and hydrogen, analogous to alkane hydrocarbons) were mentioned in the scientific literature prior to 1912, but almost everything reported was incorrect. Early in the century borane chemistry was put on a firm basis by the monumental research of the German chemist Alfred Stock, an outstanding experimentalist who was ahead of his time in the techniques

of handling air-sensitive compounds. He prepared and characterized diborane (B_2H_6), the simplest member of the series, and such higher homologs as B_4H_{10}, B_5H_9, B_5H_{11}, and $B_{10}H_{14}$.

Nevertheless, the nature of the bonding of these compounds and their structures remained a mystery to chemists for many years. The basic difficulty was that boron, unlike carbon, does not have enough electrons to form the usual electron-pair covalent bonds to all of the hydrogens and to itself. When the structure of diborane was eventually determined, it was found that two of its six hydrogen atoms form a bridge between the two boron atoms. The bonding of a bridged hydrogen to two boron atoms could be described in terms of a three-centered bond, in which three atoms are held together by only two electrons.

Although the concept of the three-centered bond was a major advance in understanding the existence of these compounds, chemists remained bewildered by the lack of a guiding principle to account for all of the known boranes; this was in clear contrast to the hydrocarbons, in which each member bears a clear and predictable relationship to the next. It was in this respect that Lipscomb made his greatest contribution to borane chemistry. He developed a topological theory of bonding for the boranes, which gave a plausible explanation of the known structures. More importantly, the theory made possible the prediction of new compounds, which guided the efforts of synthetic chemists and was largely responsible for the recent rapid developments in the field.

—Fred Basolo

Organic chemistry

Traditionally the mainstream of research in organic chemistry springs from an exclusive interest in carbon compounds. In recent times, however, it has been fed by tributaries originating in the areas of inorganic and physical chemistry and the life sciences. The course of developments within the past year reflected this diversity of interests within the field.

Organometallic chemistry. The undisputed importance of catalysis in such industrial processes as petroleum cracking stimulated interest in the interactions of organic compounds with various transition metals. One catalytic reaction that continued to attract considerable attention was the olefin metathesis reaction, in which the "ends" of two alkenes are interchanged:

$$RHC=CHR + R'HC=CHR' \rightleftarrows 2R'HC=CHR.$$

A number of research groups implicated metal carbene complexes in this process. Using a phenyltungsten trichloride-aluminum trichloride catalyst,

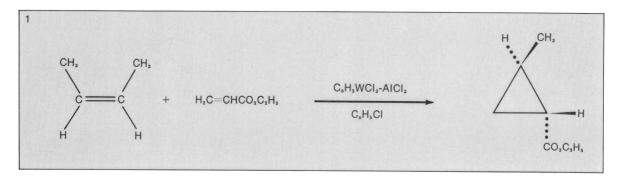

1

Paul G. Gassman of the University of Minnesota successfully trapped such intermediate carbene complexes with ethyl acrylate to give cyclopropane derivatives (1). (For additional discussion of the olefin metathesis reaction, see *1977 Yearbook of Science and the Future* Year in Review: CHEMISTRY: *Inorganic chemistry*.)

Another facet of organometallic chemistry involved the development of mild, selective synthetic reactions mediated by various transition-metal catalysts. Louis S. Hegedus of Colorado State University recently developed an intriguing procedure for the synthesis of the indole ring system using both nickel and palladium intermediates (2). The broad spectrum of indole alkaloids that occur in nature made this development a particularly promising synthetic tool.

Organoboron chemistry. The contributions of Nobel laureate William N. Lipscomb to the understanding of boron chemistry have advanced the development of organic chemistry and have made various boron hydride compounds ubiquitous, indispensable reagents in the modern organic laboratory. Herbert C. Brown of Purdue University,

West Lafayette, Ind., pioneered the introduction of a host of such reagents including, within the last year, lithium trisiamylborohydride, which afforded phenomenal stereoselectivity in the reductions of ketones to alcohols as shown in (3).

Isolation and synthesis. As organic chemists continued to screen a variety of plant and animal sources in search of biologically active molecules, nature rewarded them with an incredible diversity of structures. Intrigued by reports that ethanol extracts (moonshine) of the roots of the insectivorous plant *Sarracenia flava,* or golden trumpet, were used as a folk remedy by residents of the Okefenokee swamp in Georgia, D. Howard Miles of Mississippi State University isolated a natural paralytic agent called sarracenin. Charles J. Sih of the University of Wisconsin isolated the major hypertensive principle of tu-chung, a medicinal herb used in China for thousands of years, and the late S. Morris Kupchan of the University of Virginia reported on the isolation of a variety of antitumor agents such as jatrophone.

The existence of complex natural products also provided impetus for recent developments in synthetic organic chemistry. From a practical point of view, total synthesis offered a means for procuring scarce natural products needed for clinical testing and for obtaining analogs of natural products that possessed improved medicinal properties. Within the last year Andrew S. Kende of the University of Rochester, N.Y., and Paul A. Grieco of the University of Pittsburgh, Pa., completed stereoselective syntheses of the antitumor agents steganacin and vernolepin, respectively. Yoshito Kishi of Harvard University and Jack E. Baldwin of the Massa-

2

an indole

3

99%   1%

4

methymycin

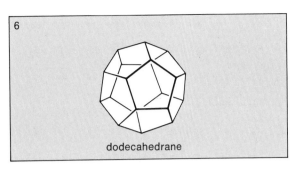

6

dodecahedrane

chusetts Institute of Technology achieved the synthesis of the antibiotics gliotoxin and penicillin, respectively, using elegant sequences of reactions.

In devising solutions to the synthetic problems posed by various natural products, organic chemists are often required to develop new methods for constructing parts of certain molecules. For example, the antibiotic methymycin (4) possesses a macrocyclic lactone subunit (shown in bold lines) for which few general methods of synthesis were available. Recently, Elias J. Corey of Harvard University invented a "double activation" procedure for linking long-chain ω-hydroxyacids to obtain macrocyclic lactones. This procedure holds great promise of being sufficiently mild to be employed ultimately in the synthesis of such natural products as methymycin.

Quite apart from the synthesis of natural products, there is interest in the construction of unusual hydrocarbons. Abraham Zilkha of the Hebrew University of Jerusalem devised an intriguing synthesis of a class of organic molecules that possess

unusual mechanical linkages. Zilkha first constructed a rotaxane (5a) in which the linear chain passing through the ring cannot "unthread" because of the bulky groups at the end of the chain. Next, he chemically coupled the two ends of the chain to afford a catenane containing two mechanically linked rings (5b). Along another line of research, a long-standing interest in highly symmetric hydrocarbons continued unabated as Leo A. Paquette of Ohio State University strove to complete the synthesis of dodecahedrane (6).

Bioorganic research. Organic chemists have developed various theories to account for the structurally diverse compounds found in nature and have sought to test these theories in ingenious ways. One broad family of fifteen-carbon compounds, called sesquiterpenes, is derived from mevalonate and is characterized by the presence of multiples of an "isoprene" unit. For example, β-bisabolene can be subdivided into the three isoprene units shown in bold outline in (7). In contrast, ovalicin cannot be subdivided in this manner. David E. Cane of Brown University, Providence, R.I., has shown, nevertheless, that ovalicin is a mevalonate-derived sesquiterpene. The specific biochemical pathway that accounts for the carbon skeleton of ovalicin was established using carbon-13 (^{13}C) iso-

5

a   rotaxane   b   catenane

ß-bisabolene   mevalonate   ovalicin

tope labels to trace a specific carbon in mevalonate to a corresponding carbon in ovalicin. A number of other research groups, notably Kenneth L. Rinehart of the University of Illinois, Edward Leete of the University of Minnesota, and Thomas M. Harris of Vanderbilt University, Nashville, Tenn., were pursuing biosynthetic studies involving other natural products.

As organic chemists unraveled the biosynthetic pathways leading to various natural products, they were attracted to the notion that they might mimic enzyme-mediated reactions in the laboratory. It was known, for example, that the acyclic molecule squalene gives rise to the tetracyclic steroid lanosterol under the influence of enzymes. In an extensive series of investigations, William S. Johnson of Stanford University incorporated this idea in the synthesis of complex cyclic structures. Recently, he demonstrated the potential value of this technique for the synthesis of corticosteroid-like systems by converting a monocyclic precursor into tetracyclic 11α-hydroxyprogesterone.

One area of bioorganic research focused on the molecular changes wrought by enzymes on small organic substrates. For example, the potential health hazard presented by certain polynuclear aromatic hydrocarbons found in the environment generated considerable interest in studying their metabolic fate. Several research groups, namely Thomas C. Bruice of the University of California at Santa Barbara, Ronald G. Harvey of the University of Chicago, Charles Heidelberger of the University of Wisconsin, and Donald M. Jerina of the National Institutes of Health, Bethesda, Md., implicated the arene oxides derived from polynuclear arenes as carcinogenic agents (8). To understand the nature of the binding of arene oxides to cellular macromolecules, the chemistry of arene oxides was un-

der active investigation. The recent isolation of an arene oxide-nucleic acid adduct suggested that arene oxides bind DNA or RNA.

Another active area of bioorganic research involved probing the nature of the active site or sites within enzymes. Two basic approaches were being taken in investigations of this type. One is exemplified by a recent study by Raja G. Khalifah of the University of Virginia who employed ^{13}C nuclear magnetic resonance (NMR) spectroscopy to study the active site of carbonic anhydrase. Emil T. Kaiser of the University of Chicago took another approach in studying the active site of the enzyme, phosphofructokinase, in which an active-site reagent was used to bind covalently a sulfhydryl group in the active-site region.

Aromaticity. The discovery of benzene, an unsaturated C_6H_6 hydrocarbon, in 1825 by Michael Faraday was followed by considerable controversy regarding its structure. August Kekule, who proposed the correct structure in 1865, called benzene and its derivatives "aromatic" compounds because of their characteristic odor. For many years aromaticity was associated exclusively with the unique chemistry of benzene and its derivatives. Although generally useful, this criterion of low chemical reactivity is not absolute because, in contrast to the chemistry of benzene, certain aromatic compounds (e.g., pyrogallol) are prone to oxidation and other aromatic compounds (e.g., phenanthrene) undergo addition reactions.

The emergence of molecular orbital theory resulted in a new definition for aromaticity which, in simplified form, stated that a cyclic, conjugated system with $4n + 2$ π-bond electrons would be "aromatic" and a system with $4n$ π-bond electrons would be "antiaromatic." Benzene, of course, is still defined as aromatic because it has 6 electrons in its π-bond system ($n = 1$). Considerable interest was generated in studying the "aromatic" character of large cyclic systems (in which n is greater than 1), and NMR spectroscopy proved an invaluable tool for probing the aromaticity or antiaromaticity of such compounds, which are called annulenes. It is interesting, therefore, that within the past year Franz Sondheimer of University College, London, discovered a reactivity criterion for

polynuclear arene   monooxygenase enzymes   arene oxide

distinguishing between aromatic and antiaromatic annulenes. For example, the aromatic [14]- and [18]annulene[c]furans undergo a Diels-Alder reaction with dimethyl acetylenedicarboxylate, whereas the corresponding [12]- and [16]annulene[c]furans prove unreactive.

—David S. Watt

Physical chemistry

Physical chemistry is the study of the structure of molecules, the nature of the chemical bond holding atoms in the molecule together, the changes in molecular structure and bonding during reaction-initiating collisions between molecules, and the macroscopic manifestation of these molecular properties in the form of the thermodynamic properties of chemical systems.

Laser chemistry. Physical chemists of the 1970s would be hard put to choose between a laser and a computer as the more useful tool. The importance of the laser can be gauged by the growth in the U.S. National Science Foundation's (NSF) chemical instrumentation budget. In 1973 NSF bought scientists about $100,000 worth of lasers and associated equipment. Three years later, however, that amount leaped to $1 million, only slightly less than one-fourth of the entire instrumentation program budget.

Laser-induced fluorescence in combination with molecular beams well illustrates the usefulness of lasers to the physical chemist. Chemists have long studied the dynamics of molecular collisions by measuring the angular distribution of product molecules when two crossed molecular beams of reagents collide in a high vacuum. But they were unable to discern which of the many internal quantum states (both vibrational and rotational) were occupied by product molecules. Because this sort of information is predictable by theory, such so-called state-to-state reaction rates are most useful for comparing theory and experiment and for allowing chemists to "fine tune" reactions.

At Columbia University, Richard Zare and Gary Pruett carried out experiments in which a beam of barium atoms and two lasers mutually intersected in a cell filled with hydrogen fluoride. An infrared laser excited some molecules of hydrogen fluoride into a more excited vibrational state as the barium beam entered the cell. A visible-light laser then electronically excited molecules of the product, barium fluoride. By observing the wavelengths of the fluorescence emitted by the excited product, the investigators were able to determine the distribution of occupied vibrational states in the product when hydrogen fluoride reactant was in either the excited or ground vibrational state.

The technique of nuclear magnetic resonance (NMR) spectroscopy has undergone great increases in speed, sensitivity, and resolution since the development of pulsed or Fourier transform NMR. The laser may lead to a comparable effect on optical spectroscopy by way of a group of phenomena called coherent optical transients. By observing the decay of these transients as sequences of laser pulses are applied to gases, liquids, or solids, physical chemists can deduce such information as the force laws governing the collisions responsible for the decay. Using Fourier transform techniques, Richard Brewer and Stephen Grossman of the IBM Research Laboratory in San Jose, Calif., were able simultaneously to resolve several closely spaced spectral lines and map out coherent transients for them in gaseous methyl fluoride.

The laser has also opened up the new field of infrared photochemistry. The energy of one quantum of infrared radiation (one photon) is not sufficient to break chemical bonds and thus drive a reaction. With lasers, however, the intensity of the light is so great that several photons can reach a given molecule at nearly the same time and combine together to break a bond. Moreover, by adjusting the laser frequency to match only the vibrational frequency of certain molecular species in a mixture, chemists can ensure that only those molecules selected by the laser can react. The ability to select specific species opens the way to new processes of chemical synthesis and possibly to new products, because heating reactants, the normal way of driving a reaction, nonselectively cause all molecules in a mixture to react.

During the past year Ernest Grunwald and his associates at Brandeis University, Waltham, Mass., began infrared photochemistry experiments with various organic molecules of the chlorofluorocarbon family and a carbon dioxide infrared laser. Of particular interest in these experiments is the fact that the gaseous compounds were at a relatively high pressure, compared with many laser chemistry experiments. This condition increased the possibility of obtaining high yields and thus made the method interesting for potential commercial application. In fact, one recent patent, issued to George Pratt of the Massachusetts Institute of Technology, seemed to cover the entire field of infrared photochemistry, including Grunwald's method. As of early 1977 MIT was in the process of trying to sign up licensees.

Centralized equipment facilities. Whereas some chemists were beginning to consider establishment of a national or regional laser facility to enable visiting scientists to use equipment they normally could not afford, computational chemists had nearly achieved a similar goal. The U.S. Energy

Research and Development Administration (ERDA) and NSF jointly agreed to support a National Resource for Computational Chemistry (NRCC). To be located at an ERDA national laboratory not yet selected, NRCC would provide visiting computational chemists access to high-performance computers for certain theoretical problems requiring exceptionally lengthy computer programs. Concurrently the NRCC staff would develop and maintain computer programs for loan to chemists to use at their own facilities.

Computational decentralization. Nearly diametrically opposing this development was the trend toward the use of high performance mini- and medium-sized computers for large-scale computation, as opposed to more mundane tasks, such as controlling experiments. Stimulated by the successful completion of a three-year experiment by Henry Schaefer and William Miller of the University of California at Berkeley, some chemists found it more economical to buy their own computer than to rely on their institution's computer center, in part because the manufacturers of small computers have been able to increase the performance of their machines without comparable increases in their prices. Schaefer and Miller felt that the cost reduction in some situations could mean the difference between doing and not doing a calculation.

Catalysis. Lasers and computers were by no means the only subjects of interest in physical chemistry. Many scientists believed that the key to advancing heterogeneous catalysis from its present status as "art" to that of science was the application of quantum theoretical and modern spectroscopic techniques to the study of metal surfaces and their interactions with adsorbed molecules. In many cases, however, clusters consisting of only a few metal atoms were easier to study; yet they still could serve as an adequate alternative model of the full surface.

In one recent set of experiments, Ward Plummer and his associates at the University of Pennsylvania took X-ray photoelectron spectra of molecular complexes consisting of one or more metal atoms and several carbon monoxide ligands. The researchers discovered that the spectra taken from clusters containing three or four metal atoms reproduced all the spectral detail they could obtain from carbon monoxide adsorbed on bulk metal surfaces. Chemists, including Earl Muetterties of Cornell University, also showed that clusters containing three or more transition-metal atoms to which organic chemical groups like carbon monoxide are attached can act as homogeneous catalysts to promote reactions that in the past had been catalyzed only by heterogeneous metal surface cata-

Recently developed techniques for the simultaneous deposition of metal vapors and vapors of organic solvents at low temperatures may yield useful catalysts. Shown are scanning electron micrographs of codeposited nickel-tetrahydrofuran before (left) and after heating and consequent sintering.

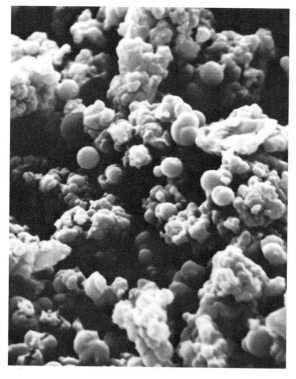

(Photos) Courtesy, Kenneth J. Klabunde, University of North Dakota

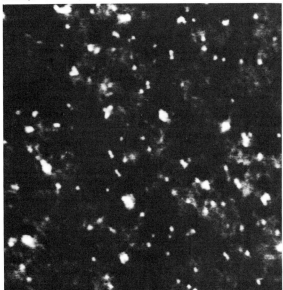

Courtesy, The University of Chicago

Using a specially built electron microscope, University of Chicago scientists obtained the first motion pictures of individual uranium atoms (bright spots). Images are magnified 5.5 million times.

lysts. For further information, see *Inorganic chemistry: Metal clusters*, above.

Atomic motion pictures. Electron microscopists are continually seeking ways to increase the usefulness of their instruments. Transmission electron microscopes and scanning electron microscopes, the two best-known varieties of instrument, operate on different principles and provide quite different types of information. In the past five years considerable interest has centered around another variety, the scanning transmission electron microscope (STEM), which combines the high resolution of transmission instruments with the ability to obtain certain additional information that the scanning feature provides.

During the past year, for example, Albert Crewe and Michael Isaacson of the University of Chicago, while attempting to view biomolecular structures with a very-high-resolution STEM built in their own laboratory, instead obtained the first motion pictures of individual atoms. During their search for techniques to make proteins and nucleic acids visible under a STEM by "staining" them with heavy atoms, which would stand out as bright spots in an electron micrograph, the investigators dried highly purified uranyl chloride (UO_2Cl_2) solutions on ultrathin carbon support films. They then repeatedly photographed a single 200×200 Å field (1 Å or angstrom $= 10^{-8}$ cm), producing about 120 successive time-lapse pictures in 2½ hours. When shown at 16 frames per second the brief com-

pressed-time motion picture revealed uranium atoms animatedly engaged in a crawling motion across the support film, presumably because of their thermal energy.

Applications of the new technique for the most part would be left to the imaginations of scientists, who might find uses for it. Meanwhile, Crewe and Isaacson were working at ways to eliminate the bothersome thermal motion, which interfered with the use of heavy atoms as a stain for biomolecules.

—Arthur L. Robinson

Applied chemistry

Man's demands on science for the necessities and conveniences of daily existence increase with each passing year—a trend no better exemplified than by the diversity of practical applications derived from chemical research within recent months. Both manufacturers and consumers of textiles seemed certain to benefit from two developments, a new synthetic fiber with properties approaching those of wool and cotton and an effective antibacterial treatment for cotton fabrics. Artificial membranes persisted as a topic of interest because of their usefulness in concentrating and isolating substances from the surrounding medium. And chemists seeking the perfect sugar substitute contributed to a better understanding of the relationship between the structure of a molecule and its taste.

ATF-1017. The desirable characteristics of wool and cotton have been closely duplicated, and in some cases surpassed, by those of a unique synthetic fiber developed by scientists at Bayer Aktiengesellschaft in West Germany. Presently code named ATF-1017, the new acrylic is 30% lighter than conventional acrylic fibers of the same diameter and possesses properties expected to make it ideal for clothing and upholstery fabrics. Emulating the wick action of cotton, ATF-1017 quickly absorbs body moisture and distributes it throughout the fabric, enhancing evaporation and thus providing coolness and comfort for the wearer. Although wool and cotton fibers can absorb as much as 40% by weight of water, they tend to swell, closing spaces within the fabric construction and reducing air circulation. ATF-1017 absorbs at least 30% by weight of water without swelling; by contrast, conventional nonswelling synthetics absorb only about 5%.

Central to the new fiber's superior qualities is a process that introduces tiny, tunnel-like capillaries throughout the entire length of each fiber as it emerges from the spinneret. To protect this delicate structure each strand is sheathed in a dense outer layer of acrylic that contains numerous porous inlets; these additional canals allow moisture to pass between the internal capillary system and the outside. As of early 1977 the new fiber was still under development, with commercial production still several years in the future.

Antibacterial fabrics. Leading a team of chemists at the U.S. Department of Agriculture's Southern Regional Research Center in New Orleans, Tyrone L. Vigo developed a treatment for cotton fabrics that inhibits the growth of pathogenic and odor-causing bacteria. Several years earlier his research group had succeeded in producing antibacterial cotton in bulk form for one-time use in hospital operating rooms by chlorination of the fibers or by a subsequent treatment that substitutes thiocyanate groups for chlorine atoms. The latest process, applied to cotton textiles, forms a stable metal-peroxide polymer coating from which peroxide groups are released each time the fabric is laundered.

For treatment the fabric is dipped in an aqueous solution of a metal acetate, a peroxide agent such as hydrogen peroxide or sodium perborate, and acetic acid; it is then mechanically processed to remove excess solution and cured at temperatures as high as 160° C (320° F). The kind of metal used in the process markedly affects the stability of the final coating; for instance, treatments using zirconyl acetate maintained effective bacteriostatic activity during 20 washings, whereas those using zinc acetate lasted through 50 washings, a practical minimum goal. Treated fabrics were tested for presence of *Staphylococcus epidermidis*, the main cause of perspiration odor, and for *S. aureus* and *Escherichia coli*, two troublesome bacteria prevalent on diapers and hospital linens.

Although the polymer coatings were found to adhere successfully to such textiles as polyester, silk, and rayon, antibacterial activity was not complete; other fibers, including acetate, wool, and nylon, did not retain the coatings well. Because peroxide is a bleach as well as a disinfectant, potential problems with certain fabric dyes were expected. Compatability of the treatment with flame-retardant chemicals and permanent-press processes were other important factors requiring investigation.

Liquid membranes. Liquid membranes made their debut in 1966 as a serendipitous discovery by Norman N. Li of Exxon Research & Engineering Co. Neglected for several years thereafter, they have only begun to be appreciated for their ability to isolate a substance from its environs or to separate it from other substances.

Liquid membrane systems are formed when an oil, water, and a surfactant are emulsified at high mixing speeds. A surfactant is any of a class of molecules, including detergents, whose structure

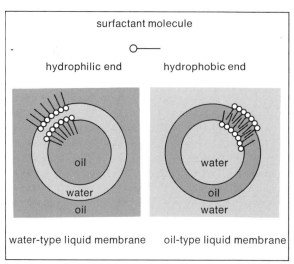

Liquid membrane systems consist typically of thin films of either water or an oil stabilized by oriented surfactant molecules.

contains a hydrophilic end (one that possesses an affinity for water) and a hydrophobic end (one that avoids water). During emulsification, surfactant molecules cluster at water-oil interfaces, directing their hydrophilic groups into the water and the hydrophobic ones into the oil, a phenomenon that forms thin stable films, or membranes. Typically, tiny droplets of water, on the order of 0.1 mm in diameter, become encapsulated in a membrane of oil; these droplets in turn become suspended in water where they aggregate into larger globules about 1 mm in diameter. Alternatively, droplets of oil may be encapsulated in a membrane of water, which is then suspended in oil.

Membranes of oil or water naturally exhibit selective permeability to various chemicals. A substance soluble in the membrane and in both of the liquids that it separates will readily diffuse through the membrane, whereas a substance insoluble in the membrane will remain isolated in either the encapsulated medium or the exterior one. Li and his co-workers found that varying the kind of surfactant or adding other chemicals to the membrane system can tune its selectivity, achieving considerable discretion with respect to the kinds of molecules allowed to diffuse and the rates at which diffusion takes place. This flexibility suggested obvious uses for liquid membranes as timed-release agents in long-term drug administration.

Of particular importance were practical demonstrations that various solutions contained in the encapsulated droplets could be used to trap molecules from the exterior medium. For example, in laboratory experiments simulating aspirin and phenobarbital overdose, two very common forms of poisoning in the U.S., oil membrane systems that encapsulated aqueous solutions of strong bases were shown effective in scavenging 95% of the drugs within five minutes from acidic, aqueous exterior media resembling conditions found in the human stomach. In each case the drug, an organic acid with good solubility in oil in its un-ionized state, diffused through the membrane into the encapsulated basic solution where it became ionized and consequently completely insoluble in oil. Studies also were mounted to determine the effectiveness of such systems in the removal of the body's own toxic waste products, such as urea, uric acid, and creatinine, which accumulate in harmful quantities in certain pathological conditions.

Passive scavenging techniques using liquid membranes were being examined for their applications in water purification and mineral concentration. The removal of phenol and such heavy metal ions as chromium(VI), mercury(II), and copper(II) from wastewater and mine water was demonstrated with systems employing acids or bases in the encapsulated liquid. A more active approach to pollution control, accomplishing chemical conversion rather than collection, was being pursued by several investigators. In one case, nitrate and nitrite ions in solution were reduced catalytically to elemental nitrogen using a membrane-encapsulated complex of isolated bacterial enzymes and cofactors. While both pollutants and their breakdown products diffused freely through the membrane, all the necessary enzymes and cofactors remained immobilized in the close proximity essential to their proper functioning as catalysts.

Oxygen-permeable polymer membrane. The past year saw announcement of another kind of artificial membrane, an ultrathin film more permeable to molecules of oxygen than to those of nitrogen. Although its molecular structure and details of its production remained a proprietary secret, its developers at the General Electric Research and Development Center, Schenectady, N.Y., described the material as a semipermeable solid polymer two millionths of an inch thick that allows gas molecules to migrate through it at rates 100–1,000 times higher than the most permeable silicone-rubber membranes in commercial use. Air drawn through the material under negative pressure emerges with a 30–50% oxygen content, compared with the normal value of 21%.

Because fuel burned in oxygen-enriched air is consumed less rapidly and produces a hotter flame, the new membrane was expected to reduce fuel costs in many industrial processes. It was also being tested as the central element of a portable oxygen-therapy unit for victims of chronic obstructive lung disease and cardiac insufficiency, who otherwise must accept the dangers and logistical problems of high-pressure oxygen in heavy tanks. Recent medical studies indicated that oxygen at 40% concentration, well within the production capability of the membrane, might be as effective a therapy for most such patients as the 100% concentration presently available.

Unrefrigerated fresh milk. Unrefrigerated fresh milk could become a reality within five to ten years because of an enzymatic process developed by Harold E. Swaisgood and co-workers at North Carolina State University at Raleigh. As presently practiced, pasteurization is only a partial sterilization technique that exposes milk to high temperatures for short periods of time, typically 72° C (162° F) for 15 seconds, to destroy the pathogenic bacterium *Mycobacterium tuberculosis* and some of the microorganisms responsible for spoilage. Left unrefrigerated, however, milk still contains sufficient bacteria to sour. Prolonged high temperatures necessary for complete sterilization—which would allow containers of milk to remain unrefrigerated until opened—imparts a distasteful flavor, a result of the unfolding of whey proteins to expose unpleasant-tasting sulfhydryl (−S−H) groups (sometimes called thiol or mercapto groups) by cleavage of the sulfur−sulfur, or disulfide, links that normally maintain the protein in its folded conformation.

In the course of his investigations Swaisgood isolated an enzyme, called sulfhydryl oxidase, that restores the fresh flavor to milk by catalyzing the oxidation of pairs of exposed sulfhydryls to disulfides. In the laboratory the reaction was carried out with the enzyme immobilized on glass beads over which heat-sterilized milk was passed, although in future commercial applications the enzyme would probably be bonded to a less expensive ceramic-bead support.

Building a better sugar substitute. Man's desire for sweet-tasting foods created the sugar extraction and refining industries, which by the mid-1970s were supplying a world demand of about 45 lb of refined sugar, or sucrose, per capita. Concomitant with heavy sugar use, such problems as

saccharin

Shown are perillartine and several of 80 synthesized oxime analogues; see text. Values accompanying each structure are: solubility in water (in molarity, M, at 25° C), taste potency (times sucrose), and ratio of the percentage of sweetness to that of bitterness (total 100%). Taste screening of the compounds was conducted by a panel of four to six experienced individuals.

weight gain and tooth decay led to early interest in artificial, non-nutritive substitutes. The most popular of these chemicals, saccharin (1), first marketed in the U.S. in the 1880s, proved at best an imperfect sweetener because of its bitter off-taste, and most other subsequently developed substitutes were found to share this feature or to possess drawbacks of their own.

One approach to finding a better sweetener has been through study of the relationship between taste and chemical structure, although the development of a unified theory in this field has been hindered by a poor understanding of the human taste-receptor mechanism and by the diversity of chemical structures found in both natural and artificial sweet-tasting compounds. Recently Edward M. Acton and Herbert Stone of the Stanford Research Institute, Menlo Park, Calif., mounted a systematic attack on the problem, using as a starting point a long-known chemical called perillartine (2), which has found usefulness only as a tobacco sweetener because of its low solubility in water, bitterness, and menthol-licorice off-taste.

The two chemists began by assuming that perillartine's aldoxime component (shown circled) was the agent primarily responsible for the molecule's sweet taste. They then proceeded to make structural changes in the remainder of the molecule, which might be considered a "carrier" group, to

calcium cyclamate

minimize undesirable properties. Ultimately creating 80 oxime analogues of perillartine, the experimenters sometimes made quite drastic modifications, such as removal of the side chain para to (opposite) the aldoxime group, changes in ring size, or cleavage of the ring.

They confirmed the necessity for the presence of the aldoxime group and its free hydroxyl (OH) group (see 3) and found that, although sweetness was retained when the ring was made smaller or cleaved, it was reduced upon insertion of a sulfur or oxygen atom in the ring (4). The double bond in the intact or cleaved ring proved necessary for sweetness, and a ring with two double bonds generally made the molecule even sweeter. They also found that the side chain affected both sweetness and solubility of the molecule. If the side chain was made too long, sweetness disappeared (5), whereas insertion of an oxygen atom in the chain improved solubility. There often occurred an inverse relationship between solubility and sweetness; structural changes that improved solubility sometimes lowered potency (6, 7). Eventually the chemists determined that a side chain consisting of oxygen incorporated as OCH_3, plus the insertion of an extra carbon atom to give CH_2OCH_3, offered the best compromise.

For its combination of solubility, potency, and negligible nonsweet tastes, one particular compound (8), dubbed aldoxime I by its creators, emerged as a potentially practical food and drink sweetener. On a weight basis, aldoxime I is 450 times sweeter than sucrose; in comparison, saccharin is about 300 times sweeter and calcium cyclamate (9), a popular sugar substitute until its ban in the U.S. in 1970 as a possible carcinogen, is only 30 times sweeter. Although preliminary screening tests indicated that the new artificial sweetener is not mutagenic, further examination would be required prior to its approval as a safe food and drink additive.

—Charles M. Cegielski

Earth sciences

During the past year the Earth sciences witnessed vigorous activity in several fields of study. Meteorologists pursued their investigations of the Earth's magnetosphere and continued preparations for an international atmospheric research experiment. Internationally sponsored deep-sea drilling revealed new data about past movements of the Earth's crust and changes in its magnetic field, and considerable attention was given to the geochemistry of trace elements and their relationship to human health. Evaluation of the success of earthquake-prediction methods in China and programs to understand and minimize the effects of drought were other significant topics.

Atmospheric sciences

During the past year in the atmospheric sciences there was an intensification of interest in the following areas of research: climate and its fluctuations; the chemistry of the ozone layer; the nature of the magnetosphere, the huge region of charged particles surrounding the Earth; and preparations for a massive international program, known as the Global Atmospheric Research Program, calling for observations of the atmosphere over the entire Earth from the surface to about 30 km (19 mi).

Climate. The series of droughts in various countries during the 1970s, along with the realization that fuel consumption, food production, and water supplies depend to a crucial extent on the weather

Flanagan—Wilmington News Journal

One of the coldest winters in many years spread misery throughout the U.S. in 1976–77. Snow and cold cause a traffic jam (above) in Wilmington, Delaware.

and climate, made scientists and statesmen aware of the need to learn more about these subjects. The effects of the daily, monthly, and seasonal weather on many human endeavors are so obvious that they hardly need be mentioned. Farmers, water engineers, and energy managers are particularly con-

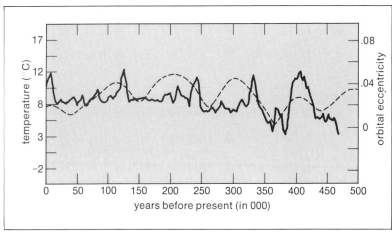

The eccentricity of the Earth's orbit around the Sun (dotted line) during the past 500,000 years varies in a pattern similar to that of water temperatures (solid line), derived from studying the remains of plankton in deep-sea cores.

Adapted from Hays, Imbrie, and Shackleton

cerned with changes of the weather or deviations from the long-term averages over a particular region. These averages, in part, describe the climate of that region. In fact, the climate of a specific area is represented by the collective of the statistical properties of its weather conditions.

Deviations of weather from average conditions or changes in climate cause problems because the way of life in a region is adapted to average conditions. When considering climate variations, it is necessary to specify the time period under consideration. During the past year there has been great interest in temperature variations of the Earth over the last 500,000 years. By studying the remains of plankton found in cores taken from the floor of the Indian Ocean, James D. Hays of Columbia University, John Imbrie of Brown University, Providence, R.I., and Nicholas J. Shackleton of Cambridge University constructed a curve showing temperatures over the last million years. They concluded that the water temperatures fluctuated over a range from 3° to 12° C (37°–54° F) and that these variations could be accounted for by changes in the Earth's orbit around the Sun.

The three geologists confirmed the ideas of the Serbian scientist Milutin Milankovitch, who in 1930 first reported orbital changes and their consequences. The orbital cycles have periods of 23,000, 41,000, and 93,000 years, caused, respectively, by alterations in the time of year the Earth is closest to the Sun, the tilt of the Earth's axis, and the ellipticity of the orbit.

In March 1976 B. John Mason, director general of the Meteorological Office of the United Kingdom, offered new evidence confirming the Milankovitch model. He argued that it is the leading contender for explaining climatic fluctuations over time periods ranging from a few tens of thousands of years to a few hundreds of thousands of years. According to the Milankovitch model, the current changes in the Earth's orbit indicate a trend toward cooler temperatures, with a new ice age to occur in a few thousand years.

In an effort to understand what might occur in the immediate future, scientists are studying various other phenomena. For hundreds of years astronomers and other Sun watchers have kept records of dark areas on the Sun called sunspots. Sunspot activity varies over a cycle of about 11 years, and has been found by many people to correlate with certain weather events. Attempts had been made to use sunspot data for long-range predictions of weather, but with little success. During the past year, however, John A. Eddy of the National Center for Atmospheric Research in Colorado confirmed earlier reports that during the 70-year period 1645 to 1715 almost no sunspots were observed. Inter-

estingly, this period coincides closely with the coldest years of the so-called Little Ice Age. Whether the absence of sunspots indicates a decrease of incoming solar energy which caused the cold period remained to be resolved. Eddy's analyses did show that over the last millennium solar activity was far less uniform than had once been supposed. The results also served as a stimulus to those scientists who have been seeking relationships between changes of solar radiation and the behavior of the atmosphere.

From about 1880 to 1940 the surface air temperatures, averaged over the Northern Hemisphere, increased about 1° C and were accompanied by a reduction of global ice cover. During the subsequent two to three decades the Northern Hemisphere underwent a cooling amounting to about 0.6° C, and the ice cover advanced toward the Equator. In the most recent years the average temperatures appeared to have leveled off, and the ice cover has remained mostly unchanged. How does one account for these variations of global temperatures? Are they chance perturbations? Are they attributable to natural events such as the injection of gases and huge numbers of particles into the atmosphere by volcanoes or alterations in the temperature of the oceans or changes in the Earth's reflectivity caused by changes in snow and ice cover? No one yet knows the answers.

A few decades ago there was genuine concern that the warming trend during the early part of the century was caused by increases of carbon dioxide in the atmosphere. The increased use of fossil fuels added huge quantities of this gas to the air. Concentration in the atmosphere increased from about 290 parts per million (ppm) in about 1890, to 315 ppm in 1958 and 332 ppm by 1977. Experts on the international Scientific Committee on Problems of the Environment projected increases to continue into the distant future with a fourfold to eightfold rise during the next 200 years. These quantities assume that coal will be the major energy source during that period.

By means of an advanced, but still not complete, mathematical model of the general circulation of the atmosphere, Syukuro Manabe and Richard T. Wetherald of the Geophysical Fluid Dynamics Laboratory at Princeton University calculated that a doubling of the present concentration of carbon dioxide would increase surface air temperatures by 2° C. If this result and the projections of multifold increases of carbon dioxide are realistic, the expected warming of the atmosphere could have serious consequences.

The calculations indicate, without doubt, the need to develop mathematical models that are closer to reality than those now in existence. It is

Wide World

Balloon is readied for launch into the stratosphere in an attempt to determine whether fluorocarbons from the Earth reach the ozone layer.

particularly important to have models that account for the interactions of the atmosphere with the oceans. In addition, it is essential to collect the data needed to monitor changes in the global climate and related phenomena.

Global Atmospheric Research Program. The Global Atmospheric Research Program (GARP) is the research component of the World Weather Program, the chief goal of which is to improve weather services to all countries. This includes better observations of the state of the atmosphere, the detection and tracking of storms, improved forecasts of significant weather events, and the transmission of weather information to those who need it.

During the last 20 years meteorologists have made major strides in understanding the behavior of the atmosphere. This has occurred, in large part, through the development of physically sound, mathematical models of the global atmosphere that can be solved numerically by means of computers. These models make it possible to examine the interactions of the various parts of the atmosphere-land-ocean-ice system as well as the radiative, mechanical, and thermodynamical processes that affect the atmosphere and the weather. As of 1977 the models still do not adequately conform to the realities of nature, particularly in accounting for air-sea feedbacks, but they continue to improve.

The efficacy of the models can be measured by how well they predict the state of the atmosphere. In order to make predictions more than a week or so in advance, it is necessary to know, for the Earth as a whole, the properties of the atmosphere, the ground, and the uppermost layers of the ocean. Unfortunately, it is difficult to obtain such information because about 70% of the Earth's area is cov-

ered by the oceans, and observations of atmospheric pressures, winds, temperatures, and humidity have been scarce in those regions. In the past they came from ships or islands. Most observations of the upper atmosphere have been obtained by means of balloon-borne radiosonde instruments.

One of the tasks of GARP is to collect data describing the complete atmosphere, *i.e.*, from the surface to about 30 km (19 mi). Since the inception of GARP there has been significant progress in the development of satellites equipped with radiometric instruments that can measure surface temperatures as well as the distributions of temperature and humidity with altitude. Also, sophisticated balloon-borne systems and buoys were developed to augment the satellite observations.

The techniques to be used in the First GARP Global Experiment, in 1978, were tested in a series of programs in various parts of the world. The last one, during the summer of 1974, included scientists and support personnel from 72 countries. The enterprise involved the study of the tropical belt extending from the Pacific coast of Central America across the Atlantic Ocean to the east coast of Africa. During the forthcoming global experiment, scientists plan to collect, for the first time, observations of the state of the entire atmosphere. Their tools are to consist of a variety of satellites, free-floating balloons, automatic weather stations in remote places, instrumented ocean buoys, airplanes, ships, and standard meteorological equipment. The data will be transmitted via satellite, radio, and land lines to central weather stations in Australia, the U.S., and the U.S.S.R., and then on to other countries.

The scale of GARP, in terms of the international commitment of personnel and intellectual resources, is unmatched in the history of science. The gains in knowledge of the atmosphere of the Earth should be great.

Weather modification. Progress in weather modification research remained slow, but at the same time in many parts of the world there were programs of cloud seeding for the purpose of increasing precipitation or decreasing the fall of damaging hail. A significant action occurred in September 1976 when the U.S. Congress enacted Public Law 94–490, known as the National Weather Modification Policy Act of 1976. It called on the Department of Commerce to conduct a comprehensive study and to develop a national policy for weather modification and a plan of action for the consideration of Congress. The act called for a report in a year's time.

Chlorofluorocarbons and ozone. In 1974 F. Sherwood Rowland and Mario J. Molina of the University of California at Irvine calculated that the release of chlorofluorocarbons (called fluorocarbons) from aerosol spray cans and refrigerating systems would lead to reductions of ozone in the atmosphere. Most of the ozone is in a layer between about 15 and 30 km (about 9 and 19 mi) high. This stratospheric ozone absorbs much of the solar ultraviolet radiation, which, if it reached the ground, could cause skin cancer and other undesirable biological effects. Following the initial reports by Rowland and Molina and other scientists, two bodies in the U.S. National Academy of Sciences examined the facts, theories, and speculations dealing with this subject.

In September 1976 the Panel on Atmospheric Chemistry and the Committee on Impacts of Stratospheric Change issued reports listing their findings and recommendations. Laboratory tests, observations of the chemical structure of the upper atmosphere, and theoretical analyses led to the conclusion that the continued release of fluorocarbons poses a serious threat to the ozone layer. The panel concluded that a continued use of the fluorocarbons at the 1973 rate could reduce stratospheric ozone by an amount most.likely to be about 7%, a quantity similar to the value predicted earlier by Rowland and Molina.

The panel also raised the question of the effects of the continued use of fluorocarbons on global temperatures and climate. Veerauhadran Ramanathan of the U.S. National Aeronautics and Space Administration (NASA) first suggested that because this substance absorbs infrared radiation in the wavelength region 8 to 13 micrometers, it would have the same warming effect as increased carbon dioxide in the atmosphere. The effect would depend on the quantity of fluorocarbons released, and even at the 1973 release rate it would not be detected for some decades. Nevertheless, it was suggested that it might be a crucial factor some 50 to 100 years in the future.

The academy reports recommended, in essence, that selective regulation of the use and release of chlorofluorocarbons be instituted within no more than two years, unless it is shown convincingly that

Rain-spattered dome protects all-sky camera used for the Florida Area Cumulus Experiment, an effort to understand the dynamics of tropical cumulus clouds and to determine whether seeding them produces more rain.

Courtesy, NOAA

ultimate ozone reductions are likely to be less than a few percent. Fortunately, home refrigerators, which are important to human health, account for less than 1% of the fluorocarbons released. Aerosol spray cans are the major sources, and there are other means by which their functions can be performed.

Magnetosphere. The Sun ejects a stream of ionized gas, which constitutes the solar wind. As the Earth moves in its orbit, the global magnetic field encounters this gas. The gas compresses the magnetic field on the sunward side of the Earth and forms a shock wave shaped like a huge bullet, the nose of which is about ten Earth radii away from the Earth. Downwind, the magnetic field stretches away in a long tail extending hundreds of Earth radii to the Moon and beyond. The cavity-shaped region defined by the solar wind contains energetic, charged particles and is called the magnetosphere.

Much remains to be learned about the nature of the magnetosphere and its interactions with the lower atmosphere. It was suggested that magnetic storms, large perturbations in the magnetic fields, may in some mysterious way have an influence on the weather. Magnetic storms are known to be associated with dramatic increases in the occurrence and intensity of auroras, the spectacular illuminations seen in the sky at high latitudes.

The years 1976 to 1979 were designated as those of the International Magnetospheric Study, with the U.S. assuming a leading role. Observations were being made by means of satellites, rockets, balloons, and aircraft. A particularly interesting experiment was to use two spacecraft, one provided by NASA and the other by the European Space Agency. They would move as a pair, with one following closely behind the other, as they cross through the magnetosphere at various places, up and downwind of the Earth. Ground-based observations for the study included arrays of magnetometers, the measurements of which would be relayed via satellite to the Space Environmental Laboratory of the U.S. National Oceanic and Atmospheric Administration.

This major research program should shed a great deal of light on the magnetosphere and magnetic storms. The latter can cause interruptions of the long-distance communications that are made by means of reflections from the ionosphere. The storms also can induce large currents in long-distance telephone and power cables, causing disruptions of the switching, amplification, and relay circuits. Better understanding should lead to better predictions of storms, allowing engineers to take precautions so as to minimize breakdowns.

—Louis J. Battan

Geological sciences

Increased awareness of the limitations of the Earth's resources focused the attention of Earth scientists on the ever growing demand for energy and minerals. The role of geoscientists in society was the theme of one conference and a prevailing concern at numerous other meetings in the United States and other nations. These were highlighted by the 25th International Geological Congress, held during August in Sydney, Australia, with Earth scientists from 73 countries in attendance. In its fourth year, the International Geological Correlation Program (with 98 countries and territories represented) expanded to 61 approved projects, including those dealing with geologic hazards, land-use problems, environmental conservation, and the search for energy and minerals.

Geology and geochemistry. The International Phase of Ocean Drilling (IPOD), begun in late 1975, enjoyed broadened financial and scientific support as the "Glomar Challenger" continued drilling in the Atlantic Ocean. Penetration into the ocean crust as deeply as was technologically feasible was a central mission of Legs 45, 46, and 49. Based on the properties of some of the deeply penetrated basalts, the researchers concluded that the Earth's magnetic field may have been largely nondipolar when those rocks were formed, perhaps during a magnetic transition. The magnetic properties of the recovered basalts deviate from seafloor magnetic lineations. This may be attributed to the bias of restricted sampling, although the origin of the lineations may be at greater rock depth than previously thought.

Some basalt samples showed striking chemical similarities at the top and bottom of a sequence. This suggests cyclical magmatic processes that may generate magmas (molten rocks) of similar composition. However, the evolved nature of some basalts sampled and evidence that not all basalt units in close proximity are from closely similar magmatic sources may reflect special mantle conditions. Perhaps heterogeneity in the upper mantle is more extensive than anticipated, thus allowing the generation of different primary magmas. The recovery of bodies of serpentinized peridotite (an olivine-rich igneous rock) in regions away from the well-defined fracture zones in the ocean floor was also puzzling. This may be explained by movements of peridotites from the hot mantle into zones of weakness in the ocean crust.

Sampling the sedimentary sequence of a passive ocean (continental) margin was achieved by drilling off northwest Africa south of the Canary Islands (Leg 47A), off Portugal (Leg 47B), in the Bay of Biscay and the Rockwall Plateau (Leg 48), and in

Photos, Deepsea Ventures, Inc.

Television camera and tripod are lowered into water 1,200 miles off the California coast (left) to search for manganese nodules on the ocean floor. Above, a scientist views picture transmitted by the TV camera from a depth of 18,000 feet.

the Morocco Basin (Leg 50). The basic premise that these margins formed by rifting with subsequent subsidence was upheld, although, as anticipated, variations in evolutional histories due to local structural and stratigraphic complexities between regions was documented. The subsidence of continental margins apparently begins as spreading is initiated and then closely follows the pattern of the oceanic crust. Continental detritus derived from neighboring slopes and shelves dominates deposition in this environment. The prominence of unconformities was exemplified on Leg 47A, where an erosion surface marking a 100-million-year time gap between the early Miocene Epoch and early Cretaceous Period was drilled.

A correlation between intensity variations in natural remanent magnetism and lithological (rock-type) boundaries was verified during drilling in the Bay of Biscay. This finding extends the potential of shipboard paleomagnetic studies, in which an absolute chronology is assigned to biostratigraphic zonations (zones of rocks with diagnostic fossils) by determining the locations of reversals of geomagnetic polarity.

New drilling programs were also conducted in both Antarctica and the Arctic during 1976. As part of the Ross Ice Shelf Project, a non-cored hole was drilled (at latitude 82°20' S, longitude 168°40' W) through the ice shelf where the ice was about 420 m thick. A planned cored hole was postponed for

the season due to technical problems with the coring apparatus. A combination of Canadian and Danish companies drilled the first Arctic well off Greenland, at about the Arctic Circle. The ship "Pelican" was used to drill this well to a depth of almost 4,000 m in 183 m of water.

Geochemistry. Geochemical studies in the oceans received a major new impetus as the first results of an extensive, systematic ocean-sampling effort were recorded and studied. Known as the Geochemical Ocean Sections (Geosecs) program, it covered the Atlantic and Pacific oceans from the Arctic to Antarctica; more than 7,000 samples were taken from the Atlantic Ocean alone. The sophisticated sampler contained rosettes of 30-liter bottles (1 liter = 1.06 quarts) along with instruments to measure dissolved oxygen content, particulate matter, pressure, salinity, and the temperature of the water. Each sample was analyzed for its chemical composition. (See *Oceanography*, below.)

Trace-element geochemistry and its relation to health and the environment received continued interest during 1976–77. Studies of selenium indicated that it is not a cancer-causing agent; in fact, the presence of selenium in the diet correlates negatively with breast cancer (based on comparisons of Asians and Africans with Americans). Furthermore, preliminary findings indicated that the incidence of both hypertensive and arteriosclerotic heart disease is significantly lower where a relatively large amount of selenium is present in drinking water. The recent identification of nickel, silicon, tin, and vanadium as essential trace elements for mammals, including humans, added them to a list already containing copper, chromium, fluorine, iodine, iron, magnesium, manganese, selenium, and zinc. Cadmium and lead were being explored as possible additions to the list.

UNESCO was concerned during the year with the applications of geochemistry to nutrition and health problems. The agency planned to co-sponsor (with the Royal Society) the First International Symposium on Environmental Geochemistry and Health. This was a useful endeavor because trace-element deficiencies and excesses are more prevalent in less developed countries than in those with broader bases of food supplies.

Organic geochemistry developed rapidly at the international level during recent months, with increasing numbers of meetings and papers. *Organic Geochemistry,* a new journal published by the International Association of Geochemistry and Cosmochemistry (IAGC), was to be devoted entirely to that subject. During the year IAGC also prepared a special volume, *Review of Modern Problems in Geochemistry,* which UNESCO agreed to publish.

Mineralogy and petrology. Research in clay mineralogy has led to a clearer understanding of the relationship between the minerals illite and smectite. A conversion of smectite to illite under conditions of deep burial was documented in several parts of the world, including British Columbia and Papua New Guinea. The possibility of a similar conversion was being applied to the search for shales that are potential source beds for petroleum. Shales that have undergone conditions of deep burial can expel any petroleum-type hydrocarbons they originally contained, providing the organic matter has matured to a fluid state during the mineral-conversion reaction. Conversely, areas in which potential source beds have not undergone conversion by deep burial are most likely barren and offer little encouragement for further exploration. Research was under way to determine the factors that control the progress of such conversion in shales so that methods used in the search for petroleum could be further refined.

An international conference allowed scientists and engineers to evaluate the fundamental physical and chemical properties of natural zeolites and to explore their applications. Zeolites, hydrated alumina-silicate minerals, are widely distributed and have unique properties that make them ideal as ion exchangers and absorbents. New and potential uses of zeolites include ammonia reservoirs and ammonium exchangers for treating feedlot-runoff and fish-hatchery waters and for removing gaseous ammonia from methane during coal gasification.

Understanding the sources and historical development of magma improved by means of studies using trace elements and radioactive isotopes. The results obtained from strontium and lead isotopes were supplemented by studies of samarium-147 and its daughter product, neodymium-143. The data indicate that magmas which have erupted from ocean ridges, oceanic islands, and continental volcanoes come from sources with slightly different compositions. In some instances these compositional differences have persisted for two billion years or more. These results lent additional credence to the view that there are distinct differences between the mantle beneath ocean basins and that beneath the continents.

Experimental research on the genesis of magma derived from the mantle led to a better understanding of how magma compositions develop. The significant role of carbon dioxide as it interacts with water and the melt received special attention. Many differences between magma compositions were explained by assuming different proportions of carbon dioxide and water in magma source areas, rather than assigning the cause to variations in pressure, temperature, or rock composition. High pressure / high temperature experiments on carbon dioxide solubility in magmas were aided by techniques utilizing radioactive carbon-14 as a tracer. When the resulting cooled glass is studied under high magnification, the decay count of the radioactive carbon-14 can be used to evaluate the role of carbon dioxide.

Energy and minerals. Dependency on foreign oil and the lack of a long-range energy plan persisted in the U.S. Domestic production of 8,158,000 bbl of oil per day in 1976 reflected a slight decline from 1975, while daily consumption rose to more than 17 million bbl (up nearly 1 million bbl), thus further increasing imports. One possibility for an improvement in the situation lies with the Atlantic continental shelf; lease sales were held for development of the Baltimore Canyon area with two test holes drilled in 1976. In addition, a new oil and gas reservoir, known as the South Slope, was found in fractured rocks 70 million–100 million years old (Late Cretaceous age) extending along the Gulf of Mexico coastal plain from the Mexican border to Louisiana. Estimates of reserves there ranged up to 7 billion bbl of oil. Elsewhere, Canadian production showed substantial declines while that of Mexico increased. Notable discoveries took place in the offshore Amazon Delta area and the Campos Basin (east of Rio de Janeiro) in Brazil, while gas reserves were found in the Barrow Island area of western Australia.

Potash mining made news when the provincial

From "An Early Ordovician Vertebrate," by T. Bockelie and R. A. Fortey, in *Nature* magazine, vol. 260, p. 36, March 4, 1976; reprinted by permission

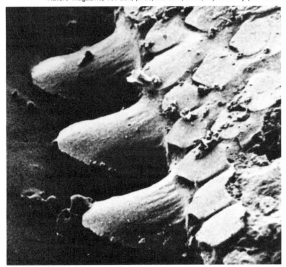

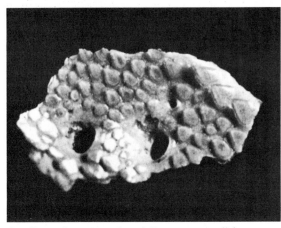

Fossil vertebrate remains of Heterostracan fishes, having an age of approximately 500 million years, were found in Norway's arctic region of Spitsbergen. At the top is part of a spinelike fragment, and in the center are scales. The circular perforations in the fragment at the bottom probably represent openings in the fish's exoskeleton.

government of Saskatchewan in Canada acquired the mine and mill complex of the Duval Corp. near Saskatoon. In 1976 the U.S. relied on Saskatchewan for two-thirds of its potash needs, but exploration for it was intensifying elsewhere. Potash in the Williston basin (Montana and North Dakota) at depths of 2,200 m was being readied for solution mining by the early 1980s.

Exploration for high-calcium limestone used in desulfurization of flue gas (the mixture of gases resulting from combustion and other reactions in a furnace) continued at an accelerated pace in 1976–77. A new plant near Maysville, Ky., began operation with a 3,000-ton-per-day capacity to supply lime for desulfurization. Other new deposits put into operation during the year included the Felipe kaolin deposit on the Jari River in northern Brazil; heavy-mineral sands (for titanium minerals) at Richards Bay, South Africa; fluorspar in South Africa; and phosphate rock from northwest Queensland, Australia, and southern Baja California.

Paleontology. Precambrian paleontology continued to command considerable interest with new finds and interpretations. Most previous reports of middle Precambrian eucaryotic (advanced, nucleus-containing) cell types probably represent degraded procaryotic (primitive) cells, suggesting that the important division between these cell types took place considerably later in the Precambrian than formerly believed. Late Precambrian metazoans (multicelled animals) from Newfoundland and other localities received special attention. Their existence promoted a reevaluation of the concept that abundant metazoans first appeared suddenly at the Precambrian-Cambrian boundary. Tubelike structures (dubiofossils) found in quartzite in Wyoming with an age of 2 billion–2.5 billion years may be organic. If so, they would extend metazoans back one billion years beyond the earliest proven finds.

The discovery of a new Cambrian lophophorate (an invertebrate animal that possesses a fan of ciliated tentacles about its mouth) with conodont-like teeth from the Burgess Shale of British Columbia was described as highly significant. It represented still another type of possible "conodont animal" found in the fossil record in the past few years and suggested that some conodonts were lophophorates. (Conodonts are small toothlike structures found as fossils in marine rocks.)

Research and publications on whether dinosaurs were reptiles or mammals continued as a prime interest among vertebrate paleontologists. Mammalian and other vertebrate fossils (fish, turtles, and an alligatorid) were recovered from Ellesmere Island, Canada, at about latitude 78° N. Their presence suggests that temperate-to-warm climatic conditions existed 50 million–60 million years ago when they lived there. Other events included finds of additional fauna from Colombia that aided scientists in determining the dispersal of terrestrial vertebrates in central America.

—Robert E. Boyer

Geophysics. During the past year a significant success in earthquake prediction and the occurrence of an unusual number of disastrous large earthquakes that were not forecast emphasized the importance of effective earthquake prediction while at the same time underlining the current imperfect knowledge of the strain buildup processes that lead to damaging shocks. Recent observations in earthquake-prone regions of Japan and California may be related to future seismic activity and offer considerable promise for studying pre-earthquake processes.

Chinese earthquake prediction. A visit to China in June 1976 by a group of ten U.S. scientists, including seven seismologists, brought new details of Chinese success in earthquake prediction. However, the occurrence one month later of an unexpected, destructive earthquake centering on Tangshan to the east of Peking underlined the fact that prediction research in that country was still in its embryonic stage.

The pragmatic approach of the Chinese scientists was continuously to monitor earthquake-prone regions by using a wide variety of geophysical measurements; little attention was paid to understanding the causative processes involved. Parameters such as tilt of the ground surface, electrical resistance, and water levels in wells were

monitored over wide regions, with the simpler measurements often being made by peasant volunteers without specialized scientific training.

This largely phenomenological approach has several distinct advantages as well as some shortcomings. Its principal strength is that much of the seismically active part of eastern China, which is highly populated, can be densely instrumented, increasing the likelihood that a precursor will be observed. The main disadvantage of so wide and diverse an effort is that many signals irrelevant to earthquake processes are recorded, and anomalies unrelated to impending earthquakes are detected and interpreted incorrectly.

Notwithstanding these shortcomings the Chinese had at least one remarkable success, and no one in the visiting U.S. delegation doubted that the large and destructive shock (magnitude 7.3) that occurred on Feb. 4, 1975, in Liaoning Province of northeast China was successfully predicted. The success seems to have been based on two factors, long-term forecasting begun as early as 1970 and detection of short-term precursors, culminating in the final prediction on the day that the shock occurred. Chinese seismologists first noted in 1970 the general increase in the numbers of earthquakes in northeast China and the migration of the large shocks of 1966, 1967, and 1969 toward the Liaoning Peninsula, and as a result began to concentrate their investigations in that area. Subsequent observations of such phenomena as crustal deformation, magnetic field changes, and a general increase in the occurrence of small earthquakes throughout the area convinced the Chinese by late 1974 that a large earthquake was approaching.

Lageos 1 satellite (below) is dimpled with prism reflectors that reflect laser beams back to their sources and thereby help geologists calculate continental drift. At the right, an earthquake-sensing device is checked before installation.

(Left) Courtesy, NASA; (right) Wide World

Residents of Peking camp out in the streets of the city in fear of an earthquake after a major shock destroyed the nearby city of Tangshan on July 28, 1976.

Careful observations were continued, and more anomalous changes were observed, but the occurrence of a swarm of small earthquakes that began on Feb. 1, 1975, and ceased abruptly on the morning of February 4 appears to have been decisive in focusing attention on the Yinkou-Haicheng area in Liaoning. Few earthquakes had previously been recorded in the vicinity of the Yinkou seismic station, and when the unusual activity abruptly ceased early on February 4 the imminent occurrence of a strong earthquake was forecast. Mass evacuations in frigid midwinter conditions were carried out, and at 7:36 PM local time the earthquake occurred. An estimated 90% of the buildings in the region near the earthquake's center were destroyed, and therefore the evacuation undoubtedly resulted in the saving of many thousands of lives.

A counterpoint to the successful Haicheng prediction was the unexpected occurrence on July 28, 1976, of an equally destructive earthquake of magnitude 8.2 near the industrial city of Tangshan, in Hopeh Province about 150 km (95 mi) east of Peking. Following this earthquake, members of the U.S. delegation, who had returned from China four weeks earlier, recalled that Chinese scientists had made a generalized forecast, based on magnetic field changes, of a large earthquake "before 1980" in the Tangshan-Tientsin-Peking area. Reports from foreign visitors who were in Tangshan at the time of the earthquake made it clear, however, that no short-term prediction was made and that damage and casualties were severe.

Other destructive earthquakes. Although the general level of seismic activity throughout the world was not abnormal during 1976, an unusually high number of large earthquakes occurred in populated regions. They resulted in considerable loss of life and severe economic dislocation in Guatemala, the Philippines, Italy, and Turkey, as well as in China.

Large earthquakes are particularly catastrophic in less developed countries, where a large proportion of the population often lives in unreinforced dwellings, as was particularly shown by the Guatemala earthquake of Feb. 4, 1976. This event caused about 100,000 casualties (among them an estimated 23,000 deaths) and left more than one million people homeless, almost 20% of the total population of Guatemala.

Although the Guatemala earthquake was not predicted, from a geophysical viewpoint a large rupture in the area was not totally unexpected: The Motagua fault system, slicing roughly east–west through Guatemala from the Caribbean coast to within 150 km of the Pacific, forms the boundary between two large crustal blocks, the North America and Caribbean plates. Horizontal motion is expected across the Motagua fault, with the block to the north moving westward ("left-laterally") with respect to the southern block. This is precisely the ground displacement that occurred abruptly at the time of the 1976 shock: 230 km (145 mi) of surface ground rupture were observed, with left-lateral slippage of from one to three meters across the fault. Secondary faults, with predominantly vertical movement on them, were also activated at the western end of the Motagua fault rupture. These faults were probably important in intensifying the devastation that took place in the valley which includes Guatemala City and the highly populated mountain hillsides to the north and west of it.

Even excluding the Tangshan earthquake, 1976 was the worst year for disastrous shocks since 1927, when a great earthquake near Nan-shan, China, took an estimated 200,000 lives. During 1976 not only were the Chinese and Guatemalan earthquakes destructive but an estimated 8,000 lives were also lost in a magnitude 8.0 event located off the west coast of the island of Mindanao in the Philippines and 4,000 died in a magnitude 7.9 shock located near Lake Van in eastern

Turkey. Also, in and around the town of Gemona in the Friuli region of northern Italy, a magnitude 6.9 earthquake on May 6 took 1,000 lives.

Earthquake prediction research strategy. Research in earthquake prediction has been turning perceptibly from preoccupation with specific models for precursory behavior to searches for observationally unambiguous anomalous changes in physical properties in the source regions of impending earthquakes. There are two principal reasons for this shift in emphasis. First, because existing data were from experiments not specifically designed for precursor studies and were scrutinized after the fact, few truly convincing anomalous changes were uncovered. Second, it has become clear that no single theoretical model seems capable of explaining the collected precursory data. This may be true because not all the "anomalies," or unexplained changes, are true precursors; seismologists have had too little experience in separating "normal" fluctuations in physical properties in seismically active regions from true earthquake precursors. Alternatively, the models suggested thus far may be incorrect. In either case, much more reliable data are needed, both to establish firmly which parameters do in fact change prior to earthquakes and to provide a firm basis upon which to construct and test physical models of pre-earthquake processes.

Detection of precursors even in relatively limited highly active areas, such as the state of California, is made difficult because of the large number of active faults and the limited number of instruments that can be deployed. Even in California an earthquake larger than magnitude 6 occurs only once every few years, and there are many hundreds of kilometers of active faults on which such an event might occur. However, the recent identification of two areas of unusual ground uplift, one in Japan and the other in southern California, has presented some unusual opportunities for prediction research. While it is by no means clear that these unexpected upheavals do portend future earthquakes, it remains true that the processes which led to the unusual effects must be understood before earthquakes can be predicted effectively.

Ground uplift. Measured against previous experience, the magnitude, rapidity of development, and large area of the recently discovered uplift in southern California are surprising to most Earth scientists, raising important questions concerning the origin and mechanism of the uplift and its possible relationship to earthquake processes. The uplift itself covers an area of at least 12,000 sq km (4,700 sq mi) of the San Gabriel Mountains and Mojave Desert north of Los Angeles, with ground upheavals of as much as 25 cm (10 in) occurring between 1960 and 1974.

Though not accompanied by any increase in seismic activity, the uplift does lie across the active trace of the San Andreas fault, which has not moved since the great earthquake of 1857. Although geological data indicate that a repeat of the 1857-size earthquake may be expected every few hundred years, available evidence suggests that the uplift is not directly related to a future earthquake on the San Andreas fault. First, motions across the San Andreas are almost totally horizontal rather than vertical. Furthermore, it was recently shown that the horizontal motions that did occur while the uplift was growing tended to lock the San Andreas fault and thereby impede slippage. At the same time, these movements increased stresses across faults that slant beneath the San Gabriel

Row of trees is offset about 3.25 meters where it is intersected by the Motagua fault in Guatemala.

Courtesy, George Plafker, U.S. Geological Survey

Slippage scars above the San Andreas fault are revealed where a hill is cut through for a highway in southern California. In this region two giant crustal plates, the Pacific and the North America, brush against each other.

Mountains, faults across which slippage is predominantly vertical. One such fault slipped about two meters during the magnitude 6.4 San Fernando earthquake of 1971, raising the mountain side of the fault and slightly depressing the valley side.

Recent analysis showed that the uplift, impressive as it is, could not by itself have increased stresses enough to cause damaging earthquakes. This does not mean that there is no earthquake risk in the uplift region, but implies that the degree of risk depends significantly on the level that stresses had reached before the uplift began about 1960. Unfortunately, there is little useful information available on this important point. Therefore, the strategy that emerged was to begin an intensive long-term monitoring program in the region in order to search for precursors, follow future development of the uplift (which recent data suggest is still evolving), and direct research toward understanding the processes that generated it in the first place. Early in the summer of 1976 the U.S. government allocated $2.1 million for uplift studies to be carried out by government agencies, university researchers, and private consulting firms. Newly initiated experiments included geodetic surveying; continuous measurement of ground tilt, gravity, and magnetic field; and careful monitoring of seismic activity.

At about the same time that U.S. scientists were discovering the California uplift, Japanese researchers were uncovering a possibly similar effect on the Izu Peninsula, 120 km (75 mi) southwest of Tokyo. There, a roughly circular area of 3,000 sq km (1,200 sq mi) was elevated as much as 15 cm (6 in)

between 1974 and 1976. Several swarms of small earthquakes in the region adjacent to the uplift also occurred during that time. Some Japanese seismologists believe that the uplift is related to the pressurization of a buried chamber of molten rock and point to the fact that the Izu Peninsula is an area of recent volcanic activity and that earthquake swarms and volcanism are often related. Whatever the mechanism, the possibility exists that the Izu uplift may be a signal of future seismic activity.

—Wayne Thatcher

Hydrological sciences

During 1976 the hydrological sciences, like many others, were the subjects of historical reviews in commemoration of the U.S. Bicentennial. Special symposia summarized the development of these sciences, and many of them resulted in valuable overviews. Especially impressive were the insights that tied the achievements of the hydrological sciences in the 1970s to technologies of the late 1700s and earlier. The reviews emphasized that the development of techniques is a combination of the slow accretion of knowledge and understanding and the apparently sudden injection of key inventions or new concepts.

Hydrology. One such concept may in the future be dated from 1976. The use of floodplains by man is almost as old as his history. They have been favored sites for development, and many major cities began as settlements along riverbanks. There the soils were productive, and the river provided water for drinking, manufacturing, and disposing of wastes. The river was also a means of transport, a supply of food, and a bulwark for defense. Later, the level land was found suitable for highways and railroads. Protection and development of these desirable attributes required dams to control stream levels and floods, dredging to facilitate transportation, and channel realignment to control erosion. Thus, a knowledge of stream and channel characteristics was an engineering imperative.

For nearly a hundred years, river control measures were based on the belief that the equilibrium of a channel was related to a steady-state condition at some given rate of discharge of the water. Recent field and flume studies, however, suggested the need to reexamine this belief. The new data, centering on the work of Thomas Maddock, Jr., of the U.S. Geological Survey, revived and reinforced the work of G. K. Gilbert early in the century. They indicate that the dynamic equilibrium of a stream channel represents reactions to the recent history of the discharges not only of the water but also of the sediment. Both the amount and size distribution of the transported sediment play major roles in determining channel changes. As of 1977 the new concept was in the early stages of being tested in relation to problems of sediment transport, erosion, channel changes, and flooding.

Drought. Droughts in various parts of North America stimulated a large number of studies of their causes, their distribution in time and space, and methods of forecasting them. Statistical evidence for relationships between 23-year and 50-year sunspot cycles and droughts had accumulated by 1977 to such an extent that some climatologists were beginning to accept the prediction of droughts on the basis of sunspot cycles and intensities.

In 1977 central California went into its third year of drought. A high-pressure system between California and Hawaii diverted northward the storms that normally bring moisture to central California. As a result, the snowpack in the Sierra Nevada in late 1976 was about one-third of normal, the lowest on record. Unfortunately, the drought area is the source of the state's two largest water projects. By 1977 irrigation requirements in central California had reduced hydroelectric power reservoirs in the region as much as 50% below their capacities. Authorities warned that any further depletion for irrigation may result in power shortages.

In Great Britain and northern Europe the drought of 1976 was the most severe since records were begun in 1727. The River Thames in England dropped several feet so that in some places it was only about half its normal width. The exposed mud-

The River Thames in May 1976 sinks to its lowest level in 40 years, a result of the severe drought affecting much of Great Britain. Scene below is at Strand-on-the-Green west of London.

Syndication International/Photo Trends

banks were grim reminders of waste-discharging practices of the past few decades. Fortunately, because of the recent reorganization of water management in England and Wales, the available water resources could be used and developed without regard to political boundaries. Industry, which used about 80% of the total water abstracted from surface and subsurface sources in the U.K., was affected in only a few local areas. Emergency measures included reduction of permitted use, recycling, inter- and intra-basin transfers, and interlinking of supply systems. These measures, however, could not stop fires on the heaths, and losses of wildlife, especially birds, lizards, and previously endangered plant species, were being evaluated.

Because of the widespread dry conditions many areas not usually associated with droughts were accelerating their collection of hydrological data. Also, in response to the droughts of recent years, particularly that of the Sahel in Africa, the United Nations scheduled a world conference on the spread of the desert. Each year, it was reported, the Sahara expands by an area four times the size of Delaware.

The need to maintain water supplies at sufficient levels to provide for agricultural demand was critical in the U.S.S.R. Schemes to divert water from north-flowing rivers to agricultural areas in southern European Russia, central Asia, and Kazakhstan had been discussed for at least two decades. To prevent such schemes from turning into ecological and financial disasters, Soviet scientists identified four criteria that must be satisfied: The resulting environmental and ecological changes must be minimal and should improve natural resources whenever possible; the project should be unified and centrally controlled; it must be designed in self-sufficient stages, each of which can be put into immediate operation so as to help amortize the enormous cost; and, finally, the project should resolve water shortages in the areas involved for all time, so far as the existing state-of-the-art allows.

Groundwater. Large-scale water transfers are not feasible everywhere, and solutions to many regional water shortages were being considered in terms of available groundwater resources. Modeling techniques, especially numerical methods using high-speed computers, were shown to be capable of solving problems involving the long-term availability of groundwater; the use, in conjunction, of surface and groundwater supplies; the interaction between hydrological and economic considerations; the migration of pollutants; and the movement of heat.

Prediction of groundwater movement in most instances is based on the simplifying assumption that aquifers are "homogeneous in their heterogeneity." Recent work in Nevada by Isaac J. Winograd and F. Joseph Pearson, Jr., of the U.S. Geological Survey, showed that this assumption is not applicable to the dense, fractured Paleozoic carbonate rocks in the south-central part of the state. For example, the carbon-14 content of groundwater at the center of a 16-km (10 mi) line of springs was found to be five times greater than that from other springs elsewhere along the line. On the basis of that and other findings, the assumption of homogeneity, basic to many programs for analyzing groundwater flow and for monitoring the dispersion of contaminants and pollutants, must be questioned before being applied to porous carbonate rocks, dense but highly fractured carbonate rocks, and volcanic rocks with lava tubes.

Subsidence. Once considered to be an unusual local phenomenon, subsidence was recently demonstrated to be widespread, especially in areas of major withdrawals of groundwater and oil. On the west side of the San Joaquin Valley of California,

Thousands of fish died when rains in September 1976 swept dirt from the streets of Paris into the abnormally low Seine River. Because the river was low there were no currents, and the fish died of suffocation.

De Sazo—Rapho/Photo Researchers, Inc.

near Mendota, the land surface subsided as much as 8.9 m (29.3 ft) from 1925 to 1975. But during 1976 subsidence in the area was greatly slowed, and there was some rebound. This resulted from the virtually simultaneous availability of surface water imported from northern California and the scientific and engineering evaluation of the relationships between subsidence, groundwater withdrawals, and the nature of the materials from which the water is being withdrawn. The use of the imported water for irrigation reduced groundwater withdrawals. By careful monitoring of subsidence rates it was possible to balance large applications of surface water and small withdrawals of groundwater to maintain present elevations and thus reduce the costs for canal repair and other releveling maintenance. If the current drought continues, however, it may be necessary to disrupt the balance by increasing groundwater withdrawals to offset reduced allocations of imported surface water. Thus, subsidence may again occur in this region.

At a symposium on land subsidence due to fluid withdrawals, subsidence or potential subsidence was reported in 14 countries representing all the continents. In Thailand, engineering and hydrological analyses of materials underlying Bangkok were made on the basis of the possibility of subsidence. The studies indicated that continued withdrawals of groundwater in the area might result in subsidence of as much as 1.1 m (3.5 ft). Because Bangkok is generally only 1 to 1.5 m (3 to 5 ft) above sea level, the city could not tolerate such an occurrence, and the government of Thailand consequently began planning both preventive and corrective measures.

UN conference. Internationally, many water-related agencies concentrated a part of their efforts on the March 1977 UN Water Conference in Argentina. This conference focused on policy matters affecting the adequacy of water supplies throughout the world. Particular attention was being given to assessing regional and continental water supplies, evaluating the usefulness of new and proven technologies in meeting future water demands, and suggesting policies that would meet some anticipated crises in water supply and water quality.
　　　　　　　　　　　　　　　　　　　　—L. A. Heindl

Oceanography. The occasional world congresses of oceanographers provide convenient milestones to measure progress in scientific knowledge of the sea. The fourth and latest of such congresses, the Joint Oceanographic Assembly, took place in Edinburgh in September 1976; previous ones were in 1959 (New York), 1966 (Moscow), and 1970 (Tokyo).

Characteristics of present-day oceanography were conspicuous in the Edinburgh program. Stud-

ies of the ocean are of international interest, and the countries of northern Europe, the Soviet Union, North America, and Japan continued to be centers of the most vigorous activity. Although the subject matter fell into the usual general categories of physics, chemistry, biology, and geology-geophysics, there was more emphasis than in previous years on interactions among fields and on the application of research findings to meeting needs of society. The importance of some problems, such as the effect of pollution on marine ecosystems and on climate, has only recently been recognized.

The nature of ocean investigation has changed markedly during recent years through the development of large-scale multidisciplinary experiments, many being carried out within the framework of the International Decade of Ocean Exploration. Some of the more noteworthy of these findings are reported below.

Paleo-oceanography. Understanding the nature of climatic change has become more urgent as scientists recognize its implications for meeting the food requirements of an ever increasing population and also become aware that human activity itself may change climate, for better or for worse. Because of its great heat capacity, the ocean dominates climatic stability. In recent months oceanographers showed that the geological records contained in deep-sea sediments can be used to study the transition between two apparently stable states of climate, the ice ages and the interglacial periods such as the present. The work was done largely within a project known as CLIMAP (Climate: Long-Range Investigation, Mapping, and Prediction). Using micropaleontological, geochemical, geophysical, and mineralogical data from the deep-sea sediments, investigators reconstructed the distributions of sea-surface temperature, ice extent, ice elevation, and continental albedo (reflectivity) during an August 18,000 years ago, the most recent period of maximum continental glaciation. Such descriptions can be used in global atmospheric circulation models, allowing a more complete assessment of the ice-age climate and giving insight into the processes whereby the present-day climate will be transformed.

A study published at the end of 1976 reported on the testing of a hypothesis for predicting the frequencies of major glacial fluctuations of the Pleistocene Epoch (2.5 million to 10,000 years ago). Again using deep-sea sediment data, the study showed that the succession of Quaternary Period (2.5 million years ago to the present) ice ages resulted from variations in the shape of the Earth's orbit. A model of future climate based on the observed orbital-climate relationship predicts that in the absence of significant man-made effects, the

ADN—Zentralbild/Eastfoto

Prefabricated rocks cast against each other and laid on a surface of polyvinyl chloride foil and asphalt matting protect the coast of East Germany's Hiddensee Island in the Baltic Sea.

long-term trend over the next several thousand years is toward another period of extensive Northern Hemisphere glaciation.

Coastal upwelling. Coastal upwelling is a phenomenon common on the eastern sides of oceans and is marked by vertical mixing of subsurface, highly productive waters into the surface layer. Symptoms of this phenomenon, among them lowered sea-surface temperatures along the eastern margins of the Atlantic and Pacific, can be recognized in paleo-oceanographic maps. The classical (Sverdrup-Ekman) theory explains the phenomenon as the product of equatorward winds along the coastal boundary and the rotation of the Earth. During recent years, the coastal upwelling ecosystem was subjected to intense study under the CUEA (Coastal Upwelling Ecosystem Analysis) program with the long-term goal of learning to predict the performance of such systems.

These studies were comparative (including the systems of western North and South America and of northwestern Africa), interdisciplinary, and quantitative. They demonstrated, among other things, that the phenomenon is generally restricted to a narrow band no wider than 50 km (30 mi), where the response of the ocean to fluctuations, or events, in the local winds is rapid. Upwelling regions are characterized by surface coastal jets and poleward undercurrents that provide a way for both nutrients and phytoplankton to be retained in the system. The location of intense upwelling depends on the shelf and slope topography, and the process varies in time both alongshore and offshore.

Each upwelling ecosystem exhibits a unique coupling between the physical-chemical environment and the life forms that are present. Relatively small differences in such conditions as bottom topography, stability of the water column, and pattern of circulation produce major consequences for the ecosystem. For example, the Peruvian system differs from that off northwest Africa by having ten times the annual fish production, despite apparent similarities between the regions. Nutrients are much more abundant off Peru, not because upwelling is more intense but because the source water is much richer. Other important distinctions are between the simple food chain and unusually high productivity off Peru and the much more complex food web and more modest productivity off northwest Africa.

Climatic change and biological effects. Climatic changes on the scales of months to tens of years have always affected the surface layer of the ocean and the plants and animals living therein. Knowledge of the natural variability in environmental conditions and of natural populations is needed if one is to recognize the additional effects of human activities. Fish populations have undergone significant increases and decreases even when unfished, and the composition of plankton populations has been changing through much of geological history.

By the mid-1970s circumstantial links had been established between some biological events and climatic and oceanic change, but the precise nature of the interaction was poorly understood. Some of these events have great economic consequences, the crisis in the Peruvian anchovy fishery being a noteworthy example.

In 1972 a major climatic event known as El Niño occurred. This phenomenon takes place at irregular intervals, fewer than ten years apart, and is locally characterized by warm surface waters off Peru, heavy rains in Ecuador and northern Peru, and reduction in the fertility of the normally highly productive waters of the Peru Current. El Niño is only the local manifestation of a large-scale environmental disturbance that was recently shown to originate in changes in atmospheric circulation across the entire tropical Pacific Ocean. Unusually strong trade winds pile up surface water in the western equatorial Pacific. When the trades relax, this warm tropical water sloshes back to the east and replaces the normal cold and nutrient-rich waters off South America. With an appropriate index of the performance of the trade winds, it should be possible to forecast this event.

The warm water, which supports only limited primary production, brings with it some tropical creatures. There is seldom evidence of a mass mortality of fish; however, in the 1972 El Niño event, adult anchovies were not abundant and were concentrated close to the coast, thereby increasing their vulnerability to fishermen. Fortunately, the Peruvian government recognized the threat to the stock and closed the fishery.

The most striking effect of El Niño on the anchovies was the reduced spawning in the years 1971–73. In the latter two years, this could be attributed to the drastically reduced spawning stock. In 1971, however, the population of breeding adults was immense, and some other explanation must be sought.

The anchovy has been exposed to similar envi-

ronmental vicissitudes for millennia and has evolved means for rapid recovery when conditions return to normal. This time, however, it may be more difficult. The anchovy stock had been subjected to heavy fishing pressure for nearly two decades prior to 1972. There is evidence from other fisheries that under such circumstances of "recruitment overfishing," recovery can be very slow. In some cases the weakened species is replaced by another, as happened when the anchovy replaced the sardine off the California coast in recent years.

Mesoscale eddies. Until a few decades ago the pattern of ocean circulation seemed simple enough—broad, smoothly flowing currents at the surface and barely perceptible drifts at middle and great depths. This simple picture arose from averaging small quantities of crude data. After World War II a series of technological developments, such as the bathythermograph and salinity-temperature-depth profilers, made it possible to resolve smaller features and to look at them more frequently. Most important, the velocity field became amenable to measurement, either at fixed locations with moored current meters, or in drifting parcels of water marked with neutrally buoyant floats. These measurements showed a much higher degree of variability than had been expected, even at great

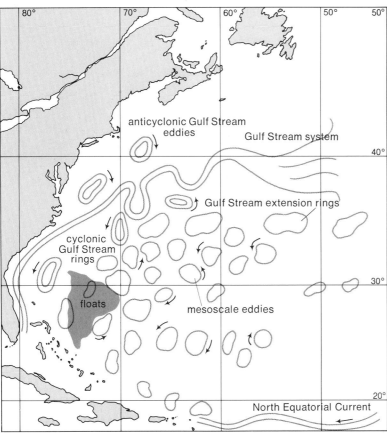

Mesoscale eddies, each a few kilometers in diameter and extending from the surface of the ocean to the bottom, are widely distributed in the Atlantic Ocean off the coast of North America. Some are seen to be associated with the Gulf Stream.

Adapted from *Oceanus*, vol. 19, no. 3, cover, Spring 1976; map by William Simmons, drawn by Nancy Barnes © 1976 by Woods Hole Oceanographic Institution

depths where the "Aries" expedition in 1959–60 found that floats at depths of 2–3 km (1.2–1.8 mi) were rapidly dispersed in all directions.

Measurements showed that much of the energy of the general circulation is contained in slow, medium-sized fluctuations, or eddying, of the flow. This variability is evident in the meanders of the Gulf Stream; it is also manifested in ring vortices pinched off from these meanders and in mid-ocean eddies. These mesoscale eddies extend from surface to bottom, are a few hundred kilometers in diameter, take several months to pass a given location, and are far more energetic than the average circulation. In many ways they are analogous to the storms and weather systems in the atmosphere. Experiments by Soviet scientists in 1970 and by U.S. and British scientists in mid-1973 provided much of the observational basis for the understanding of mesoscale variability, and theoreticians of those and other countries began analyzing models of the production and evolution of eddies and of their interactions with other scales of motion. A large U.S. and Soviet field experiment, Polymode, was scheduled for 1977–78 to test such ideas.

Geochemical studies. From the beginning of scientific oceanography, more than 100 years ago, chemists have measured the content of dissolved substances in seawater and the chemical composition of marine organisms and sediments. The great potential of chemical methods for illuminating the processes of ocean circulation and chemical cycling in the ocean has long been recognized. Until recently, however, with the exception of a few properties such as total salt content (salinity), the comparisons of chemical data required for an understanding of large-scale processes have been plagued by the uncertain standards and quality of measurements by different investigators.

This problem was being overcome by a massive program of chemical studies known as Geosecs (Geochemical Ocean Sections), in which the Atlantic and Pacific oceans were being sampled from north to south. Large numbers of water samples (more than 7,000 from 110 stations in the Atlantic alone) were taken at all depths from surface to bottom and then analyzed by standard and highly precise methods for some 23 chemical and 15 isotopic species. When sampling of the Indian Ocean is completed in 1978, data will be available for a comprehensive geochemical description of the world ocean.

Preliminary results indicate the value of a data base of high quality. As an example of these results, tritium, produced by U.S. and Soviet weapons tests in the 1950s and early 1960s, has reached the ocean surface and is being distributed and mixed into deeper water. The highest concentra-

tions in the Atlantic are found in high northern latitudes in the region where the winter sinking of surface water forms much of the deep water of the ocean. It seems likely that other pollutants may behave in similar fashion.

As another example, a comparison of nitrous oxide concentrations in the Pacific with comparable measurements ten years earlier showed an increase of 4 parts per billion. By the year 2000 this was expected to lead to a 7.4% increase in atmospheric nitrous oxide and a 1% decrease in the ozone shield that protects the Earth's surface from solar ultraviolet radiation. The increase appears to have resulted from widespread use of fertilizers and from combustion of coal and oil.

Oceanography and ocean law. While oceanographers in Edinburgh discussed the science of the sea, diplomats in New York concluded the second 1976 session of the United Nations Conference on the Law of the Sea. The negotiations, under way since 1967, have dealt with all uses of the ocean and its resources, including the pursuit of knowl-

Scientist Richard Seymour watches as computer-produced waves in a test tank pass through a model of a tethered-float breakwater he developed. The waves barely rock a toy sailboat.

Courtesy, Texaco Inc.

edge. It is clear that old uses, such as fisheries; new uses, such as the exploitation of offshore oil and gas; and future uses, such as the mining of manganese nodules, have all arisen from, or can be strongly affected by, the results of marine scientific research.

By the end of the New York sessions, it appeared likely that the eventual new legal regime for the oceans would give control over all research within 200 miles of the coast to the adjacent coastal nation. This zone encompasses approximately 37% of the area of the ocean and is the location of phenomena and processes of great scientific interest. Many scientists, particularly in the U.S. and northern Europe, fear that the pursuit of knowledge in the zone will be seriously inhibited by coastal nation restrictions.

—Warren S. Wooster

Energy

Worldwide economic recovery, unaccompanied by any truly significant energy conservation measures, caused a resurgence of total energy consumption in the non-Communist world during 1976. Preliminary data indicated that world energy demand increased by about 5% in 1976 to a level of 125 million to 130 million bbl per day in terms of oil equivalent. Essentially all of the increase was provided by petroleum, which accounted for about 45% of world energy supply. Furthermore, almost all the increased oil consumed was supplied by the Organization of Petroleum Exporting Countries (OPEC), the 13-nation group that continued its effective world oil cartel throughout 1976.

Only a little more than two years after the Arab oil embargo of late 1973 and 1974, the highly industrialized non-Communist nations had returned to the oil demand growth rates of 5–6% per year that had preceded the crisis. Thus, their dependence on OPEC oil supplies increased dramatically during 1976, following reductions in 1975 and 1974. It became apparent that most of the oil demand reductions in 1974 and 1975 had resulted from the serious worldwide economic recession and from three successive mild winters. None of the major consuming countries implemented truly effective long-range energy conservation programs nor materially increased their indigenous energy supplies. Announced plans to accelerate the development of oil, gas, coal, nuclear, and other alternate energy sources were not realized and were increasingly falling behind schedules. Thus, Western dependence on OPEC oil, most of it from Arab countries, was growing and would likely continue throughout the next decade.

Nowhere was this trend to increased oil import dependency more pronounced than in the United States, which each year accounted for approximately one-third of the world's consumption. The U.S. celebrated its Bicentennial in 1976 by going on an energy binge. In March the nation for the first time imported more oil than it produced. During several weeks, foreign petroleum imports exceeded domestic crude oil production of about 8 million bbl per day. By the end of 1976 the United States was importing 42% of its oil needs, as compared with only 29% in 1973 before the OPEC oil embargo. In 1976 these oil imports cost nearly $36 billion, or about nine times the pre-embargo bill for imports.

Despite these statistics, a Gallup Poll indicated that only 2% of the voting population in the U.S. regarded energy as the most serious national problem. The public appeared to consider the "oil crisis" over, and many deemed it a phony concoction by "big oil companies" and the Arab sheikhs to raise prices of oil products.

This complacency, however, was unjustified. The U.S. and all other non-Communist industrialized

A Mercedes-Benz, a luxury automobile from West Germany, exemplifies the wealth brought to Abu Dhabi in the United Arab Emirates by the oil field in the background.

Jacques Burlot—Gamma/Liaison

Green—Sygma

Saudi Arabian representatives at the meeting of OPEC ministers in Qatar in December 1976 joined those of the United Arab Emirates in refusing to raise the price of crude oil by 10% as of Jan. 1, 1977. The two nations agreed to limit their increases to 5%.

countries would suffer major economic damage from even a relatively short embargo or from a sizable reduction in Arab oil supplies.

Despite some strains in the cartel, OPEC maintained and strengthened its control over world oil prices during 1976. Led by Saudi Arabia, the producer with the largest excess producing capacity and largest financial resources, the OPEC members agreed to forgo an oil price increase in their May 1976 meeting. This moderate action was taken so as not to impede or reverse the slow recovery of the world economic recession. However, in their December 15–17 meeting in Doha, Qatar, the OPEC ministers were unable to reach agreement on a single reference price for crude oil. Led by Iran, Iraq, Nigeria, and Venezuela, 11 nations announced that they would increase the price of oil by 10% effective Jan. 1, 1977. Saudi Arabia and the United Arab Emirates (U.A.E.) refused to go along with those increases, announcing their determination to limit their reference crude oil price increase to 5% on Jan. 1, 1977. This split in pricing solidarity was the most serious break in the OPEC cartel since its founding in 1960; it was not expected, however, to result in a breakup of the cartel. If Saudi Arabia and the U.A.E. increase their production to meet world demands, as they are capable of doing, they will probably cause the other OPEC producers to limit their price increases to 5%.

The latest price increases raised average world crude oil prices to nearly six times those that prevailed before the 1973 embargo. The financial and economic effect of these prices continued to stagger the world's oil importers. OPEC oil exports averaged some 28 million bbl per day in 1976 and generated oil revenues of about $115 billion. Many consuming nations, especially less developed

countries, continued to amass large trade deficits and borrowed heavily to meet their oil bills.

Despite the deepening of debt, the latest oil price increase, and other negative aspects of the world energy situation, officials of the industrialized, oil-producing, and less developed nations were beginning to consider energy issues more rationally than in the past. The Conference on International Economic Cooperation (CIEC) met on a monthly basis throughout 1976 and made considerable progress in discussing political, economic, and social affairs and their effect on energy, raw materials, development assistance, and financial matters. The CIEC postponed a planned ministerial-level meeting scheduled for December 1976 but reached agreements to continue efforts to seek satisfactory resolution of energy and related issues during the resumption of the conference in the spring of 1977. Few consuming countries considered the breakup of OPEC an imminent or likely possibility or believed that real oil prices would decline in the near future. The development of new energy supplies and alternate energy sources was being accepted as a necessary evil. Oil producers were becoming more moderate in their demands and appeared to be more fully aware of the worldwide economic impact of their actions.

Petroleum and natural gas

World oil demand rebounded in 1976 to near pre-embargo growth rates of about 5–6%, after a two-year respite when annual growth rates of only 1% were realized. Oil demand in non-Communist countries increased by slightly more than 5% to average an estimated 44 million barrels per day (bpd) in 1976, or about three-fourths of total world oil consumption, which reached nearly 58 million bpd. As discussed above, the increased oil demand resulted from the worldwide recovery from the economic recession of 1974–75 and a failure of oil-consuming nations to implement sustained oil conservation measures or develop adequate non-oil energy sources.

Spurred by expectations of an OPEC crude oil price increase in December, non-Communist countries raised their imports so that oil production in non-Communist countries averaged about 46 million bpd in the last quarter of 1976 and about 44 million bpd for the year. Communist countries produced oil at an estimated rate of more than 13 million bpd in 1976. Soviet crude oil and condensate production reached nearly 10.5 million bpd, 6% more than in 1975. Despite a massive and severe earthquake in a major oil-producing area, China expanded its oil output at a rapid rate throughout 1976 and was producing an estimated 1.6 million bpd at the year's end.

Most of the non-Communist world's increase in oil production was from OPEC countries, where output expanded by more than 10% to average over 30 million bpd, the highest level in over two years. The Arab oil-producing countries of the Middle East and North Africa accounted for nearly two-thirds of OPEC output and essentially all of the increased production. Led by Saudi Arabia, the Arab countries controlled most of the world's excess oil-producing capacity. They curtailed output in order to sustain prices and increased production to meet demand at desired price levels.

During 1976 OPEC showed more restraint and a greater responsibility for its oil pricing moves than in the preceding two years. Meeting in May, OPEC delegates under the leadership of Saudi Arabia decided not to raise oil prices at mid-year but to freeze them until the end of the year. The surprising price dispute in the December meeting of OPEC in Doha, Qatar, was a further demonstration of the trend toward restraint. The Saudi Arabian and U.A.E. decision to raise oil prices by only 5% on Jan. 1, 1977, in contrast to the 11 other OPEC members' announced intention of a 10% increase on January 1 and an additional 5% increase on July 1, 1977, was certain to create considerable turmoil in world oil markets in 1977. Given the ability of Saudi Arabia and the U.A.E. to increase production by some 3 million bpd and the large stock buildup by consumers, it seemed likely that the Saudi position would prevail in early 1977 and that the average fob

Abu Rudays oil fields in the Sinai were restored to Egypt by Israel in 1975. The Arab countries accounted for most of the increased production of oil in the non-Communist world in 1976.

© Alon Reininger—Contact

(free on board) price of Saudi Arabian light crude would rise only 5%, to $12.09 per barrel. The OPEC rationale for the price increases was to recover oil revenues allegedly lost to inflation in the prices of goods and services purchased from the consuming countries.

U.S. dependency on OPEC, and especially Arab oil sources, increased alarmingly in 1976. Oil demand expanded by more than 6%, to average about 17.5 million bpd, while domestic crude oil and natural gas liquids production declined by 3.3%, to average only 10.2 million bpd. This deficit was met by increased oil imports, which averaged about 7.3 million bpd, an increase of nearly 18% over those of 1975. Direct and indirect foreign imports met an estimated 42% of U.S. needs in 1976 versus only 29% before the 1973 oil embargo. Arab countries were the source of recent increases in U.S. imports and by 1977 supplied approximately 14% of the U.S. petroleum demand, more than twice that of 1974. The U.S., therefore, was more vulnerable to an Arab oil embargo in 1977 than it was in 1973.

As insurance against the economic disruptions of any future oil embargo by Arabs or others, the U.S. government took the first step to stockpile large quantities of oil in a strategic petroleum reserve program authorized by Congress in December 1975. In December 1976 the Federal Energy Administration (FEA) announced plans for storing 150 million bbl of crude oil by the end of 1978.

Other major oil-consuming nations fared no better than the U.S. in reducing their dependency on OPEC. Despite a large increase in North Sea production, the countries of the European Economic Community increased their oil demand by 6% during 1976 and continued to import about two-thirds of their oil from OPEC countries.

Worldwide, oil and gas exploration and development activities continued at high levels in 1976 and 1977. Development of the large North Sea fields proceeded at a rapid pace. In the British sector, these fields produced about 300,000 bpd during 1976 and the bringing into production of seven more fields, now in progress, should raise output to about 2 million bpd by 1980. Norwegian North Sea fields produced about 450,000 bpd during 1976. Mexico continued development of its important Reforma fields and expanded output by more than 200,000 bpd, to average more than 800,000 bpd during 1976. China expanded its development activity as did India, Brazil, and other countries having significant recent oil finds.

In the U.S. oil and gas exploration continued at near-record levels. Well-drilling activity continued at levels averaging about 1,660 active rigs throughout 1976. Despite decreased tax benefits and continued price regulations, capital outlays by major

U.S. oil companies reached a record $25 billion in 1975, with nearly half of this total in the U.S.

Despite much concern over construction problems, the Alaskan oil pipeline was expected to be completed and to begin operation on schedule in mid-1977. This $7.7 billion, 800-mi-long pipeline would then begin delivering up to 1.2 million bpd of oil to the U.S. by the end of the year. In other actions to expand domestic oil production, the U.S. government enacted legislation permitting the development of the Naval Petroleum Reserves in California and Wyoming, and leased the first tracts in the Atlantic offshore continental shelf (OCS) area for oil exploration. The U.S. Geological Survey reported that a test well drilled in the OCS area 91 mi off New Jersey to a depth of 16,043 ft showed a potential for oil and gas.

Oil-refining capacity in the non-Communist world was expanded to nearly 60 million bpd in recent years and was greatly underutilized. In 1975 refinery capacity operated at about 75% of capacity. This rose to about 80% in 1976.

World marketed natural gas consumption increased by an estimated 9% to reach about 50 trillion cubic feet (Tcf) in 1976. Although U.S. natural

A 35,000-ton oil production platform, the largest ever built in Great Britain, is floated out to the Thirtle oil field in the North Sea. It is 606 feet high and will stand in 530 feet of water.

Central Press/Pictorial Parade

gas production continued to decline by about 5% annually, it was more than offset by large increases in Soviet and North Sea gas output. The U.S.S.R. in 1976 accounted for about 27% of marketed production, while the U.S. share, which was 97% of the world total in 1947, declined to about 45% in 1976.

World trade in natural gas of about 4.5 Tcf during 1976 continued to account for less than 10% of consumption. Natural gas delivered by overland pipelines amounted to about 4 Tcf, while seaborne shipments of liquefied natural gas (LNG) made up the remaining 0.5 Tcf. Most LNG was shipped from Algeria, Libya, and Brunei to Europe and Japan. Trade in both LNG and pipeline gas was expected to expand substantially by 1985 to about twice the present volumes. Heightened environmental concerns, however, were added to factors already complicating efforts to expand LNG shipments. With the U.S. East Coast set to become a major LNG importer, several of the coastal states petitioned the Federal Power Commission (FPC) to create strict and uniform standards for the siting and safe operation of LNG terminal facilities. The states urged the FPC to permit LNG siting only in areas of low population with buffer safety zones maintained around them.

Cars jam the road from Yugoslavia and Bulgaria to Istanbul as thousands of Turks return home from Western Europe with the cars they bought while working there.

Keystone

World reserves of natural gas were estimated at about 2,200 Tcf. The Soviet Union had 700 Tcf, or nearly one-third of the world total. The Persian Gulf states of Iran, Saudi Arabia, Kuwait, Iraq, Qatar, and the United Arab Emirates combined had reserves of more than 600 Tcf, while the U.S., Canada, and Mexico accounted for about 300 Tcf. European reserves, largely in The Netherlands and the North Sea, amounted to about 170 Tcf. In recent years the largest gas reserve additions were in the U.S.S.R., Iran, and the North Sea. Development of these reserves was being stimulated by the large recent increases in oil prices and the substantially higher prices for natural gas that ensued; however, a dramatic increase in world natural gas production was not expected in the next decade. This is because of the high cost and long lead times necessary to develop pipeline, liquefaction, transportation, and distribution systems to bring natural gas from the large producing areas to the major consuming areas of the industrialized world.

Concern in the U.S. about the nation's faltering natural gas supplies continued to grow during 1976. On July 27 the FPC announced its approval of higher interstate natural gas prices. Constituting the largest single gas price increase in history, the new rate authorized a national wellhead price of $1.42 per thousand cubic feet (Mcf) for "new" gas from wells opened after Jan. 1, 1975. This was nearly triple the "new" gas rate of 52 cents per Mcf approved by the FPC 18 months earlier. It also set new prices for "old" gas. FPC estimated the cost to consumers of their action would amount to $1.5 billion yearly. Consumer groups protested the FPC actions and set the increased cost for the first year at $2.2 billion. In October the FPC acknowledged a revised estimate of $2 billion for its July order but reaffirmed its higher rate for "new" gas. It tightened definitions and lowered slightly the rates for "old" gas to lessen the effect on the consumer to an estimated $1.6 billion. The FPC justified its actions as necessary to stimulate exploration and development of new supplies. Gas well drilling in 1976 was about 18% greater than in 1975, but much of this was in developing gas not subject to federal price regulation.

Coal

Coal consumption in the industrialized countries increased moderately in 1976. This was due to coal's sharply improved competitive position, caused by the large oil price increases since 1973, and by economic recovery in the developed countries. The demand for steam coal for power generation and industrial boilers increased by about 5% for the second year in a row, and stronger steel demand in 1976 boosted the consumption of coking coals.

World production of bituminous coal and lignite in 1976 was estimated at 3.6 billion metric tons. Led by the U.S.S.R., the Communist countries accounted for nearly 60% of the total. These nations also had nearly one-half of the estimated total world recoverable coal reserves of about 700 billion tons. The U.S. had about one-third of the world's total coal reserves and produced about 18% of the total 1976 output. Significantly, world coal consumption was less than 1% of reserves. Thus, this abundance of reserves and coal's favorable competitive position demonstrated that coal use was limited by demand and environmental constraints.

Despite a four-week wildcat strike in the coalfields, the U.S. was expected to mine a record 665 million tons of coal in 1976, about 3% more than in 1975. Domestic consumption was expected to increase 8% to nearly 600 million tons, while exports remained close to the 1975 level of 65 million tons. Investment in new and existing mines rose sharply,

signaling a substantial and sustained growth in coal production during the next decade. Much of the growth was expected to be in coal burned in electrical generation plants. Acting under legal authority, the FEA ordered that coal-burning capability be incorporated in the construction of 48 new electric generating plants in 22 states. These plants were to have an estimated generation capacity of 29,000 Mw and would be capable of burning 84 million tons of coal per year, which is equivalent to 300 million bbl of oil. The FEA action was taken so that scarce oil and natural gas could be directed to uses for which coal substitution is neither feasible nor environmentally acceptable.

In May the U.S. Department of the Interior issued new regulations for leasing and development, in an environmentally sound manner, of the vast federal coal reserves in the western states. The new system established methods for the selection of specific areas for leasing and for subjecting those areas to detailed environmental analysis and development controls before they are offered for leasing by competitive bidding. This was a step toward ending a

Giant aluminum sphere, 12 stories high and weighing 850 tons, is moved from assembly building (rear) to test stand (foreground) in South Carolina. The sphere will hold liquefied natural gas on a tanker.

Courtesy, General Dynamics

five-year moratorium on new leasing. Successful bidders would be required to develop their leases within a reasonable period or else lose them.

Electric power

The decline in the rate of growth of world electric power consumption observed in 1975 was reversed in 1976. Worldwide economic recovery, especially in industrial activity, caused an estimated 5–6% increase in demand for electricity during 1976 to a level of approximately 5.5 trillion kw-hr. This growth rate was approaching the historically high rates of 7–8% annually.

Despite average electric bills that reached their highest levels in 41 years, Americans demanded nearly 1.9 trillion kw-hr in 1976, an increase of almost 6% over 1975. As with gasoline, consumers had become more accustomed to higher energy prices and so relaxed their conservation efforts.

The primary fuels for electricity generation were the fossil fuels (coal, petroleum, natural gas), which accounted for an estimated 71% of total power output. Hydroelectric power continued to provide about 23%, and nuclear energy accounted for the remaining 6%.

Although the nuclear share of the total increased during 1976 by about 1%, construction of nuclear power plants continued to lag behind earlier expectations of growth. World capacity for generating nuclear power stood at about 80,000 Mw in 1976, with about 90% of the total located in the major industrial nations of the non-Communist world. Installed nuclear capacity in the major developed countries was expected to reach about 390,000 Mw by 1985, according to recent estimates. This figure is nearly 20% less than earlier estimates and reflects growing worldwide public concern over nuclear safety.

In the U.S. about 60 nuclear power plants with a

Coal "log" (above) is produced by feeding a mixture of finely ground coal and a tar binder into an extruder, which in turn continuously feeds the material into a pressure vessel. Coal gasifier pilot plant (left), which features improved treatment of clinkers and ash, was developed by the General Electric Co.

Courtesy, General Electric Company, Research and Development Center

capacity of 42,000 Mw were operable in 1976 and accounted for about 9% of the country's total power generation. Nevertheless, the nuclear industry continued to face serious challenges from those who questioned whether the advantages of nuclear energy outweighed the potential hazards of producing it. Responding to a court ruling that risks were inadequately considered, the Nuclear Regulatory Commission (NRC) declared a temporary moratorium on licenses for new nuclear power plants in August 1976. In mid-October the NRC issued a revised environmental impact estimate and new guidelines that it hoped would allow a resumption of licensing within the next few months. In the national elections on November 2, referenda on the issue of restricting nuclear energy plant construction were held in six states. Voters in all six decisively rejected any restrictions.

Other energy sources

The U.S. and other highly industrialized nations continued major programs to develop new and alternate energy sources in an effort to lessen their dependence on oil imports. In July 1976 President Gerald Ford signed a $9.7 billion appropriation bill for energy research and for hundreds of water and power projects. The U.S. Energy Research and Development Administration (ERDA) was provided $5.7 billion for developing new or improved energy source technologies.

Solar energy development continued to receive wide governmental support in the U.S. ERDA was authorized to spend $258.5 million on solar research and $31.9 million for solar construction and equipment projects. The agency began construction of a solar electric plant that would utilize a field of mirrors to concentrate the Sun's rays in an elevated boiler designed to generate 10,000 kw. Twenty states enacted alternate-energy-systems legislation in 1976. Half of these acts provided some form of tax incentive for stimulating increased use of solar heating and cooling in residential, commercial, and industrial buildings. A Florida law set performance standards for the solar industry, and Arizona legislated sunlight access rights for property owners.

ERDA also expanded projects for the development of geothermal and wind energy. ERDA funded or participated in many projects to test the potential of geothermal areas in the western states for both heating and electricity generation. National U.S. geothermal research efforts increased tenfold in the past five years. ERDA expenditures on wind power research and experimental projects reached nearly $15 million in 1976. In a test directed by the U.S. National Aeronautics and Space Administration (NASA), a 100-kw wind generator was successfully operated at a site in Ohio. In August ERDA announced plans for construction of a huge 1,500-kw wind generator to power 500 homes. NASA was chosen to direct this experimental project.

U.S. synthetic liquid fuel research programs were expanded, but plans to develop large-scale demonstration plants were postponed because Congress failed to pass the $5 billion–$6 billion synthetic fuels commercialization program requested by ERDA. The government-industry plans to develop the enormous western oil-shale deposits came to a virtual standstill. The Department of the Interior suspended for one year the experimental oil-shale development plans on two leased oil-shale tracts in Colorado, and the companies operating projects on two Utah tracts asked for similar suspensions. Development plans were delayed because of environmental, technical, and legal problems. The suspensions permitted the companies to delay paying $130 million of the $330 million they bid on the tracts in 1974 while they sought to overcome the impediments to development.

—James A. West

Environment

Environmental problems can be studied on many different levels. At the simplest, one considers only the effects of the environment on the individual plant, animal, or human being. At the next higher level, the interactions between populations of organisms and their environment are studied. At the third level, the focus of research is broadened to include the interactions between whole communities of species populations and the environment, and also between the populations constituting the community. At still higher levels, the roles of economic, institutional, and cultural factors in environmental problems are considered. The principal development in environmental science in 1976 was rapid maturation of research that views environmental problems from higher levels. There was also rapid evolution of research that views environmental problems from several different levels simultaneously.

Two overall findings were revealed by these new ways of viewing environmental problems. First, more and more complex patterns were exposed in the structure and dynamics of natural systems, and in the interactions between natural and human systems. Second, it was becoming apparent, in retrospect, why certain problems were not previously understood or solved; they were not being viewed either on the correct level or from enough different levels simultaneously. These introductory remarks

Alain Nogues—Sygma

Oyster farmers on the Atlantic coast of Spain try to save some of their crop from destruction by the 90,000 tons of crude oil spilled into the ocean by the wrecking of the tanker "Urquiola" in May 1976.

can be illustrated by a number of subject areas that attracted a great deal of attention in 1976 and 1977: climatic change and international sales of grain, community ecology, environmental economics, energy conservation, systems modeling, and demographic phenomena.

Climatic change and international grain sales. Climatic change and its effect on grain sales became an area of great controversy during the year, and resulted in an immense amount of activity. Large numbers of papers were published, many new books appeared, and several important committee reports were issued. It was widely recognized that the adequacy of world food supplies increasingly depended on massive grain production by a few high-latitude countries in which agricultural production is unusually vulnerable to drought, frost, or both. The controversy concerned the likelihood of a major deterioration in climate and the magnitude of the resultant impact on grain production and grain exports.

One school of thought held that rather serious climate disruptions have occurred throughout history, and that prudence dictates a number of institutional innovations to deal with such a disruption in the future. One proponent of this view was the climatologist Stephen Schneider, who wrote an elaborate analysis of this problem, *The Genesis Strategy.* The title derives from Joseph's warning to the pharaoh (related in the Book of Genesis) that in years of good agricultural production, the harvest from one-fifth of the land should be set aside as "insurance" against harvest failure and famine. Schneider extended this concept to include a broad array of institutional innovations to serve as insurance against disasters, including an Institute of Imminent Disasters.

Schneider held a view shared by many scientists: in order to gain an accurate assessment of the severity and probability of disastrous climatic impacts on grain production, it is not sufficient to examine only data from the 20th century. He, like others, argued that a longer perspective is necessary because world climate in recent decades has been unusually benign in comparison with previous centuries.

What disturbed many scientists was the estimation of the probable future severity and frequency of climatic deteriorations over the next few decades by using weather tables for the 20th century alone. If one follows this approach, the most serious climatic occurrence that can be projected for the next several decades is drought of the severity that characterized the decade 1930–39. On the other hand, if one broadens one's historical (and scientific) perspective, a qualitatively different type of climatic disaster involving low temperatures must be considered. The argument is that while new developments in irrigation can partially buffer U.S. food production against a drought, no technological innovation can buffer grain production against a large drop in temperature.

New research and publications in geophysics opened additional perspectives on this debate. Studies by J. B. Pollack, Owen B. Toon, and their associates elevated assessments of the impact of volcanic eruptions on climate to a new level of sophistication. Their calculations quantified the impact of silicate dust particles and sulfur gases from volcanic explosions on the optical properties of the atmosphere (as they affect solar radiation) and thus on the global energy budget. From their model, one can predict the magnitude of the impact on the surface temperature of the Earth that could be expected from a volcano introducing a given "dust-veil index" in the atmosphere.

In addition, the work of historical climatologists provided dust-veil indexes that resulted from volcanoes of the last three centuries. According to these climatologists, a relatively minor group of volcanoes in the 1880s, including Krakatoa (1883; Indonesia), collectively created a large enough dust-veil index so that a drop in mean surface temperature of between 1° and 3° C would have been reasonable. There appeared, however, to be a consensus in recent geophysical publications that the Krakatoa group of volcanoes generated only about a third the atmospheric dust load of Cosigüina (1835; Nicaragua) or a sixth that caused by Tambora (1815; Indonesia). Thus, one would expect to discover that Cosigüina and Tambora had much more marked impacts on U.S. climate and agricultural production than did anything in the 20th century. An inspection of U.S. historical statistics shows that this expectation is justified. The oldest set of temperature records for the U.S. is from New

Blowing dust covers a farm road in north-central Oklahoma in February 1976. Drought conditions in parts of the United States brought back memories of the "Dust Bowl" days of the 1930s.

UPI Compix

Haven, Conn. The annual mean temperature for that station never dropped below 47° F (8° C) in the 20th century, whereas it dropped to 46° F in 1817 and 45° F in 1836. While agricultural yield figures are not recorded for years prior to 1866, the U.S. wholesale price of wheat increased 62% from 1814 to 1817, and 81% from 1834 to 1838. Prices of wheat and wheat flour doubled in England in response to the Tambora eruption.

Clearly, an important new perspective on the effect of climate on grain production is introduced by relating geophysical knowledge to agronomy. As Schneider and others asserted, the policy implications are both large and urgent. There should be enough grain in storage to buffer the world against two or three consecutive years of disastrous crop reductions, and one should assume that incidents of this severity will occur not rarely but on an average of once or twice a century. The unusually good weather in the 20th century has produced a dangerous sense of false security.

Community ecology. The primary research focus of most academic ecologists used to be the dynamics of species populations. They found, however, that new insights into the behavior of species populations are revealed when viewed on the level of the community. At that level one can ask such questions as "Why are there five times as many species in one habitat as in another? What is it about the two habitats that makes for such different species packing? What does this imply about how the species populations interact with each other in the two different habitats?"

This point of view was particularly emphasized by the late Robert MacArthur of Princeton University. Twenty-one of his friends and colleagues recently wrote as a memorial to him a book that is a revealing survey of the new types of patterns in natural systems being exposed as a consequence of the maturation of community ecology. For example, suppose one asks the question, "Which particular attributes of habitats are the most useful predictors of the difference we will observe in the number of species they contain?" John MacArthur discovered that the extreme range of annual mean temperatures (usually the mean July temperature less the mean January temperature) is a useful predictor. The number of species in a habitat increases as this temperature range decreases, all other things being equal. Also, species packing increases more with a unit decrease in temperature range at small than at large temperature ranges. The explanation is that large temperature ranges oppose the establishment of new species.

Temperature, however, is not the only variable determining the population of various species in different habitats. Martin Cody, in studies of bird

Photos reproduced from UNESCO *Courier*, (left) © Stanley Chung, Hong Kong—UNESCO/Photokina/JPH; (right) Gerhard Neisins, West Germany, International Photo Competition, UN/FIAP

Shacks in Hong Kong (left, foreground) are being replaced as living quarters for the poor by high-rise towers behind them. Some behavioral scientists, however, have criticized such tower blocks for generating feelings of loneliness and anonymity (right).

communities in California, Chile, and Africa, found three distinct types of habitat measures that determine such populations. Alpha-diversity measures the species packing of a habitat. Beta-diversity measures the species turnover (the rate at which some species are lost and others gained as one moves between different habitats in a systematic way, relative to the difference between the habitat types). Gamma-diversity measures geographic species turnover (the extent to which similar habitats in different zoogeographic areas support different species).

To illustrate the types of patterns revealed by these measures, Africa is much higher than Chile with respect to beta-diversity in birds with habitats similar to California, but Chile catches up to Africa when one measures gamma-diversity. It is not yet completely clear what these different patterns mean, or how they come about.

Another matter considered by Robert MacArthur and his colleagues was the colonization of islands by species. To illustrate this phenomenon Jared Diamond presented data on the species composition of bird communities occupying islands within about 400 miles of New Guinea. Three factors were found to be associated with increased number of bird species: increased proximity to New Guinea, increased altitudinal gradient, and increased island area. Thus, a traveler hoping to see a great variety of interesting birds should avoid small, flat islands a great distance away from any large landmass.

Environmental economics. Two important (but different) landmark books on the relationship between environmental problems and economics appeared in 1976. *The Poverty of Power*, by Barry

Commoner, seeks to understand the linked environmental and economic problems of recent years by an analysis of the relationships between energy productivity, capital productivity, and labor productivity. Commoner pointed out that for several years productivity of capital in the energy sector of the economy has been dropping. This is happening because of an irrational reliance on fossil fuel energy; as these stock (fixed-supply) resources are used up, it costs more money per unit to extract the remaining, less accessible units. But the productivity of energy is also declining in energy-intensive parts of the economy. Commoner found that, as a general rule, a low efficiency in the use of energy relative to output may be interpreted as indicative of a correspondingly low efficiency in the use of capital. Furthermore, he discovered that in the last 30 years the basic design of the U.S. economy had changed so as to become lower in capital productivity (output per dollar of capital investment), but higher in labor productivity (output per man-hour of labor used). In short, the economic system has been operated as if there were a glut of capital and energy and an acute shortage of labor. In fact, the reverse situation was true.

Instead of using capital and energy inputs to increase labor productivity (a process that promotes unemployment, pollution, and rapid rates of resource depletion), Commoner advocated using labor inputs to increase the productivity of capital and energy. A root cause of the present phenomenon, he maintained, was the low price being charged for energy in the U.S. relative to the price being charged for labor. This price discrepancy promoted a high-speed substitution of cheap en-

© Gianni Tortoli

Sperm whale is captured off Pico Island in the Azores. Extensively hunted for its oil, which is used as a lubricant and in the production of cosmetics and detergents, the sperm whale is an endangered species.

ergy for expensive labor, at a time when the realities of the situation called for the opposite strategy.

The other new book on environmental economics, *Mathematical Bioeconomics* by Colin Clark, combined modern mathematical, economic, and ecological methods of analysis to analyze strategies for managing natural resources. This book is particularly timely, because one of the problems that stimulated the development of the theory in it was that of overexploitation of whales, particularly the largest (blue) whales. During 1976 there was an extraordinary rise in public awareness of and interest in the numbers of whales.

Clark's book raised the following central question in regard to whales: What is the essential defect in the thinking of modern resource exploiters that would lead them to almost exterminate valuable resources, which, if managed rationally, could yield a return on invested capital indefinitely? To clarify the following discussion, the term maximum sustainable yield (MSY) is used to designate the largest possible annual yield from the resource that can be removed each year, indefinitely, without impairing the ability of the resource stock to maintain itself.

From a strictly biological point of view, the optimal harvest strategy is to remove no more and no less than the MSY each year. This, however, constitutes a textbook example of the weakness of considering an environmental problem from the wrong perspective and from too narrow a range of perspectives. In the case of the whales, by adding economic to biological considerations, one finds that the optimal harvest strategy may be to harvest at a rate either above or below the MSY. If an industry

exploiting a renewable resource, such as whale stocks, views them strictly as a capital asset, then it follows that the optimal harvest strategy is to maximize the rate of economic return allowed through management of the asset. Unfortunately, since whale stocks only grow at 5–10% per year, harvesting so as to obtain MSY leads to a rate of economic return below that which could be obtained in possible alternate investments. Considering that situation, the manager (exploiter) of a stock of whales might well decide to increase his rate of return by managing the whales so as to drive them close to extinction. When the whale populations decline to a level at which it is no longer economic to hunt them, the assets of the whaling industry would be invested in a new business with a high rate of return.

Of course, this explains the present plight of whales, but it also exposes a defect in the strategy: continued application of it soon leaves an investor with a sharply reduced set of resources from which to derive economic gain. Also, as Clark points out, another type of economic consideration may more than compensate for the argument just presented, and may dictate an economically optimal harvesting strategy in which less rather than more of the MSY is removed each year. This economic consideration is that as the population size of the exploited stock is reduced, the cost efficiency of harvest decreases.

All the above considerations, biological and economic, lead to a new and more sophisticated theory as to how to exploit renewable resources. The intensity of harvest should depend on the relative strengths of the capital investment argument vis-à-vis the cost efficiency argument. Further complications arise because of the nature of the property rights to the resource; the price per item of the resource, which will depend on demand relative to supply; and the general inflation rate, which varies through time. Ultimately, the considerations basic to Commoner's analysis, the price of labor relative to the price of resources purchased with wages, also operate in this theory.

Clark's book is important because it brings to bear on the problem of rational management of renewable resources the full arsenal of techniques from modern economic theory and applied mathematics. Perhaps the basic and most important message in the highly technical analysis is that biologically oriented fishery scientists have had poor success in communicating their ideas about management strategies to various industries. This has been primarily because the scientists have been insensitive to what Clark has described as "time-preference phenomena," the schedules for investment, depreciation, and return that are desired by industry.

Energy conservation. Conservation of energy during recent years has become a widely publicized and highly controversial issue. Newspapers and newsmagazines have made the public aware that energy prices in the U.S. are very low compared with other countries, and that energy is used wastefully. More penetrating analyses also appeared in scientific journals. In one, Lee Schipper and Allan Lichtenberg made a thorough compari-

son of the Swedish and U.S. economies to discover how Sweden could attain a per capita gross national product essentially the same as that of the U.S. in 1971 when energy consumption per capita was only 60% as great. This study produced a number of revealing insights into the reason for the energy waste in the U.S. economy. While the Swedes use automobiles for 77% as many miles per person for trips over 30 miles as do people in the U.S., the Swedes use them for only 38% as many miles per capita for short trips (under 30 miles).

The significance of the study is that not only do Americans use large, energy-inefficient cars with a low number of occupants per car but also that a high proportion of all car trips are short. On such trips so much of the energy is used to warm up the engine that, for example, on journeys of about five miles or less, automobile fuel consumption per mile is nearly double the average fuel consumption.

This prevalence of short car trips reflects two underlying conditions: underpriced gasoline gives Americans no incentive to conserve, and the generally low availability of public transportation does not offer a convenient alternative to the car. The Swedish example makes clear how the U.S. government could stimulate efficiency in the use of automobile energy if it should become so motivated. In 1971 the Swedish gasoline tax of 50 cents per gallon raised the price of gasoline by 250% to 70 cents per gallon. In addition, automobile excise taxes and yearly fees are a steeply rising fraction of

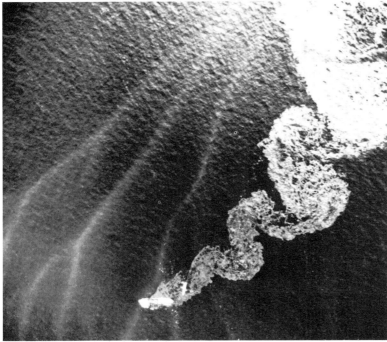

Millions of gallons of crude oil spilled by the Liberian tanker "Argo Merchant" off the coast of Nantucket Island, Massachusetts, in December 1976 drift away from the ship to form a huge slick on the Atlantic Ocean.

Wide World

vehicle weight. Consequently, the typical Swedish car weighs roughly half the typical U.S. auto.

Schipper and Lichtenberg also found that the heat exchange between homes and the external environment was about half as great in Sweden as in the U.S. The explanation is that in Sweden building codes have allowed the construction of only energy-efficient homes.

The conclusion of the study was that the U.S. uses a great deal of energy that has no positive effect on the quality of life or the economy. It is particularly noteworthy that the overall effect of this burden has been to produce a low rate of economic growth in the U.S. in the last two decades, relative to that of many other advanced economies.

Amory Lovins performed some elaborate calculations on the likely costs of alternate sources of energy in the U.S. in the mid-1980s. He made two amazing discoveries. First, all future sources of energy will be much more expensive than imported crude oil. For example, he estimated that light-water nuclear reactor energy will cost about 100 times as much per unit delivered as imported crude oil. Second, he concluded that only 29% of the cost to small customers of electric utilities is for the electricity they receive. Most of the remaining 71% is used by the utilities to purchase and maintain transmission and distribution networks. This leads to the surprising conclusion that centralization in this instance does not lead to economies but to diseconomies of scale. As this becomes more widely known, it could provide motivation for the generation of solar and wind energy at the home.

Systems modeling. During the period 1968 to 1973, there was considerable optimism that large-scale, computer-simulated models of society would be useful for solving environmental problems. More recently, books have appeared with various kinds of explanations as to why the models have not had the desired effect.

Basically, three categories of explanations have been offered. The first is that the models simply could not say anything useful because their scientific basis was not sufficiently developed; a more severe version of this is that systems analysis is really only a class of content-free logical truths. A second explanation is that for such models to be useful there must be an integrated program of problem analysis and communication with people who have a stake in the results. Furthermore, there must be a great effort to communicate by using an integrated package of words and graphics. According to this argument, nothing of this sort has yet been done on a meaningful scale. But perhaps the best explanation was provided by Walt Anderson. He pointed out the deep cultural commitment in the U.S. to growth, coupled with a cultural lack of any

clear understanding of how much change is possible in a given time. This combination of deeply held commitment to an archaic and unworkable ideal, which must be discarded very fast if disaster is to be avoided (depletion of existing energy sources before replacement technologies are in place), with the inability to change ideals fast may be trapping the U.S. The inability of the systems modelers to affect society may be due to the cultural inability of society to accept the message.

Demography. The cultural inability to accept information at odds with the conventional wisdom was nowhere more clearly exposed than in the response in the U.S. to demographic statistics. For a long time, it was a basic assumption of many types of institutions, and of the public, that growth of all types would be inevitable simply because of population growth. By late 1976, however, a new demographic pattern had continued for long enough in the U.S. so that there could be no doubt that it was a significant trend rather than a short-term statistical artifact. Because the birthrate had been dropping for so long in the U.S., many writers had argued that it would shortly turn around and start rising again. But in fact, the rate continued to decline. The U.S. birthrate per 1,000 of the population at midyear dropped from 25.3 in 1957 to 14.9 in 1974. Therefore, it dropped at an average rate of 3.07% per year over that time interval. But for the 12 months ending in August 1975 to the 12 months ending in August 1976, it declined from 15.9 to 14.5 (3.97%). On the evidence, therefore, the rate of decline is increasing.

The implications of this rate of decline for projections of future electricity requirements, airport runways, highways, and other major capital investments are, of course, profound. Perhaps that is why these numbers receive so little attention; they represent a formidable threat to the widely held dream of growth forever.

—Kenneth E. F. Watt

Food and agriculture

During 1976 the Economic Research Service of the U.S. Department of Agriculture (USDA) completed a national survey to determine how consumers' attitudes were affecting their food purchases, especially in light of increased food prices. Results were based on more than 1,400 in-home interviews with respondents who were the main food shoppers or had the major responsibility for food-purchasing decisions within their households. The general outcome of the survey was that consumers apparently are making more careful food-purchasing decisions than in the past.

Of the respondents, 30% said they were checking newspaper advertisements for food specials more than they had in 1975, and a similar percentage said they were saving and using food coupons more than in the previous year. Over one-fourth reported buying more food in volume, especially when it was sold at special rates. Those who checked newspaper ads for sales tended to be shoppers who had children living at home. Younger, better educated consumers with larger families and incomes tended to use food coupons more than others. Over a fifth said that they were making more dishes from scratch than they had in the previous year and believed this practice saved money, although some indicated that they were preparing food from scratch principally for improved nutrition and better taste. As educational and income levels increased, the practice of preparing food from scratch decreased. Overall, the survey indicated that many consumers were using various devices to lower their food costs.

The survey also showed that higher gasoline prices were affecting food shopping patterns. About one-sixth of those surveyed said they were shopping closer to home more often than in the previous year. In addition, more than 10% indicated they were making fewer trips to food stores. The results showed that average American food shoppers "did their main food shopping once a week, . . . shopped at only one store, . . . patronized stores close to home."

Higher food costs had changed the makeup of many shopping lists. More than 60% of the respondents were buying less of some types of food than they had previously, and about a fourth were purchasing more low-priced items. Cutbacks were seen particularly in beefsteaks and roasts, pork chops, bacon and ham, snack foods, dairy products, convenience foods, soft drinks, fish, lamb, veal, and canned fruits and vegetables. Economy-minded consumers purchased more hamburger, poultry, pastas, and fresh fruits and vegetables. Some consumers were changing their diets, but for reasons of health rather than cost. Principally, these were individuals who at one time or another suffered from high blood pressure or obesity or who had allergy problems. Among the major concerns were calorie intake, the amount of fat in the diet, including the relative proportion of saturated fats, and the presence of sugar. Some consumers indicated that they tried to avoid items containing artificial sweeteners, food colorings, or preservatives. Many said they used labeling information to determine the nutritional quality and ingredients of food items. However, the most used components of labeling information were prices and open dates, which indicate shelf life or storageability.

Agriculture

Short-term outlook. In reviewing agriculture in 1976, the USDA noted that total U.S. farm income was a step behind the $26 billion recorded in 1975, but realized net farm income was "a bit better than last year." U.S. farm production reached a new high, and wheat production was the second largest in history. The soybean crop, although not as large as in 1975, was still one of the biggest on record.

Retail food prices for the entire year averaged about 3% above 1975, constituting the slowest upward movement in five years. The increased cost of food is related to processing and transportation as well as wholesale and retail costs, and costs in labor, transportation, and packaging had risen substantially. All in all, both farmers and consumers could say that 1976 was not the best of years, but clearly it was not the worst.

The 1977 forecast indicated that retail food prices would rise 2 to 4% in the first half of the year compared with the same period in 1976. Red meat, poultry, and fresh produce would be most affected. Despite the improved prospects for the Soviet grain crop, the U.S.S.R. was still trying to rebuild depleted stocks, an action that would influence the U.S. market. Europe's grain crops continued to deteriorate, and increased demand from that continent would be another significant factor. Based on key indicators of cattle on feed, pig crops, and broiler hatch, U.S. livestock supplies should be plentiful in 1977. Although beef production would probably be below 1976, pork and broilers would more than make up the difference. On balance, U.S. farm exports in 1977 would be little different from the $22,150,000,000 shipped in 1976.

Long-term outlook. Modern agriculture should be viewed as a system of interrelated resources. The food industry is intricately interwoven with many sectors of the economy and encompasses far more than farming. On the input side of the farm are industries that supply such items as farm machinery and fertilizer, petroleum products for pest and weed management, and fuel to operate farm machinery. On the output side is the food-processing industry.

Some basic resources—sunlight, carbon dioxide, and oxygen—are, on the whole, poorly utilized. The same is true of nitrogen, which is a major constituent of air and essential for metabolism. Other physical resources such as soil, water, and energy are relatively limited and must be managed by deliberate human action. Water, a critical resource in agriculture, is a scarce commodity in many areas of the world. The rate of evapotranspiration from leaves, a major mechanism of water loss from plants, is an important area of study. Wheat, rice,

Adapted from "The Resources Available for Agriculture" by Roger Revelle,
© September 1976 by Scientific American Inc. All rights reserved.

	net arable area in humid tropics (millions of hectares)	arable without irrigation outside humid tropics (millions of hectares)	irrigation required for even one crop (millions of hectares)
Africa	105	490	10
Asia	80	450	15
Australia and New Zealand	0	115	2
Europe	0	170	0
North America	10	440	8
South America	300	350	24
U.S.S.R	0	325	23
Total	495	2,340	82

Potentially arable land that can support crops without irrigation comprises about 22% of the world's ice-free land surface. Water is available to irrigate another 82 million hectares (1 hectare = 2.47 acres).

and corn commonly evapotranspire thousands of tons of water per ton of edible grain produced. Moving water from where it is abundant to where it is needed is another challenge, requiring maximum mobilization of scientific and engineering know-how.

Another fundamental problem in agricultural research is to increase the amount of acreage in production. Roger Revelle of Harvard University pointed out that some 22% of the world's ice-free land surface is potentially arable land capable of supporting nonirrigated crops. He further estimated that the amount of cultivated land per person could be increased in every part of the world between now and the year 2000. In 1970 only 1,360,000,000 ha were actually under cultivation and, of that, only a fraction yielded more than one crop a year. The potential gross crop area of 4,-230,000,000 ha projected for AD 2000 could be achieved by growing more than one crop a year on roughly a third of some 2.9 billion arable ha. Rangeland potentially useful for the grazing of livestock is another of the world's relatively untapped natural resources. Improvements in range utilization by mixing native grasses with cultivated grasses were reported.

The mobilization and full utilization of resources available on the planet will require a more fully organized and orchestrated social system. In this regard, many nations are beginning to recognize the interdependence of peoples throughout the world. Thus the relatively untapped resources of Africa and South America are beginning to be developed through joint efforts of countries with capi-

tal and scientific knowledge and those with man-power and untapped resources. It is to be hoped that a significant feature of the final quarter of the 20th century will be marked improvement of food production and distribution systems on a world-wide basis.

Current research. Animal agriculture has three major needs: improvement of reproductive efficiency, disease control, and genetic manipulation to improve feed conversion efficiency. Recent research reported from USDA laboratories and several agricultural experiment stations has shown that estrus (heat) synchronization and controlled ovulation in cattle are possible and practical. Cattle can be bred "by appointment." Advantages include extensive use of artificial insemination, which permits use of genetically superior sires and greater selection of animals for ease of calving. The technique leads to a much higher rate of conception among cows, thus reducing "waste" of feed needed to maintain a barren cow.

Another technique, superovulation, is used to increase the number of ova produced by a high-quality cow at one time. Superovulation, combined with the transfer of fertilized ova from a donor cow of high quality to an incubator cow of even marginal quality, allows for the production in one year of a large number of calves from a specific mating. Theoretically, numbers in the vicinity of 60 calves per year should be possible. With such techniques, genetic improvement of cattle and other livestock bred to live in specific environmental conditions and on specific feed and forage combinations is possible.

314

Wide World

Since poultry are among the most efficient animals in converting feed energy into food energy, considerable research has been concentrated on them, particularly in the U.S. state agricultural experiment stations. Since World War II, studies of the interrelationships of genetic potential, nutritional efficiency, disease prevention, and control of light, humidity, and air movement in broiler houses have increased broiler production efficiencies in many small increments, but the cumulative result is the production of 4.5-lb birds in 8.5 weeks with a feed conversion ratio of 1.95 lb of feed per pound of live weight. On the marketing side, dark meat and turkey fat became profitable items after agricultural experiment station researchers found ways to incorporate them into such products as turkey frankfurters.

Estimates by scientists at Auburn (Ala.) University indicated that livestock and poultry diseases cost the U.S. public approximately $3.6 billion annually. One by one, animal diseases have been attacked by research scientists, but others remain unconquered. Foot rot, calf scours, and shipping fever are the principal problems of the U.S. beef industry. Current work at Colorado State University promised to reduce the 4 to 5% loss in feedlots due to foot rot. A vaccine was being developed for this disease, and a similar approach being used against shipping fever showed promise. Researchers at the University of Nebraska announced development of a vaccine that effectively produces immunity against calf scours, which causes extensive losses of range-dropped calves.

Only a small percentage of the plant and animal

James Flink, a food engineer at the Massachusetts Institute of Technology, holds a piece of synthetic fruit-like gel that can be flavored and colored to simulate such fruits as pineapples and cherries.

species available on Earth are used as food by humans. Among many efforts to expand this range, scientists at the Massachusetts Agricultural Experiment Station developed a system of converting alfalfa into human food. Alfalfa can produce up to 1,000 lb of protein per acre, compared with 500 lb

Baby yakow, a cross between a yak and a Highland cow, was bred to flourish in the uplands of Great Britain and eventually provide inexpensive meat to residents of the U.K.

London Daily Express/Pictorial Parade

for soybeans, and has an excellent amino acid profile. The technique involves the extraction of leaf juices, which contain about 50% of the plant's protein. A higher percentage of protein recovery is possible with enzymatic processing as an additional step. The residues may still be used as hay. Along the same lines, the Guam Agricultural Experiment Station initiated experiments to determine the feasibility of culturing the coconut crab, used as food on Guam for many years.

Food engineers at the Massachusetts Institute of Technology (MIT) developed a synthetic fruit-like gel that can be colored and flavored to resemble various fruits; nutrients or medicine can also be added. The most successful product was a pineapple-like food, but the MIT engineers also fabricated pieces of simulated strawberries, bananas, cherries, and peaches. The ingredients in the "fruits" all occur naturally in plants and animals. The final form is a gel that is concentrated and dried. It can be used fresh or can be frozen or freeze-dried and stored indefinitely.

—John Patrick Jordan

Nutrition

Life expectancy in the U.S. has been increasing steadily in recent years and might even reach 80 by the year 2000, compared with 71 in 1970. This seems to imply that the current health and nutritional status of Americans is good and that dietary habits and diseases are under control. However, longevity data do not necessarily show that the quality of life of the elderly is good. Henry C. Sherman, a pioneer in the study of nutrition and longevity, stressed that optimum nutrition could "not only add years to our life but could add life to our years."

At any age "we are the total of our life's nutrition," and people must have a heritage of health to ensure a vigorous and satisfying old age. The research of Bacon Chow at Johns Hopkins University, Baltimore, Md., and others supports this hypothesis. In 1900 one person in 25 was 65 or older; in 1970 the figure was one in 10. Modern medicine, among other factors, has enabled a greater proportion of the U.S. population to reach 70, but little has been done to improve the health of the elderly. Residency in an extended care facility is hardly a goal, regardless of how well these facilities cater to the needs of the residents. The rapidly increasing number of residents in such facilities belies the hypothesis that quality of life is being maintained as years are added to life.

People and nutrition. In general people are unrealistic about their health and nutritional status and in their expectations of what the medical profession can do to cure disease. A survey of 600 families conducted by the Louis Harris organization for Mount Sinai Hospital Medical Center in Chicago showed that 81% considered themselves well informed about nutrition and proper diet. Al-

Senior citizens perform yoga exercises at a social center in France, part of a national program to improve the health and well-being of the elderly.

Jean-Luce Hure—The New York Times

most half felt that they would be healthier if they ate less white bread, butter, sugar, salt, coffee, and soft drinks and more whole grain, fish, and fruit. Of the families, 85% realized the importance of exercise but only 32% had any regular exercise program. Most were aware of bad habits that contribute to heart disease and cancer, but 42% smoked. One-third believed that 60% of all lung cancer patients recover, whereas the actual mortality is 90%. Such optimism about health and medical miracles undoubtedly contributes to a lack of sound dietary and health habits. All too often, the knowledge that homemakers say they have is not reflected in the life-style of the family.

Studies have shown that people with university experience, especially those who studied food, nutrition, and/or home economics, have better dietary practices in their homes. Margaret A. Ohlson and Laura Jane Harper reported in the *Journal of The American Dietetic Association* (*JADA*; Dec. 1976) a study of 87 women, initially students in schools of home economics at midwestern universities, on whom demographic and dietary data were collected in 1935, 1944, 1955, and 1973. The data showed that their diets followed the recommended "basic four" food pattern (fruits and vegetables; meat, fish, and poultry; cereals; dairy products), in general reflecting the qualitative aspects of elementary nutrition teaching. The quantitative aspects of their diets were not so well controlled, however. Originally 77 of the 87 were judged normal in weight with 6 borderline and 4 obese. Some 38 years later, 41 were judged normal in weight, 23 borderline, and 23 obese, and many had gained and lost weight from time to time. Though mean calorie intake had decreased with age, the obese showed a greater variability in dietary practices and chose more foods with a higher calorie density from each of the four basic food groups than did those with normal weight. The obese had less structured meal patterns and ate less at breakfast (often only coffee).

A higher percentage of people over 80 had excellent food intakes than any other age group, according to Esther Brown and Sharon Hoerr, University of Illinois College of Agriculture. The subjects of their study lived independently and were responsible for their own meals. The quality of their diets was directly associated with the correct answer to these two true or false questions on a nutrition test:

People who eat dark green and dark yellow vegetables will probably be consuming sufficient vitamin A.
Bread, cereals, and flour are enriched with thiamine, riboflavin, niacin, and iron.

Were these 80-year-olds aided in reaching this age by better dietary habits based on their nutritional knowledge? Successful survival seemed to

Sidney Harris

"You'd be amazed how just a little soybean meal adds to the protein content of powdered bat's wing and newt tails."

be dependent on knowledge and practice integrated into a sound genetic pattern.

Professionals in nutrition were seeking educational expertise on how to increase the competency of the consumer in the face of what Arnold Shaefer, director of the Swanson Center for Nutrition in Omaha, Neb., described as "more quackery, misinformation, and downright stupidity about nutrition than ever."

New concepts of teaching the professional and the consumer alike were reported in the literature. Camille Bell of Texas Tech University discussed some of these in the *JADA* (Aug. 1976), pointing out that emphasis must be on the learner—how he feels about the information and how he can use it in real life situations. This type of "competency-based education" has four components: the behavior, the subject matter, the learning opportunities, and the evaluation of the learner's success. If evaluation shows less achievement than needed, the cycle can be repeated, enlarged, expanded, or modified until a certain level of competency has been achieved.

Policy on food, nutrition, and health. A report on "Food Cost, Farm Policy and Nutrition" by Desmond A. Jolly, extension consumer economist at the University of California at Davis, in the *Journal of Nutrition Education* (April–June 1976) stressed that "nutrition is a prime determinant not only of physical well-being but also of macroeconomic growth and the sociological health of

Jack Manning—The New York Times

society." Because public policy has such a significant effect on food availability and prices, Jolly believed that nutrition educators must focus more directly on the public sector. Even with full production, an explicit national food and nutrition policy is required.

At hearings before the Senate Select Committee on Nutrition and Human Needs in July 1976, nine witnesses testified on the relationship between nutrition and preventive health care and the influence of diet on various diseases. The recurring theme expressed by the witnesses was that various diseases afflicting Americans are related to nutritional and dietary imbalances. They urged nutrition education programs for all consumers and greater emphasis on nutrition in medical school curricula. They also suggested the need for people to adopt a "prudent diet" with low calorie density; less meat, saturated fat, sugar, salt, and alcohol; and more dietary fiber, unsaturated fat, fruits and vegetables, and whole-grain cereal products.

In an era when growing concern was being expressed over the "environmental impact" of various projects and developments, Sen. (later Vice-President) Walter F. Mondale, in a speech before the annual meeting of the American Home Economics Association in June 1976, asked whether the concept of "family impact" should also be invoked to test the desirability of private and governmental ventures. Do we need to develop a positive, family-oriented government policy? And, since nutrition and health constitute a major portion of the family's problems and expenditure of income (25 to 50% expended for food alone), should nutritionists, in support of a national nutrition policy, request that decision-making include a major concern for the "health and nutrition impact" of various industrial, business, and governmental activities? As an example, what is the impact of school busing on nutrition, health, and family life? Perhaps these are more crucial to the ultimate welfare of society than other legislative goals.

Current research. The relationship of selected dietary components to atherosclerotic lesions (narrowing of lumen of the arteries) was analyzed by Margaret C. Moore and others at Louisiana State University Medical Center. The analysis involved 253 deceased men for whom companions accurately reported dietary practices. Higher intakes of vegetables, proteins, carbohydrate, starch, and crude fiber were associated with fewer atherosclerotic lesions. Higher intakes of animal protein and total fat from all sources were associated with greater lesion involvement.

Mark Hegsted of the Department of Nutrition, Harvard School of Public Health, noted that the U.S. diet is high in sources of animal protein and in

Soft frozen yogurt gained considerable popularity in the United States during the year as a health food with dessert-like characteristics. The yogurt could be purchased in a wide variety of flavors.

per capita cereal consumption, which is mostly consumed indirectly in the form of animal products. In addition to their strong preference for meats, Americans have shown a great preference for fats. Increased consumption of fats occurred in the 1920s, the late '30s and early '40s, and again in the late '60s and early '70s. Consumption of vegetable fats rose, but animal sources supplied almost 60% of total usage. The amount of the polyunsaturated fatty acid, linoleic acid, in diets doubled since 1920. Consumer selection of fat and high-fat foods decreased somewhat from the all-time high recorded in 1972, but whether this trend was permanent or transitory remained to be seen.

High animal protein and high fat consumption were receiving attention regarding their possible role in the initiation and growth of spontaneous and transplanted tumors in experimental animals. Dietary differences may cause marked differences in the incidence and type of tumors and perhaps dietary modifications can influence the activity of various carcinogenic compounds in augmenting or decreasing the occurrence of tumors. Nutrition has an additional role in cancer in that malignant tissue has a high metabolic demand for nutrients which, combined with the anorexia that often accompanies the disease, can contribute to rapid weight loss. Furthermore, all the therapies for malignancies involve tissue damage with the consequent need to restore healthy tissue. Thus the patient may require an unusual feeding regimen. The location, stage of growth, and type of tumor and the patient all must be considered in planning and devising a dietary regimen that will increase the chances for recovery.

Dietary fiber was the latest dietary component to be hailed as the one that does it all. Dietary fiber should not be confused with crude fiber; it includes structural polymers of cell walls, celluloses, hemicelluloses, pectin, lignin, and undigested polysaccharides, and may be three to seven times more plentiful in a diet than the crude fiber included in food composition tables. Unquestionably dietary fiber has numerous physiological effects and functions, and researchers were attempting to delineate the exact ways in which these undigested dietary components function. Some types of fiber bind bile salts and acids, cholesterol, and other sterols, enhancing their elimination and thereby lowering their level in the blood. People need to be cautious in adding raw fiber to their diets, however, and should rely on the regular supply received from fruits, vegetables, and cooked cereal products.

—Mina W. Lamb

Information sciences

The miniaturization of computers, made possible by the technology of large-scale integration, continued to revolutionize the information sciences. The new microcomputers provided reductions in size and cost that made them likely candidates for widespread use in homes.

Computers

A variety of measurements illustrate the rapidity with which computer technology has changed in the three decades of the existence of the digital computer. Three of these are shown in the accompanying figure. Graph A illustrates that the time required to perform a single addition (of, for example, two 10-digit numbers) is approaching 10 nanoseconds (one nanosecond = one billionth of a second). Since the distance traveled by light or the electrons in an electric current in one nanosecond is about one foot, the speed of light has become a limiting factor in attempting to make computers ever faster. Only the rapid development of microelectronics in the past decade, as illustrated in graph B, has made possible the speeds that are shown in graph A.

Smaller size does not necessarily mean lower

cost because size reduction may only be achievable by expensive technology; much of the technology of the space program is a case in point. But, as graph C reveals, the cost of computing power continues to decrease rapidly because the technology of large-scale integration (LSI), which is the basis of the high speed and small size of current computer technology, is also much less expensive than its predecessors.

The result of the size and cost reductions seems certain to be a second computer revolution, marked by the proliferation of microcomputers throughout all areas where computers are used and, more important probably, into areas where computers have had little or no application to date. The remainder of this article is devoted to microcomputers because 1976 and 1977 will probably be the years from which, in retrospect, the second computer revolution will be seen to have begun.

The technology. To a generation raised on the marvels of transistor electronics, particularly in comparison to vacuum-tube electronics, it is at least reassuring to know that transistors remain the heart of the new technology. What is, however, difficult to fathom is that those transistors that one could see and handle in the early transistor radios have now, through LSI technology, become micro-

Graph indicates the changes in the past 25 years in the speed of computers (measured by the time to perform one addition), the size of computer components (measured by the volume required for a single component), and the cost (in terms of equivalent central processing units).

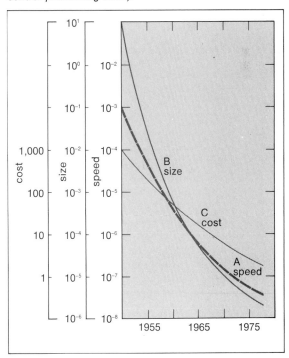

scopically small. They are, in fact, so small that a microprocessor (the arithmetic and control portion of a microcomputer) can contain 8,500 transistors in an area of 0.034 sq in. And the density of components continues to increase by about a factor of two every year.

The base or substrate of the device shown in the photomicrograph is a wafer of silicon that measures less than 0.2 in on a side, giving rise to the commonly used term "chip" to describe such microelectronic circuits. Starting from the chip of silicon, which for two decades has been the preferred material for transistors, the desired circuit is obtained by a series of chemical (etching) and metallurgical (diffusion) steps that blend conducting and insulating material into silicon. The precision necessary in the fabrication of such chips is measured in microns (one micron = one millionth of a meter).

Although the chip shown in the photomicrograph is not a complete computer but only the control and arithmetic portions of one, the same microelectronic techniques that are used to fabricate this microprocessor can also be used to produce the complete computer, which in this case would be a microcomputer. Only a power supply and basic facilities for the input of data and instructions and the output of results remain to be added to make a usable computer system.

The various chips that comprise a microcomputer can be wired together and assembled on a single circuit board with the approximate dimensions of a book. That shown in the accompanying photograph is about 8 ½ in by 10 ½ in and includes a processor, 4,096 16-bit words of memory, and various other control circuitry including a real time clock. To obtain appropriate perspective on this technology it is only necessary to note that the computer shown is as fast and powerful as computers that filled medium-sized rooms only 20 years ago.

Microprocessors. The microprocessor portion of a microcomputer or, most often, a much simplified version of it supplemented by some memory, has many uses. The most familiar perhaps is the hand-held calculator, which was made possible by LSI technology and which uses a microprocessor as the basic calculation and control element. But small calculators are only the first of what will surely be a proliferation of microprocessor applications in consumer products. For example, some automobile manufacturers probably will soon be using microprocessors to implement various engine control and monitoring functions. Some home appliances, such as microwave ovens, already have microprocessors; others, washing machines and dishwashers for example, may be expected to have

them soon in order to control the cycles and options available to the user. Children's games will also probably employ microprocessors to create inexpensively much more complex and intricate electronic games than have been possible with normal printed circuits.

The second computer revolution heralded at the beginning of this article is, however, a microcomputer rather than a microprocessor revolution. Microprocessors by themselves are rapidly becoming one of the most important technologies available to business and industry, but microcomputers may revolutionize the computing industry and with it various aspects of modern life.

Home computers. It is no accident that the largest annual computer conference in the world, the National Computer Conference, in 1977 will feature an exhibition of "personal computing." Personal computers are almost all microcomputers, sold as kits in much the same way as high-fidelity music system components and television set kits have been sold for years. By the end of 1976 more than 10,000 such computer kits had been sold, and it was estimated that 25,000 would be sold in 1977. For only $200–$600 a computer hobbyist can purchase computer kits which, when assembled, result in computers with far more processing power than any hand calculator; for no more than $2,000

LSI-11, manufactured by the Digital Equipment Corp., is one of a class of small but powerful microcomputers expected to revolutionize the computer industry.

Courtesy, Digital Equipment Corporation

Courtesy, American Microsystems, Inc.

American Microsystems AMI 6800 microcomputer consists of the power supply (far left), the microcomputer unit itself (foreground), and the input-output teletype (right).

a computer can be assembled that is more powerful than most computers of any size available in the mid-1950s.

Essentially, the computer kits consist of a variety of LSI chips that can be assembled in different ways to produce microcomputers with different capacities and capabilities. One drawback to the simplest home models is often a quite primitive input-output system, sometimes consisting only of a keyboard for input and a display register for output. With a modest additional investment paper tape and tape cassette facilities can be obtained. With a somewhat larger investment a teletype or visual display terminal may be added to the system.

Another drawback is the software. Not wanting perhaps to be outdone by vendors of larger, commercial computers, makers of home computers have developed hardware that is far ahead of the available software. Enthusiastic computer hobbyists have worked to narrow this "software gap," but it seems likely that hardware capabilities will stay well ahead of the software that could make full use of those capabilities for many years.

In the mid-1970s the first computer hobby retail stores opened in a few major U.S. cities. There can be little doubt that there will be many more such stores in the years to come. But while microcomputers built from computer kits were expected to become an increasingly important pastime in the developed countries, they would, like any hobby, affect only a small percentage of the population. The home microcomputer revolution will not be powered by kits but rather by fully assembled microcomputers that can, like television sets, be bought at an appliance store, brought home, plugged in, and used.

Home computers for a mass market will take a variety of forms and will differ in several ways from microcomputers built from hobbyist kits. Home television sets seem destined to become the standard output terminals for home computer systems. It is not difficult to use a TV set as an output device for microcomputer kits; for TV sets attached to a cable system it is equally easy to use them as output devices for home computers attached to networks, as many such computers will be.

One result of using television sets as home computer output devices may well be not just changes in the manufacture of TV sets to facilitate such usage but eventually a change in the U.S. television transmission system to one of higher resolution that will make the presentation of pictorial data on the TV screen more effective.

Many home computer systems will consist of little more than a keyboard for input, a TV set for output, and an acoustic coupler into which the handset of an ordinary telephone will be cradled. The coupler will provide the interface (the connection) between the keyboard and the TV set on the one hand and a remote computer (not a microcomputer) that will furnish computer services to many homes. When mass-produced, the cost of keyboard, acoustic coupler, and minor modifications to the home television set should be under $200. Other, more expensive home computers will be self-contained microcomputers capable of calculation on their own and also connected to a larger, remote computer to provide other services.

321

Courtesy, E & K Electronics, Ltd. of England

Acoustic coupler, into which the handset of an ordinary telephone can be cradled, will be part of many home computer systems. The coupler connects a keyboard (for input) and a television set (for output) in the home with a remote computer that will provide service to many households.

What will home computers be used for? One possible application is in education. As of 1977 computer-assisted instruction (CAI) had had only limited success, but its possibilities for continuing, tutorial, and remedial education in the home are great; with the advent of home computing, it may well be that CAI will finally realize the predictions made for it. In the area of recreation, so-called computer games that use TV sets are already popular. Some of them use microprocessors, but all are rudimentary and unsophisticated compared with the games that might be developed using real computers. Other possible applications range from travel to banking to recipe services.

Though the technology exists to mass produce home computers at a price that many can afford, there are two barriers to the rapid development of this product. The first involves communications. If home computers are to be attached to larger remote computers via ordinary telephones, then the telephone network in the U.S., although the most advanced in the world, could rapidly become overloaded. The capability to expand this network to handle home computer traffic surely exists, but it is likely that the planning for such expansion is lagging behind the need.

The second barrier is software. Hardware creates possibilities, but software is needed to realize them. To accomplish the kind of applications discussed above, considerable development of software is required. It is almost certain that failure to achieve good software will be the most serious bottleneck in the development of home computers.

Despite these barriers, the revolution is surely at hand. By the mid-1980s it seems likely that more than one million homes in the U.S. will have their own computers, and a figure of ten million is far from impossible.

Mega-micro networks. The low cost of microprocessors and the other components of microcomputers makes it possible to consider networks of microcomputers involving hundreds, thousands, even perhaps millions of such computers. Each point (or node) of the network could contain a microcomputer with special features for the solution of particular problems, or there could be many identical microcomputers to facilitate parallel computation.

To what kinds of tasks could such mega-micro networks be applied? One group includes problems that exceed the reach of the largest modern computers. An example is global weather prediction, which requires parallel computation as well as specialized computation (such as that for polar atmospheric conditions). Mega-micro networks may finally render this problem tractable.

A possible drawback of mega-micro networks involves security of data. This is an increasingly important aspect of large computer systems, especially those that deal with large data bases of a personal or other sensitve nature. When such data are transmitted from one location to another, they are particularly vulnerable, and so cryptographic techniques are used to make such transmissions more secure. But, unfortunately, mega-micro networks offer the possibility of relatively inexpensive, brute-force deciphering of such data. Thus, the use of microcomputers may well result in a need to rethink and redesign procedures to maintain data security.

—Anthony Ralston

Communications systems

A beginning of commercial data communication systems might be traced to the 1930s when teleprinter-to-teleprinter message exchange became commonplace. It is generally agreed, however, that data communication, as it is now practiced, had its first important commercial development in the late 1950s and early 1960s. At that time, banking and airline reservation systems were designed with remotely placed computer terminals connected by communication channels to a computer with its associated data files.

Advances in computer and communication technology provided a better solution for reservation systems. A single data base is kept at a centralized host computer site, where access to the data can be provided for any of hundreds of reservation systems located up to thousands of miles away. Using his terminal connected to the host computer, the agent working with the prospective traveler queries the central data base for flight status, makes the detailed reservation for the desired flight, and handles any special individual requests such as aid for the handicapped or special meals—all within several seconds or a minute or two.

Communication transmission and switching. The bulk of the communication facilities used in data communications systems are the same as those used for the voice telephone network. The data network is used in two ways: either the public switched service is used, with each terminal-to-computer transaction session preceded by a dialing signal similar to that of a normal voice conversation; or, as is the case in most large computer applications, leased lines are reserved. The signals required by the computer and the terminal are the binary digits (*bits*) familiar in computing. In order to transform these bits into analog waveforms so that they can be transmitted over the voice network, a device called a modem (modulator/demodulator) is used at each end of the communication line. The common transmission speeds used are 300, 600, 1,200, 2,400, and 4,800 bits per second (bps); higher speeds are also available.

Because the probability is low that a given communication line will be fully utilized by a single terminal, several techniques are used to combine traffic from several terminals onto one line, thereby lowering system costs. Several terminals may be attached to the same leased line in a multi-drop configuration; a master station on that line selects which terminal is allowed to transmit at a given time, to avoid confusion. Another, higher, level of combination can be done by units called concentrators, wherein data of several low-speed lines are combined onto a single high-speed line. For example, eight 1,200-bps lines may be concentrated onto one 9,600-bps line; this is useful because the expense for one line with modems capable of carrying 9,600 bps is less than that for eight with 1,200 bps capacity.

The highest level of concentration, usually done by the telephone company, occurs when the individual telephone lines are combined into a trunk hierarchy for intercity and long-distance traffic. These backbone links operate at speeds of up to six million bits per second. Equivalent deconcentration is done at the receiving end so that the destination terminal or host computer receives only the traffic destined for it at the proper rate.

New data networks. Specialized networks for data communications were being planned during the year by telephone companies in the United States, Canada, Japan, France, the United Kingdom, West Germany, Italy, Brazil, and several other countries to serve the expected large growth in data traffic. Most were scheduled for service before 1980.

These new data networks, which separate data from the voice network, have a number of advantages, both to the telephone companies and to the data users. The usage patterns of data communications are different from those of human conversation, and separate networks avoid congestion. Because digital (as distinguished from voicelike analog) transmission techniques are used, modems are no longer required. This permits a simpler and therefore less costly coupling arrangement between the terminal and the network, a factor that becomes particularly significant at speeds of 4,800 bps and greater. Additional improvements in reliability (environmental and electrical noise errors are reduced to an average rate of only 1 erroneous bit of 10^7 transmitted, contrasted with a typical 1 of 10^5 in analog systems) and in network availability (networks will be available 99.96% of the time, versus the 99.5% typical for analog) make such networks desirable to the data user. Finally, the projected costs for digital transmission are substantially less than those of their voice counterpart, in some cases as much as 50%.

Intelligent terminals. In the early 1970s a major change occurred in data communications systems.

LSI engineering techniques (see *Computers*, above) made it economically possible to produce small processors to be incorporated into terminals. Future terminals are expected to have some type of small processor, approximating a matchbox or two in size, as an integral part of their design.

This technological advance made a significant change in the capabilities of data communications systems. Prior to LSI technology, terminals had to be commanded directly by the host computer. For example, the input character produced by each keystroke frequently was transmitted at the rate of generation, and each output character was sent at a rate not exceeding that of the printer. Commands to the printer such as change-to-upper-case or advance-to-next-line had to be handled by the host computer on an individual basis. Thus, as the terminal network expanded, the workload that would be placed upon the host computer could become excessive.

LSI and "intelligent terminals" changed all of this. The small processor within the terminal could handle each of these functions independently, so that the only transmissions between the terminal and the host computer are complete messages sent at a high speed with output device control handled locally at the terminal. This substantially reduces the processing power required by the host computer or allows more terminals for a given size of host.

An equally important development made possible by LSI is that an actual application function is performed by the small processor in the terminal. For example, when a terminal is used in a retail store it is possible to add the total of individual purchases, compute the tax, and compute the amount of change, all at the terminal, with only summary information transmitted to the host.

More powerful versions of the microprocessors in intelligent terminals also can be used as cluster controllers to perform a concentration function for a group of terminals at a location, as well as additional application work. This decreases communication costs and improves interactive (immediate) response time. These controllers contain data files of up to 100 million characters and frequently attach batch terminal printers for generating reports. Thus, the controller is simply a small computer on which localized applications are run; more complex applications, or applications requiring close coordination between many controllers, are handled at the central host computer. An example of this is an insurance application; the policies and data for local customers are retained on the cluster controller, which performs functions such as simple inquiries and periodic billing; new policy rate computations or inquiries on a non-local policy are referred to the master data file kept at the host computer at regional headquarters.

Future Growth. Because of the two major advances, new data networks and intelligent terminals, significant growth is expected in data communications systems during the coming decade. It is estimated that there will be five million terminals installed in the U.S. by 1980 and an equal number in other nations. As the economies and efficiencies of electronic exchange of information are realized by advances in computer and communication technology and manufacture, many more terminal systems seem certain to become a part of everyday life, just as airline and automobile reservation systems are today. Computer systems in retail and

Calculator developed in 1976 is attached to a telephone that is connected with a computer. The device provides analysts with stock market price quotations.

NYT Pictures

Reprinted from *Electronics*, Dec. 23, 1976; copyright © McGraw-Hill, Inc., 1976

Electronic games that can be attached to home television sets enjoyed great popularity during 1976–77. A shortage in the supply of semiconductor chips prevented sales from being even greater.

food stores, to simplify inventory control for the store owner and speed the checkout process for the customer, are likely to be common. Legal and business offices can be automated with terminal typewriters directly connected to a cluster controller that stores address lists or standard legal paragraphs and edits reports and letters. Medical science can benefit by having patients' files directly accessible for the physician and hospital staff, and perhaps patient monitoring and diagnostic assistance will be commonly provided by means of terminals to physicians.

Another type of data, pictures and images, rather than letters, numbers, and words, constituted a tiny fraction of data transmission in 1977. Many manufacturers and telephone companies expect, however, that a significant amount, if not a majority, of data traffic would be of this type by 1990. About one million bits are required for a good-quality representation of an 8½-in by 11-in page (at 120 picture elements per in). Coding techniques, which remove inherent redundancy (such as whiteness), reduce the actual number of bits transmitted by factors of up to 100 times. Microprocessors at the transmitting and receiving terminals perform this coding, as well as controlling the image scanning and

inscribing devices. As this equipment is perfected and as the data network transmission capacity increases, the movement of engineering drawings, photographs, diagrams, and even "electronic mail" will become practical.

Much of this type of data does not require the rapid response time of interactive systems; usually several minutes, or even hours, can suffice. Thus, store-and-forward data networks appear likely to gain importance. In this type of network, input information is held in a large computer file, controlled either by an independent company or by the telephone system, for delivery at a later time convenient to the receiver.

Terminal networks might become very large in the future. A medium-size bank could support several hundred computer terminals, each at a teller window, connected through concentrators to one or two central computers. In a retail store, point-of-sale terminals seem certain to replace the cash registers; a large store will have perhaps 200 connected to an in-store cluster controller, which in turn communicates with computers at regional warehouses. Airline reservation systems that span nations, or may be international, will connect several thousand terminals and two or three computer sites. In manufacturing plants, computer terminals will exist initially for inventory and parts control, and later for direct control of factory equipment. Insurance companies will have two to three terminals in each local office; similarly equipped regional centers and headquarters would yield a system of 2,000 to 3,000 terminals throughout the U.S.

The cost of the entire system—terminals, telephone facilities, host computer—in each of these instances could usually be in the range of $100 to $200 or more per terminal per month. At such a cost, the gains in productivity, inventory control, or credit verification could readily amortize the expense of the data communications system and would result in substantial influence on the business and personal transactions of everyone's daily life.

—Edward H. Sussenguth

Satellite systems

Applications satellites in Earth orbit utilize their unique vantage point in space to provide services directly benefiting mankind. The major classifications of these satellite systems are communications, Earth observation, and navigation. Users are national (for domestic and military purposes), international consortiums, and private industrial enterprise. The United States and the Soviet Union continued to dominate such activities during 1976–77 because of their large launch vehicles.

Courtesy, Aerospace and Communications Operations, Aeronutronic Ford Corporation

Model of the Intelsat 5, a new class of communications satellite. Measuring about 50 feet from the end of one solar panel to the end of the other, each satellite will be able to handle 12,000 voice circuits, about twice the capability of the Intelsat 4A. The first Intelsat 5 is scheduled to be launched in 1979.

Both governments launched satellites for other nations. France, Japan, and China, however, were working on projects to develop their own space launch vehicles.

Communications satellites. The International Telecommunications Satellite Organization (Intelsat), a consortium of 94 member nations, continued its growth in size and capability. In 1976 the network of antennas increased from 123 to 151 and of Earth stations from 97 to 120. Satellite communications pathways increased from 406 to 485. Intelsat 4 and 4A satellites located in geosynchronous orbit over the Atlantic, Pacific, and Indian oceans provided global services of telephone, television, facsimile, and digital data transmission. (A geosynchronous, or geostationary, orbit is at 35,900 km [22,300 mi] altitude above the Equator. At this altitude a satellite travels at the same angular velocity as the Earth's surface. As a result the satellite remains at a constant point above the Earth. Three such satellites provide nearly global coverage.)

Comsat General Corp., a subsidiary of the publicly owned Comsat (Communications Satellite Corp.), in a joint venture with RCA, Western Union, and ITT, established a global maritime satellite communications system in 1976. Three Marisat satellites were launched to provide global coverage for the U.S. Navy as well as for commercial shipping and offshore industries. One each was placed over the Atlantic, Pacific and Indian oceans. Initially, the Indian Ocean Marisat was to serve as a standby, but onboard propulsion was available to move it around the world to any desired location.

Marisat was expected to provide greatly improved communications between ships and shore

bases. Previously, 90% of ship-to-shore communications was by hand-operated radio telegraphy, and ionospheric disturbances in poor weather often limited communications. Marisat provides high-fidelity voice, data, Telex, and facsimile services. In addition, emergency rescue operations would be speeded by immediate connection to rescue authorities such as U.S. Coast Guard bases. Two hundred shipboard terminals were being produced, initially, for lease or purchase by commercial firms.

The European Space Agency (ESA) also began building a maritime communications satellite, Marots, to be launched into geosynchronous orbit in 1977 over the Indian Ocean. Marots was to complement the two Marisat spacecraft stationed over the Atlantic and Pacific oceans.

In 1976 Comsat General Corp. launched two Comstar satellites for U.S. domestic communications use. Each satellite had 14,400 circuits. Comsat General operated the groundcontrol facilities, while American Telephone and Telegraph Co. and General Telephone and Electronics Corp. managed the communications services, which consisted of switched telephone traffic that was carried by the Bell system.

Two other U.S. communications firms, Western Union and RCA, operated domestic communications satellite systems during 1976–77. Called Westar and RCA-Satcom, respectively, these systems were proving to be more efficient, cheaper, and more reliable than ground-based cable or microwave communications networks.

In July 1976 the U.S. National Aeronautics and Space Administration (NASA) launched Palapa 1, the first of two communications satellites for the government of Indonesia. Each of these satellites was capable of providing 5,000 two-way telephone circuits, electronically linking the 3,000 inhabited islands of the Indonesian archipelago. Such space launches by the U.S. for foreign countries were performed on a cost-reimbursable basis. Canada and Brazil also had domestic satellite systems launched by the U.S. Wealthy Middle Eastern nations and countries with large areas, such as Australia, were planning their own domestic systems.

In the summer of 1976 NASA's ATS-6 satellite completed a year-long cooperative experiment with the Indian Space Research Organization (ISRO). As a part of the ISRO educational program 2,400 remote villages in India were equipped with color television sets and simple antennas to receive broadcasts from ATS-6. The villagers were exposed to Indian educational programs on a variety of basic subjects including agriculture, health, hygiene, family planning, and national integration. In addition to the 2,400 villages receiving direct broadcasts from the satellite, another 2,600 received the same programs relayed from conventional television stations. A comprehensive evaluation of the ISRO program was under way in 1977.

Palapa 1, Indonesia's first communications satellite, is prepared for launch in July 1976. The satellite united electronically the 3,000 inhabited islands of the archipelago.

Courtesy, NASA

On August 2 the ATS-6 propulsion system was activated, and the satellite began a slow drift westward from its location over equatorial Africa, in sight of India. During the next three months the U.S. Agency for International Development (AID) gave demonstrations of direct-broadcast color television aimed at showing the world community the potential of satellite communications systems for advancing economic and social development. It was a two-part demonstration, the first taking place in Southeast and South Asia, the Middle East, and East and North Africa. The second part involved countries in West Africa, South and Central America, and the Caribbean. Each demonstration included filmed and live segments, featuring officials directing attention to technological challenges facing their nations. In 1977 the ATS-6 was used for a variety of communications, scientific, and technological experiments in the continental United States and Hawaii.

A two-year cooperative test program between the U.S. and Canada began in January 1976 with the launching of the Communications Technology Satellite (CTS) into geosynchronous orbit. The experimental satellite had the capability of much higher transmission power than conventional systems. This made possible high-quality color television reception and two-way voice communications with the use of small, low-cost, user-operated ground terminals. A variety of users, including ESA, participated in the experiments. Community services such as education, health care, data communications, and public broadcasting were to be provided to regions that could not be reached by existing terrestrial or satellite systems.

ESA proceeded during the year with plans for a European communications satellite system to be orbited by a French launch vehicle. ESA was supported by Belgium, Denmark, France, West Germany, Italy, The Netherlands, Spain, Sweden, Switzerland, and the United Kingdom.

In late 1976 the emergency communications link between the leaders of the United States and the Soviet Union, the so-called hot line, was shifted from terrestrial land lines, undersea cable, and radio links to a satellite communications link. Two separate circuits, independent but parallel, were used for highest reliability. One link was through the Soviet Molniya satellite system, while the other used an Intelsat satellite.

Earth observation satellites. This category of satellites has three major forms: weather, Earth resources, and military reconnaissance.

Weather satellites. Meteorological satellites view the Earth's weather in darkness as well as light by measuring the temperature difference between clouds and the Earth's surface. In addition, sensors

Courtesy, Ford Aerospace & Communications Corporation

NATO 3-B military communications satellite undergoes prelaunch testing in California. In January 1977 the satellite was placed in orbit by a Thor Delta booster rocket.

aboard the spacecraft obtain a vertical sounding of the temperature of the Earth's atmosphere. Newer techniques not only "see through" clouds but also record rainfall over oceans, map soil moisture, and monitor temperatures and ice conditions in polar regions. In operating the National Environmental Satellite Service, the U.S. National Oceanic and Atmospheric Administration (NOAA) used two kinds of meteorological satellite systems: polar orbiting, wherein global coverage is obtained every 24 hours, and equatorial geosynchronous orbit, which provides continuous observation of about one-third of the Earth's surface. In July 1976 NOAA 5 was launched to replace NOAA 4, which was deactivated and placed in standby service. NOAA 5 continued the global survey of weather coverage, and was designed to be operational until 1986. Imagery from NOAA satellites was provided to more than 120 nations in all parts of the world as well as to academic and scientific institutions.

NOAA 5 carried four major observational systems: a scanning radiometer, a very-high-resolution radiometer, a vertical temperature profile radiometer, and a solar proton monitoring system. This last system permitted issuance of warnings of solar storms that bathe the Earth in energetic solar protons.

The Soviet Union meteorological satellites are called Meteor. Three were launched in 1976. The U.S. and U.S.S.R. continued to exchange weather photographs taken by their satellites.

Earth resources satellites. The two U.S. Landsats, which orbit the Earth over the poles, 180° apart, continued to operate successfully. Passing over the same point on the Earth at the same time and angle every nine days, they transmitted multispectral scanning data to ground stations for photographs and computer data inputs. However, the tape storage systems, designed to store data for call-up when over a receiving station, failed. Major uses of the Landsats included observation and management of agricultural, forestry, range, and marine resources; land use and mapping; environmental (pollution detection) surveys; and mineral resources and geological surveys.

An Israeli Landsat investigator outlined a mechanism that may explain the reasons for deserts and cyclical droughts in some parts of the world. Using Landsat data on ground reflectance and temperature measurements, he concluded that overgrazing by domestic animals denuded the Sinai, increasing reflectance of the Sun's radiation. In the neighboring Negev, with controlled grazing, the vegetation resulted in a darker surface that absorbs more solar heat; this absorption resulted in rising air, cloud formation, and more rainfall.

A forestry specialist at NASA using digital data of Landsat observations of a North Carolina commercial forest tract found a method of distinguishing between hardwood and pine. An accuracy of 90% was obtained compared with more expensive aerial photographs.

Argentina announced its intention to build a ground station to receive Landsat data directly. As of 1977 Brazil already had such a station. Both nations planned to cooperate to disseminate the data to other South American nations.

An advanced Landsat with greater discriminatory capability was in design stage. One application believed to be feasible in the advanced Landsat is the capability of making reliable and inexpensive traffic surveys.

Military reconnaissance satellites. As of 1977 only the U.S. and the U.S.S.R. had the technical ability and wealth to utilize spacecraft for photographic and electronic monitoring on a regular basis. No official releases were made of such activities, although both countries had long been known to take photographs from orbit and then de-orbit and recover film packages a few days to a week or more later.

During 1976 Soviet military space activities were more active than those of the United States. Of particular concern to the West was the renewal of Soviet hunter-killer satellite tests, in which an or-

Wide World

IBM systems engineer holds a four-inch data cartridge, one of 3,382 to be stored in the surrounding honeycomb-shaped unit called TELOPS. The unit will accommodate data transmitted by U.S. satellites.

biting satellite was followed by another that closed in on the first (inspection) and exploded (attack), presumably with the intent to destroy by shrapnel the orbiting satellite. In addition, one of the U.S. early warning satellites designed to spot the launch of large rockets was "blinded" in a manner that some authorities believe was accomplished by a high-powered laser beam directed from the Earth. The U.S.S.R. launched 91 missions in 1976, compared with a combined total of 25 launched by NASA and the U.S. Department of Defense.

In December 1976 China launched its seventh satellite. There is reason to believe that it was similar to its predecessors, that it was recovered, and that it was probably a developmental model for reconnaissance missions.

Navigation satellites. The U.S. Navy Transit navigational satellite system continued to be fully operational and in use by the U.S. fleet throughout the world. Although commercial ships were permitted to use this system, a shipboard computer was required to calculate position based upon the Doppler shift of the satellite's signal. The high cost of such equipment limited civilian and commercial use of the system.

Meanwhile, as an alternative to the Transit Doppler shift method, the U.S. Navy was developing a system based upon ultra-precision clocks carried on a satellite. With this system precise location is obtained by measuring the brief time required for a radio signal to travel from a satellite to a ship or aircraft.

—F. C. Durant III

Information systems

Information is needed to solve problems, make decisions, and avoid crisis situations. As problems become more complex, more information is needed, and the information is needed more rapidly. Thus it is no wonder that during a period of crisis many new information systems are created, because the scientist, the decision maker, and the public at large must have access to specialized information that can be retrieved rapidly and used effectively.

International information systems. As the world population increases, the threat of crop failure and famine becomes ever more serious. While information cannot grow food, an effective agricultural information system can facilitate sharing the available knowledge and incorporating it into national agricultural development policies and programs. AGRIS, the International Information System for Agricultural Sciences and Technology, maintains a worldwide network of participating national centers with headquarters in Vienna. A newly established Agricultural Information Bank for Asia (AIBA) joined this network and was expected to contribute agricultural research reports and other specialized literature emphasizing tropical agriculture and regional growing conditions. These reports, along with those contributed by all other nations, were processed and stored in the AGRIS computer data bank, where they were made available to agricultural scientists, administrators, policymakers, scholars, and technicians.

Less developed nations need to have access to industrial as well as agricultural technology. Therefore, a TECHNOTEC data base was designed to provide a fast and economical means for the worldwide transfer and exchange of technology, ideas, methods, and processes. This, too, was a computer-based on-line system, which, with its listings of technology wanted and technology for sale, resembled a newspaper's classified advertisement section. People and agencies seeking technological expertise to help solve industrial, scientific, or agricultural problems could obtain access to this data base via a remote teletype terminal. When a match occurred between the expressed needs and the available technology, the searcher could request the name and address of the supplier from a list of members of WORLDTEC, an organization of individuals and institutions interested in offering their financial resources, training ability, and consulting services to promote technology exchange on a global basis.

For those seeking information about patents, an International Patent Documentation Center was established in Vienna in conjunction with the World Intellectual Property Organization. This organization received weekly magnetic tapes from 27 countries covering all patents issued since 1968. Subscribers could conduct their own patent search or have it done for them, and they could order microfilm or printed copies of selected documents.

The UNESCO-UNISIST Program for International Cooperation in the Transfer of Scientific and Technical Information helped less developed countries to plan and implement national information systems and documentation centers. In Senegal the UNESCO mission was also providing essential items of equipment and helping to train a local staff. In Sudan the mission was to assist in the development of a Scientific and Technical Information Center, and in Syria it was to help prepare a plan for the establishment of the National System for Scientific Information and Documentation. All of these projects were oriented toward enabling less developed countries to participate more actively in the worldwide system for the exchange of information.

India established a series of information services for small industries and industrial development organizations. The Small Enterprises National Documentation Center (SENDOC) collected and organized information on industrial management, technology, equipment, and government programs and policies, as well as statistical data on production, employment, and capital investment. This information was gathered from books, periodicals, trade journals, and newsletters published in India and elsewhere. The SENDOC services were not yet computerized, and the collected information was stored on more than 25,000 index cards.

In order to promote industrial development and to provide a basis for reviewing requests for development loans and grants, the Israeli Ministry of Commerce and Industry established a computerized information system containing data on the nation's industrial firms and their products. If a company should request a government subsidy or loan, the system can be used to evaluate its financial status, its ability to produce more output profitably, and the domestic and export market potential of the proposed product for which development capital was being sought. In addition, the computer kept track of the loans that had already been granted and performed various statistical analyses aimed at helping the ministry formulate economic and industrial policy.

Several Eastern European countries (Bulgaria, Czechoslovakia, East Germany, Poland, Romania, and the U.S.S.R.) and Cuba, with the support of the Council for Mutual Economic Assistance (CMEA), were developing their own multinational scientific and technical information system. It was designed to store and disseminate information on science, engineering, and economics. Also to be included was an International Published Documents Information System, which was being developed at the U.S.S.R. All-Union Institute for Scientific and Technical Information. Authorities estimated that 2.5 million documents from all fields of science and technology would be processed and added to this data base each year.

Information systems and services in the U.S. In developed countries such as the United States, existing information systems need to be expanded and new ones established to cope with complex interdisciplinary problems and the increased specialization among the sciences. For example, the National Library of Medicine (NLM), Bethesda, Md., expanded its computerized bibliographic retrieval services to include specialized data bases on cancer, epilepsy, and audiovisual instructional materials in the health sciences. Access to these data bases could be gained from a typewriter-like terminal by dialing the central computer facility at NLM. One of the bases, CANCERPROJ, contains abstracts of cancer research in progress throughout the world. It could be searched by specifying broad subject

". . . and in 1/10,000th of a second, it can compound the programmer's error 87,500 times!"

Sidney Harris

areas, key words that might appear in the project title or summary, the investigator's name, and the sponsoring agency. The relevant retrieved records are transmitted to the user's terminal and typed there under computer control. EPILEPSY, a similarly organized data base, contains bibliographic citations and abstracts of articles relating to epilepsy. The AVLINE data base contains information on about 700 audiovisual instruction items in the health sciences, all of which have been reviewed and classified as "highly recommended" or "recommended." In addition to requesting these materials by subject or author, the user could limit a request to, for example, 16-mm sound motion pictures, slides, or videotape.

Also in the field of medicine, eight medical centers in the U.S. and Canada cooperated to establish an Arthritis Databank Network. Headquartered at Stanford University, it was named ARAMIS (American Rheumatism Association Medical Information System). The ARAMIS data bank contains information on hundreds of patients, including their diagnoses and the specific methods of treatment. This information was made available to physicians, and its use was expected to result in more accurate prognoses and more effective therapeutic programs.

More than 200 pollution-related data bases were compiled by various federal, state, and local government agencies as well as by many industries and universities. A single index providing access to all these files was then prepared by the Environmental Data Service.

As of 1977 more than 30 federal agencies were collecting and preparing cartographic data such as maps, charts, geodetic control points, and related information. To help make these materials more readily available, the Geological Survey of the U.S. Department of the Interior established a National Cartographic Information Center (NCIC) and began compiling records that described these holdings. By utilizing the latest techniques of microphotography and computer technology, the Center would be able to provide a "one-stop" access service to cartographic information and ultimately handle purchase orders for all the items.

A highway information data base offered trucking operators in the continental U.S. a computerized highway map used for determining the shortest practical highway routes. The data base contained information on all interstate U.S. and principal state highways plus data on normal driving speeds and mileages between thousands of points. It is continuously revised and updated as data on new road construction become available. When a user requests a route from a point of origin to any of more than 75,000 destinations, a map could be constructed and displayed by the computer, or the user could construct the route by using information contained on microfiche cards.

As an aid in guiding cargo ships through the Arctic Ocean and along the Alaskan coasts, an all-weather ice information system was devised and successfully tested. The Arctic areas suffer from serious shipping problems because of cold weather and the formation of thick ice. In many cases barges have had to turn back before reaching their destination, and their cargo had to be shipped by other, more expensive means. Data for input to this system were obtained by means of a Coast Guard plane equipped with NASA's side-looking airborne radar (SLAR) system; the plane flew over the Arctic sea-lanes and obtained daily ice data. These data were processed and used to provide interpretive navigation charts, which in turn were used as aids in scheduling and directing vessel movement through and around offshore ice.

Information research and future developments. Ensuring the privacy of information in data bases continued to be a major concern. At Purdue University, West Lafayette, Ind., an Information Privacy Research Center went into operation. One of its main tasks was to develop a methodology of information management that would protect the integrity and privacy of the collected data while still permitting the dissemination of analyzed results. The Center was to study the legal, technical, and economic issues involved in the handling of personal files by both government and private sectors. When appropriate, the Center would undertake a program that would describe the results and explain the implications of the research.

Computers and Privacy and *Computers: Safeguards for Privacy* are two reports that were recently published in the United Kingdom. The first summarized the government's thinking on the subject, and the second examined computer systems in the public sector and the rules governing the storage and the use of information contained in them. The reports recommended that legislation be introduced that would set standards governing the use of computers that store and process personal information, and that a government regulatory agency be established to oversee the use of computers in both the public and private sectors.

Experiments in providing current awareness services for blind readers were being conducted in the U.K. by the Warwick University Research Unit in conjunction with the Institution of Electrical Engineers. The project notified blind scientists of newly published material. Also, a computer-readable magnetic tape containing abstracts of recently published articles from computer science journals was processed each month to produce a Braille printout by an automatic translation program. The

Wide World

Blind man listens as computer-controlled optical scanner reads a letter aloud. The device automatically scans each line until it reaches the end of a page, at a speed of 200 words per minute. It recognizes letters, groups them into words, computes pronunciations, and enunciates words in sentences with appropriate stresses and pauses.

printouts were distributed to blind computer programmers and analysts working in the U.K., enabling them to keep up with advances taking place in computer science and thus to compete more effectively with sighted colleagues.

Information systems commonly provide access to records or documents. Dartmouth University, Hanover, N.H., however, was designing a computer-based system for retrieving visual information such as reproductions of works of art, photographs, star maps, and anatomical illustrations. The system was designed to reproduce pictorial information as color images on microfiche cards, thousands of which could be stored in a microfiche projector attached to an ordinary computer terminal. Students and faculty in an art school could, for example, conduct a computer search through an entire art collection stored in the data base and retrieve all reproductions produced in a given time period or style, including or excluding specific artists. The computer would then select all images fulfilling those requirements and would project them onto the screen of the microfiche projector in the order selected.

—Harold Borko

Life sciences

Among major concerns in the life sciences in recent months were several serious proposals for energy systems based on the metabolic or proliferative characteristics of certain plants; continued attempts to endow such important crop plants as corn, wheat, and rice with the ability to fix atmospheric nitrogen; and the development of rapid, accurate tests for the detection of carcinogenic substances. In their quest to understand the organization and regulation of genetic information, scientists exploited the ability of bacterial viruses to transfer DNA from one species of life to another. Other highlights included successful fusions of plant and animal cells and the discovery of an unusual kind of shark.

Botany

Significant developments in botany ranged over a wide selection of topics, from a consideration of certain plants as potential hydrogen "factories" to an increased understanding of the mechanism by which plants recognize pollen of their own species. Many important aspects of botany that were likely to demand attention far into the future related to fuel, food, and ecology.

Energy from plants. Plants have always been the source of most of the world's fuels; fossil fuels were formed from plant materials, and wood taken directly from trees has served as an important fuel for hundreds of thousands of years. Interest once again has centered on such renewable fuels as wood because, by definition, nonrenewable fuels— *e.g.,* coal, oil, gas, and even the fissionable elements—will run out. A number of natural systems employing plants, and thus capturing solar energy, could eventually help to produce the fuel needed for most aspects of human activity.

As a source of energy, hydrogen is both renewable and nonpolluting. It can be produced directly from water, but only at great expense, a factor that has limited its use as a fuel. Cheaper processes for hydrogen production might make it more competitive with fossil fuels. Recently, scientists discovered that hydrogen is evolved by some plant species as a by-product of nitrogen fixation. Nitrogen fixation in such plants employs a nitrogenase, or hydrogenase, enzyme system to begin the process of reducing atmospheric nitrogen for incorporation in organic compounds. Plants capable of this process comprise relatively few groups, *e.g.*, the legume family, in which a symbiotic relationship is maintained between the higher plant and a specific nitrogen-fixing bacterium (*Rhizobium* in many legumes) or blue-green alga (*Anabena* in some cases). Located in the symbiotic bacterium or alga, the nitrogenase system evolves hydrogen while fixing nitrogen, and in the presence of certain concentrations of nitrate, it evolves hydrogen more rapidly than is normal, an indication that the nitrogenase system shifts its reducing activity to hydrogen production when nitrogen compounds are directly available to the host plant. It has been suggested that such hydrogen production be harnessed and thus a new fuel source tapped.

One proposed system involves certain leguminous plants, including soybeans, which develop root nodules containing *Rhizobium* bacteria. Nitrate-fertilized crops of these plants would be raised in greenhouses and the hydrogen collected.

Symbiotic nitrogen-fixing processes within the water fern Azolla *are known to evolve hydrogen as a by-product. Exploitation of this phenomenon may one day allow large-scale production of hydrogen for fuel.*

Agricultural Research

K. R. Schubert and H. J. Evans of Oregon State University estimated that the annual production of hydrogen from 50 million ac of soybeans in the U.S. would be equivalent to the energy in 300 billion cu ft of natural gas. These figures consider only hydrogen normally released while the nitrogenase system is still fixing nitrogen. Schubert and Evans suggested, however, that technical problems of trapping, purifying, and concentrating the gas might make the proposal unworkable.

Another nitrogenase system exists in *Anabena azolla*, a blue-green alga living within the tissues of the water fern *Azolla*. Like *Rhizobium*, if a nitrate solution is provided for its host, *Anabena* will produce hydrogen by photoreductive hydrolysis of water. Large-scale utilization of this system might be difficult to achieve, but the associated problems were not as large as those of terrestrial systems.

Pursuing quite different lines of research, some botanists felt that energy could be cropped from forests and fields. Rapidly growing trees might be expected to provide a fuel source on a scale much greater than they once did, and grasses were also being considered. In fact energy cropping might ultimately provide the simplest and cheapest way to trap solar energy.

Several conditions are necessary for energy cropping. Rapidly growing perennials must be available and must be capable of rapid regrowth from shoots after harvest. To save time and money, new crops must be plantable from cuttings. Harvest of grasses must be possible every few weeks and of trees every three or four years. Possible candidates were Bermuda and Sudan grasses, sugarcane, and sorghum for high-rainfall, warm-weather areas; and poplar, eucalyptus, alder, cottonwood, and sycamore for cooler regions.

Estimated yields for warm-season grasses and trees grown closely together were 7–11 tons of dry matter per acre per year, representing a conversion of less than 1% of available sunlight. Thus, about 400 sq mi (about 250,000 ac) of land could fuel a 500-megawatt power plant. If an estimated 70 million–100 million ac in the U.S. not currently supporting food or fiber crops were used, as much as 40% of the nation's presently installed electrical generating capacity could be realized.

Salt-tolerant crops. Vast acreages of the world's land surface are unsuited to agriculture because of aridity, salinity, or both. Irrigation of arid soils is limited to available fresh water, and the practice often increases soil salinity because salt is carried up from subsoil levels. Use of saline soils is limited because crop plants are not suited to such conditions. Development of salt-tolerant crops would allow further use of saline soils as well as irrigation with ocean water.

From "Seawater-Based Crop Production: A Feasibility Study" by E. Epstein and J.D. Norlyn, in *Science*, 1977. © 1977 by AAAS

Grown in sandy dune soil and irrigated with seawater, two salt-tolerant strains of barley developed by University of California scientists show marked differences in their response to saltwater treatment. In a control experiment, in which fresh water was used for irrigation, both lines of barley achieved about the same height.

Emanuel Epstein and his associates at the University of California at Davis reported progress in discovering and developing salt-tolerant crop plants. Their work with tomatoes uncovered a clear difference in salt tolerance between *Lycopersicon cheesmanii* from the Galápagos Islands and a *Lycopersicon esculentum* cultivar (VF36) grown in the U.S. Seeds from both species were germinated and the seedlings grown in hydroponic solution in the greenhouse. Solutions were identical in nutrient content (Hoagland's ingredients), but they differed in the amount of seawater salt, which was varied to give equivalents ranging from 0 to 100% seawater.

The two tomato species varied widely in response to saline environments, with the Galápagos coastal type showing the greatest tolerance. Although all plants experienced growth-rate reduction when grown in saline solution, reduction in the Galápagos species seemed to be from osmotic stress, whereas in the VF36 plants it seemed to be from sodium toxicity. Various other differences also appeared, but the most significant one was the ability of many of the Galápagos plants to survive in full seawater. No VF36 plants survived in greater than 50% seawater. Apparently the difference is due to the ability of the Galápagos plant to tolerate relatively high levels of sodium in its leaves. Because salt tolerance has a genetic base and be-

cause the two species are interfertile, there was opportunity for hybridization studies and the possibility that salt tolerance, like productivity, could be bred into strains of tomatoes for growth on saline soils.

Epstein and associates also reported on a technique to develop salt-tolerant barley. They selected several strains likely to be salt tolerant from crosses involving strains from all over the world. The selected strains were planted in experimental plots in California, irrigated with seawater from Bodega Bay, and fertilized with commercial fertilizers containing nitrogen, phosphorus, and potassium. Most plants produced seed. The experimenters felt that further selection might produce strains of barley capable of developing into an economically feasible crop when irrigated with seawater, which supplies most nutrients (other than nitrogen and phosphorus) as well as water. Although these researchers chose barley because of its known salt tolerance, they proposed to explore the development of salt-tolerant wheat as well.

A plant defense system. The well-known problem of insect pests in agricultural, horticultural, and forest crops has been attacked in recent times largely through the application of pesticides. A growing awareness of the harmful side effects of such applications, however, has made their use less desirable and has stimulated the search for

334

alternative control measures. One emphasis has been on biological control, the utilization of natural relationships between organisms to control their increase or limit harmful effects.

Two investigators from Cornell University, Ithaca, N.Y., E. A. Pillemer and W. M. Tingey, reported on a very specialized kind of control in the field bean (*Phaseolus vulgaris*). They showed how plant hairs, or trichomes, on bean leaves actually serve to control the nymphs and adults of a major pest, leafhoppers of the genus *Empoasca*. Once the hooked hairs penetrate an opening in the insect's exoskeleton, *e.g.*, an opening between abdominal or leg segments, the hooks hold the insect fast. The ensuing struggle to escape produces further hooking, and death comes to the insect from dehydration, starvation, or even from abdominal rupture.

The study of controlled greenhouse growth of beans infested with leafhoppers led to the evidence that insect capture is proportional to trichome density and thus is well correlated with the tendency of these insects to feed on the lower surface of leaves where trichome density is greatest. In addition, young leaves, which are more often attacked by leafhoppers, tend to have higher trichome density because the leaves have not expanded to spread the trichomes out.

It also was discovered that trichomes must be relatively erect for effectiveness, thus explaining the ineffectiveness of the procumbent hairs in the lima bean, *P. lunatus*. Hybridization and selection for high density and erectness of trichomes were seen to be important criteria, especially if combined with other plant defenses.

Acid rain. Among the many probable effects of atmospheric pollution is altered plant growth. Over the last decade deleterious effects have been credited to an increase in the acidity of rainwater, a change too great to be attributed solely to carbon dioxide, the main natural cause of rainwater acidity. Because of the magnitude of change, such industrial pollutants as the anhydrides of sulfuric acid were thought to be responsible.

Laboratory investigation of the problem, although quite warranted, has been limited. In the past year, R. W. Ferenbaugh, currently of Northern Arizona University, reported some effects of acid rain on *P. vulgaris* under laboratory conditions. Various sulfuric acid solutions, ranging in acidity from that for normal rainwater (pH 5.5) to highly acidic (pH 1.5), were sprayed on different plants with an atomizer every morning. Among the relative differences in effect noted for plants treated with sprays of pH 2.5 or lower were increased bushiness due to shortened internodes, smaller and wrinkled leaves, portions of leaves killed with consequent lowering of chlorophyll content, premature leaf abscission, smaller cells, reduction in starch grain size, lowered internal pH to 4.0, and decreased production of sugar, starch, and biomass.

Similar treatment of the goosefoot (*Chenopodium quinoa*) and common barley (*Hordeum vulgare*), did not produce significant changes of the type noted in *Phaseolus*. Ferenbaugh concluded that increased acidity in rain may contribute to change in species composition of biotic communities, perhaps even food chains, because less sensitive species would be favored. Such possibilities needed to be included as considerations in environ-

Scanning electron micrograph of impaled abdomen of leafhopper nymph (left) reveals the effectiveness of erect hooked hairs (trichomes) on leaves of the field bean in trapping these insect pests. By contrast, procumbent trichomes of the lima bean (right) are ineffective as defense mechanisms.

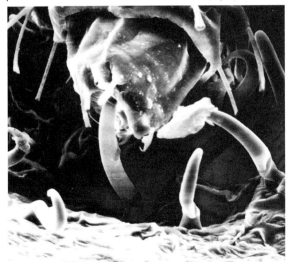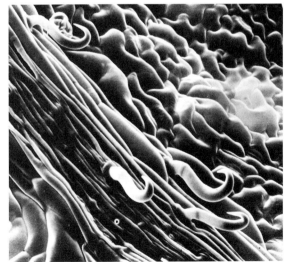

Courtesy, E. A. Pillemer and W. M. Tingey, New York State College of Agriculture and Life Sciences

mental assessments preliminary to industrial development.

Tree thermometers. The annual lateral growth of tree trunks produces the familiar ring pattern commonly used to determine the age of living trees. Comparative study of these rings also makes it possible to piece together weather patterns that prevailed when the rings were formed. In the late 1970s tree-ring laboratories existed for such purposes in Tuscon, Arizona; Munich, West Germany; and elsewhere. (For a comprehensive account of tree-ring research, see *1976 Yearbook of Science and the Future:* DENDROCHRONOLOGY: HISTORY FROM TREE RINGS.)

Recently a team of workers from the U.S. and West Germany reported their success in correlating the relative concentration of the stable isotopes oxygen-18 and hydrogen-2 (deuterium) in tree rings with the prevailing temperatures at the time the rings were formed. They established that, because of the molecular structure of wood, these isotopes do not move laterally from ring to ring; therefore, isotope measurements correspond to the conditions prevailing when each ring was formed. Combining this information with the fact that oxygen and hydrogen isotope concentrations in rainwater and atmospheric CO_2 vary with temperature, the investigators made a significant correlation between estimated temperatures from ring analysis and various other temperature records extending at least 200 years into the past. Results of studies completed on German oak (*Quercus pe-*

traea), Bavarian fir (*Abies alba*), and Japanese cedar (*Cryptomeria japonica*) suggested that temperature patterns existing before records were kept might be reliably determined from the oxygen and hydrogen isotope ratios obtained from radiocarbon-dated tree rings. Once the periodicity of such patterns became apparent, prediction of future temperature trends should be possible.

Plant cell recognition. Certain intraspecific relationships in plants involve cell recognition; that is, the ability of a cell to discriminate between cells from members of its own species and those of different species. This ability contributes greatly to the preservation of intraspecific integrity by preventing the exchange of such control substances as genes.

The most important aspect of cell recognition for flowering plants lies in the pollination process, in which the stigma of a flower usually will accept pollen only from the same plant or from another of its species. How recognition is accomplished was partly worked out by R. B. Knox and colleagues of the University of Melbourne and of the Walter and Eliza Hall Institute of Medical Research in Australia. They suggested that pollen acceptance occurs in two stages. The first is characterized by pollen arrival, hydration (swelling), and growth of the pollen tube. The second is characterized by penetration of the stigma cuticle by the pollen tube, allowing tube growth to continue through the style to the ovary where transfer of gamete nuclei effects fertilization. Pollen from unrelated plants will not

Scanning electron micrograph of papillae (fingerlike projections) on stigma of Gladiolus *species two hours after arrival of compatible pollen (left) reveals hydration of pollen grains and growth of short pollen tubes. By contrast, incompatible pollen from another plant family (right) is not accepted.*

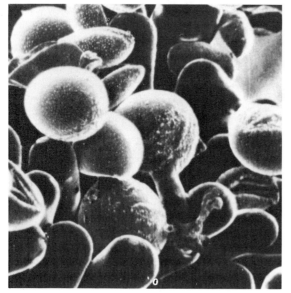 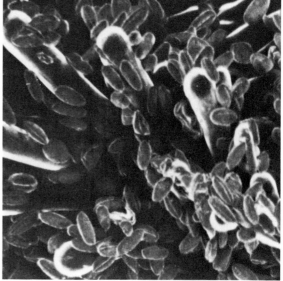

Courtesy, R. Bruce Knox *et al.*, University of Melbourne, Australia; *Proceedings of the National Academy of Sciences* of the U.S.

Based upon information supplied by the Massachusetts Institute of Technology

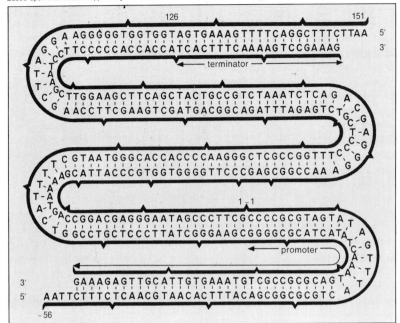

Structure of functional Escherichia coli *gene synthesized by Har Gobind Khorana is 207 nucleotides long, including its promoter and terminator. The letters A, T, C, and G represent respective positions within the paired helical chains of the nucleotide bases adenine, thymine, cytosine, and guanine. After complete assembly from chemically synthesized fragments, the gene was tested by insertion into a mutated strain of bacterial virus that depended for its infectiousness on the proper functioning of the gene.*

be recognized at the first stage; that is, the pollen grain will not hydrate or grow a tube even though it will stick to the surface of the stigma. Pollen from related plants, such as members of the same family, may be recognized at the first stage and thus may grow tubes. But these are rejected at the second step; the tubes do not penetrate the stigma cuticle.

Although Knox's group did not determine the specific factors responsible for two stages, their findings in *Gladiolus gandavensis* suggested that the first stage is promoted by mutual recognition of pollen-stigma receptors, allowing for uptake of fluid from the stigma by the pollen grain. The second stage may be promoted by mutual contribution of enzymes necessary for cuticle breakdown and tube penetration. Possible enzymes were isolated from stigma surfaces and pollen walls.

—Albert J. Smith

Microbiology

The major event in microbiology during the past year, and one that commanded considerable attention, was the U.S. swine flu vaccination program. The swine flu epidemic of 1918–19 killed more than 500,000 Americans and as many as 20 million persons around the world; on the basis of a few new outbreaks a national campaign to vaccinate Americans was announced in March 1976.

After two and a half months and about 50 million vaccinations the program was suspended because of indications that the vaccinations might be responsible for about 50 cases of Guillain-Barré syn-

drome. Guillain-Barré syndrome is a poorly understood paralytic disease from which most patients eventually recover fully; in rare cases, however, permanent injury or death may occur. As of early 1977, when nearly 900 cases of Guillain-Barré syndrome had been reported, about half among persons who had been vaccinated, statistical evidence neither supported nor refuted that swine flu vaccination was responsible. Fortunately, there was no further incidence of swine influenza outbreaks in the U.S. (For further discussion *see* Year in Review: MEDICAL SCIENCES: *General medicine*.)

Medical microbiology and genetics. Har Gobind Khorana and his colleagues at the Massachusetts Institute of Technology succeeded for the first time in synthesizing in the test tube a functional gene, one that corrects a mutational defect in a bacterial virus. Both the synthesis of the gene and the demonstration that it was functionally active were expected to have a major influence on the biological and health sciences. Khorana had won the 1968 Nobel Prize for Physiology or Medicine while at the University of Wisconsin for the synthesis of short, biologically active chains of DNA from their chemical components.

Malaria remained a serious disease in many parts of the world. As of 1977 there was no effective vaccine available and treatment of the disease was only marginally effective. A University of Georgia parasitologist recently announced success in the vaccination of chickens against a nonhuman form of malaria, and researchers from the University of Hawaii reported on the vaccination of monkeys against a human malaria parasite. Both accomplishments were highly significant in that protection against malaria through vaccination was achieved in model animal systems. These accomplishments, together with recent reports from two independent teams of U.S. investigators on the first successful long-term laboratory cultivations of a human malarial parasite, held out great promise for realizing a vaccination procedure for humans.

Awareness of the increasing resistance of microorganisms to drugs has been growing for some time. The most recent microorganism to cause such concern was *Neisseria gonorrhoeae*, the causative agent of gonorrhea. Between February 1976 and early 1977 several cases of gonorrhea caused by penicillin-resistant microorganisms were reported in the U.S. Although microorganisms with low-level penicillin resistance had been found previously, the significance of the new isolates lay in their complete resistance to even extremely high concentrations of penicillin. It was believed that these resistant forms were brought into the U.S. from the Far East. Although these forms fortunately retained their susceptibility to spectinomycin, an antibiotic substitute for penicillin, a few spectinomycin-resistant forms were encountered in the U.K. Thus, it was probable that in due course spectinomycin-resistant organisms would also be spread worldwide.

Environmental microbiology. In many cases the growth or activity of a microbial species depends upon the availability of iron. Microorganisms excrete siderochromes, which are trihydroxamates (or catechols) of low molecular weight that selectively chelate, or bind, iron. These chelator-iron complexes act as carrier molecules that transport iron across the microbial membrane and into the cell where the iron is metabolized. In nature, where there is competition among microorganisms for iron, some microorganisms produce antibiotics that are chemically similar to a competitor's siderochrome but that cannot be transported and used by the competitor. In mammalian systems there sometimes is competition for iron between the siderochromes of infectious microorganisms and such mammalian iron-binding proteins as lactoferrins and transferrins; the ability to produce disease is determined by how successfully the invading infectious microorganisms compete for iron.

Scientists in Canada formed evidence that the availability of iron is also an important factor in determining the composition and stability of aquatic ecosystems. Specifically, they noted that during blooms, or particular times of concentration, of blue-green algae, growth of other algae is suppressed. This was found to be brought about by hydroxamate chelators excreted by the blue-green algae, which tie up available iron for their own use

Agricultural Research

U.S. government scientists prepare grain treated with microbial insecticide Bacillus thuringiensis for tests. Stored grain coated with the pathogen resists infestations by larvae of the Indian meal moth.

and thus render iron unavailable for competing species of algae. Although such algae as *Scenedesmus*, which are competitive with blue-green algae, also produce small peptides that can bind iron, their systems cannot compete with hydroxamate chelators. An increased demand for iron resulting from increased rates of nitrogen fixation by blue-green algae is the apparent stimulus for the excretion of hydroxamates.

Wastewater and sewage renovation and reuse remained an important concern, and in this regard recent attention was focused on the movement and survival of viruses in soil when land disposal systems are used as the final step in wastewater treatment. Workers in Arizona and Texas reported that human disease-producing viruses did not contaminate groundwater lying 3–9 m below the soil surface when effluent from an activated sludge-type secondary sewage treatment plant was allowed to infiltrate the soil. Flooding the soil with distilled water to mimic rainfall, however, resulted in the deabsorption of viruses from the soil matrix and their further penetration into the soil.

Applied microbiology. The chemical monensin is produced by a species of *Streptomyces*, a genus of antibiotic-producing organisms that belongs to a group sometimes referred to as "higher bacteria." Although monensin is classed as an antibiotic, it has only very limited antibiotic activity; its greatest use is as an additive to beef cattle feed. Microorganisms in the rumen of cattle normally convert carbohydrates in feed to such products as acetic, butyric, and propionic acids as well as the gases carbon dioxide and methane. The acids are the animal's principle source of energy, whereas the gaseous products represent wasted energy. Monensin inhibits the formation of these gases and of acetic and butyric acids while promoting the production of propionic acid, an effect that permits more of the energy in feed to be absorbed.

Monensin was thought to be degraded rapidly when it is released to the soil in manure, and the growth of plants seems unaffected when fertilized with such manure. It was also believed that monensin did not affect the meat of animals. During the past year monensin appeared on the market as a feed additive, following its approval for use by the U.S. Food and Drug Administration.

Experiments were still under way in several laboratories on the use of microorganisms as biological insecticides. Recently workers at Western Illinois University developed strains of the bacterium *Bacillus sphaericus*, which have insecticidal activity against *Aedes* and *Anopheles* mosquitoes. *Aedes* transmits yellow fever, whereas *Anopheles* carries malaria. Some of the bacterial strains were isolated from Indonesia and the Philippines, and others were derived from a strain previously shown to have activity against another mosquito, *Culex*. More research will be required to determine whether these bacterial strains will be effective against mosquitoes under field conditions.

Microbial nitrogen fixation. Considerable interest continued to be focused on nitrogen fixation, a process by which certain bacteria and algae convert gaseous, atmospheric nitrogen to organic nitrogen (*i.e.*, combined nitrogen), which ultimately becomes available to plants. Certain nitrogen-fixing bacteria have evolved symbiotic relationships with such important legume crops as soybeans and peas. Within recent years several groups of investigators demonstrated that nonlegume crops, including corn (maize), wheat, rice, and forage grasses, also had a potential for biological nitrogen fixation. During the past year, workers at the University of Florida reported that field-grown pearl millet and guinea grass interact with *Spirillum lipoferum* and that nitrogen fixation occurred, as evidenced by higher yields from plants inoculated with this bacterium compared with uninoculated

controls. However, attempts by U.S. workers to establish nitrogen fixation in maize in temperate zones by inoculation with *S. lipoferum* were not entirely successful, perhaps an indication that the bacterium requires adaptation to temperate climates.

Nitrogen fixation by bacterial symbionts was found by scientists from the University of Georgia to constitute a major input of nitrogen to forest ecosystems. The symbiont microorganisms were shown to be established in bark and leaf samples taken from a variety of trees, including white oak, dogwood, red maple, and Eastern white pine. Workers from the University of Miami also obtained evidence that nitrogen fixation occurs in the region surrounding the root system (*i.e.*, the rhizosphere) of the sea grass, *Thalassia testudinum,* a highly productive tropical marine angiosperm. The prevalence of such a process in the rhizosphere of communities of this sea grass would help account for its high productivity.

It has long been known that microorganisms in the gut of the termite actually carry out digestion of the wood eaten by the termites. This woody foodstuff, however, is deficient in nitrogen. Recently workers at Michigan State University demonstrated that the termite gut contains a nitrogen-fixing bacterial species thought to be important in satisfying nitrogen requirements of the termite. Thus, bacterial nitrogen fixation appeared to be more widespread and to play a greater role in a diverse variety of ecosystems than formerly suspected.

One of the most novel experiments conducted during the past year was done by a pair of New Zealand scientists, who claimed to have "forced" the entry of cells of *Azotobacter vinelandii,* a free-living nitrogen-fixing bacterium, into cells of a fungus known to be mycorrhizal with (symbiotic with the roots of) a species of pine tree. The modified fungus was able to grow on media lacking combined nitrogen, an indication that the property of nitrogen fixation had been conferred onto the fungus by the forced symbiosis with *Azotobacter*. This indication was confirmed by the use of radioactive nitrogen as a tracer. Location within the fungus of the genetic information of *Azotobacter* and the degree to which the modified fungus retained its mycorrhizal relationship with the pine tree remained to be determined. Nevertheless, this appeared to be the first report of the transfer of genes for nitrogen fixation into a eucaryotic (nucleated) cell.

—Robert G. Eagon

Molecular biology

Techniques for manipulating genetic material have been improving. Over 25 years ago U.S. biologist

Norton Zinder discovered that bacterial viruses, or phages, occasionally package bacterial genes, in place of viral genes, and transfer them from one bacterial strain to another. This process is called transduction. The events Zinder studied were rare; less than one in a million virus particles would incorporate a given bacterial gene. Shortly afterward, U.S. geneticists M. Laurance Morse, Joshua Lederberg, and Esther M. Lederberg discovered that the bacterial virus lambda could transfer genes in *Escherichia coli*. Unlike the process studied by Zinder, in which any gene could be transferred but with very low efficiency, transfer mediated by lambda was efficient but restricted to a small set of genes concerned with metabolism of the sugar galactose. Although this restriction of lambda's range of transduction activity seemed to limit its usefulness, it has in fact turned out to be an exceptionally powerful tool in molecular biology because of its potential high efficiency.

Transduction as a laboratory tool. When lambda infects a sensitive *E. coli* cell, the infection can follow either of two courses with roughly equal probability. One course leads to vegetative growth of the virus followed by the death and dissolution of the bacterium and release of several hundred progeny virus particles. In the alternative course, most of the viral genes are shut off and the viral chromosome is integrated into that of the bacterium. Thus sequestered, the viral chromosome is "silent"; it is replicated as part of the bacterial chromosome and inherited in an orderly way by all descendants of the original infected cell. These descendants retain the ability to respond to certain environmental stimuli (*e.g.*, ultraviolet irradiation) by excising the viral chromosome. When this happens, vegetative growth of the virus ensues.

Lambda inserts itself into the *E. coli* chromosome at a well-defined location, called att^λ, between the genes for galactose fermentation (*gal*) and those for biotin synthesis (*bio*). When lambda excises from the bacterial chromosome, the original linkage between the genes *gal* and *bio* is usually restored. But occasionally the excision event occurs improperly and either *gal* genes or *bio* genes are removed with their erstwhile lambda neighbors. These rare events give rise to the restricted lambda-mediated transduction mentioned above. But because the viral chromosomes made in this fashion accidentally contain *both* lambda and bacterial genes, they can be replicated efficiently by the lambda DNA-replication machinery and packaged into lambda coats. Under the right conditions one can obtain populations of lambda in which 50% of the viral particles contain a particular bacterial gene (*gal* or *bio*). Such restricted transducing viruses are magnificent objects for the study of

gene organization, regulation, and function. Once formed, they breed true (if associated during infection with "helper" lambda to provide DNA replication and packaging). They can be separated from normal lambda by simple physical means and can be grown easily to provide milligram quantities of pure DNA. *E. coli* contains about 10,000 genes; hence, the incorporation of a few such genes into the lambda chromosome, which has 30 genes, represents both a vast purification and a vast amplification. More *gal* DNA can be prepared from a few liters of lambda *gal*-infected cells than from 500 liters of *E. coli*. Moreover, the *gal* genes in lambda are separated from their *E. coli* neighbors and so can be studied unambiguously.

Improved techniques. The ability of lambda to pick up *gal* or *bio* genes depends on their customary location astride the lambda attachment site in the *E. coli* chromosome. The great power to purify and amplify individual bacterial genes afforded by lambda has long been eyed with envy by molecular biologists interested in genes other than *gal* or *bio*. Over the past few years, methods for manipulating the lambda system to more general advan-

Transfer of genetic material from yeast species into E. coli *chromosome was recently achieved by splicing (at arrows) segment of yeast DNA into length of phage lambda DNA and inserting mixture into the bacterium.*

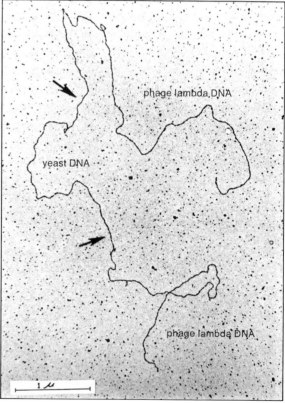

Courtesy, Ronald Davis, Stanford University

tage have been developed considerably. The first such improvement was introduced at the Pasteur Institute in Paris by Jonathan Beckwith and Ethan Signer, who transposed the lactose, or *lac*, operon (a system of genes and regulator sequences involved in the metabolism of β-galactosides) from its customary location to a new one adjacent to the attachment site for a virus called φ80 (similar but not identical to lambda), using a procedure developed at the Pasteur Institute by François Jacob and François Cuzin. The new strains of *E. coli* carrying transposed *lac* genes yielded φ80 transducing particles with *lac* genes. The transposition method works in either direction: genes in question can be moved next to the virus attachment site, or the attachment site itself can be transposed.

Further improvements are possible. In the course of studies on the specificity of lambda insertion, Max Gottesman, K. Shimada, and Robert Weisberg at the National Institutes of Health (NIH), Bethesda, Md., discovered that in bacterial strains in which the normal lambda attachment site was deleted, lambda could insert at many different chromosomal locations. Some of those insertions occurred in the interior of known genes, destroying their function. Such strains can be recognized by virtue of the lambda-induced mutation and can be induced to yield lambda transducing particles for the genes adjacent to the one invaded.

The mutagenic action of lambda in bacteria missing the normal lambda attachment site is similar to the behavior of another virus infecting *E. coli,* one called Mu (for mutator). Mu was characterized by Austin Taylor of the University of Colorado Medical Center some years ago as being able to insert at many sites on the *E. coli* chromosome, causing mutations at those sites. More recently, Arianne Toussaint of the Free University of Brussels developed procedures for incorporating genes from Mu into lambda. Using the genetic ability for insertion provided by the Mu genes, it thus becomes possible to insert lambda into the bacterial chromosome at a site previously selected by Mu insertion. Further, the particular lambda-Mu virus used this way can also contain either a part or all of the *lac* operon. Manipulations subsequent to the lambda-Mu-*lac*

insertion can be tailored to accomplish two ends: the structural gene for the enzyme β-galactosidase can be fused to the regulatory part of the operon one wishes to study; or the structural gene one wishes to study can be fused to the *lac* operator-promoter region in order to make quantities of its product. In the former case, the easily measured β-galactosidase activity is substituted for whatever gene product is governed by the regulator region in question. (See also *1977 Yearbook of Science and the Future* Year in Review: LIFE SCIENCES: *Molecular biology.*)

New studies. Transducing viruses figured prominently in the past year in studies of the organization and regulation of the genes for ribosomal proteins, protein elongation factors, RNA polymerase subunits, and ribosomal RNA. These genes control the very heart of molecular biology: RNA polymerase is the enzyme that transcribes the nucleotide sequences of DNA into those of messenger RNA, transfer RNA, and ribosomal RNA. Ribosomal RNA, together with 50 different ribosomal proteins, forms the complex structures called ribosomes, which provide the machinery for the synthesis of all proteins. It is on the surface of ribosomes that messenger RNA, transfer RNA charged with amino acids, and the protein elongation factors all interact to make the ordered peptide bonds of proteins.

A series of lambda transducing particles carrying genes for ribosomal proteins was isolated by Richard Jaskunas and Masayasu Nomura at the University of Wisconsin. They transposed *lac* genes next to the desired region of the *E. coli* chromosome and then inserted lambda *lac* there by recombination in the *lac* region. A series of rare excision events produced a family of particles capable of transducing one or more antibiotic-resistance genes known to be due to altered ribosomal proteins. The lambda derivative containing the longest segment of the *E. coli* chromosome from that region is called lambda *fus* 2; it carries genes for resistance to streptomycin, spectinomycin, and fusidic acid, as well as for 25 other ribosomal proteins, RNA polymerase subunit α, and protein elongation factor Tu. Lambda *fus* 2 DNA was used to map the genes for ribosomal proteins by cutting it with restriction enzymes,

Efficient bacterial virus phiX174, whose single chromosome seemed too short to code for the nine proteins it was known to make, was recently found to contain overlapping instructions for two proteins, D and E. Sequence of nucleotide triplets where both genes end is shown below.

protein D-- alanine —glutamic acid —glycine —valine —methionine   stop

--G—C—G—G—A—A—G—G—A—G—T—G—A—T—G—T—A—A—T—G—T—C—T--

protein E-- —arginine —lysine —glutamic acid   stop   start   serine ---protein J

Adapted from "Virus Violates an Important Biological Law," by Roger Lewin, *New Scientist: The Weekly Review of Science and Technology,* London, Oct. 21, 1976, p. 148, fig. 2

fractionating the DNA fragments so produced, and then determining which proteins can be synthesized in vitro by the DNA fragment-directed system. Another particle, called lambda *rif*d18, isolated by Joel Kirschbaum and Bruce Konrad at the University of Edinburgh, contains genes for ribosomal RNA, RNA polymerase subunits β and β', elongation factor Tu, and five ribosomal proteins. Thus, transducing particles tailor-made by manipulating genes inside *E. coli* were providing a unique look at the organization and regulation of the genes for essential components of the cell's machinery.

Recombinant DNA techniques. Other unconventional approaches to central problems of gene organization and regulation were much in the news in the past year. The terms "recombinant DNA" and "cloning" entered the lexicons of city councillors, magistrates, agency officials, and other nonscientists. The principles of the experiments causing so much public concern are very similar to those described above. In every case, the investigator transposes the set of genes to be studied onto a small DNA molecule (*e.g.*, lambda) that is capable of autonomous replication inside a bacterium. The crucial difference is that in recombinant DNA experiments, the genes so transposed need not come from bacteria. Recombinant DNA molecules are constructed in vitro; hence, the genes chosen to be purified and amplified inside *E. coli* could come from insects, mammals, plants, or even tumor viruses. The recombinant DNA molecules thus constructed contain genetic material that is never exchanged with bacteria in nature.

Introduction into bacteria of such hybrid DNA molecules, capable of autonomous replication, raises questions of risks and benefits. On the benefit side, recombinant DNA molecules provide the most powerful system known for the study of gene organization and regulation in such complex cells as those of human beings. Purification of the genes that code for rare and valuable materials, such as insulin, followed by their introduction into bacteria, could provide a cheap means of production. The same situation would hold true for human growth hormone, presently available only in experimental quantities. The risks of such experiments were largely unknown. For that reason, U.S. scientists involved in them first called for a moratorium on recombinant DNA experiments. Next, they met, eventually under NIH auspices, to develop guidelines for carrying out the experiments safely. Those guidelines, published in the *Federal Register* in July 1976, must be followed by all persons and institutions receiving NIH research-grant support.

The techniques for constructing recombinant DNA molecules are deceptively simple. One needs a small circular DNA molecule capable of replicating autonomously in *E. coli*; popular candidates are derivatives of lambda or of colEI, a plasmid that controls the synthesis of a toxin that kills sensitive strains of *E. coli*. The plasmid is cut once by a restriction endonuclease, an enzyme that recognizes and cuts at particular symmetric DNA sequences. These cuts are staggered in a way that produces short, complementary single-stranded tails. Next, the DNA from the source to be amplified is cut with the same restriction endonuclease. The fragments generated by these cuts are mixed with the cut plasmid, and the complementary ends join to produce a mixture of circular molecules containing the original plasmid into which "foreign" DNA fragments have been inserted at random. The mixture is then introduced into *E. coli* by a process similar to transformation. Plasmid-containing clones can be selected and tested for the presence of the particular genes desired. Recently this method was used to clone, for example, the genes coding for frog ribosomal RNA, for several yeast enzymes, and for chemically synthesized *lac* operator DNA from *E. coli* itself. (See also *Zoology*, below.)

—Robert Haselkorn

Zoology

Recent discoveries relating to animals include improved methods for quickly identifying potential mutagens and carcinogens, three independent reports of successful fusions of plant and animal cells, polarized light navigation by insects, and the capture of a new kind of large-mouth shark nicknamed Megamouth. Biochemical studies on respiratory enzymes (cytochromes) indicated that these were probably derived from photosynthetic systems, suggesting that the evolution of plants on the Earth preceded that of animals. A new study of the Nile crocodile uncovered complex behavior patterns, including care of the young.

Cellular zoology. During the past year new concerns arose about man-made environmental changes and their effect on animals at the cellular level. Particularly serious were reports concerning industrial chemicals, oil spills, pesticides, weed killers, drugs, cosmetics, and food additives. The list of such substances was long, and there was little agreement as to the dangers to animals.

Perhaps the most troublesome situation to deal with is cancer in man. Epidemiologists have clearly shown that cancer rates are increasing rapidly, that they are generally higher in industrial nations, and that, although sometimes they can be associated with specific chemicals or products, all too often the causes are obscure. The major problem is that chemicals presently suspect as carcinogens do not give timely data as to the extent and kind of human

Courtesy, Bruce N. Ames, Biochemistry Department, University of California, Berkeley

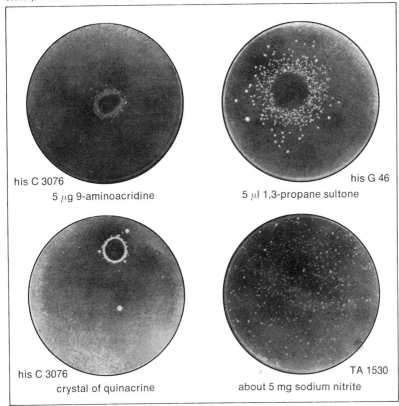

his C 3076

5 μg 9-aminoacridine

his G 46

5 μl 1,3-propane sultone

his C 3076

crystal of quinacrine

TA 1530

about 5 mg sodium nitrite

Shown are effects of four different mutagens tested with three strains of Salmonella typhimurium *that cannot grow on culture media unless a mutation is induced. One strain, TA 1530, has no protective coating, thereby increasing its permeability to chemicals. About a half billion bacterial cells are added to each plate along with the suspected mutagen. A zone of complete inhibition often occurs nearest the mutagen, surrounded by a ring of mutant colonies that marks the highest nonlethal concentration of mutagen.*

cancer they may induce many years later. It appeared, however, that significant steps toward earlier assessments were being made.

The idea that most carcinogens produce genetic mutations and that they usually produce cancer directly rather than through viral agents has been fairly convincingly established. Recently Bruce N. Ames of the University of California, Berkeley, and others demonstrated that about 90% of several hundreds of carcinogens tested produced mutations in special bacterial strains of *Salmonella typhimurium*, a close relative of *Escherichia coli*. The Ames testing system is simple, rapid, and quite sensitive. A given chemical or undefined substance is placed in the center of a petri dish containing nutrient agar and uniformly dispersed bacterial cells. Although these cells are alive, they cannot grow on the medium unless a mutation is induced. Typically, if the test substance is a mutagen, the center of the plate—where the chemical kills the cells directly—shows no growth; farther from the center, marking a zone in which lies the highest nonlethal concentration of mutagen, a ring of bacterial colonies flourishes, surrounded by fewer and fewer colonies yet farther away. The number of colonies is a measure of the mutagenic capability of the test substance.

The sensitivity of the procedure has been in-

creased by incorporation of mutants that lack normal DNA repair mechanisms (excision repair) and have a deletion through the galactose operon that renders them unable to synthesize their protective coat of lipopolysaccharides, thereby increasing permeability to many compounds. An added sophistication involves mixing the test substance with a microsomal fraction of homogenized liver tissue, a procedure that imitates the normal digestive and distribution pathway of materials taken in with food; a number of compounds were known that are not carcinogenic to animals until they have been processed by the liver.

The results of the bacterial tests are available in two days, and one technician can perform hundreds of tests per day. The significance of these microbial testing systems is that they allow mass screening and confer high sensitivity and low expense to the detection of a wide range of compounds. There was a general feeling that if a compound is a confirmed mutagen in any organism, it should be withheld from use on animals, including humans, unless it can be shown to be noncarcinogenic or nonmutagenic in laboratory animals or unless, as in the case of certain drugs, its benefits outweigh the risks.

Additional kinds and levels of testing were also developing rapidly. These require greater expense and time, but tend to assess any special features which eucaryotic (nucleated-cell) systems might possess that could be lacking in bacteria. Included were biflagellates, yeasts and other fungi, fruit flies, several higher plants, mammalian cells in culture, and, of course, mice and rats. One application of such tests was recently reported for the flame-retardant tris(2,3–dibromopropyl)phosphate (tris-BP), extensively used for children's pajamas. This compound was recently shown to be mutagenic by Bruce Ames and Arlene Blum at the University of California at Berkeley and also by Michael Prival, Elena McCoy, Bezalel Gutter, and Herbert Rosenkranz of the U.S. Environmental Protection Agency (Washington, D.C.) and New York Medical College, Valhalla. In these tests tris-BP not only acted as a powerful mutagen in the bacterial systems but also induced heritable mutations in the fruit fly *Drosophila melanogaster* as well as unscheduled DNA synthesis and chromosomal breaks in human tissue culture cells. The chemical in fabric was shown to produce hypersensitization in humans, and measurable amounts of tris-BP were detected in rats and rabbits. Blum and Ames noted that such flame-retardant chemicals were being added to many carpets, plastics, and fabrics, and therefore could present potential hazards of a magnitude equivalent to the pesticides that had been proven carcinogenic.

Because such chemicals eventually permeate the environment, not only is an increase in the human cancer rates a likelihood but there also remains the long-term hazard of significant increases in mutation rates in all animals. A crucial question is whether such chemicals can reach the germ plasm and result in sperm and eggs with defective genetic information. Such an effect on *Drosophila* has been shown for tris-BP, and it is probable that most other animals will not be exempt.

Genetic engineering. Another of the major stories and issues in biology, recombinant DNA engineering refers to recently developed techniques for excising specific pieces of DNA from an organism and enzymatically splicing it into a carrier molecule (*e.g.,* a plasmid). The DNA is inserted into a host organism, usually *E. coli*, which is then cloned in quantity. Using these techniques, four different groups in Europe and the U.S. reported the insertion into *E. coli* of a gene that codes for globin. The gene was prepared from rabbit reticulocyte messenger RNA by use of a reverse transcriptase enzyme. Even though it was shown by radioactive labeling that the gene entered the bacteria, for reasons that were not clear no globinlike gene products could be identified from cell lysates.

An entirely synthetic gene that worked, called tyrosine transfer RNA, was assembled by Nobel laureate Har Gobind Khorana and his colleagues at

Courtesy, Brookhaven National Laboratory

Fusion of tobacco-cell protoplasts and human cervical tumor (HeLa S3) cells produced a hybrid "plantimal" exhibiting three HeLa nuclei (enclosed in external projections) and two dark tobacco-cell nuclei.

the Massachusetts Institute of Technology. Also, Herbert Boyer at the University of California at San Francisco and Ray Wu at Cornell University independently synthesized the operator region of the *lac* operon, inserted it into *E. coli*, and showed that it was functional. (See also *Molecular biology,* above.)

The above experiments, though still mostly of theoretical interest, illustrate ongoing positive advances toward successful genetic engineering. On the more hazardous side, however, three narrow escapes were cited in the periodical *Science* for Jan. 28, 1977. The first of these involved the insertion of a cellulase enzyme into *E. coli* by A. Chakrabarty at the General Electric Research and Development Center in Schenectady, N.Y., using a gene-transfer technique that predated present splicing methods. The bacteria were destroyed by Chakrabarty after he reflected on the possible effect of such an organism in the human intestine. People normally do not harbor cellulase-containing bacteria, so that cellulose simply acts as roughage and gives bulk to the feces. The presence of cellulases in the intestine, however, could begin the breakdown process of cellulose; in combination with other intestinal flora the process might produce considerable gas and severe diarrhea.

Another incident involved a hybrid between the monkey virus SV40, which produces tumors in laboratory animals but probably not in man, and the adenoviruses, a group that includes some that cause the common cold. These hybrids were produced as a tool to map the genes of SV40, but should they escape, the combination might become established in humans for generations, exposing the human host to potential tumorigenic effects of SV40. Fortunately, Andrew M. Lewis, the virologist who in 1971 developed the hybrids at the U.S. National Institutes of Health, placed careful restrictions on the handling and accessibility of the hybrid.

The third example was purely conceptual, an idea by Paul Berg at Stanford University who planned to insert an SV40 into the *E. coli* genome. This kind of an experiment, though never brought to fruition, was one of the contributing factors in the development of the NIH guidelines for recombinant DNA research, published in the *Federal Register* in July 1976. These guidelines also were adopted as a model by the Committee on Genetic Experimentation, a newly formed world body that will attempt to monitor experiments in progress throughout the world and serve as a means of communication between scientists, politicians, and nations.

Cell-fusion experiments. Somewhat related to genetic engineering are the techniques of cell fusion, as illustrated in the human-mouse cell hybrids that have been so useful in the mapping of human genes on specific chromosomes (see *1977 Yearbook of Science and the Future* Year in Review: LIFE SCIENCES: *Zoology*). This work was continuing at several levels; for example, Albert Deisseroth, Ramon Velez, and Arthur Nienhuis of the National Heart and Lung Institute (Bethesda, Md.) recently reported that the much-studied globin genes, which comprise two genes that code for the α and β chains of the globin molecule, were on two different chromosomes (asyntenic) in humans, although they could not yet be assigned with certainty to particular chromosomes.

Of considerable interest were reports from three different groups of the successful fusion of animal and plant cells. Harold H. Smith's group at Brookhaven (N.Y.) National Laboratory fused human HeLa cells with tobacco protoplasts, one example of which they called a "plantimal." James Hartmann's group at Florida Atlantic University used rooster red blood cells with tobacco protoplasts to produce a hybrid facetiously dubbed "presmoked chicken." A third group from the Hungarian Academy of Science's Biological Research Center at Szeged fused HeLa cells with carrot protoplasts. Even if such combinations can be induced to undergo cell division, they probably will not develop into fully grown animal-plants. Smith's group showed that cells from two different species of to-

bacco can develop into mature plants, a finding which suggests that plant cells are more totipotent than animal cells; just how much more was a question being asked by experimenters in many laboratories.

General zoology. Insects remained fascinating in the versatility of their responses. A pioneering discovery, made about 25 years ago by Nobel laureate Karl von Frisch, was that bees are able to navigate by polarized light from the sky, a technique apparently unknown to man until about AD 1000, when the Vikings learned to use "sunstones," which are natural birefringent crystals or pebbles, as an aid to sea navigation. Recently Rüdiger Wehner from the University of Zürich described sophisticated experiments with the African ant *Cataglyphis bicolor*, a solitary forager with extraordinary directional sense. The ant begins his foraging by meandering from the nest for 100 yd or more, until it captures prey; it then runs straight back to the nest. By means of polarizing and other filters, Wehner established that the ant's directional capabilities require the use of ommatidia (individual units of its compound eye) in the uppermost one-sixth of the eye, and that sensitivity to polarization is in the ultraviolet (UV). The eye includes receptors for green and blue light; these primarily detect movement but also must give positional information. Given the ability to measure direction from UV polarization data, the ant's job still involves computing all of the angles it has turned and the distances it has traveled; this information has to be integrated continuously by the brain to enable the ant to take a straight-line return path to the nest from its foraging journey.

Many insects also have biological clocks that allow them to predict the onset of winter. These are usually photoperiod clocks sensitive to day length or night length; thus they are circadian. D. S. Saunders from the University of Edinburgh recently reported studies on the European flesh fly *Sarcophaga argyrostoma* and its wasp parasite, *Nasonia vitripennis*. The two insects have photoperiod responses that are circadian but differ in detail, corresponding to the two current models for oscillatory photoperiodic clocks. The fly displays the properties of a model of a single oscillator similar to the one proposed by Erwin Bünning of the University of Tübingen (West Germany) in 1936. In this fly, the phase of the endogenous rhythm is entrained, or set, by the entire photoperiod (24 hours) if days are short. If the period of illumination extends beyond 12 hours, however, the principal time cue is obtained from the occurrence of dusk, and the organism then exhibits long-day responses. The wasp *Nasonia*, on the other hand, seems guided by the presence of independent dawn and

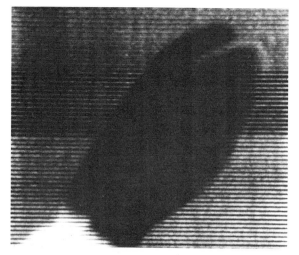

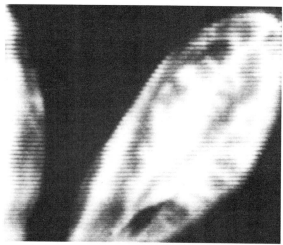

Infrared radiographs of visible outer ear (pinna) of a jackrabbit at three ambient temperatures (from top, 11°, 31°, and 45° C) reveal changes in tissue temperature through dilation and constriction of local blood vessels (warmer surfaces are of lighter shades), evidence that jackrabbit ears serve as heat exchangers.

dusk oscillators, the phase of one set by the time of dawn and the other by that of dusk. During long days, the two oscillations are partially in phase, and the insect's development proceeds without diapause (a period of dormancy or developmental arrest). When days are short, the oscillations are out of phase, and diapause occurs. It was shown that the receptors responsible for the photoperiod response are in the insect's brain and that the eye is not involved (*i.e.*, the eyes can be removed by surgery without altering this response).

A special region of the brain of the golden hamster, called the nucleus suprachiasmaticus, was shown to be involved with three different rhythms in that animal; namely, locomotor activity, estrous cyclicity, and photoperiodic photosensitivity. Milton Stetson and Marcia Watson-Whitmyre at the University of Delaware reported that destruction of the suprachiasmatic nuclei by radiofrequency lesions abolished all three rhythms. A direct neural pathway from the retina to the suprachiasmatic nuclei also was reported, an indication that the hamster eye is the original light sensor.

A somewhat different kind of rhythm, the remarkable synchronous flashing of male fireflies in Southeast Asia, was studied by John and Elisabeth Buck in the field and at the NIH Laboratory of Physiological Biology. Fireflies are beetles of the family Lampyridae. The males of some species gather on leaves of trees, not more than one per leaf, and flash in synchrony. This phenomenon relates to the more general question of how a nervous system measures time; in the case of flash synchrony a short-duration pacemaker must be involved. By using artifical flashes, the Bucks showed that the flashing of a male could be synchronized (entrained) to flash at intervals over a range of 800–1,600 milliseconds. One hypothesis derived from these studies was that synchronous flashing is an adaptation to aid mating in the dense foliage of a jungle. A second hypothesis was that the massive display tends to bring all of the fireflies together in one region. Finally, the two investigators proposed that if more than one male is competing for a female's attention, such behavior as increasing the intensity of a flash is acceptable to the female only if it is in synchrony with other males.

The current zoology of the Nile crocodile, *Crocodylus niloticus*, was recently reviewed by Anthony Pooley of the Natal Parks Board in Africa and Carl Gans of the University of Michigan. *C. niloticus* is among the largest of the order Crocodilia, weighing up to 1,000 kg (2,200 lb) and measuring as much as five meters (16½ ft) in length. It has an extensive range, occupying much of Africa including coastal waters and Madagascar, and is highly evolved as an extremely powerful predator, with advanced senses of smell, hearing, and sight, and with complex behavior patterns. Its feeding habits change as the animal matures; juveniles subsist by catching and eating small prey like snails, fish, and frogs, whereas adults regularly take antelope and Cape buffalo as large as themselves. Adults often cooperate in predation wherein certain kinds of prey are reduced to pieces that can be swallowed: the first crocodile moves a large piece of carcass toward another crocodile; the second crocodile bites the carcass and helps tear it apart. Yet each animal eats what it tears off without hostility toward the other.

Reproductive behavior of the Nile crocodile involves courtship, nesting, hatching, and care and protection of the young. At hatching time, young crocodiles call from inside the egg with an intensity sufficient to penetrate the overlying soil and carry as far as 20 m away. The female excavates the nest, and carefully picks up 16–80 unhatched eggs in her mouth. If she misses any, the young emit distress calls, which change to a softer chirping when they are in her mouth. She carries the eggs to the shallows and swings her head from side to side to release the hatchlings, who then swim to shore. Both parents remain near the crèche for 6–8 weeks, defending the young. If a juvenile in a crèche is disturbed, it sends out a loud distress call, which may be echoed by other juveniles. Adults in the area immediately move toward the sound, leaving the water if it is necessary to do so. Given the opportunity, the male also will gather unhatched eggs in his mouth and release the hatchlings into shallow water.

After several weeks the juveniles leave the crèche, looking for streams or areas not occupied by other adults. At some point they will dig a tunnel, often in cooperation with other juveniles, which they use for protection and warmth for a period of about five years. Once reaching a subadult stage, the males may challenge the territory of another adult male, but such encounters are usually more ritualistic than dangerous; the adult may chase the interloper into the water, where the subadult indicates submission by lifting his head and exposing his throat. These and other behavioral activities, together with the large brain, four-chambered heart, and other specialized anatomical features, place the Nile crocodile in a highly advanced and successful reptilian category, challenging some mammals and birds with respect to biological sophistication.

Evolution. Sharks are usually considered to be highly evolved predators of ancient lineage, preferring to feed on large prey. During the year the U.S. Navy accidently caught a 14½-ft, 1,650-lb shark on a sea anchor at a depth of about 500 ft. Upon dissection of the animal, Leighton Taylor at the University of Hawaii found that it contained in its stomach a soupy red liquid consisting of tiny shrimp. The shark has an enormous head, a peculiar snout and gill structure, and a very large mouth that seems to be associated with a capability to filter out small, planktonlike food in the manner of a baleen whale. Shark expert Leonard Compagno of Stanford University felt that the shark, which was nicknamed Megamouth, may represent a new species, genus, and family.

About 3.5 billion years ago, life arose from the primordial ooze in the form of a protocell. Evolution of this form eventually produced sulfur-dependent bacteria, which are able to tap energy available from the Sun by utilizing hydrogen sulfide present in the atmosphere. Important enzymes in this process are the cytochromes, which also have assumed fundamental roles in the life processes of higher plants and animals; they can deliver an electron either to a chlorophyll molecule for photosyn-

Reproductive behavior of the Nile crocodile includes gathering of unhatched crocodile eggs into the mouth. The animal rolls the eggs gently between its tongue and palate to release the hatchlings.

From "The Nile Crocodile," by A. C. Pooley and C. Gans, © April 1976 by Scientific American Inc. All rights reserved

thesis or to an oxidase molecule for respiration. Based on extensive studies of these enzymes, chemist Richard Dickerson at the California Institute of Technology in Pasadena advanced a seven-step scheme for the evolution of life. He concluded that the evolution of cytochrome structure suggests the early presence of the photosynthetic pathway, with respiration and animal life arising only after oxygen from plant photosynthesis became abundant.

—Darryll Outka

See also Feature Articles: THE FLIGHT OF BIRDS; THE ROLE OF ZOOS IN WILDLIFE CONSERVATION; ONCE MORE INTO THE LOCH.

Materials sciences

Significant developments in the field of materials sciences during the year included a new approach to the statistical treatment of surface-flaw distribution in ceramic materials and novel processes for the production of silicon carbide as a fiber and as a sinterable powder. Application of field ion microscopy to metallurgical studies yielded information on the behavior of atoms adsorbed on metal surfaces and on the age-hardening mechanism of metal alloys.

Taken from a 2,300° F oven only seconds earlier, glowing cube of silica-fiber insulation developed for the U.S. space shuttle program dissipates heat so quickly that it can be held in the bare hand.

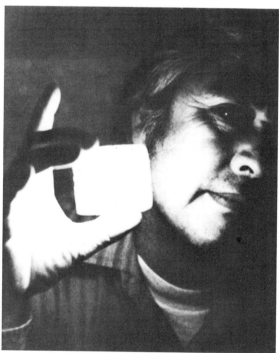

Courtesy, Lockheed Missiles & Space Company

Ceramics

Advances in ceramics during the past year were made in the development of new materials and new processing techniques, in research aimed at improved high-temperature mechanical properties, and in a range of new applications for ceramics.

New materials. Since U.S. inventor Edward Acheson discovered more than 80 years ago that silicon carbide (SiC) can be produced economically by the reduction of silica sand with carbon, SiC has ranked among the most important of abrasive and refractory products. However, SiC formed by the Acheson process is granular in form, and unlike most oxide ceramics, which sinter easily into dense, useful products, SiC resists sintering. In 1974 scientists at the General Electric Research and Development Center, Schenectady, N.Y., showed that very fine SiC powders formed by chemical vapor-phase reactions can be sintered if they contain small additions of boron and carbon. During the past year the Carborundum Co., Niagara Falls, N.Y., announced achievement of a sinterable alpha-phase silicon carbide powder starting with the Acheson process. It was reported that these powders can be sintered into complex shapes with surfaces requiring little or no expensive finish grinding, and that strengths above 85,000 psi (pounds per square inch) at 2,700° F (1,480° C) can be achieved. This powder thus joined a growing number of silicon nitride and silicon carbide powders offering great promise for use in new ceramic structural applications. Their use in high-temperature automotive and aircraft turbine engines, for example, could significantly increase efficiency and conserve strategically scarce raw materials.

Filaments of silicon carbide had been studied for many years as attractive fibers of high strength and high elastic modulus for the reinforcement of high-temperature metals. Unfortunately, until recently SiC filaments could be made only by the slow, very costly process of chemical vapor deposition on tungsten, carbon, or boron/tungsten substrates. Their cost, about $800/lb in research quantities, had severely limited their development. Thus one of the most significant events of the year was the announcement by Seishi Yajima and colleagues at Tohoku Gakuen University in Sendai, Japan, of their success in preparing SiC filaments by an entirely new procedure. An organosilicon compound, dimethyldichlorosilane, is reacted with lithium and a catalyst to produce dodecamethylcyclohexasilane, which in turn is polymerized into an organosilicon polymer, probably a polycarbosilane. The viscous polycarbosilane liquid is spun into fibers, which are then heat-treated slowly under vacuum to convert them into SiC fibers. The length and diameter of the fibers can be controlled by the spinning process; fibers produced in early work had diameters as large as about 30 microns (1 micron = 10^{-6} m). Fibers heat-treated at 1,300° C showed strengths as high as about 500,000 psi, and the highest elastic modulus attained on these fibers approached that for SiC whiskers. This process thus offered tremendous potential for the production of low-cost, high-quality SiC fibers, and there was speculation that this ability to prepare ceramics from organometallic polymer precursors might lead to many new possibilities of making a range of mixed nitrides and carbonitrides in fiber, film, and perhaps even bulk form.

Processing. Hot isostatic pressing (HIP) is an exciting new way of densifying hard-to-sinter ceramic materials into complex shapes. The pressures in traditional hot pressing, used for many years in the densification of ceramics, are severely limited by the rupture strength of the die material (typically graphite) and are very anisotropic; that is, they are unevenly distributed over all parts of the component. Pressure anisotropy, in fact, severely limits the complexity of the shapes that can be formed by standard hot pressing. In the HIP process, compaction pressure is transmitted isotropically by an inert gas, and can be as high as the cool outer walls of the pressure chamber will allow.

Although the HIP process was finding great application in powder metallurgy, its use in ceramics was just beginning. A. Traff and P. Skotte of ASEA, an engineering research and development company in Sweden, recently used the HIP process to close the remaining porosity in traditionally sintered alumina tool tips used for the machining of

metals. The postdensification HIP treatment increased tool-tip lifetime by at least 25%. In the same way, the rupture strength of boron carbide components was more than doubled. Especially promising were recent indications in the U.S. and elsewhere that silicon nitride, which does not sinter or even hot press without the aid of generally harmful additives, might densify to acceptable strength levels under the simultaneous high temperatures and very high pressures of the HIP process. If this could be done, the long-term high-temperature properties of silicon nitride should be significantly improved.

One of the serious problems facing the introduction of silicon nitride and silicon carbide parts of complex shape in applications where dimensional tolerance were critical was the tremendous expense of diamond grinding and surface finishing these dense, hard ceramics. As a result, processes with the potential for producing shapes close to final configuration, such as HIP treating and the newly emerging injection molding of sinterable ceramic powders, and more efficient machining processes received much greater emphasis in the past year.

Mechanical properties. Many modern ceramics can be processed to very high strength levels, but they are still inherently brittle, fracturing with little or no discernible plastic deformation. They also generally rate very low in fracture toughness, so that even very small flaws present as a result of imperfect processing or surface machining can cause catastrophic failure at operating stress levels. It is essential, therefore, that the designer of a ceramic component calculate very accurately the

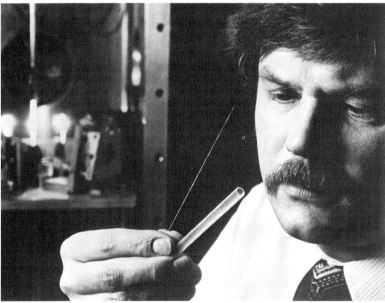

Scientist holds single-crystal sapphire fiber and tube, each formed by newly developed laser-beam technology. The fiber has a tensile strength in excess of 1.4 million pounds per square inch.

NYT Pictures

mechanical and thermal stresses to be encountered and that he apply a probabilistic approach to the strength of the ceramic material to be used. Until recently, the relatively simple flaw-distribution function introduced by W. Weibull in 1938 had been the basis for these probabilistic treatments. During the past year a new, much more general statistical treatment of surface-flaw distributions was reported by J. R. Matthews, F. A. McClintock, and W. J. Shack of the Massachusetts Institute of Technology. Their results for several glasses, which indicated that differences in flaw distributions between materials and between various surface treatments can be determined very effectively by straightforward indentation tests, should have a great influence on future fracture-mechanics treatments of the strength and service life of ceramics.

While nothing was done to reduce the brittleness of ceramics, some progress was made last year in improving their fracture toughness. Several studies showed that partially stabilized zirconia, when properly processed, can have surprisingly high toughness values. Nils Claussen of the Max-Planck-Institute in West Berlin demonstrated that the addition of very finely divided unstabilized zirconia can double the toughness of alumina, apparently by forming a very fine network of microcracks at the second-phase zirconia particles. Since the cracks intentionally induced this way are extremely small, increased toughness is achieved at the expense of only a modest decrease in strength. This toughening technique, which may be widely applicable to many structural ceramics, should be especially valuable for applications where thermal shock resistance is important.

Applications. Ceramic thermal-protection materials were to play a major role in the U.S. National Aeronautics and Space Administration's pair of space shuttle orbiters, scheduled for initial space flights in 1979. Since the shuttle concept was initiated to reduce the cost of space operations by reusing the expensive orbiter stage, perhaps as many as 100 times, the shuttle orbiters must be protected from the intense heat generated upon reentry into the Earth's atmosphere. To this end the Lockheed Missiles and Space Co. developed an extremely lightweight insulation (9 lb/ft^3), made of high-purity amorphous silica fibers, which emits heat so effectively that a block of the material can be held in the bare hand while its center is still visibly red hot. The insulation was being machined into individually shaped tiles to match the orbiters' contours and coated to prevent moisture absorption. Tiles for the underside of the orbiters were designed to protect the aluminum skin against reentry temperatures as high as 2,300° F (1,260°C). About 70% of the surface of each orbiter was to be covered with this reusable insulation, requiring the fabrication of about 34,000 tiles per spaceship. Orbiter nose caps and wing leading edges, which would be subjected to the highest reentry temperatures (approaching 3,000° F), would be protected by a reinforced carbon-carbon composite.

In view of current energy requirements and national concerns about the environmental safety of nuclear power systems, there was great interest in the possibility of using ceramics as a means of safely storing radioactive wastes. Several groups, including the Pacific Northwest Laboratories in Richland, Wash., were studying the incorporation of nuclear-reactor wastes into solid, perhaps glassy, ceramics that offered stability and ease of handling. (*See also* Feature Article: NUCLEAR WASTE DISPOSAL.)

—Norman M. Tallan

Metallurgy

The past year saw a significant increase in the application of field ion microscopy to the study of metallurgical phenomena, with the result that, for the first time, direct observation of a range of atomic-scale structures and mechanisms was made possible. Field ion microscopy is unique in that, by providing a magnification of one million times, it permits visual observation of the images of single atoms located on a metal surface and, hence, observation of the atomic arrangements and atomic processes occuring on such surfaces.

Experimentally, the technique involves establishing a voltage difference in a vacuum chamber between a positively charged metal wire (the specimen) and a grounded fluorescent screen toward which the metal wire is pointed. The wire, which is typically 0.005 in in diameter, is previously sharpened to a rough point by chemical polishing. As the voltage difference between the specimen and the screen is increased, the more prominent atoms on the rough metal surface at the tip of the wire are ionized and ejected from the surface by the electric field; this process is termed field-evaporation of the surface. Thus, with increasing voltage the surface of the tip of the wire is smoothed until it comprises perfect crystal planes. Helium gas at low pressure is then leaked into the system, and if the electric field adjacent to the individual atoms on the metal surface is greater than the ionization potential of helium, helium atoms coming into this vicinity are ionized and repelled by the field toward the screen. By means of an image intensifier, contact of the helium ions with the screen is observed as a pattern of fluorescent spots, the arrangement of which faithfully duplicates the arrangement of the atoms on the metal surface.

Courtesy, William R. Graham, University of Pennsylvania

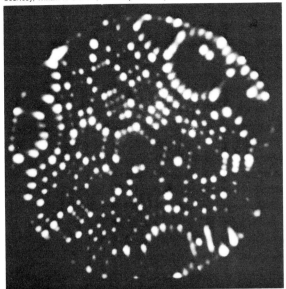

A field ion micrograph of the crystal surfaces of tungsten. A pair of tungsten adatoms on the (211) plane appears within the ring of surface atoms at the upper right-hand corner.

This technique recently was applied to direct observation of the diffusion behavior of atoms adsorbed on metal surfaces (so-called adatoms) and to observation of the precipitation of the second phase in age-hardening alloys.

Diffusion of atoms over metal surfaces. In studies of the behavior of adatoms on metal surfaces, adatoms were deposited on the metal surface by thermal evaporation from a filament incorporated in the vacuum chamber. Such atoms were then observed directly as spots on the fluorescent screen. Preparation of a perfect surface and adsorption of the atoms from the vapor phase were conducted at the temperature of liquid helium (about 4 K or − 269° C), a temperature at which adatoms are immobile on the metal surface. In the absence of an electric field, the specimen was then rapidly heated to some desired temperature, held at this temperature for a desired time, and rapidly recooled to liquid helium temperature. The high-voltage field was turned on and direct measurements were made of adatom movement on the surface during the time for which the surface was held at the elevated temperature. Repetition of this procedure yielded the diffusion coefficient, D, of an adatom as $D = <R^2>/4\tau$, in which $<R^2>$ is the mean square displacement of the adatom from its initial position in time τ, the duration of one diffusion interval. Measurement of D as a function of temperature yielded the energy of activation required for an atomic jump, or change of position.

Study of the movement of rhodium atoms over five different crystal planes of face-centered cubic rhodium showed that the magnitude of the diffusion coefficient depends greatly on the crystal plane over which the adatom is moving. This is caused by a dependence of the activation energy required for atomic jumping on the degree of "atomic roughness" of the crystal plane. It was found that the activation energy increases with increase in the degree of "atomic roughness" of the plane; *e.g.,* the activation energy increases from a value of 15 kilojoules (kj) per mole on the (111) plane, the smoothest plane, to a value of 84.5 kj per mole for diffusion on the (100) plane, the least close-packed plane.

Study of the diffusion of tungsten adatoms on the surface of body-centered cubic tungsten showed that when deposition occurs on the (211) plane, one-dimensional diffusion occurs along the [111] channels on this plane. It also showed that when two such atoms, deposited in adjacent channels, eventually meet they form a stable pair of atoms that migrates more rapidly than a single adatom; the activation energy for diffusion is decreased from 73 kj per mole for diffusion of a single adatom to 36 kj per mole for diffusion of a pair. The migration of the pair occurs by a "walking" action in which one of the atoms makes a single jump, followed by the second atom making the corresponding jump. This behavior is attributed to the strong attractive interactions between the two adatoms, and the observation that two adatoms migrate independently of one another when they are further apart than seven angstroms (Å; one angstrom = 10^{-8} cm) gives an indication of the shortness of range of the interactive forces.

Studies of the diffusion of pairs of adatoms on different metals revealed subtle differences in behavior. For example, if the migrating pair is likened to a pair of walking feet, a tungsten pair spends more time with feet together than with one foot in front of the other. The opposite is true for a pair of rhodium atoms, and a pair of iridium atoms hops, rather than walks, along the channels.

Mechanism of age-hardening. Age-hardening is a well-known metallurgical phenomenon whereby the strength and hardness of an alloy, which initially is a single-phase supersaturated solid solution of a metal solute in a metal solvent, increase with time because of the slow precipitation of a second phase in the alloy. Although it was reasonably assumed that the mechanical properties of the aging alloy are determined by the shape, size, number density, and composition of the precipitated second-phase particles, it was often found that the aging alloy acquired its maximum strength and hardness before the precipitated particles grew large enough to be observed by elec-

Courtesy, International Business Machines Corporation, Research Division

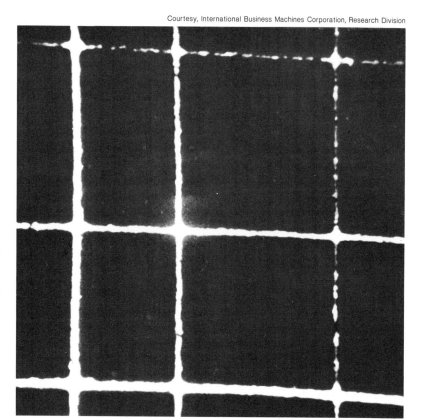

Ultrathin metal lines (left to right), approximately 150, 80, and less than 50 angstroms wide (1 angstrom=10⁻⁸ cm), may be useful in the fabrication of X-ray lenses. The lines are defined by polymerization of impurities on the surface of a metal film by scanning it with an ultrahigh-resolution electron beam 5 angstroms in diameter. The metal unprotected by the polymer lines is then sputter-etched away, leaving the lines intact.

tron microscopy. This greatly hindered understanding of the fundamental mechanisms of the process and, hence, understanding of the influence of the precipitation process on mechanical properties.

Application of field ion microscopy to the study of age-hardening at 500° C (930° F) in an iron-copper alloy containing 1.55% by weight of copper provided virtually complete information on the process. By field-evaporating layers from the surface of an age-hardened specimen, the sizes of the precipitated particles were measured through determination of the thickness of matrix that field-evaporated between the initial appearance of a particle at the surface and its final disappearance. Coherent precipitates were detected by virtue of the property that field-evaporation nearly always affects the relative magnifications of the precipitate and the matrix, and coherency of such precipitates with the matrix was confirmed by observation of the matching of lattice planes across the interface between the particle and the matrix.

It was found that nearly all of the particles are spherical, and the smallest particles observed were 8 Å in diameter. It was determined that maximum strength in the alloy is achieved when the mean particle diameter reaches 24 Å. When the particle size exceeds 50 Å the matching of lattice planes across the interface disappears, which indicates

that such particles are no longer coherent with the matrix. Measurement of the rate of increase of particle size confirmed that particle growth rate is controlled by the normal volume diffusion of copper in iron.

Within one hour of aging at 500° C the number density of particles was $10^{18}/cm^3$. This density remained nearly constant until maximum strength was achieved after three hours of aging, after which it gradually decreased to less than $10^{16}/cm^3$ in 120 hours. It thus was shown that more than 99% of the particles precipitated eventually redissolve in the matrix. From measurement of the number density and mean size of the particles it was determined that the total volume fraction of the precipitates does not rapidly reach a constant value, as had been assumed previously, but continues to increase until the mean particle size exceeds 100 Å.

In this study the chemical composition of the precipitates was determined by an arrangement in which the material that had field-evaporated from a selected area on the specimen surface was allowed to pass through a pinhole in the fluorescent screen into a time-of-flight mass spectrometer. In this manner it was determined that, although the equilibrium second phase in iron-copper alloys is virtually pure copper, the copper content of the precipitates after one hour of aging is less than 50% and does not approach 100% until more than 100 hours of aging time have elapsed. This experimental evidence provided elegant confirmation of the predictions of thermodynamic analysis of the nucleation of copper precipitates in iron.

—David R. Gaskell

Mathematics

The major news from the world of mathematics was that one of its oldest unsolved problems was resolved in 1976 by an unprecedented technique combining abstract mathematical reasoning with extensive computer computation. Not only did this work verify a century-old conjecture but it also provided striking evidence for a promising new research strategy in the mathematical sciences.

The problem, known popularly as the four-color conjecture, is rather simple to state: can every map (on a plane surface) be colored with four colors so that adjacent regions receive different colors? The first confirmation of this conjecture was published in 1879 by a London barrister, A. B. Kempe, but it proved to be incorrect. The recent verification, carried out by Kenneth Appel and Wolfgang Haken at the University of Illinois, was simply a very elaborate correction of Kempe's oversight. While the solution to this problem is of no practical use to cartographers, the century-long endeavor to solve it generated a whole new branch of mathematics called graph theory that has been of crucial importance to the development of such fields as operations research and computer science.

The idea that four colors are sufficient for coloring any map first occurred to the British student Francis Guthrie in 1852. Since neither Francis nor his brother Frederick could confirm this hunch, they relayed the question to Frederick's mathematics tutor, Augustus De Morgan, who in turn posed the query to the most famous British mathematician of the time, William Rowan Hamilton: "Cannot a necessity for five colors or more be invented?"

It is easy to verify (figure 1) that three colors are too few. Moreover, it is not too difficult to show that it is impossible for five countries to be arranged so that each of them is adjacent to the others. The reasoning, repeatedly rediscovered by many who have worked on the conjecture during the past 125 years, appears to show that four is exactly the right number. But it actually conceals a hidden flaw that is typical of those that have undermined many purported proofs of the four-color conjecture. In figure 2 six countries are arranged in such a way that no four countries are mutually adjacent. If the reasoning given above were correct, then it should follow for this particular map that three colors will suffice. But in fact four are required, one for the central country and three for the ring of countries surrounding it.

This simple example illustrates well the subtleties of the four-color conjecture. A correct proof must deal not only with the adjacency patterns of various countries but also with all the possible serpentine configurations in which various chains of countries can entwine themselves around other regions. Kempe's proof foundered on just this type of problem; he overlooked a single exotic configuration. Haken and Appel surmounted this hurdle by a massive computer search, requiring several thousand hours of computer time and hundreds of pages of what even the authors termed "ridiculous detail." Yet for all its modern sophistication the

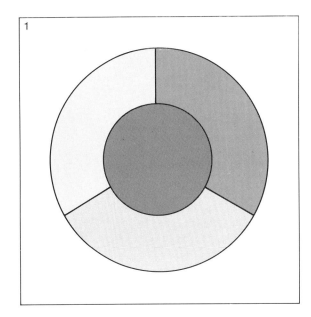

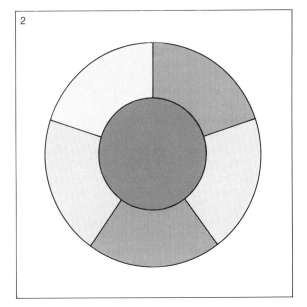

proof devised by Haken and Appel is a strikingly direct descendant of Kempe's proof.

Kempe began his argument by showing, correctly, that it was sufficient to verify the conjecture for "normal" maps, those in which no more than three regional boundaries meet at each point; any map containing points where more than three boundaries meet can be modified to a normal map that will be more difficult to color than was the original because more regions are adjacent. Kempe then used a remarkable formula developed by the 18th-century mathematician Leonhard Euler to show that any normal map must contain regions with fewer than six neighbors.

Euler's formula is as follows: the number of vertices plus the number of regions equals the number of edges, plus two. (In symbols, $V + R = E + 2$.) In a normal map $2E = 3V$. By combining this fact with Euler's formula, Kempe proved an astonishing result about normal maps: if each country in a normal map is labeled with a number equal to 6 minus the number of its neighbors, then the sum of all these labels — no matter how large or complex the map — is always 12. However, if each country had six or more neighbors, then each label, and hence their sum, would be zero or less. Because this is not the case, some country must have fewer than six neighbors.

Armed with this information concerning "unavoidable" regions, Kempe tried to show that whenever a region with fewer than six sides appeared in a normal map, the map could be reduced to a smaller one whose coloring was no easier; if the reduced map could be four-colored, then so

could the original map. Such a reduction strategy would prove the conjecture, for it would ensure that any map could be reduced by repeated steps to a simple map, say with only four regions, which could be easily colored. Then by reversing the process the original map could also be colored.

Kempe's proof was simple and correct for regions with two, three, or four sides, but for pentagonal regions his proof was incomplete. In 1890 Percy J. Heawood, a mathematician at the University of Durham, gave an example of a normal map with 25 regions which contained a pentagon that could not be reduced according to the methods used in Kempe's proof. Heawood's map could be colored, but not by Kempe's method. Heawood's analysis of the Kempe proof demonstrated that the problem was far more subtle than had at first been believed.

The problem attracted the attention of amateur and professional mathematicians throughout the world. It was generalized (and often solved) on surfaces more complicated than a plane. (Figure 3 shows a map on the surface of a doughnut that requires seven different colors; Heawood showed that, for a doughnut, seven is the correct minimum number of required colors.) But not even the best minds of the 20th century could solve the conjecture in its original formulation. Laborious modifications of Kempe's argument revealed only that the conjecture is true for maps with 40 or fewer regions. These efforts climaxed, in a way, with Martin Gardner's publication of a now-famous hoax counterexample in the April 1975 issue of *Scientific American.*

Haken and Appel adopted Kempe's method by assigning to each country a "charge" equal to 6 minus the number of its neighbors. Because positive charge occurs only in regions with fewer than six neighbors, one can be sure, based on the positive total, that such regions are unavoidable in normal maps. Kempe had tried unsuccessfully to show that this set of unavoidable configurations was also reducible; where Kempe failed, Haken and Appel succeeded. But to do so they had to replace his one flawed case (pentagonal regions) with 1,936 complex configurations.

Positive charge provides a clue to the presence of reducible configurations. The strategy behind the Appel-Haken proof was to redistribute the charge on the map in such a way as to improve these clues, always subject to the constraint that the total charge must remain unchanged. They did this by a step-by-step procedure called a "discharging algorithm" that treated one region at a time. When the discharging algorithm was completed, then each of the configurations identified by the remaining positive charges must be re-

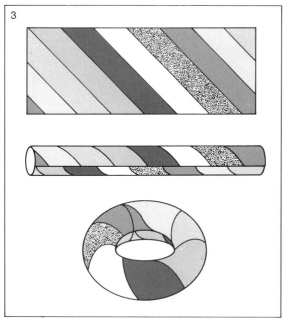

3

From Beck, Bleicher and Crowe, *Excursions into Mathematics*, p. 67, 1969

duced, just as Kempe had reduced the cases of two-, three-, and four-sided regions.

The first step in this program, the design of an appropriate discharging algorithm, took about three and one-half years of counterpoint between man and machine. For each region with positive charge produced by the draft algorithm, Haken and Appel tried to find a reducible configuration around it. (For assistance in this task they employed specially designed computer algorithms.) If no reducible configuration was discovered in a reasonable time, perhaps half an hour of computer search, they assumed that none existed and went back to modify the discharging algorithm to avoid such situations.

Their goal in this work was to reduce the likelihood of misleading or useless clues. Positive charge remaining in a configuration that could not be reduced would yield an insurmountable obstacle identical to the one that destroyed Kempe's proof. Moreover, positive charge remaining in a location where the smallest candidate for reducibility is too large to be checked is completely useless. Either difficulty, if remaining in the final step, would prevent completion of the proof.

When they were finally convinced that they had an algorithm that located only reducible configurations, Appel and Haken began the systematic verification of reducibility for all cases of positive charge produced by the algorithm. The resulting catalog contained 1,936 reducible configurations, each requiring a search of up to 500,000 options to verify reducibility. This last phase of the work took six months and was completed in June 1976. Final checking, part of which was carried out by the researchers' teenage children, took the entire month of July, and the results were officially communicated to the *Bulletin of the American Mathematical Society* on July 26, 1976: "Every Planar Map Is Four Colorable."

The announcement of the Haken-Appel proof sent several different shock waves through the mathematical world. The verification of a century-old conjecture that had baffled the 20th century's best mathematicians was an astounding accomplishment. But a solution based on computerized case analyses involving nearly 2,000 cases and 10 billion logical options is the complete antithesis of the idealized "elegant" mathematical proof. The Haken-Appel proof is the first example of a major mathematical problem solved by an essential symbiosis of theoretician and computer. Many mathematicians believed that this result is only the prelude to better, shorter, more conceptual proofs. "We aren't going to go through eternity," vowed one mathematician, "saying 'And the computer said . . . .'"

In defense of their formidable method, Haken and Appel observed that their proof was close to optimal within the Kempe tradition of seeking unavoidable sets of reducible configurations. Every configuration that must be reduced is surrounded by a ring of neighbors that determines whether or not it can be reduced. The size of this ring has great bearing on the difficulty of establishing reducibility. Several years earlier Edward F. Moore of the University of Wisconsin had developed a strategy for disproving the four-color conjecture (if indeed it were false) by creating maps that excluded all known reducible configurations almost as fast as such configurations were discovered. The map in figure 4 (flattened out from the surface of a sphere; each polar region bounded by the top and bottom lines is a nine-sided region) is one Moore created in 1963 that contains no reducible regions with ring size smaller than 11. The Haken-Appel proof requires configurations with a ring size that is no larger than 14.

The Moore graph shows, therefore, that no proof based on an unavoidable set of reducible configurations can be even moderately short, since it must deal with ring sizes at least as large as 11. The Haken-Appel proof, while somewhat longer than necessary, deals with configurations only a few sizes larger.

Because of the success of Haken and Appel others might be inclined to support computer attacks on all famous unsolved problems. But the crucial first step in any computer attack is a difficult theoretical maneuver, the reduction from an infinite to a finite number of cases. This is possible in the four-color problem because of the intricate geometry of maps. It is not likely to be as easy with problems in number theory, such as the "last theorem" of Fermat that only for $n = 1$ or 2 are there solutions in positive integers to $x^n + y^n = z^n$. The finitization of such problems will be very difficult, perhaps impossible. And no computer assault can work until finitization is complete.

But even if a problem is finite, it may be impractical to implement on even the fastest computer. The

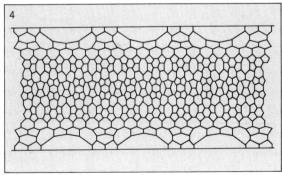

From Edward F. Moore, *Mathematics Magazine*, p. 220, September 1976

Haken-Appel proof is just on the border of the possible; had the attack required configurations of ring size 15, the time required for computer search of reducibility would have made the present proof totally impossible. The achievement of Haken and Appel reveals the existence of a new class of mathematical theorems that are true but for which no simple proof exists. And it implies the existence of theorems that are true but for which no proof is presently possible.

The logician Kurt Gödel showed in 1931 that what is true may not, even in theory, be provable. Haken and Appel demonstrated by their work that what is true and theoretically provable may not be actually provable because the shortest possible proofs are too long for computation or comprehension. Their work thus helped to establish the boundaries of what is possible. Exploration of these boundaries by mathematician-computer teamwork is likely to be a major challenge for mathematicians in the final quarter of this century.

—Lynn Arthur Steen

Mechanical engineering

Mechanical engineers strive to make living more interesting and comfortable for others by creating, designing, producing, and operating all kinds of moving structures such as toys, printing presses, weaving machines, tools, bicycles, and locomotives. They are also occupied with energy management, ranging from natural resources such as oil and gas to final uses such as heating and cooling homes and powering automobiles. Part of their interest in energy stems from the fact that no machine can be kept in motion without a supply of energy. Thus, mechanical engineers are cast in roles that influence every facet of modern living. This range of influence may become more evident by considering four examples of their current searching and inventiveness: human thermal comfort, precision in cutting, safety in high-rise building fires, and the need for better fuel mileage and lower exhaust emissions from automobiles.

Human thermal comfort. For comfort in the summer many buildings and vehicles are air-conditioned. In winter these spaces are heated, for thermal comfort is one of the ancient desires of man. Tests of many races of people show that they prefer the same general range of surrounding temperatures and humidities. Recent experimental studies show that this feeling of comfort is related to a very narrow range of skin temperatures. For each activity level, people generate within their bodies thermal energy that must flow to the body's surface. There it is transferred to the surrounding air

Courtesy, Lasercraft, Division of Optical Engineering, Inc.

Engraving in wood was achieved by a laser, which carves by vaporizing material rather than by tearing or shearing it. The finished products are generally precise in outline and splinter-free.

by heating the air and sweating. The blood vessels under the skin bring more or less warm blood to the skin areas depending upon the skin temperature that is necessary to maintain the central organs or core of the body at a nearly constant temperature of 98.6° F(37° C). The average temperature of human skin varies significantly. A sedentary person feels progressively cooler as skin temperature falls below 93.5° F (34.2° C). If it rises above that value, there is a feeling of progressive warmth. Temperature, humidity, air motion, and clothing determine average skin temperature and, therefore, comfort for any given activity level.

In contemporary industrialized societies about one-third of the total energy resources is used to create an environment that produces a comfortable skin temperature. For the very young, the very old, and the sick such climatic control has been shown to be medically beneficial. But for all others, while it may be comfortable, it is not necessarily beneficial. Military hot-weather acclimatization studies indicate that good physical conditioning requires frequent sweating. This, of course, will not occur in an air-conditioned environment.

Faced with this evidence, how should mechanical engineers manage a reduction in energy consumption and still meet the human desire for thermal comfort? Some of their recent efforts to accomplish this goal include the following: production of better insulation materials and better designs of buildings to reduce heating and cooling requirements; improved designs and more effective use of clothing; and experiments with humans to establish more accurately the boundaries between comfortable and warm and comfortable and cool climates. Subsequent setting of cooling and heating controls to those boundaries rather than at the middle of the comfort zone can produce a significant reduction in energy requirements.

Engineers were also attempting to improve the performance of heating and air-conditioning equipment. During recent years energy was so cheap that cost-cutting methods of design were acceptable even though they resulted in less efficient utilization of energy. As an example, the elimination of the pilot lights in gas stoves and heaters by replacing them with electronic ignition systems could have saved significant amounts of natural gas. This is now being done.

Precision in cutting. A laser carves by vaporization of the material rather than by shearing and tearing, as is done by a sharp knife, a drill, or a lathe. The laser produces a stream of energy that is 30 times the intensity of the Sun at the Sun's surface. This intense stream has the characteristics of light so that it can be easily directed and focused.

The result is a precision carving instrument that never dulls yet transforms to vapor the solid against which it is directed. The results are very precise, chip-free, and splinter-free carving and drilling of a wide assortment of woods, ceramics, plastics, and some metals.

High-rise building fires. Because a major goal of engineering is to improve the physical well-being of man, it is important to engineers to pay attention to the safety aspects of designs. The risk to life in occupied high-rise buildings when a fire occurs can be quite high. During the year mechanical engineers worked on this problem with architects, fire departments, and government agencies, but they did not succeed in devising satisfactory life-saving procedures. Fire ladders that can reach above seven stories of a building do not exist, and their utility would be questionable if they did. Smokeproof and fireproof furnishings at reasonable prices have also not been developed, and not all high-rise buildings contain sprinkler systems.

Upon examining the curricula of the schools in areas of the U.S. having the greatest number of high-rise buildings, it becomes apparent that they contain few courses or programs relating to the science and technology of unwanted fires. Yet in

Fire breaks out on the 20th and 21st floors of the Occidental Tower in Los Angeles on Nov. 19, 1976. Three firemen were injured while trying to put out the blaze, which posed particular difficulties because it was beyond the reach of fire ladders.

Los Angeles Times Photo

other countries such programs do exist. During recent months engineers and community leaders began efforts to rectify this educational deficiency.

Fuel mileage and exhaust emissions. Pressure from the public and legislators for reduced exhaust emissions and improved mileage for automobiles posed a challenge to engineers. It stimulated a revolution in thought about the long-established method of inducting fuel and air into the automobile engine. The conventional equipment consists of a venturi carburetor and an intake manifold. Air is drawn through the carburetor by the action of the pistons in the engine. The velocity with which the air is drawn determines the amount of fuel that is to be mixed with it. Then, in a very short section of the intake manifold, the metered fuel and air are mixed and directed to the individual cylinders.

The mileage and emissions from the vehicle are closely related to the air-fuel metering and mixing process. Though they became progressively more elaborate, the conventional venturi carburetor and intake manifold neither satisfactorily improved mileage nor reduced emissions. The maldistribution of fuel and air among the cylinders remained unsatisfactory, causing emissions that were too high and mileage that was too low. Fuel injection systems were being explored as an alternative to the carburetor and manifold. The fuel is metered and injected separately for each cylinder. Shockwave carburetion was another alternative. In this case, high turbulence is created in the proximity of the fuel-air mixing point to improve mixing of the fuel with the air.

As of 1977 it was not yet clear as to which of the several alternatives would be the most successful. But the mechanical engineering design goal was clear: an engine must be produced that would use less energy and produce fewer emissions, and this must be accomplished without a major increase in cost or a sacrifice in dependability.

—Richard K. Pefley

Medical sciences

Two protracted events dominated medical news in recent months—the investigation and eventual identification of the cause of a mysterious killer disease and the implementation of the U.S. swine flu immunization program. Ongoing study of diabetes mellitus shed new light on its causative factors and offered therapy. Treatment of the mentally ill became increasingly dependent on advances in molecular biology and brain chemistry, and the spread of rabies became a matter of growing concern. One highlight was the discovery of a 4,500-year-old dental bridge in Egypt.

General medicine

For most physicians the past year was fraught with increasing medical-practice regulations, governmental intervention, social and economic pressures (particularly consumerism), and concern with continuing medical education (CME) and "recertification." There were advances on most medical fronts, but nothing sufficiently significant to counterbalance widespread public criticism, at times scornful, concerning "unnecessary surgery," skyrocketing malpractice costs, the uneven geographic distribution of doctors, the soaring costs of medical care, and the lack of personal consideration by the physician.

Whether a general practitioner or a specialist, virtually every physician in the U.S. was concerned about increasing requirements for recertification. A concept of multiple criteria for recertification was emerging, based generally on demonstrated attendance at CME courses, a practice audit, and satisfactorily passing an examination. All 22 medical specialty boards in the U.S. approved a policy advocating recertification, and by March 19, 1977, eighteen states and the District of Columbia re-

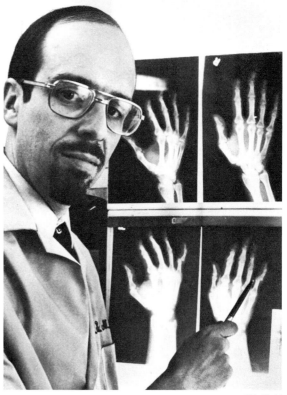

Leonard Berlin points to X-ray of little finger of Mrs. Harriet Nathan, who had sued the physician for malpractice. Berlin countersued and won.

Wide World

quired participation in CME programs for "reregistration." By February 1977 there were 16 state medical societies requiring attendance at CME courses as a condition for renewal of membership.

Although it was difficult to list accurately the exact number of CME programs in both general and specialty medicine, most recent estimates (1974–75) showed a total of 10,184 courses (sponsored by almost 1,200 different agencies) attended by more than 270,000 individual physicians, some of whom were taking several courses. Obviously, CME is a rapidly burgeoning field of endeavor and can be expected to become an integral and necessary part of every physician's life.

Important medical developments and clinical advances of recent months included investigation of a mysterious malady known as Legionnaire's disease, the swine flu immunization program, a new diagnostic method in radiology called computerized axial tomography, and an innovative surgical approach to facial paralysis.

Legionnaire's disease. When approximately 2,300 American Legionnaires gathered in Philadelphia, Pa., in July 1976, none had the slightest foreboding that their convention, held at the Bellevue-Stratford Hotel, would be more than a pleasant reunion. Yet within two weeks of their four-day meeting at least 180 persons developed a strange illness and 29 died. Characterized by fever, generalized pain and muscular aching, headache, cough, and upper respiratory symptoms, the disease was first thought to be "flu." However, when several patients stated that others at the convention had developed the same illness, physicians notified local health authorities and finally the U.S. Public Health Service Center for Disease Control (CDC) in Atlanta, Ga.

As the world's largest epidemiologic center, with 3,800 physicians, public-health specialists, laboratory technicians, and epidemic intelligence officers, the CDC had studied scores of troubling and, at times, puzzling epidemics. To solve the Legionnaire's disease, as the outbreak was soon named, its largest campaign for any public health problem was instituted.

A team of doctors, statisticians, and engineers was sent to Philadelphia to conduct a multifaceted analysis of the meeting place and the participants. Legionnaires were interviewed about their lifestyles and their activities at the convention. There was detailed examination and inspection of all parts of the hotel, including water and ventilation systems, kitchens, elevators, and waste-disposal and sanitation equipment. After all common probable causes of disease and death were considered and excluded, the esoteric possibilities were investigated. Investigators from local health depart-

Wide World

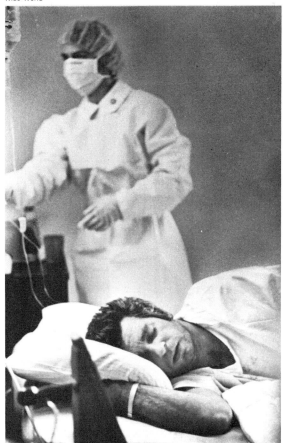

Patient being treated for Legionnaire's disease only delivered a load of canned goods to one of the hotels involved in the American Legion convention.

ments as well as workers from the CDC tested for bacteria, viruses, various chemical toxins, poisonous gases (*e.g.*, phosgene, nickel carbonyl, carbon tetrachloride, and freon), herbicides, pesticides, and even the paint on pencils used (possibly as swizzle sticks) at the meeting.

After several weeks it was admitted that no usual etiology for the disease and its symptoms could be found. Tests at the Pennsylvania State Health Department had eliminated the possibility of any of 13 viruses, 18 bacteria, 18 fungi, 3 rickettsia, or parasites. Rare diseases associated with pigeons, parrots, monkeys, and hamsters, such as Marburg's disease and psittacosis, were eliminated. Neither were any of 17 toxic metals found responsible.

Some general assumptions could be made on the basis of the clinical behavior of Legionnaire's disease. It was not particularly contagious because only a small number of those attending the convention were infected. It was not contagious enough to spread to contacts because no instance was recognized in any person who was not present at the

359

convention (although one pathologist at Hahnemann Medical College and Hospital in Philadelphia developed symptoms of the disease two weeks after studying a lung specimen of one of the victims). It was moderately fatal because more than 10% of those who became ill did die. In addition, the disease was thought to have traveled along an airborne route. One piece of evidence for this belief was the fact that most of those afflicted were cigarette smokers, this group providing a more susceptible respiratory tract.

Finally, after almost six months of countless tests and studies, when it seemed as though all possibilities had been considered and no answer could be found, the breakthrough came. According to Charles C. Shepard, chief of the leprosy and rickettsia branch at CDC, a routine search for rickettsia uncovered the presence of a "bacteria-like organism" not visible in the microscope and not previously known. Its existence later was proven

A final "victim" of Legionnaire's disease, Philadelphia's Bellevue-Stratford Hotel suffered a severe decline in business after the convention and was forced to close.

Martin Adler Levick—Black Star

through reactions with blood samples from infected patients.

The microbe was isolated by injecting lung tissue from dead patients with Legionnaire's disease into guinea pigs, which within a few days became ill. Material from the spleens of these animals was then injected into chick embryos, which died. When the yolk sacs of the embryos were examined microscopically, clusters of rodlike bacteria, different from any known organism, were found. When solutions of the microbe were mixed with blood from surviving patients who had had the disease, antibodies that reacted against the organism were found in 29 of 33 instances, a phenomenon that did not occur with blood samples from noninfected people.

The microbe is hard to grow and does not resemble any agent of disease presently recognized; it possibly represents a new species or class of bacteria. It also appears to be the same organism that in 1966 caused an outbreak of pneumonia at St. Elizabeths Hospital in Washington, D.C., which resulted in at least 16 deaths. The presence of antibodies to this new organism was demonstrated in blood preserved from the 1966 victims.

The final "fatality" of Legionnaire's disease was the Bellevue-Stratford Hotel itself, the "Grand Old Lady of Broad Street." Because of intense adverse publicity the hotel's occupancy declined markedly until November, when extensive financial losses forced it to close.

Swine flu immunization program. To many the flu is an annoying illness of several days duration, with symptoms of fever, generalized muscle aching, sore throat, headache, fatigue, and perhaps abdominal pain and diarrhea. Few, however, appreciate the seriousness of some types of influenza, especially those of a highly contagious nature that are often accompanied by development of a fatal pneumonia.

The 1918–19 flu pandemic was one of the world's greatest medical crises. Approximately 20 million people died, including more than 548,000 Americans and 12.5 million in India. Fifty times the number of deaths were estimated to have had the disease. Its spread was so rapid that the entire North American continent was involved within one month; simultaneously it was noted in places as distant as the southern U.S.S.R. and Greenland.

The "Asian" flu of 1957 caused at least 70,000 deaths in the U.S. and afflicted about 45 million people. The "Hong Kong" epidemic of 1968–69 caused 30,000 deaths in the U.S. and involved approximately 50 million people. In most such epidemics the greatest mortality was among the very young and the aged; in 1918–19, however, a far greater proportion lay in the 20–45-year age group.

UPI Compix Wide World

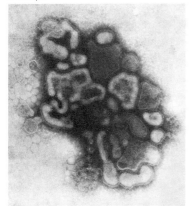

Virus magnified 132,300 times (above) is influenza A/New Jersey/76 and was found among military personnel at Ft. Dix, New Jersey, in 1976; it resembles the virus of the 1918—19 pandemic. At the right, logistics for combating a possible flu epidemic are plotted on a cathode-ray tube.

Whereas the influenza virus apparently plagued even the ancient Greeks and Romans, the virus as an entity was not identified until the 1930s. Humans never acquire complete immunity to influenza because the virus is capable of rearranging its eight genes either through mutation or recombination to produce new types that are not susceptible to previously developed antibodies. In considering immunity to influenza one author has likened the body to an outmoded military strategy—well prepared for the tactics and weapons of a previous war but incapable of dealing with the innovations of a new one. In the late 1970s there was no cure for influenza. The only effective way to manage the disease is to prevent the virus from attacking and damaging the cells of the respiratory system; this can be done only if the individual has the proper kind of antibodies.

On Feb. 4, 1976, a young army recruit at Ft. Dix, N.J., reported at sick call with a sore throat, headache, congested nose, and a feeling of general discomfort. He was given the proper advice to remain in his barracks, but despite this instruction, he participated in a training march the following day, during which he collapsed and died.

An autopsy revealed an influenzal pneumonia in both lungs. Further testing showed that the causative agent was a new strain of influenza virus, thus explaining clinically his rapid fulminating course

terminating in death, a progression quite different from the usual course of influenza.

This particular virus resembled a type ordinarily found as a cause of infection in swine; it also resembled the virus of the 1918–19 pandemic. Further investigation showed that 12 other soldiers at Ft. Dix had swine-virus influenza, fortunately all nonfatal, and extensive blood testing revealed that at least several hundred other recruits probably had been infected.

Previously, the swine flu virus generally had caused disease outbreaks only in swine; its rare human victims had always been in rural locations and in contact with swine. Only a few of the recruits at Ft. Dix, however, were from farms or had had contact with swine. Thus, it was significant that this outbreak represented a transmission of swine influenza not from swine to man, but from man to man.

Subsequent discussion and study by federal, state, industrial, and academic experts weighed heavily the possibility that the new virus was potentially dangerous because of its virulent nature and the lack of antibodies in the population. Was the new virus, named A/New Jersey/76, a mutation of the swine flu virus, a mutation of the common type A human virus, a combination of swine and human virus, or a reappearance of the 1918–19 virus? Should there be a national commitment to develop

361

a vaccine and inoculate the country's population, or at least the high-risk segments, *i.e.*, the elderly and chronically ill, schoolchildren, and pregnant women?

According to Edwin D. Kilbourne, an internationally recognized expert on viruses, the real concern was that the virus appeared to be a major mutation. "From our past experience," he stated, "we know that the appearance of a major influenza mutation heralds a pandemic worldwide epidemic. The identification of a new strain of influenza at Ft. Dix has given us the opportunity, for the first time in history, to do something about a pandemic in advance. . . . Our response to flu pandemics has always been too little and too late."

In late March, after appropriate consideration of scientific recommendations and alternatives, U.S. Pres. Gerald R. Ford announced a vaccine development effort and a nationwide voluntary immunization program at a cost of $135 million. Concurrently, he directed the Department of Health, Education, and Welfare to develop plans for vaccination between the beginning of September and the end of November. It was expected to require several months to produce the vaccine, culturing the virus in fertile chicken eggs.

Legislative hopes and efforts, however, were soon thwarted. In any immunization program the possibility of side effects from the inoculations can occur, usually because of unknown or unsuspected allergies. When the U.S. pharmaceutical industry sought malpractice insurance sufficient to meet possible claims and suits that might arise from the mass inoculations, insurance companies either demanded excessive premiums or declined to issue any insurance. Consequently, four pharmaceutical companies, which had prepared about 120 million doses of the vaccine, refused to release them.

In July deaths from the mysterious flulike Legionnaire's disease inflamed public opinion and spurred Congress by mid-August to pass legislation placing the swine flu vaccination program under the Federal Tort Claim's Act. This made the U.S. government the primary defendant in any action in which an adverse reaction might occur from a swine flu shot. If an error in manufacturing should be found, the government would proceed with a suit against the industry.

On October 1, one month behind schedule, mass vaccination began. Actual inoculation was done chiefly by state and local health agencies, although the vaccine was obtainable from private clinics and physicians. The vaccine was free in the public clinics. High-risk individuals—those over 60, with respiratory or lung disease, or with debilitating problems—were given priority. The physicians of such people decided whether they should receive the A/New Jersey strain alone or a bivalent combination A/New Jersey and A/Victoria strains; the latter was a type of flu more common and less virulent.

In mid-October another setback to the program occurred when three elderly recipients died within hours after inoculation in the same clinic in Pennsylvania. A nationwide investigation subsequently revealed a total of 35 such deaths "shortly after" inoculation; the victims in this group had an average age of 71–72 years. Adverse publicity alarmed the public and prompted 11 states by late October to close their flu shot clinics until thorough retesting of the vaccine and a dispassionate consideration of these deaths indicated that for this age group the death rate was no higher than usual.

By late December another roadblock to the program became evident. The surveillance system established as part of the immunization program reported several instances of a poorly understood

Inoculation against swine flu, part of a nationwide program in the United States, is performed in Watsonville, California

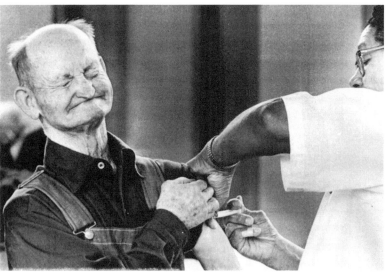

UPI Compix

malady, called the Guillain-Barré syndrome, in patients recently immunized with swine flu vaccine. Guillain-Barré syndrome is a clinical combination of muscular pain and tenderness with weakness and ascending paralysis. The disease is of gradual onset, usually lasts for several days, and disappears without residual defects. In some instances, however, paralysis becomes severe enough to interfere with breathing, and death can occur.

Early figures, covering October 1 through mid-December, indicated that about 50 of more than 100 reported victims of Guillain-Barré syndrome had received swine flu vaccine. By late December, as more detailed data became available, the number of patients with Guillain-Barré syndrome rose to 496, including 19 fatalities. Of these, 242 (11 fatal) had received the A/New Jersey influenza vaccine from lots produced by all four manufacturers. Of the remainder, 234 (8 fatal) had received no influenza vaccine, 16 (none fatal) were unknown regarding their vaccination status, and 4 (none fatal) had received influenza B/Hong Kong vaccine. The majority of cases in vaccinated persons occurred two to three weeks after their vaccinations. (As of March 15, 1977, the number of reported victims of Guillain-Barré syndrome exceeded 870, of which more than 440 were recipients of A/New Jersey vaccine.)

The incidence of the Guillain-Barré syndrome was about 1 per 150,000 vaccinees, 7.5 times the incidence in the unvaccinated population. The mortality from this neurologic disease was estimated at about 1 per 2.5 million vaccinations. Nonetheless, concern was aroused and, more importantly, the expected outbreak of swine flu had not occurred. Only three cases of swine flu had been documented since the outbreak at Ft. Dix, two in Wisconsin and one in Minnesota; all of the victims worked on farms and with pigs. A moratorium on swine flu vaccination was declared on Dec. 16, 1976, and the entire program was suspended.

Further consideration was postponed until the new president, Jimmy Carter, took office in January 1977. After a review of the matter the new secretary of health, education, and welfare, Joseph Califano, Jr., decided to resume bivalent shots in early February 1977 for the elderly and chronically ill because of a growing threat from A/Victoria flu, for which no monovalent vaccine had been manufactured.

Computerized axial tomography. Medicine has entered an era in which internal organs of the body and their diseases are being made accessible by noninvasive procedures. Such capabilities may effect a revolution in medicine comparable to that stimulated in the last century by the introduction of anesthetics and asepsis.

In a conventional X-ray exposure, a large cone-shaped beam of X-rays emanating from a single source is passed through the body, and different degrees of tissue density are recorded as shadows on photographic film. However, in this technique the images of various body structures overlap, often making it difficult or impossible to distinguish one organ or tissue from another when only minor density differences are present.

A major improvement, called tomography, was devised in 1922. In this technique the X-ray source moves past the subject in one direction and the film in another. Thus only one plane of the body remains stationary with respect to the film; all other planes are blurred. Tomography helps greatly to obtain better detail and more information by separating one plane and its body structures from the others.

Most recently the marriage of radiology and computer science has resulted in a further diagnostic method—computerized axial tomography (CAT)—that promises to replace many previous radiological and nonradiological techniques because of its noninvasive nature, its convenience, its decreased amount of radiation, and its amenability to selective data retrieval and manipulation.

Computerized axial tomography consists of passing a fan-shaped beam of X-rays through a patient's body to radiation detectors on the opposite side as the patient or X-ray apparatus is rotated stepwise around a single axis. By measuring the X-ray density along each diameter of the complete rotation, data is acquired for each plane of the body being studied. This computed system of tomography can detect a contrast change of 0.2%, making it 10–25 times more sensitive than a conventional X-ray picture; it is this quality that makes CAT distinctive.

One can visualize a plane through the body as a grouping of small squares or picture elements (pixels) of X-ray density data. By mathematical manipulation of the data, each pixel can be assigned a density number, a quantity related to a standard substance of known X-ray density. The complete picture can then be presented as a two-dimensional (vertical and horizontal) array of figures, easily displayed as varying shades of light and dark on a television screen. Further, the varying densities can be readily translated into color if desired.

The idea and development of CAT was chiefly due to the efforts of British engineer Godfrey N. Hounsfield and the Central Research Laboratories of EMI, Ltd., in the U.K. The first EMI scanner, which began clinical use in 1973 at the Mayo Clinic in Rochester, Minn., was used to obtain information about the brain. Previously, to study the brain and its diseases (e.g., tumors, blood clots, and congeni-

Photos, courtesy, Cornell University Medical College

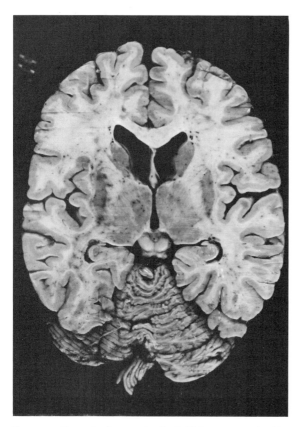
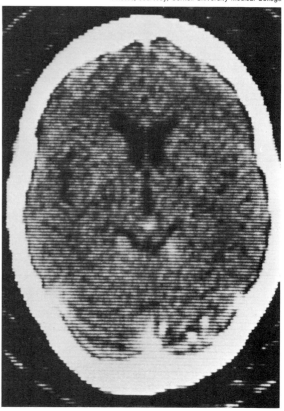

Cross-section of a human brain (left) is compared with a scan of a brain cross-section (right) in the same plane achieved by computerized axial tomography. This noninvasive procedure provides information for diagnoses previously obtainable only by exploratory surgery.

tal abnormalities) it was necessary to inject a liquid opaque to X-rays into the carotid arteries (a technique called cerebral arteriography) or a bolus of air into the spinal-cord canal or the ventricles of the brain (pneumoencephalography). Although both methods could secure information about the contents of the skull and abnormal conditions of the brain, they were difficult, time consuming, occasionally painful, and infrequently dangerous.

After four years of experience with the EMI scanner and with several variations designed and constructed by other companies, it is generally accepted that CAT is not only more convenient for patients and physicians alike but also more informative. The images so produced can distinguish between normal blood, clotted blood, fatty tissue, and tumors. When this method and contrast media are used in conjunction, additional diagnostic information can be supplied. Because it is basically noninvasive and without undesirable side effects, it is feasible to apply this examination not only to diagnostic problems but also to the screening of patients for tumors or other abnormalities at a much earlier stage than is possible with traditional methods.

Refinements in equipment and examining techniques have permitted CAT scanning of other parts of the body. In the abdomen it is particularly suited for the detection of tumors and abnormalities involving the liver, the pancreas, and the space behind the peritoneum—disorders difficult to diagnose and study by other methods. For abnormalities of the chest it is of benefit in detecting tumors in the mediastinum and the peripheral chest wall. It also is helpful in diagnosing disorders of the breast. In 1977 further studies were in progress for the heart, in which X-ray pulses triggered by heartbeat are used to compensate for the movements of this organ.

Although it has been well demonstrated that the internal structure of any part of the body can be diagrammatically expressed by this method, CAT does not yet yield the fine detail expressed on a conventional X-ray film. CAT exposes the patient to less radiation per scan than do conventional machines, thus limiting the amount of information that can be obtained. When increased resolution (detail) is desired, it is necessary to divide the body into smaller and smaller pixels, thus markedly increasing required computer time.

Facial-nerve grafting. Help for patients with a damaged facial nerve (secondary to trauma or deliberate sacrifice in parotid tumor surgery) and consequent paralysis of one side of the face has been provided by an ingenious operation that exploits recently developed techniques for tissue transfer and microsurgical anastomosis (joining) of fine-structured tissues. Called transfacial nerve grafting, the procedure translocates either of two nerves from elsewhere in the body: the great auricular nerve from the neck below the ear (for short grafts) or the sural nerve from the calf (for long grafts).

After careful anastomosis, using the microscope, of the nerve graft to the facial nerve or to its branches on the functional side of the face, the graft is tunneled across to the paralyzed side and anastomosed to nerve endings in comparable areas of the paralyzed muscles. By this method of cross-face grafting, restoration of some of the facial movements of the paralyzed side is achieved, and quality of facial expression after this technique is better than that in patients who have undergone other procedures.

—C. Frederick Kittle
See also Feature Article: PLASTIC SURGERY

Diabetes research

A number of recent advances have been made in the disorder known as diabetes mellitus, both in understanding its causative factors and in developing effective therapy. Most studies have continued to support the concept that in diabetes there is either an absolute or a relative deficiency of insulin,

the small protein hormone secreted by specialized cells, called beta cells, located in the pancreas. Normally about one milligram of insulin is secreted daily into the bloodstream; hence, its concentration in blood is relatively small, about one part in one billion.

Insulin in normal individuals controls the concentration of various fuels, especially glucose, in body fluids. After a meal, insulin concentration rises, signaling the cells of the body to take up and utilize or store incoming fuel. Between meals or during fasting, insulin concentration lowers, summoning stored fuels back into circulation to provide the body with energy until the next meal. The availability of the immunoassay for insulin in biological tissues and fluids, originally developed by Solomon Berson and his colleague Rosalyn Yalow at the Veterans Administration Hospital in the Bronx, New York, allowed many important studies to be mounted. Some of these revealed barely detectable or absent insulin concentrations in the juvenile-onset diabetic. By contrast, in the maturity-onset diabetic, insulin concentration may be normal or higher than normal, but insulin release is either insufficient or temporarily delayed.

Furthermore, studies showed that obesity in individuals with or without diabetes somehow inhibits the capacity for insulin to exert its effects on tissues. In the obese nondiabetic, the beta cells are able to meet the challenge by releasing excess quantities of insulin; however, the obese individual who has an inherited predisposition to diabetes appears unable to produce this extra insulin and therefore suffers relative insulin deficiency.

The reason why obesity causes resistance to

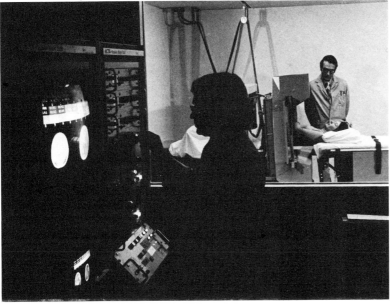

Scanner uses the method of computerized axial tomography to provide pictures of almost any part of the body.

Ray Gora—The Chicago Tribune

one's own insulin was being examined by many workers. Jesse Roth and his colleagues at the National Institutes of Health, Bethesda, Md., showed that the surfaces of various body-tissue cells and blood cells, when derived from a fat animal or fat human, have fewer insulin receptors. On the other hand, Pedro Cuatrecasas and Dean H. Lockwood, at Johns Hopkins University in Baltimore, Md., suggested that the inability for cells from fat people to respond to insulin is a deficiency within the cell. It seemed probable that both mechanisms are involved.

Many data demonstrate that cells in individuals with the predisposition to diabetes behave as if they were much older than the chronological age of the donor. In concurrence with such tissue senescence, diabetics or those predisposed to the disorder often experience accelerated atherosclerosis (sometimes leading to gangrene, heart attack, and stroke) and the early and severe onset of such related phenomena as senile cataract and softening of the bones (osteoporosis).

Juvenile-onset diabetes. Causation in juvenile-onset diabetes, which is usually associated with a progressive total insulin deficiency, has been a very active topic for many research efforts. A decade ago Willy Gepts of the Free University of Brussels, in examining the pancreases of children who died from recently developed diabetes, found the beta cells to be surrounded by inflammatory cells, suggesting either a viral etiology or an autoimmune reaction, whereby the body responds to a compo-

nent of itself as if it were foreign tissue. Subsequently, British workers David Gamble of West Park Hospital in Epsom, England, and Keith Taylor at the University of Sussex found that juvenile-onset diabetes occurs in the U.K. in small clusters and that each of these clusters is associated with the appearance of antibodies against one of the common groups of viruses; namely, Coxsackie. Concurrently, John Craighead of the University of Vermont and the late Jurgen Steinke of Boston discovered another virus that attacks beta cells in certain specific strains of mice. Gamble and later Sidney Kibrick of Boston University and his colleagues in the U.S. demonstrated that human Coxsackie virus could likewise cause diabetes in some experimental animals. Paralleling these developments, however, was the finding that most children with recently developed juvenile-onset diabetes possess one or more antibodies against components of their beta cells or else certain immune-type cells that recognize beta cells as foreign tissue. Hence, diabetes appeared to be a combined effect of both viral infection and autoimmunity, with perhaps the former initiating the latter.

In addition, the tendency to develop juvenile-onset type diabetes has been correlated with certain specific genes located on the sixth chromosome of man, and it is these same genes that give to each individual the unique cell-surface proteins that identify self from nonself. This cluster of genes and the multiple substitutions that can be made at each gene make up in man the major histocompati-

Microscopic examination of pancreatic islands of Langerhans often serve to discriminate between the different forms of diabetes. In juvenile-onset type, islands are smaller than normal, beta cells are reduced in number and appear damaged, and increased numbers of alpha cells may produce excess glucagon. In maturity-onset type, although island size and alpha cell count are normal, some beta cells may be replaced by hyalinization, the deposition of proteinlike substance.

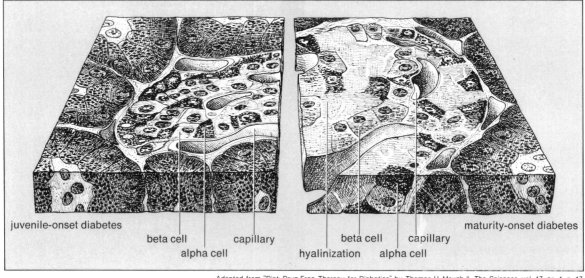

juvenile-onset diabetes

beta cell   capillary

alpha cell

hyalinization   beta cell   capillary   maturity-onset diabetes

alpha cell

Adapted from "Diet: Drug-Free Therapy for Diabetics" by Thomas H. Maugh II, *The Sciences*, vol. 17, no. 1, p. 17, January/February 1977, © 1977 by The New York Academy of Sciences. All rights reserved

bility locus; it is these properties that surgeons try to match as closely as possible when tissues are transplanted from one individual to another. Originally Jørn Nerup of the Gentofte Hospital and his colleagues in Copenhagen noted that at one of these gene locations, namely the B locus, two unique substitutions (or alleles) were much more prevalent in juvenile-onset diabetics than in the nondiabetic population. Subsequently, specific markers at other genes, such as at the C and D loci, likewise were found to be correlated with diabetes.

The current hypothesis, as put forth by Nerup and other workers in the U.K. and the U.S., suggested that an aberrant immune mechanism closely related to the aforementioned genetic markers gives to certain individuals the unfortunate predilection to turn against their own beta cells once the beta cells have become virally infected. With further research into the mechanism of immunity and with the possibility of identifying that target on the beta cell surface against which the immune system reacts, therapeutic approaches should be possible in the not-too-distant future.

Insulin studies. Another area of rapid development is the technology and biology of insulin. Donald Steiner of the University of Chicago demonstrated that, in the process of making insulin, beta cells first synthesize a larger, precursor molecule, from which a subsection is then removed. Both insulin and these connecting sections are normally stored together in granules within the beta cells, later to be released as needed. This extra factor, termed the "connecting" peptide or C-peptide, can be identified in blood by an immunoassay developed by Steiner and Arthur Rubenstein. This test allows treatment of an individual injected with animal insulin that has been purified of its C-peptide component, while monitoring the patient's C-peptide concentration as an index of insulin production within the body. This useful tool demonstrated that youngsters with recently developed diabetes produce some insulin, because for the first few months or years they have C-peptide. Later, production disappears, usually at the same time that a single injection of insulin given in the morning is no longer able to sustain the individual through a full 24-hour cycle.

Another by-product of Steiner's research stemmed directly from the observation that animal-insulin preparations of several years ago contained very small amounts of insulin precursors, and that these precursors were the likely agents responsible for adverse reactions to insulin in some individuals, inducing either acute allergies or antibody formation against insulin (insulin resistance), which necessitated greater insulin doses. On the basis of this discovery, commercial preparation of insulin

was improved and such adverse reactions were all but eliminated.

To return to the causation of juvenile-onset and maturity-onset diabetes, David Pyke at King's College Hospital and his London colleagues amplified the work of Marise Gottlieb and Howard Root at the Joslin Clinic and Harvard University, who had observed that when one member of identical twins has documented maturity-onset diabetes, the other member is also found almost always to have diabetes, an indication of a very strong hereditary contribution. By contrast, when one member of young identical twins develops juvenile-onset diabetes, only about 50% of the second twins develop the disease. Furthermore, Pyke showed that if second members do not develop juvenile-onset diabetes within two or three years of the first, they never will. The observations on juvenile-onset diabetes support the viral causation theory. Yet, there is also obviously a strong hereditary contribution because in Caucasian populations, in both Europe and the U.S., the prevalence rate of juvenile-onset diabetes is fairly large, approximately 1 in 300. On the other hand, data collected by the U.S. National Commission on Diabetes suggests that maturity-onset diabetes occurs eventually in about 5% of the adult population. Thus there exists a strong hereditary predisposition in both types of diabetes, although a greater one in the maturity-onset type.

Complications of diabetes. Another area of research that has seen recent progress relates to the chronic complications of diabetes, particularly the abnormalities that develop in the eye, the kidney, and the nerves. Animal models developed in the past few years showed that correction of the insulin deficiency prevents the appearance of these lesions, and, in a lesser way, partial correction of the insulin deficiency results in complications that are more delayed and less severe. Ronald Engerman and James Bloodworth at the University of Wisconsin at Madison showed that insulin treatment of diabetic dogs prevents lesions in the eye to a marked degree, and a large team of workers in Minneapolis demonstrated that correction of insulin deficiency in diabetic rats was able to reverse some of the changes found in the kidney.

One of the first prospective randomized studies in man, recently reported by Georges Tchobroutsky of the Hotel Dieu in Paris, indicated that aggressive therapy with multiple daily insulin injections resulted in decreased progression of problems in the eye. Biochemical studies likewise showed that simple lowering of elevated blood-sugar levels corrects many abnormalities in white cells, red cells, and some tissues. Thus the old argument that many diabetic complications result from an independently inherited predisposition has

(Top) Courtesy, Wah Jun Tze, University of British Columbia; (bottom) adapted from "Implantable artificial endocrine pancreas unit used to restore normoglycaemia in the diabetic rat," Wah Jun Tze et al., Nature, vol. 264, no. 5585, p. 466, Dec. 2, 1976

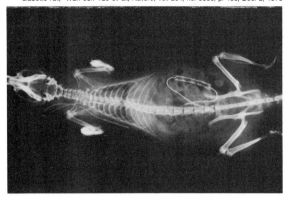

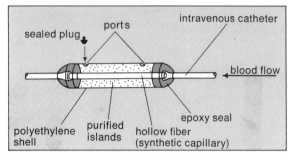

X-ray (top) reveals implanted artificial pancreas used to normalize high glucose level in diabetic rat. Synthetic capillary within the device (bottom) separates island cells from animal's blood supply but allows free diffusion of insulin.

become less tenable, and research in diabetes has leaned increasingly toward correcting the insulin deficiency. Particularly interesting were approaches that adjust insulin dosages to fuel concentrations, producing a feedback control such as exists in the nondiabetic individual. Along this line researchers were attempting to develop total pancreatic transplantation or transplantation of the small isolated pancreatic tissue, called the islands of Langerhans, that are the source of beta cells. The logistics, however, have provided problems; namely, the source of suitable pancreatic tissue and the need to diminish the recipient's capacity to reject the transplant. Thus, the bulk of individuals who received pancreatic transplants to date were already receiving immunosuppressive treatment for kidney transplants following diabetes-related kidney failure.

J. Stuart Soeldner in Boston and Samuel Bessman at the University of Southern California were trying to develop an implantable mechanical pancreas that could detect the circulating blood-sugar concentration and respond to it with proportional releases of insulin into the bloodstream. In tests using diabetic human and animal subjects, A. Michael Albisser and his colleagues at the University of Toronto demonstrated that instruments which continuously monitored glucose concentrations by chemical means external to the body, when connected to a computer that could deliver glucose, insulin, or both, were able to maintain perfectly normal blood-glucose control. The concept of a better insulin-delivery system with feedback control that may minimize or negate blood-vessel complications prompted the development of better programs to educate both diabetic patients and the professionals and paraprofessionals responsible for their care. To cite one example, the National Commission on Diabetes recommended that diabetes centers be established in about 10–15 areas of the U.S. to develop model teaching centers and to educate health professionals in the necessary techniques.

Along another line of research Roger Guillemin and his colleagues at the Salk Institute for Biological Studies in San Diego, Calif., characterized a small peptide of 14 amino acids extracted from the base of the brain. Subsequently, the substance was found to inhibit the release of growth hormone from the pituitary gland and hence was named somatostatin. It was soon found that this material inhibits many other physiological processes, such as the release of insulin from pancreatic beta cells and of glucagon, another hormone, from pancreatic alpha cells.

The role of glucagon itself in diabetes was the topic of much research, particularly by Roger Unger of the University of Texas Health Science Center at Dallas, who demonstrated that diabetics have excessive levels of glucagon, which acts to increase blood-glucose concentration. This observation incriminated glucagon as a possibly significant agent in diabetes, and it was suggested by John Gerich, now at the Mayo Clinic in Rochester, Minn., that a long-acting somatostatin preparation which suppresses glucagon might help in the day-to-day control of diabetics who require insulin. Also under study, especially by Knud Lundbaek of Århus, Denmark, is the use of somatostatin by long-term administration to suppress not only glucagon but also growth hormone, in line with the hypothesis that excess growth hormone in the uncontrolled diabetic might also be promulgating complications of the small blood vessels in the kidney and the eye.

The laser has become an important tool in the management of diabetic retinopathy. First, it is used to destroy leaking blood vessels on the retina by coagulating the blood in the vessel itself. However, a more interesting use was the application of hundreds of scattered, pinpoint-sized burns to the retina. This treatment results in little or no visual loss, yet it markedly reduces the formation of new leaking vessels elsewhere in the eye. The effectiveness of such therapy was clearly shown in a large

Reprinted from *Electronics*, January 6, 1977; copyright © McGraw-Hill, Inc., 1977

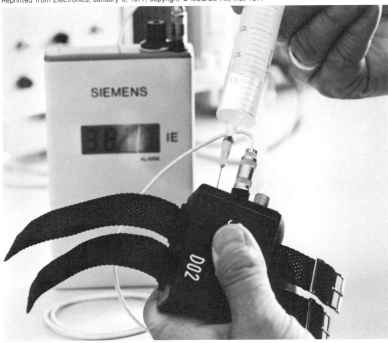

Electronically controlled Micro-Dosage System developed by West German firm can continuously release highly concentrated insulin into the bloodstream through a catheter at rates on the order of microliters per hour. About the size of a cigarette pack, the experimental device should offer an attractive alternative to diabetics requiring daily insulin injections.

multicentered study in the U.S. coordinated by the National Eye Institute and reported in March 1976.

Other questions continued to haunt investigators. What causes small blood vessels in the kidney of the diabetic to become increasingly leaky and eventually to close off, often leading to kidney failure? And in the eye, what causes a similar increase in leakiness, followed by closure of many of the small vessels and new vessel growth into the fluids of the eyeball, a chain of processes that contributes to blindness? Many workers offered hypotheses that related these changes simply to increases in glucose concentrations. Helen Ranney of the University of California at San Diego, Frank Bunn of Boston, and Anthony Cerami of Rockefeller University in New York City, all blood experts, found the hemoglobin molecule in red cells of the diabetic to be different, suggesting that other proteins in the diabetic might be similarly altered.

—George F. Cahill, Jr.

Psychiatry

Since the early 1800s psychiatrists have been involved in a continuous waxing and waning of therapeutic zeal, pessimism, humanistic concern for the individual, and emphasis on the social climate. During World War II the intensified need for effective psychotherapy led to recognition of well-trained psychiatrists who utilized comprehensive knowledge of the total personality as well as knowledge of immediate verbal and somatic modalities. In the post-World War II period these

men, who were to become leaders in the teaching of psychiatry, brought new enthusiasm to the field. A renascence of interest in the social climate of the individual took place in the late 1950s, and publication in 1961 of the elaborate study *Action for Mental Health* served to stimulate both public and legislative interest and gave rise to the community psychiatry movement.

The traditional one-to-one doctor-patient relationship was thus deemphasized. Simultaneously, the political protest movements of the late 1960s and early 1970s led to polarizing debates between advocates of demedicalization of psychiatry, who depicted psychiatrists as self-oriented members of the medical "establishment" using a "myth of mental illness" to maintain dominance, and those who held psychiatry to be a medical discipline. By 1977 this debate had largely abated. Attention had shifted to the substantial scientific developments that had been accumulating and to the intensified interest of the public in psychiatry, which was being expressed largely through social, judicial, and legislative actions.

Research developments. Attempts at understanding mental functioning during the period 1895 to 1960 led more readily to formulations about psychological events—divorced from brain matter—than they did to formulations about brain function. The psychiatrist looked upon mental life as if it were "functional"; *i.e.*, purely psychological. Effective somatic treatments for certain conditions existed; however, there was a tendency toward naively simplistic hypotheses about the underlying

Sidney Harris

*"Delusions of grandeur?
I am grand!"*

organic etiology of mental illness. Beginning substantially in the 1960s, experimental psychiatric research began to move into the vanguard of biochemistry and neuropharmacology in a clinically useful manner. One example is the study of neurotransmitters, chemical compounds that relay electrical impulses from one nerve cell to another. Fascination with neurotransmitters and their landing sites or "receptors" stemmed from the observation that certain types of mood-altering drugs also bring about dramatic changes in the state of certain neurotransmitters. In the mid-1960s Joseph J. Schildkraut and co-workers hypothesized that some, if not all, depressions might be associated with a neurotransmitter deficiency at crucial transmission sites and that, conversely, manias might be associated with increased neurotransmitters. Of particular interest was norepinephrine, a member of the class of compounds called catecholamines. In animals several mechanisms were discovered by which mood-altering drugs brought about the hypothesized direction of change in norepinephrine and its by-products.

Moving from animal to human study, Schildkraut investigated a measurable indicator of catechola-

mine activity—a urinary breakdown product known as MHPG (3-methoxy-4-hydroxyphenylglycol). MHPG was found to fluctuate in accord with clinical state in subtypes of depressive illness such as bipolar (manic-depressive) illness. Studies suggest that MHPG may be useful as a basis for predicting which person may respond well to which drug; for example, people with relatively high levels of MHPG have responded well to the drug amitriptyline, while those with lower levels have not. Schildkraut and other investigators who have published similar findings have avoided drawing grandiose conclusions. Yet it is reasonable to assume that clinically useful information will result from each successive deepening of understanding. This was not the case with research in somatic therapy in previous psychiatric eras.

In another example of the scientific discovery of clinically useful information, Richard I. Shader and his co-workers studied the effects of two anti-anxiety agents, chlordiazepoxide and oxazepam, on human volunteer subjects selected for their measurable tendency toward anxiety. Two groups of subjects were given, respectively, one of the anti-anxiety agents and an inactive compound, and were asked to perform certain tasks. Frustration was introduced into the situation—the groups were told that they had done poorly on the previous task and would have to repeat it—and the effect in producing a measurable form of hostility was studied by means of a standardized rating scale. It was found that one of the drugs, chlordiazepoxide, significantly increased hostility while the other drug, oxazepam, and the inactive substance did not. Such research designs hold promise for discovery of drugs that are both highly specific for certain kinds of emotional distress and free from untoward emotional side effects—a far cry from the older "shotgun" use of barbiturates.

Therapeutic developments. The ceaseless effort to shorten psychiatric treatment included behavior therapy, designed to alleviate specific symptoms through a process of conditioning; time-limited therapy, a melding of pragmatic and psychoanalytic concepts; and biofeedback techniques, which attempt to enhance an individual's voluntary control over significant bodily functions with the aid of an electronic instrument. An example of the latter was reported to be effective in the treatment of migraine; in this study control over blood flow was signaled by finger temperatures and recorded by a biofeedback instrument.

There was enormous concern with the continued problem of delivery of adequate psychiatric care, particularly to those with severe mental illness. Although the need for improved community facilities was recognized, funding problems often stymied plans. The relatively limited benefits for many patients from the drug treatment of schizophrenia were more openly discussed, and a National Institute of Mental Health research study pointed to comparable outcomes in patients receiving minimal antipsychotic medication in an active hospital milieu and patients receiving more usual drug treatment.

Sociopolitical issues. Since the early 1800s waves of concern for the rights of the patient have developed as an extension of concern for human rights in general. These upsurges have led to judicial and political action which, while well intended, sometimes impeded the adequate professional care of patients; e.g., commitment laws intended to protect the mental patient sometimes blocked early and appropriate treatment. The human rights movements of the 1960s stimulated renewed attention to the rights of those who could not help themselves, including mental patients. Many psychiatrists supported these principles out of their recognition of social injustices; for example, the abuse of involuntary hospitalization as a means of political repression. However, by 1977 it appeared that excessive emphasis on the "rights" of the individual might subordinate other important considerations.

Confidentiality has been assured by law unconditionally to lawyers and the clergy, but efforts to extend this privilege to psychiatrists have met with only partial success. Recent court decisions seriously attenuated whatever privileges exist. A West Coast psychiatrist was even imprisoned for refusing to reveal his records of a former patient who was involved in a lawsuit not connected with his treatment.

In the Tarasoff case of 1969 a psychiatrist warned police at the University of California, Berkeley, that his patient was threatening the life of the patient's girl friend, but when the homicide occurred the psychiatrist was held to be negligent in not having warned the victim. The decision was made that psychotherapists have a legal duty to warn the intended victims of patients they determine to be dangerous. While many psychiatrists recognized the necessity for reconciling the public's need for protection and the patient's need for confidentiality, the Tarasoff decision was considered by many to be a counterproductive legislative incursion into a highly complicated issue. Thus far there has been

Hundreds of synaptic vesicles containing a chemical transmitter await release from motor-nerve terminal into space between terminal and muscle-cell receptors. Malfunction of such mechanisms, which also serve to relay electrical impulses from one nerve to another in the brain, have been linked to depressive illnesses.

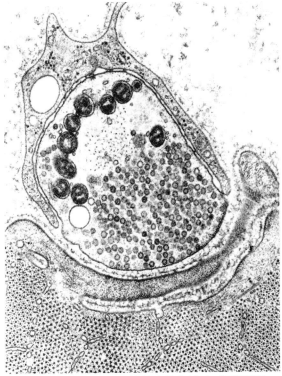

Courtesy, John E. Heuser, University of California Medical Center, San Francisco

no reliable research that establishes the predictability of serious violence. While psychiatry has moved ahead gradually with "hard data" on complicated sociopsychiatric issues, the courts placed expectations on psychiatrists that far exceeded their professional capacities.

Other issues involved the control of electroconvulsive therapy and psychosurgery, the right to due process and a hearing for children under consideration for involuntary commitment by parents, the right to treatment, and the right to refuse treatment. In general, funds to help carry out psychiatric treatment under new rulings had not been made available, and discrepancy existed between mandates and their performance, as well as detrimental discrepancies deriving from overly literal interpretation of the laws.

These developments were superimposed upon the background of day-to-day psychiatric practice, requiring empathy, objective assessment, nonjudgmental but firm intervention, and personal integrity. While forms of therapy rose and fell, solid helpful principles of psychotherapy continued to be taught in medical schools and psychiatric training centers. What the emerging psychiatrist was more apt to realize in 1977 than in previous decades was the need for understanding his or her role in changing social-medical-judicial circumstances.

—Arthur E. Reider and Benjamin Simon

Dentistry

In anticipation of efforts by the new U.S. administration to implement some form of national health insurance, the American Dental Association (ADA) revised its guidelines for participation in such a program. At its annual session in Las Vegas, Nev., in November 1976, the ADA reiterated its viewpoint that the dental profession should take an active part in the design of a program that includes dental care. It was emphasized, however, that dental care delivery must be based on the "traditional efficient private system." The ADA also reaffirmed its "fundamental belief" that the use of public funds for direct health benefits should be limited to providing dental services for those who cannot otherwise afford them. The guidelines place priority on comprehensive dental services for children and emergency dental care for all eligible individuals.

On another issue of consumer interest, dental costs, ADA officials continued to stress that dental fees, unlike other health care costs, had not been inflationary but had merely kept pace with increases in the general economy. The chief reason for this, they said, was increased productivity of dentists achieved through expanded use of dental auxiliary personnel and more advanced treatment methods.

Even in localities where water is fluoridated, the pits and fissures of children's molars show a greater susceptibility to cavities than smooth tooth surfaces. However, sealing these pits and fissures reduces the rate of new molar cavities by 40%, according to Sydney T. Pollard of the New York State Department of Health. The finding was based on a three-year study involving 2,000 first- and second-graders in Rochester, N.Y. "Based on our findings," Pollard said, "we recommend the application of a pit and fissure sealant to all newly erupting first permanent molar sites with the exception of the cheek side of the lower first molars. Here our study showed no cavity reduction in the sealed sites." He also recommended the replacement of lost sealant during periodic dental examinations.

Rapid periodontitis, a dental disorder involving swift bone destruction, red swollen gums, massive plaque and calculus deposits, and painful abcesses, was being treated successfully with tetracycline and gum surgery. Sigmund Socransky of the Forsyth Dental Center, Boston, has identified several important organisms implicated in the disease. He noted, however, that destroying too many bacteria in the mouth by antibiotics can also harm helpful organisms. For example, mouth fungi, usually kept in check by bacteria, can thrive when these microorganisms are destroyed.

Two health educators, John R. Seffrin of Purdue University, West Lafayette, Ind., and Delmar J. Stauffer of the ADA, suggested that the dentist is one health professional who has a good opportunity to reach patients who smoke and can use this position to attempt to modify their behavior. "By advising and counseling, providing helpful literature, creating an environment in which smoking is prohibited and setting a good example, the dentist can have a significant role in his patients' education on cigarette smoking. Since the harmful effects of smoking on oral health have been well established, the practicing dentist can focus on the specific oral health hazards, and then relate the message to the overall health of the patient."

A 4,500-year-old dental bridge found in Egypt by University of Michigan dental researchers seemed to offer proof that some kind of dentistry was performed in that country as early as 2500 BC. The discovery was reported by James E. Harris of Ann Arbor, Mich., and Zaki Iskander of Cairo at the 54th general session of the International Association for Dental Research, held in Miami Beach, Fla., in March 1976. The device, apparently part of a four-unit dental bridge, consists of three teeth linked together by a gold wire wrapped around two teeth and passing through a drilled hole in the third.

Photos, courtesy, Robert G. Schallhorn, Denver, Colorado

Previously there had been considerable skepticism that dentistry was actually practiced that early.

Zia Sheykholeslam and Melvyn Oppenheim of the New Jersey Dental School examined two ways to repair chipped teeth and found them equally effective. The older system involves a special ultraviolet-light gun and the newer method employs a bonding agent. Both methods resulted in natural-looking and functional restorations of chips or cracks. The ultraviolet "gun" is about the size of a hand-held hairdryer and serves to harden the resin used in the restoration. The newer bonding agent hardens quickly by itself. Both processes take about 45 minutes and cause no discomfort to the patient.

Diabetes may be responsible for many chronic oral sensory complaints, such as pain in the face and jaws, and may even be an underlying factor in patients whose oral sensory problems appear to have originated from other disorders, according to Vernon J. Brightman of Philadelphia. In addition to pains in the face and jaws, oral sensory problems may include a burning sensation of the tongue and other parts of the mouth, dryness, abnormal taste, and loss of taste sensitivity. The ability to accentuate other disease processes is a well-known feature of diabetes, probably resulting from the extensive damage to small blood vessels in many tissues that is characteristic of the disorder. The increased severity of periodontal disease that often accompanies diabetes also probably results from these small blood vessel changes.

University of Illinois dental researchers helped relieve severe facial pain by using biofeedback techniques that teach patients to relax muscles and thus stop clenching and grinding their teeth. The patients suffered from myofascial pain dysfunction syndrome, which involves facial pain, muscle spasms, jaw clicking, and limited jaw motion. Theories on the cause and treatment of this disorder vary, but according to Daniel M. Laskin, research findings consistently indicate that in most cases the cause is teeth clenching and grinding in response to psychological stress. Laskin and his co-workers found that a variety of treatments—including placebos—all provide relief, suggesting that the prospect of relief reduces anxiety and thus breaks the cycle of tension, clenching, spasms, and pain. "An advantage of the biofeedback technique is that the patient learns to control muscle tension without medication or prosthetic devices."

Calcium lactate has strong potential for reducing tooth decay caused by the fermenting of foods such as candy and sugar-containing cereals, according to a report by Buddhi M. Strestha of the University of Rochester, N.Y. When candy and cereals were fermented with calcium lactate and

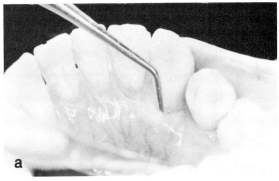
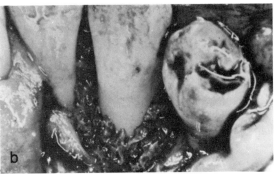
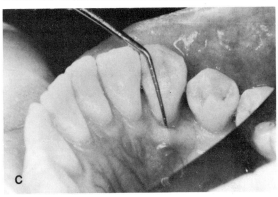
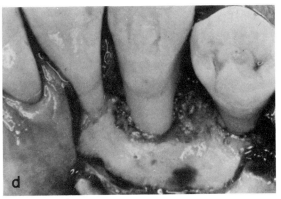

Deep pocket between lower cuspid and gum (a) is sign of periodontal disease that has destroyed part of underlying jawbone. Defect is filled and reattachment to tooth effected through bone graft (b). Three years later, regenerated bone has nearly filled pocket (c), as confirmed by surgical reentry (d).

enamel in saliva, the calcium lactate reduced dissolution of the enamel by 50–60%. In "orofax" tests, which involved a simulated oral system using human saliva, caries-like lesions were reduced by 17–85% when calcium lactate was added to snack foods.

Despite such advances, no dietary agents — even fluoride added to drinking water — make it possible for children to nibble sugary snacks throughout the day without developing tooth decay, according to William H. Bowen of the National Institute of Dental Research (NIDR). Speaking at the ADA annual session in Las Vegas, Bowen dispelled many myths about sweets and tooth decay and discussed the role of substitutes for sucrose or table sugar. The most promising substitutes are the sugar-alcohols such as sorbitol, used in the U.S. in the so-called sugarless chewing gums and candy, and xylitol, available in Finland and being tested by the NIDR National Caries Program. Bowen explained that while sorbitol is about 60% as sweet as sucrose, xylitol is about equal to sucrose in sweetness.

Stanley L. Handelman of the Eastman Dental Center, Rochester, N.Y., reported on laboratory experiments in which small doses of low-intensity direct electric current were found to kill mouth bacteria that cause infection. By means of a tiny generator powered by two watch batteries, silver electrodes, which are not harmful to human tissue, were used to conduct small doses of electric current and silver salts to the bacteria. The silver ion is probably the effective antibacterial agent.

Electric burns and cuts from sharp objects placed in the mouth frequently cause injuries to the oral tissues of children, and parents should be alert to prevent such accidents. Robert A. Goepp of the University of Chicago warned that, while chewing of electric cords by toddlers is not a common event, the burns may vary from first to third degree. In most cases first-degree burns probably are treated by parents, but second- and third-degree burns require professional treatment, and in severe cases reconstructive surgery is needed because of extensive scarring. A sharp object like a pencil held in a child's mouth can cause perforation of the hard palate and even injure the soft palate, which may result in speech impairment.

—Lou Joseph

Using a king-size brush, a young visitor cleans the teeth of a hippopotamus at the Tokyo Zoo. The brushing was part of a campaign to teach children the importance of dental hygiene.

Keystone

Veterinary medicine

Rabies. Rabies became a matter of increasing concern in the U.S. and Great Britain during 1976. Although the human death toll from this dreaded disease had been minuscule in the developed countries, the perceived threat had a real basis inasmuch as about 30,000 persons annually in the U.S. required antirabies injections following animal bites. The disease is almost universally fatal once symptoms develop. The Pasteur treatment, so-called because it is essentially the same as that developed in 1885 by Louis Pasteur, involves a series of up to 21 injections of modified rabies virus. Depending on the vaccine type, these may be painful and occasionally fatal. Nor is the treatment 100% effective; the first rabies death in the U.S. in 1976 was that of a Maryland woman who began the full series only 44 hours after being bitten by a rabid bat. Between 1960 and 1976 a total of 20 persons died of rabies in the U.S., and 1974 was the only year during the past two centuries in which no rabies deaths were recorded.

Once common, major outbreaks of canine rabies became almost nonexistent after vaccination of dogs was made mandatory for licensing throughout most of the U.S. Although perhaps half or more of the dogs in some localities had never been vaccinated, the level of compliance was high enough to reduce the total incidence among dogs from several thousand annually to 129 in 1975. An outbreak in Laredo, Texas, during late 1976, possibly origi-

Photos, *Agricultural Research*

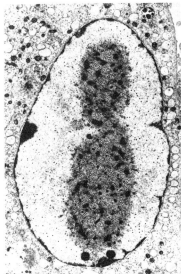

(Left) Researcher removes blood sample from a heifer injected with adenoviruses found in calves suffering from weak calf syndrome in an effort to find the causes of this disease of newborn calves. (Right) Microphotograph shows one of these substances, a bovine adenovirus, in an infected cell.

nating in Mexico, reached serious proportions before adequate control measures could be instituted. With the declining incidence of canine rabies, wildlife became the primary reservoir of the virus. Of the 2,677 confirmed cases reported in the U.S. during 1975, domestic animals accounted for only 433, as compared with 2,241 involving wildlife (including 1,226 skunks, 514 bats, and 278 foxes).

As a means of reducing the number of human treatments, which are virtually mandatory unless the biting animal can be positively identified as nonrabid, the Center for Disease Control (CDC) in Atlanta, Ga., urged, in 1976, the identification of "rabies-free" areas. Once this was done, CDC officials said, physicians in such areas would be "advised to avoid unnecessary treatment of persons bitten by certain domestic animals," *e.g.,* dogs, which account for the vast majority of human bites but only 5% of animal rabies cases.

During 1975 the District of Columbia, Hawaii, Idaho, Vermont, Guam, and the Virgin Islands were the only U.S. jurisdictions that reported no animal rabies cases. The states with the greatest number of cases were Texas (326), California (290), and Minnesota (184). The populations theoretically at greatest risk, however, were those of Montana (172), North Dakota (103), and South Dakota (85), where the animal cases per 100,000 human population were about 245, 172, and 125, respectively, versus 50 in Minnesota, 30 in Texas, and 14 in California. Some caution is advisable in interpreting these statistics, however, since there is considerable variation in the efficacy of reporting by states.

Beginning in central Europe after World War II

and spreading westward nearly 1,000 mi during the next three decades, epizootic rabies involving primarily wildlife increased alarmingly. Britain had been free of rabies for 50 years, but in 1975–76 officials expressed fears that its proximity to the English Channel would result in introduction of the disease despite efforts to keep it out. Although heavy fines were imposed for attempting to circumvent the stringent animal quarantine regulations, scofflaws continued to smuggle dogs and cats into Britain, in one instance by parachute.

The shift from domestic animals to wildlife as a reservoir of the rabies virus in Europe involved primarily foxes rather than skunks and bats. If rabies were to gain a foothold in the fox population of Britain, officials feared that effective control would be difficult if not impossible. Although large-scale extermination was considered impractical, authorities in some areas were mapping out their fox populations to determine what level of reduction might be effective if the unthinkable should be required. Meanwhile, the veterinary profession had begun a vigorous dog-vaccination campaign.

Swine influenza. The controversial swine flu inoculation program in the U.S. (see *General Medicine,* above) was instituted after 13 cases of swine type A influenza, one of them fatal, occurred among recruits at Ft. Dix, N.J. It had been known for many years that the virus, which differs from the human type A virus, could be transmitted from swine to human beings, but the Ft. Dix outbreak was the first time transmission between persons had been clearly demonstrated. The original source of infection could not be identified.

It is known that swine have harbored the flu virus at least since 1918, the year of the devastating worldwide outbreak of human influenza. Later research showed that the swine virus had antigenic features in common with the virus that caused the 1918–19 pandemic. Although it would be pure speculation to say in retrospect that the swine virus was in fact the responsible agent, the impossibility of proving otherwise was a factor in the decision to proceed with the human immunization program. However, as pointed out by Bernard C. Easterday, veterinary virologist and consultant on influenza to the U.S. National Institutes of Health and the World Health Organization, the program was lacking in one important concept. Assuming that the swine virus might be dangerous to people, logic would have dictated that something be done about the host reservoir in swine, about 1% of which die of the disease annually.

Influenza in swine could be prevented by vaccination, but the mortality from the disease has been considered an acceptable risk by swine producers since it is less expensive to take this loss than to vaccinate two pig crops every year. About 50% of all pigs in the U.S. become infected, and a substantial number of persons having direct contact with swine develop antibodies to the virus, an indication of subclinical infection. In one survey, 13 of 114 swine practitioners had swine influenza antibodies, unquestionably derived from contact with swine. At Ft. Dix 68 of 308 persons tested were serologically positive. But how many of these cases were due to human transmission rather than earlier swine contact could not be determined. Slaughterhouse workers are susceptible, but the virus cannot be transmitted by pork products. In swine, the virus inhabits only the respiratory tract, usually without causing clinical infection, and with only casual contact a pig would have to cough directly into a person's face for transmission to occur.

Other developments. In May 1974 the U.S. had been declared free of hog cholera (swine fever), 12 years after an intensive eradication program had been instituted, but sporadic outbreaks requiring local quarantines were more or less expected. After one such episode in Texas in 1975, outbreaks occurred in New Jersey in February 1976 and a month later in New England. That the two may have been related was suggested by the fact that pork from the affected New Jersey herds had been shipped to the New England area. Another possibility was the use of vaccine, production and interstate shipment of which has been illegal since 1971. Some 20,000 pigs were destroyed at a cost of about $2.5 million, but the disease had been costing producers more than $50 million annually before eradication was begun. The last quarantines were lifted in June 1976.

Several veterinarians accompanied the wagon train that traveled across the U.S. to Valley Forge, Pa., in 1976 to commemorate the U.S. Bicentennial, and many others provided services along the route. There was some concern for the animals' (horses and mules) welfare, but few problems developed. All animals were required to have health certificates acceptable to each state they crossed, and most had been given anti-influenza vaccine.

The first successful transplant of a nonhuman primate (baboon) embryo was accomplished by Duane C. Kraemer, Gary T. Moore, and Martin A.

The first successful embryo transfer of a nonhuman primate was achieved in 1975. The baboon embryo, removed from the donor five days after ovulation, was similar to that shown at left. The infant, 63 days after birth, is shown with the donor mother (right) and the recipient mother (left).

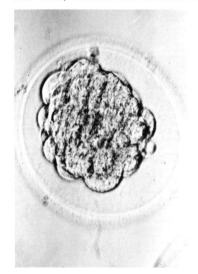

Courtesy, Duane C. Kraemer, Texas A. & M. University, College of Veterinary Medicine, and the Southwest Foundation for Research and Education

Kramen. Kraemer was the veterinarian who pioneered the commercial application of embryo transfer in purebred cattle in 1971. In cattle the purpose of embryo transfer is to increase the number of calves that can be produced by an especially valuable cow. Similarly, the primate research had potential for increasing the productivity of individual animals with genetic characteristics that make them especially useful as models for the study of human disease.

The latest in a series of studies on the future supply and demand for veterinary services in the U.S. projected a shortage of 7,000 veterinarians by 1985, increasing to 17,000 by 2020 unless substantial efforts were made to train more students. Meeting the projected demand, based on conservative estimates, would require increasing the current veterinary population of about 30,000 to 53,000 in 1985 and to 70,000 in 2020. The report concluded: "Failure to provide an adequate number of veterinarians could lead to a decreased level of animal health, increased cost of food production, and the delay of research advances."

—J. F. Smithcors

Optical engineering

During the past year there were a number of advances in optical engineering. The success of the first use of optical navigation in space, which led to placing Viking 1 in orbit around Mars, was followed by an impressive sequence of photographs transmitted back to the Earth from the Martian surface by the Viking lander vehicles. A new technique was developed for making images of atoms in crystals. Substantial progress was reported in the enrichment of uranium by lasers. The Bell System's prototype lightwave communications system performed well, and the British installed the first fiber-optic link in a distribution system for television.

Diamond turning. Pitch lap polishing has for centuries provided a relatively simple and practical way of producing optical flats (transparent disks with one or both sides accurately plane) and spherical components. Even aspheric components, those departing slightly from the spherical form, have been produced, but technical difficulties, the long time required to fabricate a single component, and high cost prohibit their use in many applications. Diamond turning has changed that. By 1977 aspheric components were being fabricated for use in laser resonators, infrared imaging systems, and X-ray microscopes and telescopes. The precision micromachining of components with a single-crystal diamond tool became quick, versatile, and cost effective.

Diamond turning of optics, that is, the use of a diamond tool on a precision lathe to fabricate an optical component, is not a new technique. In recent years, however, significant engineering improvements vastly increased its usefulness for fabricating ever larger nonconventional aspheric optics. These improvements include an air-bearing spindle, dynamic balancing by sophisticated electronic techniques at the operating rpm (revolutions per minute) of the lathe, and an oil shower to thermally stabilize the complete machine. Diamond machining produces optical surfaces on aluminum, brass, copper, gold, silver, nickel, lead, platinum, zinc sulfide, germanium, and many plastics. The list continues to grow as research proceeds.

Laser fusion experiments require optical components of high quality. In such experiments laser light of extremely high intensity is shone onto a pellet of deuterium and tritium, thereby heating it to 100 million degrees Kelvin and causing a microscopic thermonuclear explosion. The long-range goal is practical power production to relieve the energy shortage.

Future high-powered lasers will require large, cooled, nonconventional-shaped optics for resonators and beam processing. The resonator is the cavity within which laser light is reflected back and forth to amplify the light intensity. A new procedure for increasing the active volume and the power output of large lasers is to fabricate an annular resonator in which the lasing medium (gas or chemical reactants) flows radially outward from an inner cylinder. A light beam of relatively low intensity must be allowed to enter the cavity and trigger the amplification process, extracting the required energy from chemical reactions or electronically excited gases. A means must also be provided for extracting a high-intensity laser beam from the cavity resonator.

One successful design for a laser incorporated a compound axicon at one end of the resonator. An axicon is a mirror with a conically shaped surface. By machining an internal axicon and an external axicon on the same substrate, a compound axicon is produced. When a beam of light enters the cavity resonator along its axis and is directed toward the compound axicon, it is shaped into an annular beam that passes through the lasing medium and, after amplification, can be extracted as a higher-intensity beam. The fabrication of compound axicons and other components was successfully achieved with diamond turning. Some optical components with diameters as large as two meters were made by this method.

It is striking and impressive to observe the mirrorlike surfaces of high optical quality produced by diamond turning. The optical reflectance is compa-

Adapted from *Proceedings of the Society of Photo-optical Instrumentation Engineers*, SPIE, vol. 93, August 1976, J. B. Arnold *et al.* "Advances in Precision Machining of Optics"

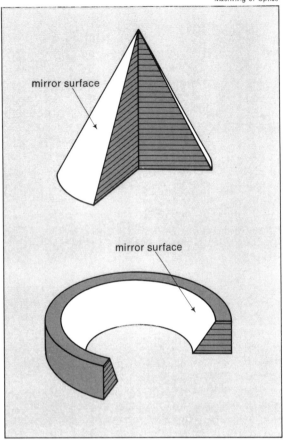

Axicons, mirrors with conically shaped surfaces, can be fabricated by diamond turning in both external (top) and internal (bottom) configurations.

rable to vacuum-evaporated coatings and is superior to the infrared reflectance of polished samples. The superb optical characteristics of diamond-turned components also make the process useful for the fabrication of optical components for infrared imaging systems.

Another application of diamond turning has been the fabrication of components for X-ray microscopes and telescopes. X-rays can be reflected with high efficiency from smooth metal surfaces at glancing angles and then focused to form an image on a suitable detector. At the California Institute of Technology an X-ray telescope consisting of four nested aluminum mirrors was under construction. The mirror surfaces were machined at Oak Ridge (Tenn.) National Laboratory.

For use at X-ray wavelengths, diamond turning is followed by polishing. The cost per mirror is less than $10,000 as compared with $125,000 using standard grinding and polishing techniques; the latter method, however, achieves an accuracy within 2 arc seconds as compared with 20 arc seconds for diamond turning.

Adaptive optics. Atmospheric turbulence and thermal effects can cause appreciable distortion in both the space and time dependence of a wavefront in a light beam propagating through the atmosphere. If the beam is broken down into smaller beams of sufficiently small cross section, the distortion across each small beam is quite uniform. Separate servomechanisms can correct this local uniform distortion of the wavefront in each small beam. The individual small beams can then be recombined to form a nearly perfect image. This process of real-time corrections of wavefront distortion is known as adaptive optics.

One approach to adaptive optics, pursued by Hughes Research Laboratories, utilizes a laser beam. An outgoing beam is split into many smaller beams by passing through a series of beam splitter plates. Each of these glass plates is oriented at the correct angle to minimize reflection losses, and each has a small aluminized reflective patch on it to select out a small beam. The small beam is one element in an array that makes up the total outgoing beam.

As the procedure continues each small beam is reflected off a mirror backed by a piezoelectric oscillator. It is phase shifted and tagged with its own modulation frequency. The recombined total beam is then reflected off a target. A sample of the interference pattern reflected by a bright area of the target too small to be resolved (a glint) is observed, and is tracked if necessary to follow a target in motion. Elements of the reflected signal can be sorted out, and servomechanism-controlled, phase-correction signals can be sent to the original optical phase shifter array in order to modify the outgoing beam. When the servomechanism system has maximized the irradiance on the glint, the phase variation across the received wavefront has been compensated. The array will be properly phased even if a time-varying phase disturbance is introduced anywhere in the optical path, provided the time variation is within the response capabilities of the servomechanism loop.

Other approaches to adaptive optics utilized flexible mirrors. A flexible mirror with several hundred actuators for wavefront correction was fabricated and successfully tested.

Future prospects for adaptive optics include large systems with up to a million individual elements; long-range laser communication with reduced power requirements; greatly improved resolution of large earthbound telescopes using angle-of-arrival fluctuations at two different wavelengths, thus allowing correction by deforming a mirror in the optical train of the telescope; and delivery of maximum energy in high-power–pulse propagation in lasers.

Camera Press/Photo Trends

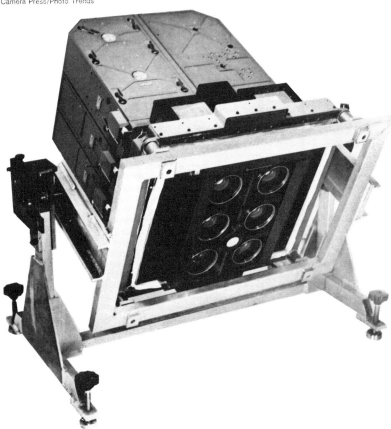

OPS, a multispectral camera developed jointly by the Soviet Union and East Germany, is similar to the one installed on the Soviet Soyuz 22 spacecraft launched in September 1976. Photographs from the camera were used by Soviet scientists to analyze the Earth's surface for "economic purposes."

Optics in the Soviet Union. The Soviet Union, largely under the guidance of the State Optical Institute (Vavilov Institute), was encouraging research and development in all areas of optical engineering. These included the development of fiber optics for communication systems in order to conserve copper resources, methods for automatic processing of information, thermal imaging, holography, and laser technology. A particular desire expressed in the tenth Five-Year Plan, which began in 1976, was to refine the entire structure of the research and production organization. One goal was the widespread application of modular construction methods to the design of optical instruments. This was viewed as being of some urgency in order to reduce the work load of those involved with the pilot production of various optical components and assemblies.

A number of specific recent achievements in the Soviet Union were of some importance. One was a holographic instrument that makes it possible to reconstruct a three-dimensional pattern of the distribution of particles in a stream. It can be applied to the study of the combustion products in the exhaust gases of engines, thus being of value in solving problems in engine design. The development of a luminescence microscope expanded the possibilities for studying organisms at the cellular level. It permits viewing and flash photography in luminescent light, in polarized light, and with dark-field illumination. The development of a laser Doppler velocimeter, an instrument that simultaneously measures the three components of velocity, was also reported. Such measurements are desirable for the study of three-dimensional flows, as in turbulence.

—Frederick Wooten

Physics

Confirmation and controversy proved effective stimuli to research efforts in physics during recent months. High-energy colliding-beam experiments yielded convincing evidence for the existence of subatomic particles possessing the quantum property called charm, and charge-density waves, developed as a theory nearly two decades ago, were discovered to be important phenomena in the electronic behavior of certain solids. Data suggesting the presence of primordial superheavy elements in ancient samples of mica were collected during the year, but they failed to be substantiated by subsequent investigations.

Courtesy, Fermi National Accelerator Laboratory

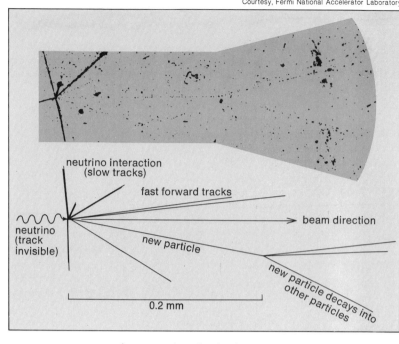

neutrino interaction
(slow tracks)

fast forward tracks

neutrino
(track
invisible)

beam direction

new particle

new particle decays into
other particles

0.2 mm

First recorded track of a suspected charmed particle was captured in three-dimensional nuclear emulsion at the Fermi National Accelerator Laboratory near Batavia, Ill., by a multinational collaboration of physicists. Microscopic examination of the emulsion revealed a track of 0.18 mm, which corresponds to a particle lifetime of about 5×10^{-13} sec. Studies of the particle's decay characteristics apparently ruled out the possibility of a conventional "uncharmed" entity.

High-energy physics

In 1976 conclusive evidence was finally found for the existence of "charmed" baryons and mesons. Such particles had been theoretically predicted in 1970 by Sheldon Glashow of Harvard University and collaborators, and their detailed properties, such as mass and decay patterns, were worked out in a series of articles in 1975. Also, indirect evidence for such particles had been found in 1975 by a number of experimental groups using high-energy neutrinos. However, these earlier experiments had been somewhat equivocal, whereas the new data agreed so well with theoretical expectations that no other interpretation was plausible.

The idea of charm arose as an extension of the quark model of hadrons. Hadrons are subatomic particles that can undergo strong interactions; *i.e.*, they can transform into each other rapidly either by spontaneous decays or in collisions at high energy. Two classes of hadrons are known: mesons, whose intrinsic angular momentum, or spin, is an integer multiple of Planck's constant (h) divided by 2π; and baryons, whose spin is a half-integer multiple of the same quantity. By the early 1960s hundreds of baryons and mesons were known, each distinguished by some value of mass, spin, and electric charge. It became clear that in such numbers these hadrons could not be "fundamental" objects.

An important step beyond the hadrons was made in 1964 by Murray Gell-Mann and by George Zweig, two U.S. theorists. They pointed out that it was possible to understand the pattern of known hadrons by assuming that hadrons were composite objects, made of a small number of presumably simpler objects, which Gell-Mann called quarks, after a line from James Joyce's *Finnegans Wake*. According to this model, there are three types of quarks, each with spin $h/2\pi$. Baryons contain three quarks, which might be of various types. Mesons contain one quark and one antiquark, which is the antiparticle of a quark. The rules for adding spins are such that this model accounts for the observed array of baryon and meson angular momenta.

Two of the quarks (usually labeled by u and d) have approximately equal mass. The third (labeled by s) has a somewhat higher mass, and those hadrons containing s quarks tend to have higher mass than those containing only u and d quarks. In order to explain the observed electric charges of hadrons, it is necessary to ascribe an electric charge of $+2/3$ that of the proton to the u quark and $-1/3$ that of the proton to the d and s quarks. Each antiquark has an electric charge opposite to that of its corresponding quark. Finally, because all efforts had failed to detect individual quarks directly, or to produce them separated from each other, physicists somewhat reluctantly accepted the idea that quarks are confined; that is, permanently kept near one another by strong forces that do not allow them to be pried apart. Only combinations of three quarks, of three antiquarks, or of equal numbers of quarks and antiquarks are immune to those strong forces and can be observed as isolated objects, such as hadrons.

Although three types of quark were sufficient to account for all of the hadrons known until recently,

James Quinn

Rectangular electromagnets (lower left) inside the main ring of the Fermi National Accelerator Laboratory's proton synchrotron enclose a small tube through which protons are accelerated to within a fraction of the speed of light. To produce a beam of neutrinos for experiments such as that described on the facing page, a proton beam is extracted from the main ring and directed toward a stationary metal target. The very energetic collisions create particles that decay primarily into neutrinos, antineutrinos, and muons, the last of which are filtered out by passing the beam through a kilometer-long mound of earth.

certain theoretical arguments led Glashow and collaborators to hypothesize a fourth type of quark, which they called a charmed, or c, quark. This c quark, like the u quark, has an electric charge of $+2/3$ that of a proton. Its mass is much greater than that of the other quarks; consequently, it was expected that hadrons containing c quarks would have higher mass than corresponding hadrons containing the other quarks. This higher mass would help explain why such charmed hadrons had not been previously observed. None of the four types of quark can convert into one of the other types through the strong interactions of hadrons. However, it is possible for a quark-antiquark pair of any type to change into a pair of another type. As a result a hadron containing a single c quark cannot convert via strong interactions into one not containing a c quark and so should be distinguishable on that basis. The existence of many such hadrons was predicted, with a c quark substituted for one of the other quarks in a known hadron, similar to the way that chemists substitute one element for another in a given molecule.

For example, it was predicted that a meson with spin-zero should exist containing a c quark and a u antiquark. This meson would have charge $+2/3 +(-2/3) = 0$, and consequently was labeled D^0. Another meson would contain a c quark and a d antiquark and have a charge $+2/3 + (+1/3) = 1$, the same charge as a proton; it was labeled D^+. Because u and d quarks have about the same mass, the D^+ and D^0 should also have about the same mass. Finally, a meson of slightly higher mass, called F^+, should exist, composed of a c quark and

an s antiquark. There would also be antiparticles for all of these mesons, with opposite electric charge and identical mass.

In order to predict the masses of the hadrons containing c quarks, it was necessary to know the mass of the c quark itself. This number was inferred from an interpretation of the J or ψ meson, a particle discovered in 1974 by two independent groups of U.S. physicists. (Team leaders Burton Richter of the Stanford Linear Accelerator Center, or SLAC, and Samuel C. C. Ting of Brookhaven National Laboratory were awarded the 1976 Nobel Prize for Physics for their discovery; *see* Year in Review: SCIENTISTS OF THE YEAR.) According to that interpretation, the J/ψ is composed of a c quark and a c antiquark and thus can decay by strong interactions into other hadrons; hence, its observation was not regarded as conclusive evidence for c quarks. However, from this interpretation and from the known mass of the J/ψ, it was possible to infer that the c quark would have a mass equivalent to a rest energy of about 1.5 GeV (billion electron volts). This information, together with previous calculations about the masses of the lighter quarks, allowed Glashow and his co-workers to predict that the D^0 and D^+ mesons should have rest energies of about 1.8 GeV and the F^+ meson a rest energy of about 2 GeV.

Although c quarks cannot convert into other quarks by strong interactions, they can do so by weak interactions, which are some 10^{10} times smaller in their effects. These weak interactions then could allow D mesons to decay into hadrons containing other quarks, with a half-life of about

10⁻¹³ seconds; such decays are fast by ordinary standards, but very slow compared with decays that go through strong interactions, which have half-lives of 10⁻²³ seconds. The weak interactions of *c* quarks were predicted to involve primarily a conversion of *c* quarks into *s* quarks. This would imply that, in the decay of D mesons, at least one particle containing an *s* quark should appear. The least massive of such particles are two mesons labeled $\bar{K}^0$ and K^-, which differ from D^+ and D^0 by having an *s* quark in place of a *c* quark. It was expected, therefore, that K mesons and their antiparticles (K^0, K^+) would be among the decay products of D mesons.

The first direct evidence for the production of D mesons, followed by their decay into hadrons, came from experiments done at SPEAR (Stanford Positron-Electron Asymmetric Ring) by a group of physicists from the University of California at Berkeley and from SLAC headed by Gerson Goldhaber. In these experiments, opposing beams of electrons and their antiparticle positrons were made to collide. The electron and positron each have equal energy, varying from 2 to 2.3 GeV. During a collision they combine to produce a photon, which, after an instant of existence (10⁻²⁴ seconds), converts with various probabilities into sets of other particles, one of which might be a set of hadrons. In the first experiment of the Berkeley-Stanford group, some 29,000 examples of electron-positron annihilation into hadrons were observed. The hadrons included charged K mesons and charged π mesons (pions), which are less massive particles made of *u* and *d* quarks and antiquarks. Some events also included neutral K mesons, but these were harder to analyze because the hadron detectors were insensitive to neutral particles.

The hadron-detection system was able to measure the momentum of the particles—and with some uncertainty, their velocity—by means of a so-called time-of-flight system. These quantities together allow determination of the mass of a hadron and so allow differentiation of a K meson from a π meson. Thus for every charged hadron produced, the type, energy, and momentum could be ascertained. Suppose that a D^0 meson is produced, which decays into a K^- meson and a π^+ meson. According to the conservation laws of energy and momentum, the sums of the energies and momenta of the decay products must equal those of the D^0. Although each of these quantities may vary for each instance of D^0 production, according to Einstein's relativity theory, a certain combination of the energy and momentum, known as the invariant mass, of the D^0 meson will always be the same, and will be equal to the mass of a D^0 meson at rest. Therefore, in every case in which a K^- and a π^+ are produced by the decay of a D^0 meson, a specific combination of the total energy and momentum of these particles should be the same. When the K^-

First direct evidence for the production of D mesons, followed by their decay into hadrons, came from experiments that measured and plotted the invariant mass for various combinations of their decay products. A large surplus of decay events observed for the Kπ combination corresponded to a rest energy of 1.86 GeV, suggesting that a particle of this energy was being produced. See text.

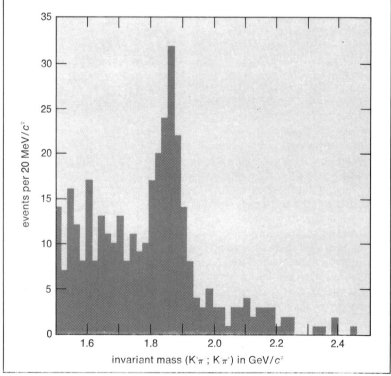

From Gerson Goldhaber, Lawrence Berkeley Laboratory

and π^+ are produced by other methods, this combination of total energy and momentum will not have a unique value, but will vary from event to event.

The experiments measured and plotted the invariant mass for every $K^- \pi^+$ combination and for every $K^+ \pi^-$ combination observed. When this was done (see figure) they found a large surplus of events in which the invariant mass of the $K\pi$ combination corresponded to a rest energy of 1.86 GeV, suggesting strongly that a particle of this energy was being produced. Further evidence for this interpretation came from analysis of events in which a charged K meson and three charged π mesons were produced, with all charges adding to zero. A similar analysis of invariant mass for these events again showed a peak in the number of events with an invariant mass corresponding to an energy of 1.86 GeV. This was interpreted as showing that the K-1π and K-3π are alternative decay modes of the same particle. The decay mode $K^+\pi^-$ is evidence for the antiparticle of D^0.

Subsequent experiments of the same type by the Berkeley-Stanford group found evidence for particles with positive electric charge that decay into a charged K meson and two charged π mesons. This particle has a rest energy approximately 10 MeV (million electron volts) higher than the first particle and was a clear candidate for D^+, which was expected to have slightly higher energy than D^0.

To be sure that the new particles contain charmed quarks, it was considered necessary to verify that they decay via weak interactions. Several features of weak interactions could be used to do this. One is that weak-interaction decays involving leptons (such as muons and neutrinos), together with K mesons, should be observable in addition to the purely hadronic decays mentioned above. Some evidence for such decays was reported from experiments done elsewhere, but this evidence was not conclusive. A second way of showing that the D^+ and D^0 mesons decay by weak interactions would be to find some instances of decay that involve pions alone, for only weak interactions allow both types of decays by a single type of particle. Some small amount of evidence for such purely pionic decays appeared in the SPEAR experiments, but more data were needed to definitely establish this fact.

It was expected that many more hadrons containing c quarks would be discovered in the future. Evidence already existed for such mesons of spin $h/2\pi$, produced together with D^+ and D^0, and for such baryons with spin $1/2$ produced in other experiments. The detailed study of these hadrons promised to keep physicists busy for the next few years.

—Gerald Feinberg

For a comprehensive discussion of subatomic particles and quantum properties, see *1977 Yearbook of Science and the Future* Feature Article: PARTICLE PHYSICS: A REALM OF CHARM, STRANGENESS, AND SYMMETRY.

Nuclear physics

Significant events in nuclear science during the past year included a report of the creation of element 107, controversy over evidence for the existence of naturally occurring supertransuranic nuclei, and initial results in the search for man-made nuclear states of abnormally high density.

Supertransuranic nuclei. For years the dream of many nuclear scientists has been the creation of nuclear species much heavier than those presently existing in nature and indeed possibly much heavier than have ever been created in nature. During the year a group of Soviet physicists, working at the Joint Institute for Nuclear Research at Dubna under Georgi N. Flerov, announced creation of element 107 as the heaviest transuranic species yet found. There was every reason to believe that such elements existed in early stages of the universe, but because of their very short lifetimes, measured in millionths of seconds, they have long since disappeared. Recent studies on existing heavy nuclei in the lead-uranium range have permitted scientists to extrapolate their new-found structural knowledge to predict possible groups of new supertransuranic elements having about 114 or 126 protons that could be stable—or almost stable with very long lifetimes —if only ways could be found to produce them or to detect them should natural traces still exist.

Substantial excitement, therefore, was generated in 1976 when Robert Gentry of the Oak Ridge (Tenn.) National Laboratory and colleagues from Florida State University and from the University of California at Davis announced what appeared to be rather compelling evidence for the existence of naturally occurring element 126; this implied a lifetime measured at least in tens of thousands if not hundreds of thousands of years.

It had long been recognized that highly charged energetic particles emitted in the radioactive decay of heavy nuclei can cause permanent damage in any crystalline or glassy material in which these nuclei may be imbedded and that under proper conditions this damage can be made visible as a signature for the decay. Gentry and his colleagues focused on special naturally occuring halos in mica. Rather common, halos had long been assumed to be markers of the damage resulting from the radioactive decay of tiny specks of uranium or thorium trapped in the mica during its geological

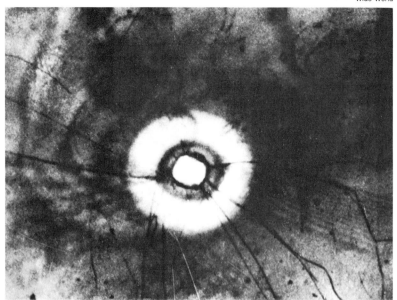

Under 100-power magnification, fragment of mica reveals giant halo and central inclusion of the type that yielded what first appeared to be good evidence for the existence of naturally occurring superheavy elements. Subsequent investigations soon made this interpretation untenable, but the incident served to further scientific inquiry.

crystallization; the observed halo radii corresponded roughly to the distance their decay products might be expected to travel in mica, about 5–20 microns (1 micron = 10^{-6} m). Over an extended period Robert Gentry had been collecting rare halos with much larger radii that, taken at face value, would have required for their production alpha particles of 14 MeV (million electron volts) rather than the 4 MeV characteristic of uranium and thorium emissions. Although no known element emits such high-energy alpha particles, decay energies of sufficient magnitude had been predicted for the quasi-stable supertransuranics.

Gentry and his collaborators bombarded the central specks of a number of giant halos with beams of low-energy protons from a Van de Graaff accelerator and measured the characteristic X-rays emitted. It was known that under proton bombardment some inner atomic electrons are dislodged and that, as outer electrons from the atomic cloud cascade in to fill these vacancies, X-rays having energies uniquely characteristic of the number of nuclear protons are emitted. The experimental data showed a well-marked X-ray line at 27 keV (thousand electron volts), exactly the value that had been predicted for element 126.

Because of its extreme importance in nuclear science this finding stimulated worldwide studies of mica inclusions and halos. Unfortunately, three different pieces of new evidence soon made untenable the suggestion that element 126 had been found. In a systematic study of possible alternate sources for the 27-keV radiation, John Fox and his collaborators at Florida State University found that low-energy proton bombardment of the element

cerium, a known component of mica, produces nuclear gamma radiation at precisely this energy when an incoming proton displaces a neutron in the cerium nucleus. Dirk Schwalm at the GSI, Darmstadt, West Germany, showed that, when a very large number of halos were examined systematically, they did not separate simply into normal and giant classes. Rather there was a normal probability distribution of radii centering on the so-called normal radius but extending all the way to giant radii. This suggested that various physical and chemical processes at the individual halo sites had determined their radii, rather than the energy of the radiation emitted. And, finally, Gentry and others exposed nine giant halo inclusions to the very intense synchrotron X-ray source at Stanford University's SPEAR electron-positron colliding beam facility. Intrinsically this is a much more powerful and precise method of inducing X-ray emissions characteristic of the elements present; no evidence for element 126 was found. Despite these negative results, however, the excitement and new work generated by the Gentry experiment greatly increased the tempo of worldwide search for the totally new physics and chemistry that would result from identification of stable or quasi-stable supertransuranic elements.

Pions probe nuclear structure. Although it is relatively easy to add neutrons to nuclei to make increasingly heavy and unstable new isotopes, it is much more difficult to add protons to produce lighter isotopes far from stability. Vadim V. Volkov and his associates at Dubna used heavy-ion beams and Arthur Poskanzer and his colleagues at the University of California at Berkeley used very-high-energy proton beams to create such neutron-rich isotopes as sodium-33, which has 11 more neutrons than does naturally occurring sodium-23. Very recently Robert Burman and his collaborators at the Los Alamos (N.M.) Meson Physics Facility reported an entirely new reaction involving a positive pion projectile and a negative pion product; in essence this (π^+, π^-) reaction changes two nuclear neutrons to protons. Burman's group produced and studied the mass-16 and mass-18 light proton-rich isotopes of neon using corresponding mass-16 and mass-18 oxygen targets. In addition to giving access to new light isotopes these double-charge-exchange reactions are expected to provide a powerful tool for the study of single-particle aspects of nuclear structure because they can be thought of as a method for changing the charge of two nucleons without otherwise changing the nuclear structure of the original target.

Giant nuclear multipole oscillations. In parallel with this new probe for single-particle aspects of nuclear structure, other probes are being developed for studying collective phenomena, those wherein all neutrons and protons present participate together. Perhaps the simplest of such mo-tions are the so-called giant resonances. In the simplest of these, the monopole, the nuclear radius oscillates, as does the density; in the next most complex, the dipole, all the neutrons oscillate against all the protons; in the next, the quadrupole, the nucleus oscillates between doorknob and football shapes; and in higher multipoles even more complex oscillatory shape changes occur. The nuclear dipole resonance has long been known and understood in terms of both its collective character and the underlying more complicated individual motions of its component nucleons. During the past year substantial new experimental information was obtained on the giant quadrupole, and George Bertsch of Michigan State University succeeded in understanding it on fundamental microscopic terms.

Most important, however, has been a tremendous expansion in the ability of physicists to excite and study giant resonances using high-precision electron beams. Because the electromagnetic force, the only one through which electrons interact with nuclei, is a long-range one, it was expected that electrons would be effective in exciting collective nuclear oscillations. William Bertozzi

Under construction at Sandia Laboratories, Albuquerque, N.M., 44-foot-diameter accelerator will subject BB-sized pellets of deuterium and tritium to extremely short and powerful pulses of electrons in efforts to trigger small thermonuclear explosions for electric power generation.

Courtesy, Sandia Laboratories

and his collaborators at the Massachusetts Institute of Technology obtained sufficiently precise electron beams from the Bates linear accelerator to excite and study the lowest seven multipoles in a variety of nuclei.

Totally independent evidence concerning some of the lower new multipole resonances was obtained by F. S. Dietrich and his collaborators at the University of Washington in Seattle; in these latter measurements protons of precisely known energy were swept over the energy range of interest, and gamma radiation that was emitted when they were captured via giant resonances was observed. Again use was being made of the fact that because the range of the electromagnetic forces — which is reflected in the wavelength of the gamma radiation — is very much larger than nuclear dimensions, all nuclear constituents experience essentially the same force. These studies on the new resonances posed a very stringent and important test of the detailed understanding of nuclear structure and dynamics that has been accumulated over the years.

High-density nuclei. Some years ago T. D. Lee and Gian-Carlo Wick of Columbia University, New York City, predicted the possibility that at very high energies, several hundred MeV to a few GeV (billion electron volts) per nucleon, an entirely new kind of matter might be created in heavy-ion collisions. This new matter would have a density substantially higher than normal and, if stable as the calculations suggested, would have truly remarkable properties. Among them would be stability in the atomic-number range from 350 to 100,000; in addition would be the possibility of "storing" essentially unlimited numbers of neutrons, and hence energy, in entirely new fashion.

With the development of the super-HILAC/Bevalac combination at Berkeley and of the Synchrophasotron at Dubna, which were capable of producing beams up to 2 GeV and 6 GeV per nucleon, respectively, major interest focused on the search for nuclear states of abnormal density and thus for possible production of this postulated new kind of matter in very-high-energy, heavy-ion collisions. As of early 1977 results from Harry Heckman and his collaborators at Berkeley were negative. Erwin Schopper and his collaborators from the University of Frankfurt, West Germany, however, obtained higher energy data at Dubna, and preliminary analyses of these data suggested that some of the effects expected to characterize the increased density states may be present. Should subsequent studies, which may be possible only at Dubna in this higher energy range, confirm these early findings, it would be one of the most important discoveries in nuclear science since fission.

International aspects. The uniqueness of this facility at Dubna points up a rapidly growing trend in nuclear physics. At lower energies both the West German UNILAC at Darmstadt and the French GANIL under construction at Caen far exceed the capabilities of anything either under construction — or even approved for construction — in the U.S. Major initiatives in this most rapidly growing salient of nuclear science are being taken also in Israel, Japan, the Scandinavian countries, Italy, and the United Kingdom. In an area of science developed and brought to vigorous maturity in the U.S. and possessed of a very high potential for important new results, initiative and leadership are passing from this country. Unless reversed by forceful federal action in the near future this is a trend that could have serious negative consequences.

—D. Allan Bromley

See also Feature Articles: NATURE'S NUCLEAR REACTOR; NUCLEAR WASTE DISPOSAL.

Solid-state physics

To a large degree, crystalline, three-dimensional metals and semiconductors were well understood in the 1970s, and for both practical and fundamental reasons increasing attention was being paid by solid-state physicists to more complex materials and phenomena. Recently, two such examples came into clear focus. One is a newly discovered phenomenon, the occurrence of charge-density waves in two-dimensional materials. The other relates to the optical transmission of glasses, which collectively constitute a class of amorphous materials.

Charge-density waves. One of the most fascinating aspects of condensed matter is the number of ingenious ways that nature has found to reduce its total energy through atomic rearrangement. A common example, resulting from subtle phase changes in the solid state, is the effect of temperature upon ferromagnetic materials. Above a characteristic temperature, called the Curie temperature, the magnetic moments associated with individual atoms in the ferromagnetic solid lose their order, and thus the solid loses its magnetism. Below the Curie temperature, order is restored and the magnetism reappears.

Other subtle phase transitions occur in solids, all of which serve to lower the energy of the solid. One newly discovered and important example involves the phenomenon of charge-density waves, a concept developed in the 1960s by A. W. Overhauser of the Ford Motor Co. Research Laboratories (later of Purdue University, West Lafayette, Ind.). Basic to an understanding of charge-density waves is a realization of the key role the ordering of atoms plays in

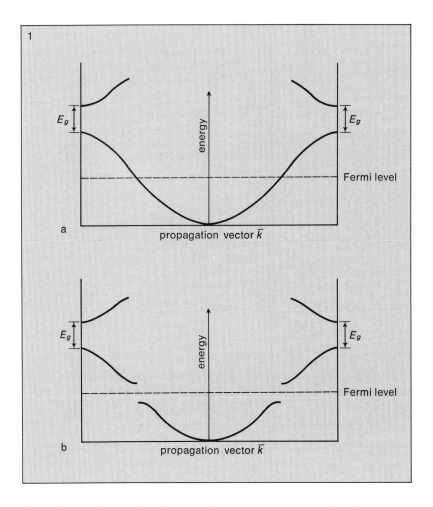

E_g

energy

propagation vector $\bar{k}$

E_g

Fermi level

a

E_g

energy

propagation vector $\bar{k}$

E_g

Fermi level

b

determining the electronic and vibrational quantum, or energy, state of crystalline solids. As was established by Louis de Broglie and others early in the 20th century, electrons (as well as vibrations of the crystal lattice) have a wave nature and, like light, can suffer reflection and constructive and destructive interference. When the wavelength of the electron matches the period of the lattice (*i.e.,* the minimum distance between lattice atoms that must be traveled to find identical surroundings), such interference takes place, and the traveling-wave quantum states, which ordinarily characterize electrons in solids, are transformed into standing-wave states. Depending on their phase, and thus on their interaction with the ions that make up the lattice, the energy of the standing waves is either increased or decreased, creating a bandgap; *i.e.,* an energy range over which no quantum states are allowed.

In (1) the quantum states of a metal are depicted in terms of the energy of the electron and the propagation vector, $\bar{k}$, of the electronic state. The quantity $\bar{k}$ is a vector whose direction specifies the direction of motion of the electron and whose magnitude is inversely proportional to the wavelength (λ) of the electron. When $n\lambda = 2a$ (*a* is the characteristic lattice periodicity in the direction of motion of the electron; *n* is an integer), the condition for a standing wave is achieved, and the bandgap, E_g, opens up, as indicated in (1a).

Depending on the magnitude of the bandgaps and the number of electrons available to fill the available states, a solid may be an insulator, semiconductor, or metal. For a solid to exhibit the properties of a semiconductor or an insulator, bandgaps must exist in all directions of electron motion and there must be only enough electrons to fill up a certain number of bands to their maximum energy. If excess electrons exist, they must go into states on the high-energy side of the bandgap; in such a case the solid exhibits the properties of a metal.

The Fermi level is the highest quantum state filled by an electron in a solid at a temperature of absolute zero ($-273°$ C). Thus, there are empty states available just above the Fermi level. In an insulator or semiconductor, the Fermi level lies in the bandgap and is often well separated from the band edges. In a metal, the Fermi level lies near the middle of the band, as shown in (1a).

In forming a bandgap, the states that are to lie below the gap are moved to lower energy and those that are to lie above the gap are moved to higher energy. Thus, if a bandgap could be opened at the Fermi level of a metal, as shown in (1b), the total energy of the solid would be decreased because the energy of the highest-lying filled states would be lower. But how could this happen if the periodicity of the lattice does not allow for a standing wave to occur at the Fermi level?

Overhauser recognized that it might be energetically favorable for the required periodicity to be produced by a rearrangement of the electrons within the crystal. This new periodicity would be established by the charge redistributing itself in such a manner that it has a periodic, wavelike density distribution—hence the term charge-density wave. For example, in the case shown in (1b), the periodicity of the charge-density wave must be twice as large as that of the crystal lattice because the magnitude of $\bar{k}$ is proportional to $1/\lambda$.

That experimental observation of this phenomenon took nearly two decades is partially attributable to the fact that it is very difficult to meet the conditions necessary for its occurrence in three-dimensional metals; this is because of the necessity of satisfying the standing-wave condition in three dimensions simultaneously. As one might expect, it is easiest to satisfy the standing-wave requirements in one dimension and next easiest in two dimensions. Of course, one may ask, do one- and two-dimensional metals actually exist? The answer is that certain solids form fiber-like chains that give a strong one-dimensional nature to their conductivity , and there exists evidence for charge-density-wave formation in some of these materials; for example, $K_2Pt(CN)_4Br_{0.3} \cdot 3H_2O$.

In the last few years, a large amount of research was being devoted to quasi-two-dimensional materials. Such compounds as TaS_2, $TaSe_2$, and MoS_2 are micalike in that they have strong bonding in two dimensions but only very weak bonding in the third dimension. Their crystals are made up of two-dimensional sheets only three atoms thick that are very loosely bonded to other sheets in the third dimension. As a result, these materials, which have only partially filled bands, act as two-dimensional metals. From investigations of their electrical, optical, and magnetic properties, a number of unusual characteristics were discovered that were not well understood until the importance of charge-density waves was recognized. One example is the conductivity-versus-temperature curve for one of the crystalline forms of TaS_2, shown in (2).

As a bandgap opens up, one would expect to see

Adapted from *Advances in Physics*, by J. A. Wilson *et al.*, vol. 24, p. 117, fig. 3

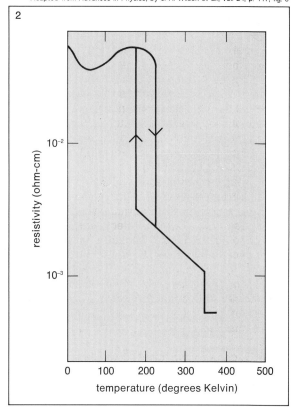

a sharp increase in resistivity, because the material is transformed from a metal to a semiconductor with a very small bandgap. This effect can be observed by measuring the resistivity while the temperature is lowered through the transition temperature for formation of charge-density waves. However, the actual behavior, shown in (2), is more complex than might be expected. This is due to a number of complicating factors. For example, in general the Fermi level will not lie just at the middle of the band, as shown in (1). Further, the positive ions of the lattice will move in response to the shift in electron charge produced by the formation of charge-density waves. As the temperature is reduced, additional changes in the lattice are produced that attempt to bring the periodicity of the crystal and that of the charge-density wave in better registry. The sharp increase in resistance at 352° K shown in (2) is due to the first formation of charge-density waves; these are poorly matched to the crystal lattice. The gradual increase in resistivity as the temperature is lowered to 200° K and the sharp increase at 200° K are due to small rearrangements of the lattice ions that bring the lattice and the charge-density waves in better registry. Electron diffraction proved a decisive tool in establishing the occurrence of charge-density waves in two-dimensional metals and aided greatly in working out the details of both the periodicity of charge-density waves and their effects on lattice periodicity.

Optical studies of amorphous materials. Among the major practical developments in solid-state physics of recent years has been the emergence of fiber-optics systems to replace standard electrical transmission lines in communications. In these systems, a semiconductor device transforms an electrical signal into an optical signal, which is then transmitted through a very thin, flexible glass fiber to a semiconductor detection device. Because of the relatively high frequencies that can be transmitted through a fiber with a diameter as small as 0.1 mm, much more information can be carried over glass fiber than over electrically conducting wire of comparable size. Of course, in many practical applications optical fibers also must be able to transmit optical signals over several kilometers without large losses from optical absorption. The development of optical fibers arose from the technology of glasses. Glasses are a class of amorphous materials, and therein lies an interesting story.

Solids come in two forms: crystalline, in which all the atoms are arranged in an ordered array that repeats itself over and over again; and amorphous, in which there is no long-range order. The crystalline semiconductors that constitute the sources and detectors of lightwave communication systems were relatively well understood theoretically. On the other hand, as of the late 1970s there was no comprehensive theoretical understanding of the basic optical and electrical properties of amorphous materials such as those that constitute optical fibers.

Vacuum chamber (in background) recently built by two IBM scientists approaches the near perfect vacuum range of about one molecule per cubic centimeter.

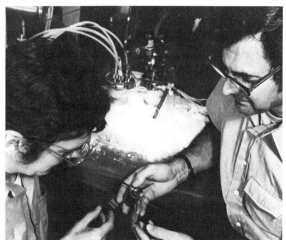

Courtesy, International Business Machines Corporation, Research Division

In the late 1960s, when work on optical fibers was just under way, there was surprisingly strong agreement among solid-state theorists that, because of their lack of long-range order, the bandgaps of glasses would not be well defined but would contain a large density of quantum states similar to those found in very impure crystalline materials. As a result, glasses would be quite absorbing. However, fundamental studies of amorphous germanium about 1970 showed that the bandgaps are much sharper and that optical absorption is much weaker than prior work had indicated.

Meanwhile, practical work on glasses demonstrated that optical transmission could be increased by removing impurities. With great care in preparation, silicate glass fibers were produced in which as little as 20% of the light is absorbed after transmission through a kilometer of glass at the wavelength of maximum transmission (about one micron, or 10^{-6} m). In addition, new theoretical work indicated that the earlier approximations which had predicted large absorption may be incorrect, and an increasing body of knowledge is appearing that justifies the large transmission value recently achieved experimentally.

—William E. Spicer

Psychology

In psychology, as in many other disciplines, the pendulum continued to swing strongly toward applied and away from pure scientific interests. A concrete indication of this trend could be seen in the results of a survey conducted by the American Psychological Association (APA) on the proportion of openings in various areas of graduate study in psychology. A sharp drop (from 21.2 to 13.2% of the total) was noted for experimental psychology, which was supplanted as the most frequent area of study by clinical and counseling psychology. This fact reflected primarily the poor academic job market, because that is where most experimentalists are employed, but it was also true that the applied areas were the most popular with students.

Psychoanalytic theory. Despite the decline in the field, large numbers of academic psychologists continued to work on a vast array of experimental and theoretical problems. It was especially encouraging during the year to note what appeared to be a firm beginning of the systematic application of sound experimental methodology to some of the fundamental theoretical problems of psychoanalysis. Under the intriguing title "Psychoanalytic Theory: The Reports of My Death Are Greatly Exaggerated," Lloyd H. Silverman described two independent research programs, each spanning a full decade, which used laboratory techniques to test some of the central psychoanalytic tenets. Silverman, at New York University, used subliminal presentation of wish-related stimuli, while J. Reyher, at Michigan State University, employed posthypnotic suggestion; both research programs attacked the proposition that psychopathology is stimulated by unconscious wishes, and both seemed to have amassed considerable amounts of generally positive results. Silverman's data were derived from 16 separate experiments; stimuli designed to stir aggressive wishes (such as a picture of a snarling man or the message "Cannibal eats person") when presented subliminally resulted in a brief increase in "ego pathology," compared with control stimuli (such as a picture of a man reading a newspaper or a neutral message such as "People are walking").

The prime importance of Silverman's presentation was that it directly called these programs to the attention of a wide audience of psychologists. While it was too early for counterattacks and critiques to have appeared, a large number of them were expected. But, as Silverman himself pointed out, it is time for psychoanalytic theory to be modified on the basis of just such experimentally oriented critiques.

Intelligence. Perhaps the biggest bombshell of the past year in psychology was the furor created by attacks upon the experimental results and the reports of British psychologist Sir Cyril Burt. The first psychologist to be knighted, Burt was long a towering figure in intelligence testing and theory. His study of the intelligence of identical twins raised in separate environments has been one of the mainstays of those who believe in the importance of heredity in determining intelligence; for example, he reported a high correlation between test scores of such twins (.771, compared with .944 for identical twins reared together). Burt's data have been suspect for several years, however, and doubts began surfacing more regularly after his death, at age 88, in 1971. Mainly, these doubts centered on the curious constancy in certain of the correlations cited (including the pivotal two given above) even as additional sets of twins were supposedly added to the data base. Burt's credentials were apparently too strong to permit widespread questioning except by a few skeptics, in particular Princeton University psychologist Leon Kamin, one of the most vigorous critics of the hereditarian position.

The controversy was brought to a focus when the Oct. 24, 1976, issue of the *Sunday* (London) *Times* carried a story by investigative reporter Oliver Gillie. Despite a thorough search of the records of London University and interviews with 18 of Burt's colleagues, Gillie had been unable to find any evidence of the existence of Burt's two collaborators, Miss Margaret Howard or Miss J. Conway. He concluded that possibly they "never existed, but were the fantasy of an aging professor who became increasingly lonely and deaf." The newspaper subsequently reported that Miss Howard had apparently been a member of the faculty of University College, London, in the 1930s. However, questions concerning the mystery (such as, if Howard and Conway did not collect the twin data, who did?) spawned many hypothetical explanations (such as, Burt simply fabricated the data). However these questions are resolved, substantial damage was done to Burt's reputation and, to a lesser degree, to the hereditarian position on intelligence that he spearheaded.

Of much greater long-range significance, for an understanding of intellectual function, was the application by University of Michigan psychologist Robert Zajonc of his previously announced family-configuration theory to the increasingly disturbing problem of the steady decline in U.S. high-school seniors' performance on the Scholastic Aptitude Test (SAT). This theory won for Zajonc and his University of Michigan colleague, Gregory Markus, a political scientist, the 1975 Social-Psychological Prize of the American Association for the Advancement of Science. In essence, their theory holds that intelligence depends in part upon the intellectual environment of the family, and that the greater the mean intellectual functioning of other family members during a child's early development the greater his or her intellectual growth is likely to be.

Applied to the SAT problem, this theory neatly explains the continuing drop in mean scores in the U.S. (from 490 in 1962 to less than 460 in 1974) as a function of the increasingly large families, with relatively short time intervals between children, of the years immediately following World War II. Thus, for example, a person who took the SAT test in 1962 was likely to have been the first-born in the family and to have therefore enjoyed the relatively high-level intellectual environment provided by his parents; his younger brothers and sisters, on the other hand, were likely to have been born into increasingly larger families with correspondingly lower mean levels of intellectual functioning. Because family size began to decline during the 1960s, Zajonc predicted a corresponding rise in SAT scores, beginning about 1980.

This startlingly simple view was subjected to large-scale statistical tests in a number of studies of family size and intelligence conducted in Western Europe. The results of the tests consistently supported the theory. While it is admittedly not the entire story, the family-configuration view is a re-

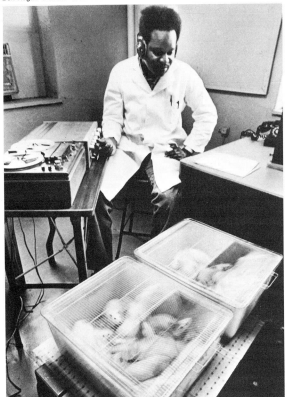

Don Hogan Charles—NYT Pictures

Rats of a breed subject to high blood pressure were placed in plastic cages and for 16 weeks were subjected to vibrations and loud subway noise twice a day. Four of the 25 rats died compared with no fatalities in a control group not subjected to noise and shaking.

freshing change from and may help to defuse the emotional confrontation of the traditional hereditary and environmental positions on intelligence.

Environmental psychology. One of the strong new tides that could be observed in the contemporary development of psychology was the growing interest in research upon long-neglected facets of what may be called, for want of a better term, the quality of life. One prominent focus of this new interest was the environment as it relates to behavior. The job of pinpointing problems, resources, and personnel in this emerging area was undertaken by an APA Task Force on Environment and Behavior, which in 1976 completed its three-year study. Along with an increasing number of college courses and graduate programs on the subject, the Task Force noted the well-attended meetings of the Environmental Design Research Association and the establishment of the journal *Environment and Behavior.* An especially noteworthy feature of environmental psychology is its necessarily interdisciplinary character; psychologists work closely with, among others, geographers, anthropologists, ar-

chitects, urban planners, interior designers, civil engineers, economists, and political scientists.

Examples of the research that was being carried out in this field included: a study of sensory responses to air pollution, at the Yale School of Medicine; a survey of the effects of urban crowding on such behavioral functions as aggression, family interaction, political activity, and sexual activity, at the University of Nebraska; and an investigation at the U.S. National Bureau of Standards into the abatement and control of noise pollution.

If environmental psychology is to realize a substantial part of its early promise, the research in the field must bear a close relation to the recognized needs of society so that its utility will be apparent to the legislative bodies that do most of the funding and to the federal and other agencies that make use of it. In this respect the recent emphasis in the field seemed appropriate; relevant titles from 1976 papers in the *American Psychologist* included "Environmental Psychology and the Real World" and "Concern for the Environment: Implications for Industrial and Organizational Psychology."

Health care. While psychologists continued to interest themselves in the behavioral aspects of health care, the courts in the U.S. continued to issue rulings designed to redress individual grievances against various institutional practices and, thereby, increase the potential need for attention to behavioral concerns. Thus, a federal judge ruled that the patients in the federally operated St. Elizabeth's Hospital in Washington, D.C., especially those capable of living outside the institution, must have improved care and treatment. Another federal judge issued far-reaching orders requiring correction of the "cruel and unusual punishment" found in the Alabama prison system (overcrowding, understaffing, highly inadequate physical facilities, unwholesome food, and no meaningful classification system). Meanwhile, the case for the rights of children to due process when being committed to mental hospitals by their parents was being heard by the U.S. Supreme Court in a class-action suit filed by a group of 14 organizations.

Promotion of improved lifestyles was being actively pursued by Canada's minister of health, Marc Lalonde. After the satisfactory completion of a one-year pilot project in British Columbia, Lalonde announced the initiation of a national program in which lifestyle-information centers would be placed in pharmacies across Canada. In 1976 he began a check-insert program expected to reach two-thirds of the country's people; enclosed with federal checks was a "Lifestyle Profile" designed to allow each individual to assess the hazards in his own lifestyle, to be followed by pamphlets with tips on improvements. Further, a nationwide "Dialogue on Drinking" program was launched in October, by means of media advertising.

Sex therapy. Of the several major areas in which behavioral improvements were being promoted, none was so fast-growing or so controversial as sex therapy. Between 4,000 and 5,000 clinics and treatment centers were operating in the United States in 1977.

The most crucial problem in the field was the high percentage of quackery. As of 1977 the practice of marriage counseling was regulated by only five of the states, and in no state were there laws to enforce minimum training standards for sex therapists. A review of the problem and a guide to accredited marriage counselors were published in the March 1976 issue of *Psychology Today*.

Perception. It is impossible in a review of this length to do more than hint at the scope and intensity of the experimental and theoretical researches actively pursued by psychologists in such fields as neuropsychology, human memory and cognition, and animal learning and memory. Some of the most interesting research reported during the year in these areas was on perception in pigeons.

Increasingly in use since first introduced as a behavioral subject by B. F. Skinner, pigeons have been trained by means of operant-conditioning procedures to perform in various unusual ways, such as playing table tennis and selecting imperfect pills in a drug assembly line. In recent months, however, attention turned to an assessment of certain of the pigeon's natural capacities, such as the

Upon being shown a toothbrush, Lucy, a seven-year-old chimpanzee, makes the sign for it that she had been taught. Lucy achieved a vocabulary of approximately 75 signs.

Paul Fusco—Magnum

depth of its conceptual and perceptual abilities. In research at Cambridge University, British psychologists trained pigeons in a free-living colony to "conceptualize" the letter A. They found that the birds were able to discriminate "A" from "2" in 18 different typefaces and to transfer this discrimination very well to 22 new typefaces (and in one case to handwritten letters). The hypothesis that the pigeons had stored a kind of "template" was given provisional support by additional experiments that utilized partial figures and other letters.

In another research program, at Harvard University, pigeons were found to be capable of some exceptionally accurate identifications in discrimination tests of common objects (trees, bodies of water, and a particular woman) shown pictorially in varied settings. For example, they were able to reject such superficially treelike materials as vines and stalks of celery, as well as the particular woman's husband wearing her scarf and another woman in her apartment. Moreover, once they had been trained, they were almost as effective at appropriate discriminations the first time they saw the test pictures. The novel feature of this research was that it demonstrated in the pigeon a high level of perceptual ability with real-life materials of a sort that are normally not used in laboratory research. It also suggested previously unsuspected cognitive processes, which called for further analysis.

—Melvin H. Marx

Space exploration

The highlight of the year in space exploration was the landing of the Viking 1 and Viking 2 unmanned spacecraft on the surface of Mars. The two craft and their associated orbiters transmitted a wealth of data to Earth. In other developments work continued on the U.S. manned space shuttle, and the Soviet Union launched several manned Earth-orbital missions as well as unmanned probes of Venus and the Moon.

Manned space flight

In 1976–77 the United States did not conduct any manned space flight missions. Development efforts continued on the space shuttle, and the first orbiter spacecraft was delivered in the fall of 1976. The European Space Agency also continued development of a space laboratory designed to be flown onboard the space shuttle orbiter in 1980. The Soviet Union launched three manned missions. As a part of the Soviet manned space program two unmanned missions also were accomplished, one to orbit a Soyuz spacecraft in order to validate

UPI Compix

Space shuttle orbiter "Enterprise" is rolled out for its initial presentation at Palmdale, California, on Sept. 17, 1976.

long-term systems operations and the other to place a Salyut spacecraft in orbit. The Soviet Union also announced a new cooperative space program with the Soviet-bloc nations. As a part of this program cosmonaut candidates would be selected from those nations, trained in the Soviet Union, and flown as crewmen in joint programs.

Space shuttle. The U.S. space shuttle program reached a major milestone on Sept. 17, 1976, with the delivery of the first orbiter spacecraft, "Enterprise." The space shuttle was designed to provide unique capabilities for the U.S. and members of the European Space Agency to conduct near-Earth orbital space exploration. The reusable orbiter spacecraft is about the size of a DC-9 jetliner; it will be launched by rocket into space, orbit the Earth, and then reenter Earth's atmosphere and land much like a conventional airplane. The orbiter cargo bay (60 × 15 ft [20 × 5m]) will be used to transport unmanned satellites and other payloads into Earth orbit and will provide the capability to conduct in-orbit servicing of satellites. The cargo bay is also designed to be used to transport specialized laboratories (Spacelabs) into space for manned studies in the life sciences, Earth resources, astronomy, and other scientific disciplines, and the Department of Defense planned to use it for military research. European and U.S. scientists submitted scientific experiments to be conducted on the first Spacelab mission.

The first orbiter was to be used in a flight-test program at NASA's Dryden Flight Research Center, Edwards Air Force Base, California. A modified Boeing 747 jet aircraft would transport the orbiter to altitudes of approximately 28,000 ft above the Earth. The orbiter astronaut crew would separate the orbiter from the 747 jetliner and then demonstrate approach and landing techniques that would be used following orbital space operations. These tests were scheduled for completion in 1977.

In July 1976 NASA issued a call for space shuttle astronaut candidates. Two types of candidates were to be selected: pilot astronauts, who would fly the space shuttle, and mission specialists, who would be responsible for implementing in-flight scientific and engineering studies. (*See* Feature Article: THE SECOND GENERATION OF ASTRONAUTS.)

Soyuz 20/Salyut 4. Soyuz 20 was the first Soviet unmanned mission to be completed in 1976. It began with the launch of a Soyuz spacecraft from Tyuratam on Nov. 17, 1975. The objective of the mission was the verification of the functions of the spacecraft systems for long-term manned operations. The spacecraft was placed in near-Earth orbit and successfully accomplished rendezvous and docking with the orbiting Salyut 4 space station on Nov. 19, 1975. Salyut 4 had been launched in December 1974 and had been used in two previous manned missions during 1975. The Soyuz 20 mission lasted 91 days and appeared to be a demonstration of long-term spacecraft capability aimed at exceeding the 84-day mission record set by the U.S. Skylab 3 crew. Soyuz 20 was deorbited by ground controllers and landed on Feb. 16, 1976.

Soyuz 21/Salyut 5. The first Soviet manned spacecraft mission of 1976 was started with the launch of the unmanned 20-ton Salyut 5 space station on June 22, 1976. Unlike previous space stations, Salyut 5 was modified to include two docking points, thereby permitting the simultaneous docking of two spacecraft. In addition, the space station was equipped to accommodate up to six persons.

On July 6, 1976, Soyuz 21 was launched from Tyuratam. The mission commander was Col. Boris Volynov, and the flight engineer was Lieut. Col. Vitaly Zholobov. After docking with and boarding

Tass/Sovfoto

The Soviet Union's Soyuz 22 spacecraft with two cosmonauts on board lands safely by parachute near Tselinograd in Kazakhstan on Sept. 23, 1976, after eight days in orbit.

the Salyut 5, it seemed likely that the crew would attempt to break the 84-day record of Skylab 3. However, the Soyuz 21 mission was terminated after 49 days.

The docked Soyuz 21 / Salyut 5 complex circled the Earth every 89.6 minutes in an elliptical orbit ranging from an apogee of 168 mi to a perigee of 152 mi above the Earth (1 mi = 1.61 km). The first Moscow television transmission of the space mission took place from the Salyut 5 on Thursday, July 8, showing the two crewmen relaxed and comfortable at the spacecraft's control panel. Scientific experiments conducted by the crew included observations relative to the development of fish eggs and film documentation of the behavior of fish under weightless conditions; the formation of alloys containing bismuth, lead, tin, and cadmium; the growing of crystals under weightless conditions; and studies of fluid dynamics and surface tension. The data from the last experiment were to be used in the design of capillary pumps devoid of moving parts and appropriate for use under weightless conditions.

Other limited scientific investigations conducted on the mission included operation of an infrared telescope-spectrometer to determine the transparency of the atmosphere in order to measure its components. Specific measurements were made of atmospheric ozone, nitrogen oxide, and water vapor in different layers of the atmosphere. The crew also performed medical experiments, which consisted of assessments of the cardiovascular system similar to those conducted on earlier Soviet crews. Vacuum suits applied negative pressure to the

lower half of the body in order to obtain information concerning adaptation of the cardiovascular system during flight and to provide in-flight data for predicting the degree of difficulty in resuming an erect posture that might be expected upon return to Earth.

Earth resources photography was also one of the scientific objectives of the mission. Specific targets on the Earth were photographed in an effort to locate potential mineral deposits and to aid in the study of seismic activity. Areas in danger from mud slides were photographed, as well as potential locations for new dams and rail lines.

After 43 days in space, and considerable emphasis from the Soviet press concerning the fact that both cosmonauts were "feeling very well," the Soviet newspaper *Izvestia* reported that the two men were suffering from a "psychological problem" described as a "state of sensory hunger, which occurs when a human is cut off from the sights, sounds, and smells to which he is accustomed." *Izvestia* said that one sign of the problem was "the increase in their need for communication evidenced by the fact that they were asking the ground control operators with ever increasing frequency for news from Earth." On the advice of psychologists, ground control began playing music to the cosmonauts.

On July 24 the two cosmonauts began preparing to return to Earth. Soyuz 21 returned to Earth on August 24 in an area 125 mi southwest of the town of Kokchetav in Kazakhstan. Salyut 5 continued to orbit the Earth with all of its systems "performing normally."

Soyuz 22. The second Soviet manned mission of 1976 was Soyuz 22. The two-man crew was commanded by Col. Valery F. Bykovsky, a veteran of a five-day space flight aboard Vostok 5 in 1963. The flight engineer was Vladimir Aksenov, who had had no previous space flight experience.

The mission was launched on Sept. 15, 1976, from Tyuratam and was designated by the Soviets as an Earth photography mission. A newly developed MKF-6 multispectral space camera, fabricated by the Electronic Institute of the East German Academy of Science, was flown for the first time on this mission. The camera could take simultaneous photographs in six distinct wavelengths of the visible spectrum in order to permit scientists to study the land surface characteristics, oceans, vegetation, cloud formation, and weather systems. During the flight of Soyuz 22 there were simultaneous aerial photographic surveys made from aircraft using a similar camera system. In addition, Soviet scientists performed "ground truth" studies at selected ground sites in order to validate and aid in the interpretation of the results obtained from the Soyuz 22 and aircraft photography. Similar test flights had been made by the U.S. in the Apollo and Skylab programs.

The Soyuz spacecraft remained in near-Earth orbit at an altitude of approximately 160 mi for eight days. The crew ended the mission by successfully landing the spacecraft on Sept. 23, 1976, near Tselinograd, Kazakhstan.

Soyuz 23. The third Soviet manned space flight of 1976 began with the launch of Soyuz 23 on Oct. 14, 1976, from Tyuratam. The two-man crew was commanded by Lieut. Col. Vyacheslav Zudov with Lieut. Col. Valery Rozhdestvensky as the flight engineer. The spacecraft was launched into an initial elliptical orbit of 116 × 139 mi and later maneuvered into a new circular orbit to rendezvous with the already orbiting Salyut 5 space station. During the 17th orbit of Soyuz 23, the Soviet crewmen encountered difficulty with their rendezvous system while attempting to dock with Salyut 5. This marked the seventh failure of the last 11 Soviet attempts to complete various space station missions.

Immediately following the failure to dock with the space station, the crew prepared to terminate the flight. On the 33rd orbit the crewmen fired their retro-rockets and landed on October 16 in Lake Tengiz, 400 mi northeast of Tyuratam. The water landing was the first in the Soviet manned space flight program and was obviously not planned. Recovery operations took several hours due to the remoteness of the landing site and the night and heavy snow storm conditions, but the crewmen were recovered in good health.

—Richard S. Johnston

Space probes

For exploration by space probes 1976 was clearly the year of the Viking. Other significant events did take place, however, including the landing of a probe on the Moon that returned a sample of its soil to Earth.

Probing Venus. The orbiter sections of Venera 9 and 10, Soviet probes that landed on Venus in October 1975, continued to provide information about the planet, even though the landers had ceased functioning after an hour on the surface. As 1976 began, the orbiter section of Venera 9 had made 46 orbits of Venus, while that of Venera 10 had completed 44 orbits. Both Venera missions officially ended on March 22, but useful scientific data continued to flow from the two orbiters.

Among the information derived from experiments aboard the orbiters was a value for the density of Venus of 0.81485 based on a value of 1 for the Earth. Optical instruments aboard the two probes provided new data on the structure of the planet's cloud cover. Its upper limit is about 39 or 40 mi, and the clouds of Venus are more transparent than those of the Earth. Thus, they absorb little of the solar radiation falling on them and scatter radiation only in the visible and near-infrared range of the spectrum.

The same instruments reported that the thermal radiation from the planet was practically the same in intensity from both the night and day sides of Venus. They also discovered a luminescence on the night side of the planet that seemed to come from

Sidney Harris

a narrow band of clouds in high altitudes. Other instruments designed to detect magnetic fields failed to find such a field generated by the planet itself, but they did reveal magnetic fields created by the solar wind.

By June the orbiter of Venera 9 had ceased to function, but that of Venera 10 was still operating. On June 16 radio transmissions from the probe were beamed within 900,000 mi of the Sun's surface to perform studies of the flows of its plasma at those comparatively close distances to its surface. An early analysis of data indicated that such flows are extremely nonuniform and are subject to rapid changes in time. The experiment had a practical side as well. Further analysis of the data was expected to help determine the extent to which commands to future probes would be disturbed when passing through such a region in space.

Later in the year, Soviet scientists formed some tentative conclusions about the surface of Venus, based upon data received from the landers during their brief existence. The rocks near the two landers exhibited natural radioactivity that suggests they are similar to those of terrestrial basalts. Specifically, the instruments in the landers found that radioactivity in such rocks was caused by potassium, thorium, and uranium.

Also, the Venera 9 lander indicated that the wind in its area ranged between 0.94 and 1.56 mph. Similar conditions were reported at the landing site of Venera 10, with winds there being between 1.78 and 2.90 mph.

Viking on Mars. With the successful landing on Mars by Vikings 1 and 2 in 1976, a unique milestone was reached in the history of man's exploration of his celestial environment. *Astronautics & Aeronautics* magazine noted that the U.S. Congress in 1803 appropriated only $2,500 for Lewis and Clark to explore the territory west of the Mississippi. The price tag for Viking, 173 years later, was approximately $1 billion.

Following attempted launches marred by mechanical setbacks, the two probes finally spent ten months on a largely uneventful, 450 million-mile voyage through interplanetary space to their target planet. Viking 1 entered orbit about Mars on June 19, and its lander vehicle touched down on the planet's surface on July 20 in Chryse Planitia. Viking 2, following seven weeks later, entered orbit on August 7, and its lander touched down on September 3 in Utopia Planitia.

Even though the Viking 1 lander successfully touched down, it suffered a few malfunctions. Its seismometer refused to uncage upon command and remained out of order permanently. Thus, no data on Marsquakes could be recorded. The all-important surface sampler arm and scoop also became balky, but it was later adjusted and worked satisfactorily.

The first photograph made by the lander was of one of its own feet and the area adjacent to it. Engineers at the Viking Control Center at the Jet Propulsion Laboratory in Pasadena, Calif., wanted to see to what extent the craft had sunk into the Martian soil. The picture revealed a firm but rocky ground into which the foot had sunk little more than an inch. The lander's cameras then began taking panoramic views of the landing site. These revealed a terrain surprisingly like the deserts of the western U.S. Once the colors had been adjusted,

Soil sampler collector arm of Viking 2 (right) pushes a rock several inches on the surface of Mars in October 1976. Soil from the depression beneath the rock (far right) was collected and tested because some scientists believed that if there are life forms on Mars they might seek rocks as shelter from the intense ultraviolet radiation of the Sun.

Photos, courtesy, NASA

the pictures revealed not only a reddish soil and rocks but a pink sky as well.

Meteorological instruments indicated that winds in the vicinity of the lander gusted up to 34 mph but generally were no more than 20 mph. They blew from the east in the late afternoon and shifted to the south at night. Temperatures in the area ranged between a daytime high of −20° F (−30° C) and a nighttime low of −121° F (−85° C). The atmospheric pressure was 7.12 mb. (The pressure at the Earth's surface is about 1,000 mb.) The temperature just under the soil during the day indicated 24° F (−4° C).

The three biology experiments proceeded as planned after the sampler arm was returned to working order. The Martian soil proved active in all three experiments. Soil samples dampened with water vapor in the gas-exchange device indicated a release of oxygen. The labeled-release test, using radioactive carbon in a nutrient solution, indicated a rapid rise in the amount of carbon dioxide detected. The pyrolytic-release experiment showed that radioactive carbon had been extracted from the atmosphere of the test cell and taken up by the soil sample.

Control experiments were then run on sterilized soil samples, and the results were negative. Thus, scientists were left no more the wiser for their efforts. The tests did not prove or disprove that there is a form of life on Mars similar to the Earth's bacteria. The results could have been produced by chemical reactions rather than the metabolic activity of bacteria. As of early 1977 no firm judgment had been made. The official National Aeronautics and Space Administration (NASA) position, however, was that Viking had not detected life on Mars, although many scientists associated with the project refused to abandon the possibility of life on the planet.

Investigations of the inorganic content of the Martian soil showed it consisted of 2–7% aluminum, 15–30% silicon, 3–8% calcium, 0.25–1.5% titanium, and 12–16% iron. A quantitative analysis of the atmosphere revealed that it is composed of 95% carbon dioxide, 0.1–0.5% oxygen, 2–3% nitrogen, and 1–2% argon.

After touching down, the Viking 2 lander experienced some of the same troubles as those that plagued its sister craft. The sampler arm and scoop acted up, but mission engineers were able to overcome the problems and put the device into service. The first pictures from the lander disclosed a terrain similar to that photographed by the Viking 1 lander. However, many rocks within camera range showed deeply pitted surfaces. Scientists speculated that they could have been of volcanic origin. Additionally, the pictures in the close vicinity of the

Viking 2 lander showed clearly how the fine Martian soil was blown about on the surface, forming small dunes and piling up against rocks.

Temperatures reported were much the same as those at the Viking 1 lander. The high was −23° F in the afternoon, and the low was −114° F in the early morning. The temperature just beneath the surface of the soil was 30° F. The barometric pressure was only slightly higher, 7.72 mb. Analyses of the atmosphere by instruments aboard the Viking 2 lander revealed the presence of krypton and xenon. Their discovery as constituents of the Martian atmosphere was expected to permit scientists to deduce how the atmosphere evolved.

On October 25 the sampler arm of the Viking 2 lander performed an intricate maneuver in its search for soil that might contain bacterial forms of life. Early that morning the arm nudged a rock aside and scooped up a sample for analysis by the biological instrument package. The reason for the process was that scientists believed that the soil beneath the rock would have been protected from the fierce ultraviolet radiation of the Sun. Hence, the probability of bacteria surviving would be greater. No signs of life were detected from the sample, however.

On November 7 the seismometer on the Viking 2 lander registered what may have been a Marsquake. The event lasted about 30 minutes and appeared to have had an epicenter several thousand miles from the lander. The response of the instrument was similar to data recorded by instruments left on the Moon by Apollo astronauts.

Three days later, on November 10, Mars went behind the Sun, and the spacecraft was temporarily out of communication with the Earth. As Mars emerged from behind the Sun, ground controllers sent the first commands to the Viking landers on December 16 and 17. Both craft responded without trouble.

While the landers were busy on the surface of the planet, the Viking 1 and 2 orbiters were equally occupied circling Mars. In addition to acting as radio relays from the landers to Earth, the two craft also performed scientific experiments and took detailed pictures of the planetary surface. By the end of the year, the two probes had taken more than 8,000 pictures, sometimes at a rate that overloaded the processing computers at the Jet Propulsion Laboratory.

Both craft performed "an orbital walk" or had the inclination of their orbits to the equator of Mars changed to permit their cameras to cover more of the surface. Additionally, the "walk" of the Viking 1 orbiter permitted it to search for a possible landing site for the Viking 2 lander. In late September the inclination angle of the Viking 2 orbiter was changed from 55.3° to 75° to permit closer study of the northern polar region of the planet.

One of the most dramatic pictures returned by an orbiter was of Phobos, one of the two natural satellites of Mars, from a distance of only 545 mi. Mission controllers devised a method that prevented the picture from being blurred because of the relatively close distance of the satellite to the probe. The picture showed primary and secondary craters and also an unexpected feature, striations or grooves in roughly parallel patterns.

Measurements of the temperature in the polar regions also produced a surprise for scientists, who had estimated that it would be about −190° F (−125° C). However, readings made over the northern polar area showed that the temperature was only −90° F (−75° C). Such a "high" temperature would not permit the formation of frozen carbon dioxide ("dry ice"), which scientists had assumed made up the polar caps. Scientists therefore concluded that the polar caps are composed of ordinary ice produced by frozen water vapor. (See also Feature Article: THE VIKING MISSION TO MARS.)

Probing the Moon. Launched on Aug. 9, 1976, the Soviet probe Luna 24 made a soft landing in the Moon's Sea of Crises on August 18. The landing site was approximately 300 mi from the place where Neil Armstrong and Edwin Aldrin had landed in 1969. The probe was apparently a replacement for Luna 23, which was launched into the same area but was damaged in landing on Nov. 6, 1974.

Luna 24 successfully sank a core drill about 6.5 ft into the soil and returned the sample to the Earth on August 22 for study by scientists at the Vernadsky Institute of Geochemistry and Analytical Chemistry in Moscow. The core showed distinct layers of material, indicating that the lunar soil had been laid down in successive deposits. Soviet scientists said that it compared in color and consistency with samples returned by the earlier Luna 16. Several grams of the material were presented to U.S. scientists for testing.

Pioneering in space. Pioneer 10, which had been launched on March 2, 1972, continued its journey through outer space. On Feb. 10, 1976, it crossed the orbit of Saturn. In 1987, when it is scheduled to pass Pluto, the probe will become the first man-made object to leave the solar system. In case it is ever found by intelligent life outside the solar system, Pioneer 10 carries a pictorial mes-

Rock and soil from the Moon collected by Luna 24 are stored within the concentric rings of the ampule returned to the Earth by the Soviet probe.

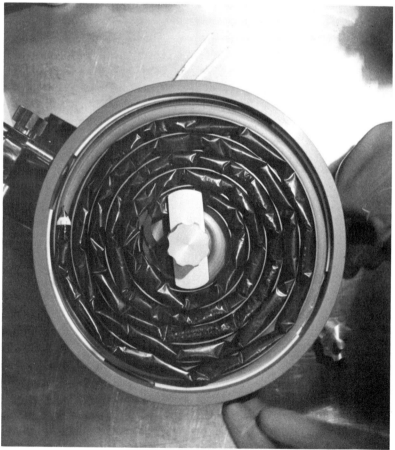

Novosti/Sovfoto

sage explaining where it came from. The extremely large tracking antennas of NASA's Deep Space Network should be able to receive signals from Pioneer 10 as far away from the Earth as the orbit of Uranus (2 billion mi), which it is scheduled to cross in 1979.

In March, Pioneer 10 discovered that Jupiter has an enormous magnetic tail, about half a billion miles long, completely spanning the distance between the orbits of Jupiter and Saturn. Considering the size of the huge envelope, scientists predicted that Saturn should enter it once every 20 years, with the next encounter occurring in April 1981. Such a meeting should produce interesting magnetic phenomena if they could be detected and measured. Previously, some scientists had thought that Jupiter's tail would be very short or even wound around it because of the rapid rotation of the planet.

On May 25 mission controllers at Ames Research Center (California) applied a correction to the path being taken by Pioneer 11 on its way to Saturn. The successful maneuver ensured that the probe would pass the planet within a distance of 2.5 Saturn radii. The next day Bradford Smith of the University of Arizona announced his opinion of the proposed trajectory of the probe, which would take it inside the rings of Saturn.

"If the decision is made to fly inside . . . it is very likely to be a kamikaze mission," he said to a conference on the planet Jupiter held at Ames Research Center. Smith based his opinion on the fact that he believes the apparently empty spaces between the rings are filled with particulate matter. In the meanwhile, instruments aboard Pioneer 11 furnished the first evidence that the Sun's magnetic field has a structure similar to those of the Earth and Jupiter, a simple dipole form.

Future outlook. As might be expected following the outstanding success of the two Vikings on Mars, scientists, particularly those at the Jet Propulsion Laboratory, began advocating a Viking 3 mission. The lander would be mounted on tracks, like an army tank, and could roam over the surface of the planet. Because NASA had a lander that could be modified for the purpose, the project would be both practical and, to a degree, economical. Despite the enthusiasm for it in some quarters, however, no such project was authorized for fiscal 1978.

Pioneer Venus, scheduled for launch in May or June of 1978, continued on schedule. As 1976 ended, its heat shield and parachute system were tested at the White Sands Missile Range in New Mexico. The probe was dropped from a balloon at an altitude of about 20 mi to simulate conditions that exist 67 mi above the surface of Venus.

Courtesy, NASA

Test model of Pioneer Venus reveals four large probes mounted on the spacecraft body. The probe is scheduled for launch in 1978.

Preliminary studies were under way at the Jet Propulsion Laboratory for a probe that would rendezvous with Halley's Comet in March 1986. To propel the craft to a distance of 1 astronomical unit from the Sun, designers suggested either an ion engine, with power supplied by solar energy, or solar sails, which would use the pressure of solar radiation. Such sails would have a width on each side of 2,625 ft. To stabilize the craft they would be rotated like a gyroscope, with solar radiation providing the force to produce the rotary motion. Eight to 12 vanes, like those of a windmill, would be used for the purpose. Each of the two sails would have a length of some 18,600 ft, making the overall diameter of the probe just over 7 mi.

Mikhail Y. Marov of the Soviet Institute of Applied Mathematics revealed during the year that work on future Soviet probes of Venus would depend upon a full analysis of data from Venera 9 and 10. Such future probes would probably be completely redesigned. He also stated that the U.S.S.R. was working cooperatively with French scientists in developing the next generation of probes of Venus. One concept proposed by the French was the floating in the Venusian atmosphere, after release by a Soviet probe, of pressurized balloons with instrument packages.

—Mitchell R. Sharpe

Transportation

Government continued to play a major role in transport technological developments during 1976–77. While this took the form mostly of financial backing, it also affected the research and development laboratories of private industry through the issuance of rules and regulations relating to both safety and the environment.

Air transport. Despite strong objections by U.S. air carriers, U.S. Pres. Gerald Ford decided to order the extension of noise standards applicable to new air transports to about 1,550 older transports with takeoff weights exceeding 75,000 lb. The standards were to be applied over an eight-year period beginning Jan. 1, 1977. The U.S. Department of Transportation (DOT) implemented this executive order with the following schedule: B-747s within six years, with one-half completed within four years; B-727s, B-737s, DC-9s, and BAC 1-11s within six years, with one-half in four years; and B-720s, B-707s, DC-8s, and CV-990s within eight years, with one-fourth in four years and one-half in six years.

The airlines had two choices. One was to retire the old aircraft and replace them with new transports that meet the noise standards. The other was to retrofit the old aircraft with noise suppressors, which airlines claimed would cost $3 billion–$5 billion. They preferred the former solution, but doubted whether they could generate the estimated $26 billion (assuming a 6% annual inflation factor) needed to replace their obsolete and noisy jets during the next ten years. In 1977 efforts were being made by DOT to help the airlines finance this program, with indications pointing to earmarking of a portion of the existing air travel user charges (8% ticket tax and 5% cargo waybill tax) for that purpose.

The U.S. Federal Aviation Administration (FAA) certified the new, special-performance B-747SP, a

Bell Helicopter XV-15 is rolled out at Arlington, Texas, in October 1976. Featuring a rotor that can be tilted (top and bottom), the craft was designed to combine the precision hovering and low downwash of a helicopter with the long range and high speed of a fixed-wing airplane.

Photos, Wide World

shorter but longer-range version of the original jet transport. Pan American World Airways became the first airline to offer long-range service with the modified jet, and it began nonstop service between Los Angeles and Tokyo and New York and Tokyo. The 266-seat aircraft cut 3 hours 45 minutes off the previous New York–Tokyo schedule. Another Pan American B-747SP set an around-the-world record for a commercial flight, flying a New York–New Delhi–Tokyo–New York route in 46 hours; the old record of 62½ hours was set in 1965 by a B-707.

Lockheed Aircraft Corp., seeking to capture a sizable share of the 300 potential orders for air transports to replace obsolete B-707s and DC-8s, proposed a shortened, long-range version of the L-1011, a three-engine, widebody transport. While it did report some orders for the new model, its total sales of all L-1011 models failed to meet a goal of 300 by nearly 50%. Lockheed, therefore, announced that it had begun a gradual $515 million write-off of the cost of the project.

Airbus Industrie, builders of the European twin-engine, widebody A300 Airbus, was likewise concerned about failure to attract orders. As of early 1977 it had been able to obtain orders for only about 25% of the 350 aircraft sales needed to break even. To help boost sales and tap the large potential air-freight market, the firm began to market a convertible passenger / cargo version of its longer-range model, A300B4 FC (freighter conversion). This version had a capacity of 345 passengers, or could provide a variety of upper-deck cargo and passenger configurations.

The extremely high costs and risks of new aircraft technology forced U.S. and foreign aircraft manufacturers to consider joint projects, thereby sharing research and development risks and reducing competition for what they believed to be limited markets. One such project was an approved, but not finalized, joint venture by McDonnell Douglas Corp. and France's Dassault-Breguet and state-owned Aérospatiale. They planned to build and sell the Mercure 200, a stretched and more economical 174-seat model of the 150-seat Mercure 100, at a development cost of $250 million. A study for the French government warned, however, of possible losses up to $600 million if this venture is carried through, citing strong competition from the B-727 and the B-7N7; the latter is an advanced trijet with a passenger capacity of about 200 and in 1977 was on the drawing boards. The big advantage of the B-7N7 is its very high bypass ratio, which allows it to generate more power with much less noise and fuel consumption than the B-707s and DC-8s that it would replace. Its development and tooling costs, however, could total $1 billion.

The Boeing Co. reported that it was making a final evaluation of a four-year plan to join with aircraft manufacturers in Japan and Italy in developing a new medium-range, 200–240-seat jet airliner at an estimated cost of $680 million. Boeing foresaw possible sales of about 1,000 such planes for more than $1 billion.

Long-awaited commercial supersonic air passenger service finally got under way, with the British-French Concorde operating between Paris–Rio de Janeiro and London–Bahrain. Air France reported that its flight to Rio, including a fuel stop, took about 7½ hours, 5 hours less than the regular time; British Airways said that its flight to Bahrain took about 3½ hours, a reduction in flight time of about 3 hours.

Because of strong opposition to expected high noise levels of the Concorde, flights to the U.S. were limited during 1976 to the federally owned and operated Dulles International Airport near

Supersonic passenger airliner Concorde takes off from London's Heathrow Airport on Jan. 21, 1976, its first day of commercial service, for a 3,500-mile flight to Bahrain.

Keystone

William E. Sauro—NYT Pictures

Roosevelt Island cable car undergoes performance tests in New York City. The car will run from Second Avenue and 60th Street in Manhattan to Roosevelt (formerly Welfare) Island in the East River.

Washington, D.C. Even this was not easy to accomplish, the decision of then Secretary of Transportation William T. Coleman, Jr., to allow a 16-month test of Concorde service to both New York and Washington having been vigorously challenged. While Coleman's decision for service to Dulles was upheld by a U.S. appellate court, the Port Authority of New York and New Jersey was allowed to block service temporarily to the John F. Kennedy International Airport pending the results of noise and environmental impact tests to be made of all Concorde landings and takeoffs at Dulles. Results of those tests indicated far less impact than opponents of the SST had claimed would occur. For example, the FAA reported confirmation of earlier predictions that the SST is about 50% louder than the B-707 during takeoff but is quieter when landing.

The aerospace ministers of both France and Great Britain, while expressing satisfaction with the performance of the Concorde, recognized its cost disadvantage by announcing their governments' decision not to extend production beyond the 16 planes already in service or being built. They also said that they were discontinuing their feasibility study of an advanced SST for the 1990s.

The Soviet Union continued to report troubles with its Tu-144 SST, which was providing mail/cargo service between Moscow and Alma-Ata, and it suspended further flights indefinitely. U.S. observers expressed the belief that the Tu-144's problems included excessive fuel consumption, vibrations, and pressurization.

A new aircraft landing safety device, called the Minimum Safe Altitude Warning (MSAW), was installed at both Dulles and Los Angeles International airports. MSAW warns air-traffic controllers audibly with a horn and visually with a radar screen message if a plane drops or will drop below a safe altitude. Plans called for its installation at about 65 of the nation's airports by mid-1977 at a cost of $2.9 million.

Urban mass transit. Despite strong efforts by the U.S. Urban Mass Transportation Administration (UMTA) to encourage the development of a standardized urban transit bus with advances in comfort, safety, fuel economy, and noise and emission controls, its well-publicized Transbus program met resistance and thus delay because urban transit authorities preferred buses individualized for their particular needs. UMTA did, however, set a standard for any urban buses funded in large part with federal aid, by announcing that after Feb. 15, 1977, all such vehicles must have an effective floor height of 24 in, as compared with the current 34–35 in, or have a kneeling feature that permits entry and exit at the 24-in level.

General Motors Corp. offered its RTS, a bus designed as part of the Transbus program, for urban service. The 40-ft, 47-seat bus was built from welded modules and was equipped with the kneeling feature for easy boarding and exiting.

European bus concepts were being transferred to the U.S. for urban bus service. Seattle, Wash., was selected for operation of a fleet of articulated diesel buses by late 1977, a first in the U.S. despite long use of such buses in Europe. They were to be built by AM General Corp. In New York City, eight double-decker city buses entered service in Manhattan in a two-year, UMTA-sponsored demonstration project. The buses, built by British Leyland Ltd., had 68 seats, 25 more than conventional single-level buses, and required only the driver to operate them. A similar project was under way in Los Angeles with buses built in West Germany.

UMTA awarded Santa Clara County, California, approximately $4,150,000 to buy 80 new propane-powered transit buses, which would give that county the nation's first all-purpose fleet of buses of that type. UMTA said that the 138 propane-powered buses already in service throughout the U.S. are practically smog-free and have had excellent performance and economy records.

The "world's first gas turbine/electric rail commuter cars" began revenue tests on the Long Is-

Wide World

Articulated diesel buses, widely used in Europe, are being produced by a subsidiary of American Motors Corp. for use in Seattle, Washington.

land Railroad. The cars obtained their power from either a third rail or their gas turbine generators. The $14.8 million program was being funded equally by UMTA and New York state; the eight prototype cars were built by General Electric Co. and the Garrett Corp., four by each.

Rohr Industries, Inc. decided to end its involvement in rail rapid transit but said it would meet its existing contracts, including the building of 300 cars for Washington, D.C.'s Metro system and seven turbine-powered trains for Amtrak. Rohr said that it was getting out of the business because of its unprofitable nature.

Among many UMTA-backed research and development programs for urban mass transit, one was a test in New York City of two flywheel-driven, energy-storing subway cars. These cars were designed to store energy in the flywheels during braking for use during acceleration, with expectations of a reduction in power needs up to one-third.

The future of Downtown People Movers (DPM) got a big boost from UMTA when it announced grants totaling $245 million to four U.S. cities (Cleveland, Houston, Los Angeles, and St. Paul) to help build and demonstrate a variety of systems for inner-city travel. DPM's generally utilize automated buslike vehicles operated by computers along fixed guideways built of concrete. UMTA stressed, however, that it was not promoting futuristic systems that still must prove their feasibility, but instead wanted to see an expansion of the relatively simple systems already being used successfully at some airports and recreational centers.

In furtherance of its program to try to divert downtown travelers from their cars to public transit, UMTA announced the selection of five cities

(Boston, Memphis, Providence, R.I., Tucson, and Burlington, Vt.) to participate in designing auto-restricted zones in downtown areas.

Highway transport. Transportation Secretary Coleman, in a highly controversial decision, decided not to require the installation in new cars of air bags that automatically inflate in crash emergencies and thus prevent occupants of the front seat from being thrown forward and possibly penetrating the car's windshield. He said that the bags work, but lacked public acceptance. As an alternative, he was negotiating with several automakers to persuade them to offer the safety devices in about 500,000 new cars, possibly 1980 models, at a below-cost price partially subsidized by the government and the automakers. In the interim, the Department of Transportation was trying to promote greater use of auto seat/shoulder belt systems, claiming a potential saving of 11,500 fewer annual fatalities if 70% of drivers used them rather than the approximately 15% who did so in 1976.

The drive to improve auto fuel economy continued at full speed, stimulated by tight fuel-mileage standards imposed by the U.S. government on auto makers. The U.S. Environmental Protection Agency (EPA) reported good progress on auto fuel economy, and it predicted that 1977 model cars would average 18.6 mpg, or 6% better than 1976 cars, which would exceed statutory standards set for 1978. Further help could come from EPA's dropping of a phased reduction of lead content in gasoline because of concern about an auto fuel shortage during the summers of 1977 and 1978. This action was taken despite the upholding by a U.S. appellate court of EPA's authority to require gradual removal of lead from gasoline. EPA did, however, set an Oct. 1, 1979, deadline for a sizable one-step reduction to less than one-third of present levels.

Ford Motor Co. announced plans to offer with its 1979 light trucks an optional engine that automatically cuts out half of its cylinders when full power is not needed, for a 10% fuel saving. Another fuel-saving innovation was the unveiling by Sandia Laboratories of a variable displacement auto engine, developed through a $270,000 grant by the U.S. Energy Research and Development Administration (ERDA), which allows the driver to alter the piston stroke and thus adjust power to fit driving conditions. This permits the elimination of the normal throttle for a possible 40% fuel saving, offset in part by a 10–12% increase in weight and cost.

The EPA declined to set standards for sulfur emissions for 1979 cars, saying that the problem had been overestimated and that federal regulations were not needed at this time. The EPA also announced noise standards for new trucks over 10,-000 lb, specifying a maximum of 83 decibels after Jan. 1, 1978, and 80 decibels after Jan. 1, 1982. It said that existing trucks of that size average about 86 decibels. EPA estimated the cost of compliance at about $225 million a year, but predicted a 25% drop in urban traffic noise.

The Japanese government, confronted with growing concern about auto pollution in many of Japan's crowded cities, announced the development of an electric auto with a range of 250 mi — twice that of previous electrics — through use of a new hybrid battery combining iron-air and lead-storage principles. While production costs were about three times those for conventional vehicles, operating costs were only about one-half the amount.

ERDA predicted a major switch to electric cars in the U.S. by the year 2000 because of fuel costs. The agency proposed a program to encourage production of about 1 million electric cars by 1985 and 10 million by the year 2000.

ERDA awarded a $200,000 contract to Lear Motors Co. to evaluate the feasibility of specific flywheel technology for small automobiles. Plans called for the use of a four-hp motor to charge the flywheels when the cars are parked, for the purpose of storing sufficient energy to permit the car to operate up to 50 mi.

Pipelines. The record-cold winter of 1976–77 placed a severe strain on the network of pipelines supplying natural gas for heat and energy in the U.S. By late January pipeline transmission companies could not put enough gas into their systems to meet the greatly increased demand. States and regions served by only one or two pipelines generally suffered the greatest shortages.

Despite serious problems with welds on the 798-mi trans-Alaska pipeline, Alyeska Pipeline Service Co. continued to predict that it would begin operating in mid-1977. It reported at the end of 1976 that the overall project was nearly 90% complete, with major attention centered on completion of the pump stations and the terminal at Valdez, Alaska. Inflation and construction problems pushed estimated total costs to $7.7 billion. Alyeska submitted to both U.S. and Alaskan agencies its oil-spill contingency plans, which provided for rapid detection and corrective action.

Since the U.S. West Coast region cannot possibly use all the Alaska crude oil that will start to flow in 1977, the highly controversial problem arose as to how to transport it to refining and consumption

Traffic controllers in Tokyo monitor their instruments and view a city map showing the major automobile arteries. Tokyo's computerized system has helped alleviate traffic congestion in the city.

Hirotaka Yoshizaki—NYT Pictures

Courtesy, Santa Fe Railway

Storage facility for the Gulf Central Pipeline at Hermann, Missouri. Increased use of the pipeline caused it to be expanded to more than double its previous capacity.

areas throughout the country. Environmentalists, fearing tanker spillages along the coasts and at ports, strongly opposed plans to build terminals and new pipelines to Middle Western refineries. With time rapidly running out, it appeared that much of the surplus crude must be shipped by tanker by all-water routes to refineries on the Gulf of Mexico, either through the Panama Canal or around South America. Maritime laws required the use of both U.S.-built and U.S.-manned ships for the movement of such domestic waterborne commerce, and studies indicated that there were not enough U.S.-flag tankers to handle such a volume. While the U.S. Department of Commerce could make exceptions in an emergency and permit the use of foreign vessels, such a decision would be a difficult one because of strong opposition from U.S. maritime unions and shipbuilders.

If part of the excess crude oil is to be transported by pipeline, one proposal appeared to have the advantage of quick construction. It called for conversion of existing natural-gas pipelines as the major portion (700 out of 1,050 mi) of a line from the Los Angeles area to western Texas.

A new U.S. pipeline went into operation. Seaway Pipeline, 510 mi long and 30 in in diameter, began moving crude oil from tanker berths at Freeport, Texas, to Cushman, Okla. Plans called for a tie-in with Seadock, a deepwater terminal in the Gulf designed to handle the huge supertankers unable to berth at U.S. coastal ports because of their deep drafts. The crude oil would be transferred from those tankers via underground pipelines to storage tanks on the shore.

Rapid growth in traffic of the 1,900-mi Gulf Central Pipeline, which transports anhydrous ammonia fertilizer from Louisiana to Middle Western corn-belt states, spurred a $42 million expansion program to more than double its capacity. Its tonnage between 1970 and 1975 increased from 247,000 to 865,000. The Soviet Union fully recognized the great boost such a pipeline could give to agricultural production, and chose Williams Brothers Engineering Co. to provide the conceptual design for a 1,500-mi ammonia pipeline in that country. It was to have a greater capacity than any other pipeline in the world, with a 360 metric tons-per-hour flow rate in the 14-in-diameter main line. While the construction itself was to be done by workers in the Soviet Union, the designing and material procurement were to be done in the United States and France.

Sharp differences over the need for coal slurry pipelines in the U.S. continued to delay plans for building many such lines. As many as seven coal slurry lines totaling 5,361 mi were under active consideration, but inability to obtain right-of-way authority at the state level—because of opposition by railroads and environmentalist groups—blocked actual construction.

Though the operational feasibility of coal slurry pipelines had been clearly established, through successful operation of a 273-mi line from mines in Black Mesa, Ariz., to a utility in Mohave, Nev., improvements continued to be sought. Keller Corp. announced a new process to reduce the amount of water needed in such pipelines by as much as 80%. This process moves crushed coal suspended in

405

Courtesy, ConRail

ConRail, a federally aided company, took over the operation of seven bankrupt railroads in northeastern U.S.

methyl alcohol or a mixture of alcohols, called methacoal when mixed. Keller claimed that methacoal would flow through lines at steep grades up to 10 ft per second, and said that the process moves an 80% coal mix as compared with only 50% in a water slurry.

Railroad transport. The new Tank Train of GATX Corp. began commercial runs for Cirillo Bros. Petroleum, which had leased 10 of the 23,150-gal-capacity cars to deliver fuel oil from a deepwater terminal in Albany, N.Y., to commercial customers in the northeast region who were formerly served by truck. The special train could load and unload very quickly by using a single outlet, because all the cars in the train were linked by a single hose system. GATX and some western railroads visualized the use of Tank Trains for immediate movements of excess Alaskan crude oil from West Coast ports to Middle Western refineries.

GATX also unveiled a TankTainer intermodal container, a heavy-gauge tank with solid end frames, designed for movement via rail, highway, and ship. Its standard 8-ft by 8-ft by 20-ft size could hold up to 5,200 gal and 55,000 lb at up to 600 psi. GATX claimed that the use of such containers on railroad flatcars could make railroads competitive with tank trucks.

Pullman Standard demonstrated its new Blue Ox wood-chip pulpwood car to shippers and railroads in Panama City, Fla. The car could unload chips, short logs, or long logs, which previously required three different types of cars, in just a few seconds through use of a 51-ft side door. The prototype car could carry 7,000 cu ft or 87.5 tons. While paper companies favored carrier ownership of the cars,

the railroads were resisting the capital outlay until they could get assurances of large-scale use.

U.S. railroads continued a variety of projects to increase freight-car utilization. One, a joint program of the Association of American Railroads, Interstate Commerce Commission, and 11 railroads, attempted to coordinate car use through a clearinghouse system that permitted lines to borrow one another's cars and to reduce the empty cross-hauls caused largely by the return of empty cars to owner roads. The program was started in late 1974 by three railroads (Missouri Pacific Railroad, Milwaukee Road, and Southern Railway System), and progress reports indicated car utilization improvements up to 20%.

In the rail passenger field, Amtrak began service with the first of four French-designed Turboliners, built by Rohr, on three routes between New York City and Albany/Buffalo/Syracuse, respectively. Each of the five-car trains seated 265 persons. Budd Co. unveiled a new self-propelled rail passenger car, SPV-2000, which it said would be able to operate at speeds of 100–120 mph singly or as trains at fuel savings up to 50% compared with present equipment.

Water transport. A major development of great interest to ocean tanker lines and oil pipelines was Secretary Coleman's decision to approve 20-year licensing of the first two deepwater oil ports in the U.S. The ports were subject to many conditions, such as availability to all shippers and stiff environmental-protection regulations. Whether or not the oil companies building them would agree to the strict conditions was debatable, although some indicated that they could not accept them without

Courtesy, Boeing Marine Systems

The Jetfoil, a 224-passenger hydrofoil manufactured by the Boeing Co., began experimental service between Seattle, Washington, and Victoria, British Columbia. Jetfoils were also in use in Hawaii, Hong Kong, Venezuela, the Sea of Japan, and the English Channel.

modification. The two projects included an $865 million deepwater terminal beyond the Texas coast, and a $738 million project off the coast of Louisiana. While such offshore terminals are common in other parts of the world, they had not previously been permitted off U.S. shores.

A trend in maritime ocean shipping toward greater use of roll-on/roll-off and oceangoing barges appeared to be accelerating. Some ship operators expressed concern about overtonnages of such ships, similar to complaints about container ships several years earlier. Large oceangoing barges were being built for roll-on/roll-off service. An example was formation of Euro-Arab Sea Trailer (EAST) to provide such service between Europe and Saudi Arabia, utilizing what it called the "world's largest trailer barge," a 430-ft, triple-decker towed by a 10,000-hp deep-sea tug.

Futuristic water craft moved closer to full-scale commercial use. Boeing's 224-passenger, two-deck advanced hydrofoil, Jetfoil, began experimental service between Seattle and Victoria, B.C. It was designed to cruise at speeds up to 50 mph. Rohr won a $160 million contract from the U.S. Navy to design a 100-mph, 3,000-ton surface-effect ship, which could lead to construction of a prototype by 1982.

UMTA selected New York City for a $995,000 grant to conduct a two-year test of air-cushion vessels in urban commuter service. Three 84-passenger Hovermarine vessels were to replace conventional Staten Island ferries at night, link Manhattan and other points during rush hours, and provide Manhattan–LaGuardia airport shuttle service.

—Frank A. Smith

U.S. science policy

Prediction is very difficult—especially about the future.
—Niels Bohr

Whether or not the quote is apocryphal, it is typical of the great Danish physicist, who once told a visitor that he had nailed a horseshoe over the door—not because he believed in the efficacy of magic but because he understood it worked whether one believed in it or not.

It also serves to point up the situation in which science found itself in 1977—called upon not only to explain the past but also to predict the future. To the extent that the future would be determined by the effects of science and technology on the human condition, many political leaders felt it to be a reasonable demand. Had not the British scientist-novelist C. P. Snow claimed that scientists were better equipped than most in such an enterprise? They had the future "in their bones."

The sometimes cloudy crystal ball. One who called upon the scientific community for such leadership was a good political friend, Sen. Edward M. Kennedy of Massachusetts. To those in attendance at the 100th anniversary meeting of the American Chemical Society (ACS) in April 1976, he declared: "What we need desperately are institutional changes ... which foster better planning for the future.... We have to honestly assess future trends and options—not to lay out a precise master plan to impose on the public—but to present them with the full range of alternatives, including their relative costs and benefits. We need truth-in-packaging for the future. Only in this way can

407

our citizens make informed choices on the vital issues before us.''

Another speaker at the ACS centennial meeting suggested that confidence in the scientific community's prognosticative ability was not entirely misplaced. Linus Pauling noted that, at the 25th anniversary meeting, Harvey W. Wiley had predicted that by 1976 there would be 225 million people in the United States and that the annual federal budget would be $4 billion. His prediction on population was only 7% too high; estimated expenditures in 1976 were $373 billion, but this is not as far from Wiley's estimate as it seems if inflation since 1901 is taken into account.

Wiley also predicted in 1901 that by 1976, ''by a general comprehension of the principles of nutrition, food will be more wholesome and more potent. The general acceptance of the principles of hygiene will make the average life of man longer and his usefulness more fruitful. Man will not only live longer, but he will be happier and practically free from the effects of enzymatic, contagious, and epidemic diseases.''

Some might protest that man is not much happier in 1976 and that, while average life expectancy has been extended, the lifespan of human beings has not. And Wiley was wrong on one other count. In anticipating what his successor as keynote speaker might say 75 years later, he ventured to predict, ''The orator who will address you on that day is perhaps not yet born.'' Pauling took great pleasure in pointing out that, on that day in 1901, he was already six weeks old.

Pauling took his own turn at the crystal ball. Although he saw a world in 2076 from which armed conflict and massive unemployment had been almost entirely eliminated, he was considerably less sanguine about the near term, predicting that, because mankind refused to plan ahead, the next 25 or 50 years would see ''the greatest catastrophe in the history of the world.'' It might result from a world war, ''which could destroy civilization and might well be the end of the human race, but civilization might end because of the collapse of the systems on which it depends.'' Among possible causes, he listed global famine, weather changes due to man's tinkering, fatal reduction of the ozone layer, and the accumulation of poisonous wastes in the atmosphere and the oceans.

''The human race might survive,'' he concluded optimistically. ''By 2076, we shall, I hope, have solved these problems and from then on we may have a world in which every person who is born will have the opportunity to lead a good life.'' Considering the average age of the audience, it was doubtful whether they were greatly reassured by his final remarks.

Sidney Harris

''Our sun is more than four billion years old and has already reached about half its life expectancy. It is now time to plan for the future of mankind, and a positive first step is the election of someone who is willing to face this vital problem. . . .''

The capability of scientists as a group to predict the future, while much in demand, has not—in truth—been well demonstrated over time, despite the emergence in recent years of research institutes entirely devoted to technological forecasting and related fields of futurism. The available evidence suggests that scientists are better equipped to make predictions concerning the physical universe than on anything having to do with the relationship between the physical universe and human society. For example, M. King Hubbert, an exploration geophysicist then in the employ of a large oil company, prophesied in the mid-1950s that U.S. oil production would reach its peak at the end of the next decade and then begin to decline. Although Hubbert repeated his predictions in a report of the National Academy of Sciences to the federal government in 1962, the government only a few years later began creation of the multibillion-dollar interstate highway system, which, as it turned out, assured the nation's eventual dependence on foreign oil. On the other hand, the Club of Rome, which published *The Limits to Growth* in 1972, to the accompaniment of extraordinary publicity, found it necessary to refine its dire predictions a short while later because the authors of the original cry of doom had not cranked into their computers the capacity of human beings to respond intelligently to changes in their physical and socioeconomic environment.

Technology assessment. Of all the attempts to predict the technological future, only one has been officially incorporated into the apparatus of the federal government. That was technology assessment, or TA. Established in 1972 as an analytical arm of the U.S. Congress, the Office of Technology Assessment (OTA) was expected to predict not only the economic consequences of new technologies but also their social costs and benefits. Indeed, its proud parents in Congress and in academic science had visualized it as predicting the effects of new technologies on all aspects of society. It was not enough, they said, to anticipate the immediate impact of technological advance; the second- and third-order effects must be gauged as well.

Early in the OTA's history it became clear that Congress, during a period of some anxiety about the economic health of the country and its competitive position vis-à-vis other nations, was becoming increasingly unconcerned over the need to anticipate the negative effects of technology. Accordingly, the agency turned its main thrust toward studies of the relative promise of new technologies to solve national problems. Even in this far more limited sphere, however, questions were raised with respect to its performance.

In a letter made public in mid-1976, Harold Brown, then president of the California Institute of Technology and later secretary of defense, resigned as the first chairman of the Technology Assessment Advisory Council with the observation that "few of us on the Council, I believe, would say that we are satisfied with what has been accomplished, compared with what we hoped for and still believe possible." As leader of the council, a group of 12 outside authorities called upon to advise the congressional board directing OTA, Brown said that the agency was failing "to provide an early warning system for the Congress so that [it] can consider the social and other impacts of technological advances . . . before those effects are upon us."

Even more critical words came from the Commission on Information and Facilities, established by the House of Representatives to survey such enterprises. In its initial report, the commission found that "OTA remains substantially short of reaching levels of performance reasonably expected of an information resource of its size and cost and access to expertise."

A gentler appraisal of technology assessment came from one of its progenitors, Harvey Brooks, Benjamin Peirce professor of technology and public policy at Harvard University. Brooks, who had served as chairman of the National Academy of Sciences committee that recommended the establishment of OTA, agreed that the "record on implementation of TA has not been particularly happy" but argued that it is in the nature of TA in the political process that answers will be demanded before adequate information is available. TA, he argued, has to be a continuous learning process, in which the first assessment can often do no more than identify areas where more research is needed. Furthermore, the very fact that TA takes place in a political context lessens the likelihood that purely rational analysis will carry the day. The development of the supersonic transport continued despite numerous unfavorable assessments, and "the history of auto emission legislation is explained better by political dynamics than by a rational evolution of choices based on improved technology assessments." In the end, Brooks concluded, "I think the question can only be answered by saying some knowledge is better than none. It is better to proceed with incomplete or inadequate information than with none and some risks will have to be taken."

Science policy and the public interest. By the end of 1976 there was ample evidence that science policy decisions would have to be made on the basis of inadequate information and that some risks would have to be taken. The most highly publicized example was the ill-fated swine flu inoculation program. A group of scientific experts including Jonas Salk and Alfred Sabin, the developers of polio vaccine, advised the government to begin mass inoculations to forestall an epidemic of a new and possibly highly lethal strain of influenza. But the program was beset by problems from the beginning and was finally halted after a statistically significant number of recipients developed an obscure form of temporary paralysis. (See Year in Review: MEDICINE.)

Sometimes one answer conflicted with another. After a public-interest group had succeeded in obtaining legislation mandating the addition of flame retardant to children's sleepwear, another found that the flame retardant used caused cancer in laboratory animals. Consumer's Union, one of the oldest and largest consumers' groups, recommended the use of smoke detectors with ionization chambers using a tiny amount of radioactive americium as the best protection against fatal home fires. But Sidney Wolfe, director of the Health Research Group, condemned the radioactive material as being too dangerous for general use and recommended that photoelectric detectors be employed instead.

One of the staunchest friends of such public-interest groups, the liberal *Washington Post*, rebuked the Health Research Group for responding too quickly to the threat of radiation. The failure to conduct a carefully balanced analysis of risks and benefits, said the *Post* editorially, "is going to be a growing problem for organizations which are created to push specific public-interest programs. It is quite easy for them to slip over the line which the public sees as dividing special-interest groups from public-interest groups."

The warning was especially timely in view of 1976 legislation establishing a program within the National Science Foundation (NSF) aimed at strengthening the technical expertise of public-interest groups. The program originated with a member of Senator Kennedy's staff, and Kennedy persuaded the Senate to authorize funding at a $3 million level. The House Committee on Science and Technology, however, worried about too close a relationship between the NSF and the activist groups. As James W. Symington, chairman of the House Subcommittee on Science, Research, and Technology, told a June 1976 colloquium on science and government: "It is not that we in the House shy away from controversy, nor should the NSF and the scientific community remain aloof from subjects simply because they are controversial, but that we have a genuine concern as to whether the funding of public advocacy groups is a proper function of the NSF." As in the case of much legislation, the committee expressed its anxieties in dollar terms, allowing the foundation only $300,000 in its version of the authorization bill. That was, in fact, all the foundation had asked for. If the House was worried about NSF funding of militant activists, the foundation, it appeared, was equally concerned.

When the authorization bill finally emerged from conference committee it bore the mark of compromise. A total of $1.2 million had been allocated for the controversial Science for Citizens program, including increased funding of the more traditional NSF program to promote the public understanding of science. The bill also specified that no grants were to be made to registered lobbies, and none at all would be made without prior approval of the blue-ribbon National Science Board, the foundation's top policymaking group.

When scientists collide. Underlying these concerns was the growing realization that even the best scientific advice was not sufficient to provide clear guidance on many of the technical questions confronting policymakers. In some cases, it was because the facts eluded scientific grasp. This was pointed out by Alvin Weinberg, director of the Institute for Energy Analysis in Oak Ridge, Tenn., writing in the November 1976 issue of the *Bulletin of the Atomic Scientists*. For instance, he said, it can be easily demonstrated that a dose of 500,000 milliroentgens of radiation is harmful to humans, but if one were to ask whether one milliroentgen per year (1% of natural background) is harmful, science would not be able to answer. Such questions he termed trans-scientific. "Yet questions of this sort," he said, "underlie much of the debate on the deployment of new technology.... The line between science and trans-science is never sharp, nor is it fixed.... The scientist who engages in public debate has a clear responsibility ... to say when he speaks with the full weight of science, when he speaks in a trans-scientific mode."

Many among the scientific leadership held that colleagues who became impassioned about some question of environmental risk lose their scientific objectivity; even worse, they may employ a double standard, speaking carefully to their scientific peers but with loose exaggeration to the public. Philip Handler, president of the National Academy of Sciences, proposed to the bicentennial meeting of Phi Beta Kappa that the code of scientific ethics be extended: "When describing technological risks and benefits to the nonscientific public, the scientist must be as honest, objective, and dispassionate

Early airplanes are among the exhibits at the National Air and Space Museum in Washington, D.C. The museum opened in July 1976.

Dennis Brack—Black Star

as he knows he must be in the more conventional, time-honored, self-policing scientific endeavor."

One approach to the problem of the scientific controversy in which experts contradict experts was to make sure that all such controversies took place within public view. This found somewhat more support outside the scientific community than within. The minutes of a White House advisory group convened to lay the groundwork for restoration of the White House Office of Science and Technology Policy (*see* below) disclose that, at its April 23, 1976, meeting, Chairman Simon Ramo "expressed some concern over the problem of handling controversial topics in a public discussion, where the risk of misunderstanding was very high. Perhaps OSTP should not use public groups for discussion of highly controversial issues."

No such reticence was found among public officials. When workers at several universities announced plans to conduct research in a new field of genetics involving the creation of new variants of living organisms (recombinant DNA), local public officials demanded the right to participate in the

A space suit like that worn by the Apollo astronauts on the Moon is displayed at the Alabama Space and Rocket Center in Huntsville, Alabama.

Teresa Zabala—NYT Pictures

establishment of laboratory requirements to ensure public safety. The fact that a respectable set of universal guidelines had already been issued by the National Institutes of Health was not considered adequate. In an April 1976 address before the American Society for Public Administration, David L. Bazelon, chief judge of the U.S. Court of Appeals for the District of Columbia, insisted that the courts too had a role to play in technical controversies. Their role, he said, was to monitor the decision-making process "to make sure that it is thorough, complete, and rational, and that it takes into account all relevant information and testimony."

The science court. The burgeoning interest in public participation in science policy during 1976 brought sudden attention to an idea that had been seeking acceptance for almost a decade. The idea was called, variously, an Institute of Scientific Judgment, Board of Technical Inquiry, or, most popularly, the science court. Its first (and, for many years, only) sponsor was Arthur V. Kantrowitz, best known for his work in the field of magnetohydrodynamics and financially independent as the result of his success in industrial technology.

Kantrowitz's basic idea was that in most controversial policy issues, it is possible to separate questions of technical fact from questions of value judgment. He argued that the two kinds of questions were confused in the mind of the policymaker, and that if the scientific questions could be plucked out of the debate and brought before a technically trained and objective group for judgment, much of the controversy would vanish and the residual policy question could be resolved in the political arena.

He proposed to deal with these technical questions by adapting some of the processes of traditional courtroom procedures, primarily by employing "case managers" who would argue opposing positions before a panel of scientific judges. Should cyclamates be permitted as artificial sweeteners in soft drinks? In that typical policy issue is imbedded a technical question: Do currently available data from tests on laboratory animals provide reasonable proof as to the safety of the compound? This latter question would be brought before the panel, presumably argued on one side by a case manager from industry and on the other by a case manager from a consumer group. After testimony from both sides and cross-examination by the case managers, the panel of independent scientists would deliver its judgment.

Numerous objections had been raised over the years concerning the validity of the concept, the most serious, perhaps, being that there is no satisfactory way to separate technical from value-laden judgments. Other questions were raised at a

411

Courtesy, *Chemical & Engineering News*

H. Guyford Stever is sworn in as director of the White House Office of Science and Technology Policy by U.S. Vice-President Nelson Rockefeller on Aug. 12, 1976, as President Gerald Ford and Mrs. Stever look on. As the director of the OSTP, Stever also served as science adviser to the president.

colloquium on the science court idea held in September 1976. Margaret Mead found unacceptable the idea that scientific questions could be decided by the adversarial process. James Turner, a lawyer for several consumer activist groups, pointed out that there is a basic difference between the scientific and the legal process. The first, he said, sought truth and the second, justice; the truth is not always just, and justice does not necessarily follow from the discovery of truth.

Despite these reservations, most of the speakers at the meeting, organized under the joint auspices of the Department of Commerce, the National Science Foundation, and the American Association for the Advancement of Science, were friendly to the idea—at least to the extent of trying it out. NSF officials indicated that funds would be available for a trial demonstration. Additional support came from a presidential task force chaired by Kantrowitz and a group of presidents of scientific societies. Questions remained, however, about how such an experiment might be conducted, and where. A proposal to conduct it at the Massachusetts Institute of Technology, where Kantrowitz was a visiting university professor, was rejected by a faculty committee.

Science in the White House. On May 11, 1976, with a flourish of Gerald Ford's pen, U.S. science regained its privileged access to the presidential ear. The signature brought into being Public Law 94–282, "An Act to establish a science and technology policy for the United States, to provide for scientific and technological advice and assistance to the President, to provide a comprehensive survey of ways and means for improving the Federal effort in scientific research and information handling . . . and for other purposes."

The in-and-out history of the White House science office began in November 1957, when Dwight D. Eisenhower, in response to the launching of the first Soviet artificial satellite, organized the President's Science Advisory Committee. Under John F. Kennedy, the staff of the president's science adviser was reorganized into an Office of Science and Technology within the Executive Office of the President. Its influence in the White House dwindled during the administration of Lyndon B. Johnson, and in January 1973, Richard M. Nixon reduced the entire apparatus and transferred it to the National Science Foundation.

There was a delay in the response of the scientific leadership, due in part to shock and in part to the realization that the Nixon White House in 1973 had more to worry about than access to scientific advice. Nixon's appointment of Gerald Ford as vice-president to replace Spiro Agnew signaled the beginning of a thaw, and when Ford became president, the new administration let Congress know that it would look with favor on new enabling legislation. It was this new legislation that President Ford signed on May 11.

The distractions of a presidential election campaign interfered with the prompt establishment of the new White House Office of Science and Technology Policy. Eventually H. Guyford Stever, who had served as both director of the National Science Foundation and informal science adviser to Presidents Nixon and Ford, was named full-time adviser to President Ford and director of the new office. Several months had elapsed since the signing of the bill, however, and it was apparent that OSTP had been moved to the back burner.

And there it stayed during the conventions and the election. Although Jimmy Carter named an advisory committee of scientists during his campaign, he showed no sense of urgency in appointing individuals to fill the principal scientific posts in his new administration. In March 1977, however, he nominated Frank Press, a geophysicist at MIT, as his science adviser and director of the Office of Science and Technology Policy.

—Howard J. Lewis

Scientists of the Year

Honors and awards

The following is a selective list of recent awards and prizes in the areas of science and technology.

Anthropology

Distinguished Service Award. The American Anthropological Association named Margaret Mead and Lita Osmundsen joint recipients of its Distinguished Service Award. Mead, former president of the American Association for the Advancement of Science, has long been recognized as a leader in her field. Osmundsen directed the activities of the Wenner-Gren Foundation in New York, which provides substantial financial support for anthropological research.

Architecture and civil engineering

Acoustics Medal. Theodore J. Schultz, technical director of architectural acoustics and noise control at Bolt Beranek & Newman Inc., in Cambridge, Mass., was awarded a 1976 Silver Medal in Architectural Acoustics by the Acoustical Society of America. He was cited for contributions related to acoustical design parameters and to criteria governing spaces that are used for musical performances.

Brown Medal. The Franklin Institute of Philadelphia named E. Dale Waters recipient of its 1976 Frank P. Brown Medal for "development of heat pipes for stabilization of foundations in Arctic regions." Waters conducted his research at the Westinghouse-Hanford (Conn.) Engineering Development Laboratory.

Honor Awards. A jury of the American Institute of Architects singled out ten structures or building complexes for 1976 Honor Awards because they represented "the highest standard of where [architecture is] today." The list included: R. Crosby Kemper Jr. Memorial Arena in Kansas City, Mo. (C. F. Murphy Associates); Occupational Health Center in Columbus, Ind. (Hardy Holzman Pfeiffer Associates); Waterside apartment complex in New York City (Davis, Brody & Associates); Center for Creative Studies in Detroit (William Kessler & Associates); a student facility at State University College of New York at Purchase (Gwathmey Siegel Architects); Douglas House, a private residence at

Harbor Springs, Mich. (Richard Meier & Associates); Old Boston City Hall, a renovated 1865 landmark (Anderson Notter Associates); Butler Square, a 70-year-old warehouse converted into a luxury hotel with shops and offices, in Minneapolis, Minn. (Miller, Hanson, Westerbeck, Bell, Inc.); Whig Hall, the restoration of a fire-gutted building at Princeton (N.J.) University (Gwathmey Siegel Architects); and Marcus House, a 1910 carriage house converted into a residence in Bedford, N.Y. (Myron Goldfinger).

Astronomy

Founders' Prize. The Texas Instruments Foundation awarded a special one-time Founders' Prize of $10,000 to Frank J. Low for his development and application of the low-temperature germanium bolometer for improved detection of infrared radiation. A research professor at the University of Arizona, Low worked at both the Lunar and Planetary Laboratory and the Steward Observatory; he was also associated with Rice University in Houston, Texas.

Holweck Award. The French Society of Physics and the Institute of Physics in London alternately name the winner of the annual Holweck Medal and Prize. In 1976 the French Society bestowed the honor on Harry Elliot of the Imperial College, London, for studies of cosmic rays and their interaction with geomagnetic and interplanetary magnetic fields.

Hughes Medal and Maxwell Award. For "distinguished contributions to the application of general relativity to astrophysics, especially to the behaviour of highly condensed matter," S. W. Hawking of the University of Cambridge was awarded the 1976 Hughes Medal by the Royal Society. For the same work he also received the Maxwell Medal and Prize from the Institute of Physics in London.

Lenin Prize. The Presidium of the Supreme Soviet awarded 1976 Lenin State Prizes in Science and Technology to Galina Bazilevskaya, Agasi Charakhchyan, Taisiya Charakhchyan, and Yury Stozhkov for their studies of cosmic ray bursts from the Sun and for research on solar modulation of galactic cosmic rays.

Pierce Prize. J. Roger Angel of the Steward Observatory in Arizona was given the 1976 Newton Lacy Pierce Prize by the American Astronomical Society. Using optical-polarization measures, he interpreted radiation from degenerate stars and developed techniques in precision spectropolarimetry to study cool and dust-shrouded stars, and to explore the angular structure of Seyfert galaxies.

Russell Lectureship. Cecilia H. Payne-Gaposchkin of the Smithsonian Astrophysical Observatory,

Harvard University, was named 1976 Henry Norris Russell Lecturer by the American Astronomical Society. Her areas of specialization included stellar atmospheres, galaxies, variable stars, and spectral classification.

Smith Medal. The National Academy of Sciences bestowed the 1976 J. Lawrence Smith Medal on John A. Wood of the Smithsonian Astrophysical Observatory for "influential works over the past decade on the structure, classification and evolution of meteorite bodies."

Warner Prize. The American Astronomical Society selected Stephen E. Strom, an astronomer at the Kitt Peak National Observatory in Arizona, to receive the 1976 Helen B. Warner Prize. His chief interests included young stellar objects associated with circumstellar and interstellar dust and gas clouds. More recently, he has concerned himself with research involving the chemical composition and evolution of galaxies.

Chemistry

Adams Award. William S. Johnson of Stanford University was named by the American Chemical Society as recipient of the 1977 Roger Adams Award in Organic Chemistry. The biennial award, which includes an honorarium of $10,000, acknowledged the importance of his work in total synthesis of natural products, particularly steroids.

Bingham Medal. The Society of Rheology bestowed its 1976 Bingham Medal on Lawrence E. Nielsen, an employee of the Monsanto Co. in Missouri. Besides investigating the rheological behavior of concentrated suspensions, he undertook extensive research on the relationships linking the mechanical properties of high polymers and composite materials to their molecular and colloidal structure.

Chandler Medal. Columbia University honored Kai Siegbahn of Uppsala University in Sweden by presenting him with the 1976 Charles Frederick Chandler Medal. The award called attention to Siegbahn's pioneer work in developing ESCA (electron spectroscopy for chemical analysis), a "powerful method (that) has proven to be of fundamental importance in the understanding and elucidation of (the) composition, electronic configuration and structures of molecules."

Gold Medal. The American Institute of Chemists selected Kenneth S. Pitzer of the University of California, Berkeley, as recipient of its 1976 Gold Medal Award. Pitzer's contributions to physical chemistry include the elucidation of relations between the chemical and physical properties of compounds and the shapes and internal motions of their respective molecules.

Lippincott Medal. The Coblentz Society, the Optical Society of America, and the Society for Applied Spectroscopy chose Richard C. Lord, Jr. as first recipient of the Ellis R. Lippincott Medal. Lord, director of the Spectroscopy Laboratory at the Massachusetts Institute of Technology, applied infrared and Raman spectroscopy to the solution of structural problems in biology and chemistry.

Nobel Prize. The Royal Swedish Academy of Sciences awarded the 1976 Nobel Prize for Chemistry to William N. Lipscomb, Jr., of Harvard University. In 1949 he began experimenting with boranes —chemical compounds containing the elements boron and hydrogen—and eventually discovered the unusual manner in which the atoms are bonded together to form borane molecules. Though scientists knew that pairs of atoms in hydrogen compounds are bonded by pairs of electrons, they could not explain the bonding of boranes in this way because the compounds lacked sufficient electrons. When Lipscomb demonstrated that a pair of electrons could be shared by three borane atoms, he simultaneously provided a plausible explanation for a vast array of other molecules whose structures had long mystified chemical scientists. After World War II Lipscomb obtained his Ph.D. (1946) from the California Institute of Technology. He then spent 13 years at the University of Min-

William N. Lipscomb, Jr.

Wide World

nesota, where he used X-ray diffraction to determine molecular structures. After moving to Harvard University he was named Abbott and James Lawrence professor of chemistry.

Pfizer Award. Stephen J. Benkovic of Pennsylvania State University was chosen to receive the 1977 Pfizer Award in Enzyme Chemistry for his research in anomeric specificity, the biochemistry of folic acid, and studies of the mechanisms of phosphoryl transfer.

Potts Medal. Paul W. Morgan and Stephanie L. Kwolek of E. I. du Pont de Nemours & Co. were each awarded a 1976 Potts Medal by the Franklin Institute in Philadelphia for discovering liquid crystals of polyamides and developing technology for spinning exceptionally strong and stiff fibers from those polymers. Herbert Blades was given a Wetherill Medal for contributing to the success of the same project.

Priestley Medal. Henry Gilman, professor emeritus at Iowa State University, was named recipient of the 1977 Priestley Medal. In announcing its most prestigious award, the American Chemical Society called attention to Gilman's leadership in developing organometallic chemistry, which has been of great importance in synthesis, catalysis, and enzyme research.

Royal Medal. John W. Cornforth, an Australian-born organic chemist, was awarded a gold medal by the Royal Society, London, for fundamental contributions to an understanding of the biosynthesis of steroids.

Welch Award. The 1976 Robert A. Welch Award in Chemistry was given to Neil Bartlett of the University of California, Berkeley. He became the third recipient of the $100,000 Welch Foundation prize for being the first scientist to produce a compound containing a noble gas.

Earth sciences

AAAS-Rosenstiel Award. Gordon A. Riley, professor emeritus at Dalhousie University, Nova Scotia, Canada, received the 1976 American Association for the Advancement of Science-Rosenstiel Award in Oceanographic Science. He was presented with the $5,000 award for being "the first to consider biological oceanography in terms of differential equations and to cast conceptual ideas in rigorous form, thus advancing theories and understanding."

Agassiz and Ewing Medals. The National Academy of Sciences named Walter H. Munk of the University of California at San Diego recipient of the 1976 Alexander Agassiz Gold Medal for "experimental and theoretical research on the spectrum of motion in the oceans and the earth." The American Geophysical Union also named Munk

first recipient of the Maurice Ewing Medal "for outstanding leadership in global geophysics and oceanography and (for) inspired contributions to studies of the rotation of the earth, tides, internal waves, and ocean dynamics."

Day Medal. Each year the Geological Society of America presents the Arthur L. Day Medal "for outstanding distinction in contributing to geological knowledge through the application of physics and chemistry to the solution of geological problems." In 1976 the medal was awarded to Hans Ramberg of the University of Uppsala, Sweden, the author of numerous articles dealing with mineral chemistry, thermodynamics, petrology, tectonics, and geodynamics.

Environmental Quality Award. David M. Evans, a consulting engineer in Denver, Colo., was selected to receive the 1976 National Academy of Sciences Award for Environmental Quality. Evans, who received a $5,000 honorarium, was cited "for his key discovery that injection of liquids deep underground can generate earthquakes, and for his subsequent studies . . . of the environmental implications."

Founders' Prize. The Texas Instruments Foundation of Dallas, Texas, awarded its $35,000 Founders' Prize to Carl I. Wunsch of the Massachusetts Institute of Technology for combining data processing techniques with hydrodynamic theory to generate new oceanographic information.

Horton Medal and Warren Prize. The American Geophysical Union bestowed its first Robert E. Horton Medal on Walter B. Langbein "for outstanding contributions to the geophysical aspects of hydrology." Langbein, long associated with the U.S. Geological Survey, was also named recipient of the 1976 G. K. Warren Prize, administered by the National Academy of Sciences.

Meisinger Award. The American Meteorological Society named Roger A. Pielke of the University of Virginia recipient of its 1977 Meisinger Award. He was cited "for fundamental contributions to mesoscale meteorology through numerical modeling of the sea breeze and interactions among the mountains, oceans, boundary layer and the free atmosphere."

Penrose Medal. Preston Cloud, a biogeologist with the U.S. Geological Survey, received the 1976 Penrose Medal from the Geological Society of America. He was widely recognized as an expert on such subjects as the evolution of the primitive Earth, the evolution of ecosystems, and the problems of man and his finite resources on the Earth.

Rossby Medal. The 1977 Carl-Gustaf Rossby Research Medal of the American Meteorological Society was awarded to Akio Arakawa of the University of California at Los Angeles "for his formulation of physically realistic methods to incorporate convective clouds and boundary layer processes into large-scale prediction models of the atmosphere, and for his contributions in numerical methods of weather prediction.''

Second Half Century Award. The American Meteorological Society bestowed its 1977 Second Half Century Award on Syukuro Manabe, a meteorologist with the U.S. government's Geophysical Fluid Dynamics Laboratory in New Jersey. Manabe was cited ''for his outstanding contribution to the understanding of the influence of radiative processes on the climate through numerical simulation of the dynamics and physics of the atmosphere.''

Special Award. The American Meteorological Society gave a Special Award in 1977 to the Viking Meteorological Flight Team ''for the scientific and engineering achievement which has brought us daily weather reports from Mars. This new capability to compare the atmospheric dynamics of two planets marks a major and historic step forward in the science of meteorology.'' Seymour L. Hess was the team leader and Jack A. Ryan his deputy.

Sverdrup Medal. The 1977 Sverdrup Gold Medal of the American Meteorological Society was presented to Raymond B. Montgomery, professor emeritus of Johns Hopkins University, Baltimore, Md., for ''important contributions to air-sea interactions, isentropic analysis, the study of spatial and temporal analysis of sea-level, and the equatorial current system.'' Montgomery's profound influence on a whole generation of oceanographers and meteorologists was also noted.

Energy

Bohr Medal. Every three years the Danish Society of Chemical, Civil, Electrical and Mechanical Engineers in Copenhagen presents a Niels Bohr Gold Medal to one who has made outstanding contributions to the peaceful use of atomic energy. The Society selected Hans Bethe of Cornell University to receive the 1976 award.

Distinguished Associate Award. John Clarke of the Oak Ridge (Tenn.) National Laboratory was given the 1977 Distinguished Associate Award by the Energy Research and Development Administration, an agency of the U.S. government. Clarke was honored for ''his leadership of a fusion program of unparalleled scope and depth covering theoretical and experimental work in both tokamak and mirror concepts, technology development in the fields of neutral beams and superconducting magnets, and major conceptual design work for next-generation tokamaks.''

Founders Award. The National Academy of Engi-

neering presented its 1976 Founders Award to Manson Benedict, professor emeritus of Massachusetts Institute of Technology, for ''his contributions to the development of atomic energy technology and his leadership in nuclear engineering education.''

Petroleum Chemistry Award. The American Chemical Society Award in Petroleum Chemistry, which includes a $5,000 honorarium from the Lubrizol Corp., is normally given each year to ''recognize, encourage, and stimulate outstanding research achievements in the field of petroleum chemistry.'' Recipient of the 1977 award was Sidney W. Benson, long associated with the University of Southern California and the Stanford Research Institute.

Environment

Fermi Award. The Energy Research and Development Administration, an agency of the U.S. government, named William L. Russell recipient of the 1976 Enrico Fermi Award. Besides a gold medal, Russell received an honorarium of $25,000 for outstanding contributions ''to the quantitative evaluation of the genetic effects of radiation in mammals which serve as a major scientific base for national and international standards for radiation protection of populations; for his major contributions to the principles of genetic theory; and, most recently, for his vigorous efforts to evaluate in animals the mutagenic potential of chemical pollutants arising from nonnuclear energy sources.''

Tyler Award. The $150,000 John and Alice Tyler Ecology Award, administered by Pepperdine University in California, was shared in 1976 by three research scientists. Charles Elton, a biologist at the University of Oxford, formulated the basic principles of modern ecology and wrote *Animal Ecology* (1927), a seminal work of vast importance. René Dubos, professor emeritus of Rockefeller University in New York City, is a microbiologist whose abiding concern was to elucidate the interaction between microorganisms and man. Abel Wolman, professor emeritus at Johns Hopkins University, Baltimore, Md., was primarily responsible for the chlorination of water supplies, which markedly improved public health throughout the world.

Food and agriculture

Babcock-Hart Award. Harold S. Olcott, professor of marine food science at the University of California, Davis, was presented with the 1976 Babcock-Hart Award by the Institute of Food Technologists. The award, sponsored by the Nutrition Foundation, honored Olcott for developing ''a new class of antioxidant substances which provided a basis for a new theory of how antioxidants in general, and vitamin E derivatives in particular, work."

Corson Medal. The Franklin Institute bestowed its first award in nutrition on Nevin S. Scrimshaw, head of the department of nutrition and food science at the Massachusetts Institute of Technology. He was presented with the Bolton L. Corson Medal for discovering new and novel sources of protein for human nutrition. India and South America have notably benefited from his work.

Goldberger Award. Charles E. Butterworth of the University of Alabama School of Medicine was named recipient of the 1976 Goldberger Award. The American Medical Association selected Butterworth for his research in clinical nutrition and on the disease tropical sprue.

Humboldt Award. The $10,000 Alexander von Humboldt Foundation Award, sponsored by the Alfred Toepfer Co. of Hamburg, West Germany, was given in 1976 to John D. Axtell of Purdue University for improving the nutritive quality of sorghum. The citation noted discoveries made by Axtell and his colleagues on tannin protein relationships that "will affect the livestock economy of the world" and made it possible "for plant breeders to markedly enhance the diet of hundreds of millions of people."

McCormick Medal. Each year the American Society of Agricultural Engineers presents a Cyrus Hall McCormick Gold Medal to one of its members for engineering achievement in agriculture. The 1976 honor was bestowed on Lester F. Larsen, who designed and developed testing equipment for tractors used in the production of food.

Information sciences

Goode Award. The American Federation of Information Processing Societies presented its 1976 Harry Goode Memorial Award to Lawrence G. Roberts, president of Telenet Communications Corp. The selection was based on his "contributions to the architectural design of computer-communication systems, his leadership in creating a fertile research environment leading to advances in computer and satellite communications techniques, his role in the establishment of standard international communication protocols and procedures, and his accomplishments in the development and demonstration of packet switching technology and the ensuing networks which grew out of this work."

Marconi Award. Hiroshi Inose of the University of Tokyo was named recipient of the 1976 Marconi International Fellowship, which was supported by 22 corporations. The $25,000 award recognized Inose's expertise in computer technology and his important contributions to the development of switching systems.

Turing Award. Michael O. Rabin of the Hebrew University of Jerusalem, and Dana S. Scott of the University of Oxford shared the 1976 A. M. Turing Award, which is presented each year by the Association for Computing Machinery to one or more individuals for making "a contribution of a technical nature to the computing community."

Zworykin Award. The National Academy of Engineering bestowed its $5,000 Vladimir K. Zworykin Award on C. Kumar N. Patel, who has been director of the Physical Research Laboratory at Bell Telephone Laboratories. He was cited for "outstanding achievement in the field of electronics applied in the service of mankind with particular note of his original contributions in the area of laser technology."

Life sciences

Adler Prize. Edward A. Boyse of the Sloan-Kettering Institute for Cancer Research, New York City, and professor of biology at Cornell University Medical School, became the first person since 1947 to be named recipient of the $10,000 Isaac Adler Prize. Boyse received the award from the president and fellows of Harvard College for his research on the surface of the cell and the manner in which genes

Edward A. Boyse

Wide World

determine its composition in higher organisms, such as man.

Copley Medal. Dorothy M. C. Hodgkin of the University of Oxford was awarded the 1976 Copley Medal for outstanding work on the structure of complex molecules, particularly penicillin, vitamin B_{12}, and insulin.

Franklin Medal. Mahlon B. Hoagland of the Worcester Foundation for Experimental Biology in Shrewsbury, Mass., was given the 1976 Franklin Medal for his research on protein synthesis and its relationship to DNA and RNA.

Gairdner Award. Eugene P. Kennedy of the Harvard Medical School, Boston, was awarded $10,000 by the Gairdner Foundation in Willowdale, Ont., for his elucidation of the biochemical pathways involved in triglyceride and phospholipid synthesis.

Hardy Prize. Frederick Sanger of King's College, University of Cambridge, received the William Bate Hardy Prize from the Cambridge Philosophical Society for his research on the sequencing of DNA.

Horwitz Prize. The $20,000 Louisa Gross Horwitz Prize for 1976 was shared by Seymour Benzer of the California Institute of Technology and Charles Yanofsky of Stanford University. The prize committee noted that "nothing goes on in the field of molecular genetics today that is not built on their findings." Benzer was cited for establishing the field of fine-structure genetics and Yanofsky for establishing the fundamental validity of the one-gene–one-enzyme hypothesis.

Jubilee Award. Arthur Kornberg of the Stanford University School of Medicine was named recipient of the 1976 Jubilee Award of the Biochemical Society, London. Kornberg became widely known for his research on the role of enzymes in the replication of DNA.

Levy Medal. David M. Auslander, Carl B. Huffaker, and George F. Oster, all of the University of California at Berkeley, received 1976 Louis E. Levy medals from the Franklin Institute as co-authors of a paper entitled: "Dynamics of Interacting [Insect] Populations." Although Oster and Huffaker are entomologists, Auslander holds the position of associate professor of mechanical engineering.

Lilly Award. Robert G. Roeder of the Washington University School of Medicine in St. Louis, Mo., was given the 1977 Eli Lilly Award in Biological Chemistry. Throughout his career, Roeder's chief interest centered on the activities of RNA polymerases in animal-cell nuclei.

Tillyer Award. The Optical Society of America selected Floyd Ratliff of Rockefeller University, New York City, to receive the Edgar D. Tillyer Award for 1976. Ratliff was honored for his work on spatial and temporal interactions among the various receptors of the eye of the horseshoe crab.

Materials sciences

Douglas Medal. The American Institute of Mining, Metallurgical and Petroleum Engineers (AIME) bestowed its 1977 James Douglas Gold Medal on Carleton C. Long for "uniquely distinguished contributions to the metallurgy of zinc, lead and their alloys."

Glazebrook Award. The Institute of Physics in London selected Sir Montague Finniston of the British Steel Corp. to receive the 1976 Glazebrook Medal and Prize for his leadership in the application of science to the large-scale manufacture of steel.

Lucas Medal. The 1977 Anthony F. Lucas Gold Medal was given to Marshall B. Standing by the AIME for longtime contributions "to the knowledge of reservoir and well performance and to the effective teaching of their practical applications."

New Materials Prize. The American Physical Society presented its 1976 International Prize for New Materials to William G. Pfann and Henry C. Theuerer, research scientists at Bell Telephone Laboratories in New Jersey. The two were cited "for their outstanding work on the development of methods for purifying semiconductors and growing epitaxial crystals from the vapor phase. This effort has been of vital importance in the growth of semiconductor technology."

Richards Award. Denis F. Kelsall received AIME's 1977 Robert H. Richards Award for "outstanding contributions to mineral processing in the theory, operation and development of equipment," including the Cyclosizer.

Mathematics

Lenin Prize. The Presidium of the Supreme Soviet of the U.S.S.R. awarded 1976 Lenin State Prizes in Science and Technology to Nikolay N. Krasovsky, Aleksandr B. Kurzhansky, Yury S. Osipov, and Andrey I. Subbotin for their work on the mathematical theory of control systems.

Sylvester Medal. The Royal Society, London, presented its 1976 Sylvester Medal to David G. Kendall of the University of Cambridge for his contributions to probability theory and its applications.

Waterman Award. Charles L. Fefferman of Princeton University was named first recipient of the Alan T. Waterman Award, established by the U.S. Congress in 1975. The award, administered by the National Science Foundation, consists of a gold medal and a grant of $150,000 spread over a three-year period so that Fefferman can conduct research or study at any U.S. institution of his choice. The citation noted "his researches in Fourier analysis, partial differential equations, and several complex variables that have brought fresh insight and renewed vigor to the classical areas of mathematics and contributed signally to the advancement of modern mathematical analysis."

Mechanical engineering

Lenin Prize. Valentin D. Shashin, minister of the Soviet Union's petroleum industry, Feliks G. Arzhanov, Valeri I. Grayfer, Valentin V. Karibsky, Aleksandr V. Sinelnik, and Tevgat S. Gaynutdinov were each given a 1976 Lenin State Prize in Science and Technology by the Presidium of the Supreme Soviet for contributing to the automation of petroleum production.

Medical sciences

Award of Merit. The Gairdner Foundation in Willowdale, Ont., presented a special $25,000 Award of Merit to Godfrey N. Hounsfield of the Central Research Laboratories at EMI Limited in Middlesex, Eng., for "his outstanding contribution to the care of patients by the pioneer development of computerized tomography."

Gairdner Awards. The Gairdner Foundation presented 1976 awards, each worth $10,000, to George Klein of the Karolinska Institutet in Stockholm and to George D. Snell of the Jackson Laboratory in Bar Harbor, Maine. Klein was honored for contributing to an understanding "of the biology of neoplastic cells and [for] his distinguished work in tumour immunology." Snell was cited for "his identification of the major histocompatibility complex in mice, and for establishing methods of study fundamental to immunogenetics." An additional award of $10,-000 was shared by Thomas R. Dawber of the Boston University School of Medicine and William B. Kannel of the Public Health Service in Framingham, Mass. Each was cited for "careful epidemiologic studies, revealing risk factors in cardiovascular disease which have important implications for the prevention of these disorders."

Lasker Awards. The $10,000 Albert Lasker Basic Medical Research Award for 1976 was presented to Rosalyn S. Yalow, a senior medical investigator with the U.S. government's Veterans Administration. She was cited "for her role in discovering and developing the technique of radioimmunoassay for identifying and measuring, in blood and other body fluids, the concentration of hundreds of substances," including "hormones, drugs, vitamins, enzymes, and viruses."

The Albert and Mary Lasker Foundation also announced two 1976 Clinical Medical Research Awards. The $10,000 prize was shared by Raymond P. Ahlquist of the Medical College of (Augusta)

Georgia and by J. W. Black of the University College of London. Ahlquist was selected "for his concept of alpha and beta receptors, which opened the door to the development of propranolol, a milestone drug in the treatment of heart diseases and severe high blood pressure." Black, who based his research on Ahlquist's concept of the adrenergic receptor mechanisms, developed propranolol in 1964. This new medication directly benefited countless patients afflicted with various forms of heart disease as well as those suffering from dangerously high blood pressure.

A Special Public Health Service Award of $10,000 was given to the World Health Organization "for its historic achievement in the imminent eradication of smallpox, the first and only disease ever to be eradicated from the Earth."

Nobel Prize. The Nobel Prize for Physiology or Medicine was shared in 1976 by Baruch S. Blumberg and D. Carleton Gajdusek. The two virologists, each of whom received an honorarium of about $80,000 administered by the Karolinska Institutet in Stockholm, were honored "for their discoveries concerning new mechanisms for the origin and dissemination of infectious disease." While visiting Australia on one of his many travels, Blumberg discovered that the blood of an Aborigine contained a protein also found in the blood of hepatitis victims. He later learned that this "Australian antigen" was part of the virus that causes hepatitis B infection and might also be linked to cancer. An antigen test for hepatitis B infection was subsequently developed to prevent virus transmission through blood transfusions. Blumberg received his medical degree from Columbia University's College of Physicians and Surgeons and a Ph.D. in biochemistry from the University of Oxford. He has been associated with both the Institute for Cancer Research in Philadelphia and the department of anthropology at the University of Pennsylvania and did research at the National Institutes of Health.

Gajdusek sought to determine the nature and cause of a mysterious fatal disease that the Fore tribe in New Guinea called *kuru* ("trembling"). After learning the language of the Fore, Gajdusek studied their culture and in a makeshift field laboratory performed autopsies on kuru victims. He concluded that kuru is an infectious neurological disease transmitted by the ritual eating of human brains. Later experiments with chimpanzees confirmed his suspicions that the destructive agent within the brain tissue was a slow-acting virus that could remain dormant for an extended period of time. His discoveries may also provide the clue to understanding such other puzzling nervous disorders as multiple sclerosis and Parkinson's disease. Associated with the U.S. National Institutes of

Wide World

Baruch S. Blumberg

Wide World

D. Carleton Gajdusek

Health in Bethesda, Md., Gajdusek earned his medical degree at Harvard University and did post-doctoral studies there and at the California Institute of Technology.

Royal Medal. James L. Gowans of the Medical Research Council Cellular Immunology Unit, Oxford, England, was honored in 1976 by the Royal Society "for his distinguished research in the field of immunology, especially as regards the recirculation and immunological role of lymphocytes."

Schwartz Award. The American Medical Association presented the 1976 Arnold and Marie Schwartz Award to Alton I. Sutnick of the University of Pennsylvania School of Medicine "for his studies of atelectasis, pneumonia, and pulmonary embolism."

Scientific Achievement Award. The American Medical Association's Scientific Achievement Award for 1976 was given to Harry Goldblatt of Mt. Sinai Hospital in Cleveland, Ohio, for determining the relationship between kidney disease and hypertension.

Wightman Award. The Gairdner Foundation announced a new $25,000 award in 1976 and selected K. J. R. Wightman, the man after whom it is named, as the first recipient. The Gairdner Foundation Wightman Award, created to honor Canadians who demonstrate outstanding leadership in medicine and medical science, was given to Wightman for his active role in education and for promoting the establishment and activities of numerous medical groups, especially in the Toronto area.

Optical engineering

Inventor Award. Emmett N. Leith and Juris Upatnieks of the University of Michigan received the 1976 Inventor of the Year Award from the Association for the Advancement of Invention and Innovation. The two were cited for their use of a laser light source to construct and display true three-dimensional holographic images.

Ives Medal. The Optical Society of America awarded its 1976 Frederic Ives Medal to Arthur L. Schawlow of Stanford University, who has performed significant research in the field of lasers and optical and microwave spectroscopy.

Lomb Medal. The biennial Adolph Lomb Medal of the Optical Society of America was presented in 1976 to Marc D. Levenson of the University of Southern California. Levenson was selected for his work in laser spectroscopy, including the development of two-photon absorption spectroscopy without Doppler broadening and the spectroscopic technique called three-wave mixing.

Richardson Medal. The Optical Society of America awarded its 1976 David Richardson Medal to John H. McLeod of the Eastman Kodak Co., an expert in applied optics. Besides developing optical-production machinery, plastic-transfer molding techniques, and unique equal-path interferometers, McLeod invented the axicon, a mirror with a conically shaped surface used in various optical instruments.

Physics

Bonner Prize. The 1976 Tom W. Bonner Prize in Nuclear Physics was given to John P. Schiffer of the Argonne National Laboratory in Illinois. In presenting the award, the American Physical Society cited Schiffer's "contributions to the understanding of nuclear structure through studies of nuclear reaction, particularly his work on nuclear Coulomb energies and the effective residual interactions in the shell model."

Born Award. The German Physical Society in conjunction with the Institute of Physics in London presented the 1976 Max Born Medal and Prize to Hermann Haken of the University of Stuttgart, West Germany, for his contributions to quantum optics and solid-state physics. Haken was the first to establish a quantum-mechanical theory of laser discharge. He also calculated the binding energy of the exciton (the "Haken potential").

Buckley Prize. George Feher of the University of California at San Diego received the 1976 Oliver E. Buckley Solid State Physics Prize from the American Physical Society for his "development of electron-nuclear double resonance, and the application of spin resonance to a wide range of problems in the physics of condensed matter."

Europhysics Prize. Wolfgang Helfrich of the Free University of Berlin was selected by the European Physical Society to receive the 1976 Hewlett-Packard Europhysics Prize of 20,000 Swiss francs (about $8,000) for contributing to an understanding of the physics of liquid crystals.

Guthrie Award. The Guthrie Medal and Prize of the Institute of Physics, London, was given in 1976 to Abdus Salam for his contributions to the theory of fundamental particles. Salam was associated with both the Imperial College of Science and Technology in London and the International Center for Theoretical Physics in Trieste, Italy.

Longstreth Medal. The Franklin Institute awarded its 1976 Edward Longstreth Medal to Walter L. Bond of the W. W. Hansen Laboratories of Physics at Stanford University "for his contributions to the science and practice of crystallography."

Nobel Prize. Two U.S. scientists shared the 1976 Nobel Prize for Physics for a revolutionary discovery in high-energy physics. Samuel C. C. Ting of the Brookhaven National Laboratory in New York and the Massachusetts Institute of Technology (MIT) directed a team that discovered a new subatomic particle, designated J. Almost simultaneously Burton Richter of the Stanford Linear Accelerator Center-Lawrence Berkeley Laboratory in California headed a group that used a quite different procedure to discover the same particle independently; it was named psi. The discovery of the J/psi particle brought scientists one step closer to understanding the ultimate components of the universe. Whereas previous research had led physicists to postulate the existence of three fundamental particles called quarks, the J/psi particle has unique properties that seem to point to a fourth quark with a special quality called charm.

After receiving his Ph.D. from the University of Michigan, Ting worked at the European Organization for Nuclear Research (CERN) in Geneva and taught physics at Columbia University in New York City. He then joined MIT and Brookhaven Laboratory. Richter obtained his doctorate from MIT and moved to Stanford University in 1956.

Oppenheimer Prize. The Center for Theoretical Studies at the University of Miami presented its 1976 J. Robert Oppenheimer Memorial Prize to Yoichiro Nambu of the University of Chicago. His contributions to physics included the formulation of

Samuel C. C. Ting

Wide World

Burton Richter

Wide World

the Bethe-Salpeter equation, used to describe fundamental-particle interactions through fields.

Planck Medal. The 1976 Max Planck Medal of the German Physical Society was given to Ernst C. G. Stueckelberg, emeritus professor at the University of Geneva, for his work in quantum field theory, molecular physics, and thermodynamics.

Rutherford Award. Roger J. Blin-Stoyle of the University of Sussex and Joan M. Freeman of the U.K. Atomic Energy Authority were named recipients of the 1976 Rutherford Medal and Prize by the Institute of Physics, London. Both were honored for their significant studies on beta-radioactivity of complex nuclei.

Schottky Prize. Franz Wegner of the Institute for Theoretical Physics at the University of Heidelberg, West Germany, was given the 1976 Walter Schottky Prize by the German Physical Society for his theoretical work in the areas of phase transitions and elementary particles.

Wetherill Medal. James W. Cronin of the Enrico Fermi Institute in Chicago and Val L. Fitch of Princeton University each received a 1976 John Price Wetherill Medal from the Franklin Institute "for their discoveries implying failure of time reversal invariance for elementary particles."

Herbert Blades of E. I. du Pont de Nemours & Co. also received a Wetherill Medal for discovering liquid crystals of polyamides and developing technology for spinning exceptionally strong and stiff fibers from those polymers. Two colleagues received Potts medals (*see above*) for the same work.

Wood Prize. Theodore H. Maiman received the 1976 R. W. Wood Prize from the Optical Society of America for developing (1960) the first laser. His success in producing an intense beam of wholly coherent light by means of a rod of synthetic ruby led to the development of other types of lasers, which have been of immense value in industry, medicine, and other fields.

Psychology

Applications in Psychology Award. The American Psychological Association (APA) named Fred S. Keller recipient of its 1976 Distinguished Contribution for Applications in Psychology Award. He was cited for making "an extraordinary range of boldly creative contributions to instructional procedures. . . . By showing how a subject can be mastered step by step in a carefully constructed program, he has freed both student and teacher from the aversive by-products of crucial examinations, and in doing so has made learning not only more effective but more humane."

Kittay Award. The $25,000 International Kittay Award for 1976 was presented jointly to James Olds

© Karsh, Ottawa; courtesy, Kittay Scientific Foundation

Hans Selye

of the California Institute of Technology and to Hans Selye of the Institute of Experimental Medicine and Surgery at the University of Montreal. Olds was honored for adding "a new dimension to the understanding of human motivation"; Selye was selected for opening "new perspectives for the field of psychosomatic medicine." Neither was directly seeking the information that turned out to be of such great importance to psychiatry. While Olds and a colleague were testing avoidance centers in the brains of rats, they mislocated an electrode and discovered a pleasure center that the rats later repeatedly stimulated by pushing levers. When Selye injected mice with impure extracts and toxic drugs as part of his study of sex hormones, the mice manifested what is now recognized as the three classical stages of the stress syndrome: alarm, adaptation, exhaustion. This discovery was later related to such disorders as hypertension, ulcers, and colitis.

Professional Contribution Award. The APA named John C. Flanagan and David Shakow corecipients of its Distinguished Professional Contribution Award for 1976. Flanagan directed the program of Aviation Psychology during World War II. "Through ingenious test development and careful validation, this program . . . demonstrated the potential of this kind of classification testing on a nationwide basis, more recently exemplified by Project TALENT." Shakow was cited for "his leadership in creating a training model for clinical psychology that would retain the unique quality that characterizes a psychologist, and (for) his research contributions in the psychological study of schizophrenia."

Courtesy, Kittay Scientific Foundation

James Olds

Scientific Contribution Award. The APA named four persons recipients of 1976 Distinguished Scientific Contribution Awards: Beatrice C. Lacey and John I. Lacey, Theodore M. Newcomb, and Roger N. Shepard. The Lacey citation read in part: "With superb technology and meticulous experiments, they have demonstrated that complex patterns of autonomic response are measurable, characteristic of individuals, stable across years, and predictive of individual-environment transactions."

Newcomb was selected for work that "led the way to a greater interdisciplinary involvement of social psychology, especially with sociology and anthropology, not only on the conceptual level, but also in the application of interdisciplinary conceptions to pressing social problems." Shepard's citation mentioned, among other things, "his pioneering work in cognitive structures, especially his invention of nonmetric multidimensional scaling, which has provided the social sciences with a tool of enormous power for uncovering metric structures from ordinal data on similarities."

Space exploration

Fahrney Medal. William H. Pickering of the California Institute of Technology, a former director of NASA's Jet Propulsion Laboratories, became the first recipient of the Fahrney Medal. The Franklin Institute chose Pickering for his leadership in science and technology in space programs.

Foucault Prize. The French Society of Physics named J.-P. Taran recipient of the 1976 Foucault Prize for his work in applied physics. Taran worked with the Office National d'Études et de Recherches Aérospatiales near Paris.

Transportation

Brown Award. Each year the Institute of Civil Engineers in London provides the S. G. Brown Award and Medal to foster mechanical inventions. In 1976 the Royal Society selected Frank Mackley of J. T. Mackley & Co. for contributing to the development of the Hover Platform.

Gold Medal. The 1976 Gold Medal of the Royal Aeronautical Society, London, was presented to William J. Strang who, as joint technical director of the Concorde project, had a key role in developing supersonic commercial transportation.

Science journalism

AAAS-Westinghouse Awards. Each year the American Association for the Advancement of Science administers journalism awards sponsored by the Westinghouse Electric Corp. A $1,000 prize is assigned to each of three categories: articles appearing in U.S. newspapers having a daily circulation exceeding 100,000; articles appearing in newspapers having a more limited circulation; and articles appearing in magazines intended for the general public. The first of the 1976 awards went to Paul G. Hayes for "Mountains of Oil," which appeared in the *Milwaukee* (Wis.) *Journal* (Oct. 3, 1976). Don Alan Hall, writing for the *Corvallis* (Ore.) *Gazette-Times*, was selected for "Trees of Conflict" (Aug. 4, 1976). The magazine award was given to Jonathan Eberhart for 25 articles on the Viking mission to Mars, which were published in *Science News* (June–November 1976).

AIP-U.S. Steel Award. The 1976 winner of the American Institute of Physics-United States Steel Foundation Science-Writing Award in Physics and Astronomy was Jeremy Bernstein of the Stevens Institute of Technology in New Jersey. The seven judges chose him for a two-part article entitled "Physicist: I. I. Rabi," published in *The New Yorker* (Oct. 13 and 20, 1975).

Grady Award. The 1977 recipient of the James T. Grady Award for Interpreting Chemistry for the Public was Patrick Young, a science reporter with the *National Observer*. In bestowing the award, the American Chemical Society called attention to eight of Young's articles, including "Moon Gives up Some Secrets, Puzzles Remain"; "Nuclear

Tools Added to Fight on Disease"; and "Science Seeks a Salt-Water Garden."

Washburn Award. Each year the Museum of Science in Boston presents a gold medal and an honorarium of $5,000 to an individual "who has made an outstanding contribution toward public understanding of science, appreciation of its fascination, and the vital role it plays in all our lives." The 1976 Bradford Washburn Award was given to Loren C. Eiseley, an author and anthropologist at the University of Pennsylvania.

Miscellaneous

Boys Prize. S. D. Smith of the Heriot-Watt University in Edinburgh received the 1976 Charles Vernon Boys Prize from the Institute of Physics, London, for his contributions to the design of scientific instruments in physics and meteorology.

National Medal of Science. The U.S. government's highest scientific award, the National Medal of Science, is presented annually by the president of the United States to persons who have done outstanding work in the physical, biological, mathematical, or engineering sciences. The 15 recipients of 1975 gold medals were: John W. Backus, a computer scientist at IBM San Jose (Calif.) Research Laboratory; Manson Benedict, a nuclear engineer, professor emeritus of the Massachusetts Institute of Technology; Hans Bethe, a physicist, professor emeritus of Cornell University; Shiing-Shen Chern, a mathematician at the University of California, Berkeley; George B. Dantzig, a computer scientist at Stanford University; Hallowell Davis, a physiologist, professor emeritus of Washington University, St. Louis, Mo.; Paul György (deceased), pediatrician, late professor emeritus of the University of Pennsylvania's School of Medicine; Sterling B. Hendricks, an agricultural chemist, formerly with the U.S. Department of Agriculture; Joseph O.

Hirschfelder, a chemist at the University of Wisconsin; William H. Pickering, space scientist, director emeritus of the Jet Propulsion Laboratory in Pasadena, Calif.; Lewis H. Sarett, a chemist, vice-president of Merck & Co.; Frederick E. Terman, an electronics engineer, emeritus vice-president of Stanford University; Orville A. Vogel, an agronomist, professor emeritus of Washington State University; E. Bright Wilson, Jr., a chemist at Harvard University; and Chien-Shiung Wu, a physicist at Columbia University.

Science Talent Awards. The 36th annual Science Talent Search, sponsored by the Westinghouse Educational Foundation and administered by Science Service, produced the following winners in 1977. The first-place award, a $10,000 scholarship, was given to Richard C. Schirato, a senior at Skyline High School in Dallas, Texas, for his research in photochemistry. Schirato studied the unstable intermediate complexes (exciplexes) that are produced when certain chemical reactions are stimulated by light. He found a simple correlation between the wavelengths of light emitted by exciplexes in solution and the known parameters of various solvents. The second-place $8,000 scholarship went to James G. Propp, a senior at Great Neck (N.Y.) North Senior High School. In his mathematics project he sought to prove or demonstrate properties of sequences of integers. Winner of the third-place $8,000 scholarship was Annie L. Murray, a senior at Melbourne (Fla.) High School. Her investigation centered on the microorganisms that destroy gum tissue and cause tooth decay. Three other winners each received a $6,000 scholarship: Evan M. Tick of Jamaica (N.Y.) High School for developing a computer simulation program for modeling rapid transit systems; Grant H. Stokes of Los Alamos (N.M.) High School for investigating gamma radiation that results when a positron, a form of antimatter, encounters an electron; and

Richard C. Schirato

James G. Propp

Annie L. Murray

Photos, courtesy, Science Service, Inc.

Douglas W. Laske of the Bronx (N.Y.) High School of Science for his research on the biochemistry of enzyme systems. Four additional students each received $4,000 scholarships: Daniel D. Blau of Stuyvesant High School in New York City; Paul A. Cahill of East High School in Akron, Ohio; Kenneth J. Lohmann of West Lafayette (Ind.) High School; and Glenn C. Poole of Annandale (Va.) High School.

Silver Medal. The Acoustical Society of America presented a 1976 Silver Medal in Engineering Acoustics to Hugh S. Knowles, president of Knowles Electronics and of Industrial Research Products. The citation called special attention to the technical contributions he made to improve hearing.

Szilard Award. Richard L. Garwin of IBM's Thomas J. Watson Research Center received the 1976 Leo Szilard Award for Physics in the Public Interest. He was honored by the American Physical Society Forum on Physics and Society for publicly elucidating such major technological issues as those connected with supersonic commercial passenger transportation.

Wildhack Award. Ernest Ambler of the National Bureau of Standards received the William A. Wildhack Award from the National Conference of Standards Laboratories for his numerous contributions to metrology.

Obituaries

The following persons, all of whom died in recent months, were widely noted for their scientific accomplishments.

Aalto, (Hugo) Alvar Henrik (Feb. 3, 1898 – May 11, 1976), Finnish architect, had an influence on modern design that rivaled that of any of his contemporaries. Most of his finest creations were built in Finland and manifest a deep affinity with Finnish landscape and culture, though his works can also be seen in France, Germany, the U.S., and other countries. Among notable early works were the Turun Sanomat newspaper offices in Turku (1930); the tuberculosis sanatorium at Paimio (1933); and the Municipal Library at Viipuri (1930–35). His Säynätsalo town hall buildings (1950–52) exemplify Aalto's mature style, his awareness of individual settings, and his predilection for regional materials. He also designed furniture, often using laminated or bent birchwood. Aalto was trained at the Technical Institute of Helsinki and counted among his many honors the Gold Medal of the American Institute of Architects (1963).

Bullen, Keith Edward (June 29, 1906 – Sept. 23, 1976), New Zealand seismologist, became a pro-

Courtesy, Consulate General of Finland

Alvar Aalto

tégé of Harold Jeffreys at the University of Cambridge, where in the early 1930s the two began compiling travel-time measurements of earthquake pulses. Considering the imperfections of scientific equipment at the time and the irregular distribution of seismological stations throughout the world, the Jeffreys-Bullen Tables (1935, 1940), still widely used today, were a remarkable achievement. Bullen's lifelong study of the distribution of the density of the Earth, which included development of the Bullen A and Bullen B models, was summarized in his book *The Earth's Density* (1975). He was professor of applied mathematics at the University of Sydney from 1946 to 1971 and served as president (1954–57) of the International Association of Seismology and Physics of the Earth's Interior.

Curme, George Oliver (Dec. 24, 1888 – July 28, 1976), U.S. chemist, developed processes for commercial production of a wide variety of aliphatic chemicals, particularly ethylene glycol for use as an antifreeze in cars, and numerous derivatives of petroleum-based hydrocarbons. His research contributed significantly to the expansion of the chemical industry in the U.S. After obtaining his Ph.D. (1913) from the University of Chicago, Curme went to Germany, which at the time led the world in

Henrik Dam

organic chemistry. Early in his career he joined Union Carbide and in 1948 was named a vice-president in charge of chemical research. Though he retired in 1955, he remained as a director of the company until 1961.

Dam, (Carl Peter) Henrik (Feb. 21, 1895—April 18?, 1976), Danish biochemist, shared the 1943 Nobel Prize for Physiology or Medicine with Edward A. Doisy of the U.S. In the early 1930s, while studying laboratory chicks that suffered from internal bleeding when restricted to a certain diet, Dam discovered the existence of vitamin K, a naphthoquinone compound that acts as an antihemorrhagic agent. In 1939 he and Doisy, working independently, isolated the vitamin from alfalfa (lucerne). Thereafter, vitamin K played a vital role in saving the lives of many newborn infants and patients undergoing surgery. Dam graduated from the Copenhagen Polytechnic Institute (1920) and the University of Copenhagen (1934) and taught in Copenhagen until 1939. During World War II he was on the faculty of the University of Rochester in New York. From 1946 to 1965 he was professor of biochemistry and nutrition at the Polytechnic Institute in Copenhagen and from 1956 to 1963 headed the biochemical division of the Danish Fat Research Institute.

Flint, Richard Foster (March 1, 1902—June 5, 1976), U.S. geologist, was the author of *Glacial and Quaternary Geology* (1971), considered the most comprehensive and up-to-date presentation of the subject available in any language. In all, Flint published more than 150 research papers and mono-

graphs, including *Glacial Geology and the Pleistocene Epoch* (1947) and *Glacial and Pleistocene Geology* (1957). He was also chairman of the National Research Council committees that compiled the Glacial Map of the United States and the Glacial Map of North America, and he assumed an active editorial role in several scientific journals. Flint obtained his Ph.D. (1925) from the University of Chicago and then joined the faculty of Yale University, where he remained until his retirement in 1970.

Friis, Harald Trap (Feb. 22, 1893—June 15, 1976), Danish-born electrical engineer, was one of the most creative radio communications experts of his time. Friis received a degree in electrical engineering (1916) from the Royal Technical College in Copenhagen, where he was later granted a doctorate of science (1938). In 1919 he moved to the U.S. and joined the Western Electric Co., where he designed the first commercial double-detection superheterodyne broadcast radio receiver, the forerunner of the modern radio. With Karl Jansky he designed (1932) the first antenna to trace the cause of one type of radio interference to emissions from the center of the Galaxy and thus initiated radio astronomy. The rhombic antenna used in shortwave radio telephony was designed by Friis and Edmond Bruce. Friis also designed the multiple unit steerable antenna and the horn-reflector antenna now in worldwide use. The Bell System microwave radio facilities for long distance telephone circuits were likewise initially designed by Friis.

Frumkin, Aleksandr Naumovich (Oct. 24, 1895—May 27, 1976), Soviet electrochemist, specialized in surface phenomena and evolved theories of kinetics in electrochemical reactions and the quantitative influence of an electrical field upon molecular adsorption. Frumkin was at the Karpov Institute of Physical Chemistry in Moscow from 1922 to 1946 and in 1930 was named to the chair of electrochemistry at Moscow University. He also served as director (1939–49) of the Institute of Physical Chemistry at the Soviet Academy of Sciences and in 1958 became director of the Institute of Electrochemistry at the same academy. Among other awards, he received a 1931 Lenin State Prize in Science and Technology.

Haddow, Sir Alexander (Jan. 18, 1907—Jan. 21, 1976), British pathologist, was a research scientist whose experiments helped demonstrate conclusively that certain hydrocarbons in coal tar can cause cancer. He was also among the first to recognize the possibility of treating cancer effectively through chemotherapy. Haddow, who became a fellow of the Royal Society in 1958 and was knighted in 1966, graduated from the University of Edinburgh. He was professor of experimental pathology at the University of London (1946–72) and director of the Chester Beatty Research Institute of the Institute of Cancer Research, Royal Cancer Hospital, London (1946–69). He also served as president of the International Union Against Cancer (1962–66).

Heisenberg, Werner Karl (Dec. 5, 1901 – Feb. 1, 1976), German physicist, revolutionized modern physics when he discovered (1925) a way to formulate quantum mechanics in terms of mathematical matrices. Two years later he published his uncertainty (indeterminacy) principle: namely, that the position and the velocity of an object cannot both be measured exactly at the same time. Indeed, the very concept of exact position and exact velocity taken together has no meaning in nature. The principle is vital to an understanding of subatomic particles because of the intimate connection between such particles and waves. Heisenberg graduated from the University of Munich, then studied under Max Born at Göttingen and Niels Bohr in Copenhagen. After World War II, as founder and director of the Max Planck Institute for Physics and Astrophysics, he studied a broad range of topics and became widely known as a philosopher of science through such books as *Philosophic Problems of*

Werner Karl Heisenberg

The New York Times

Nuclear Science (1948; Eng. trans. 1952). In 1932 he was awarded the Nobel Prize for Physics.

Lysenko, Trofim Denisovich (Sept. 29, 1898 – Nov. 20, 1976), Soviet plant geneticist, dominated a large segment of his country's science for many years by persuading Joseph Stalin and Nikita Khrushchev that environment can effect heredity changes in plants, a view that supported Marxist theory. Lysenko's refusal to sanction research that did not meet his approval seriously impeded Soviet research in genetics and biology. He graduated from the Kiev Agricultural Institute (1925) and four years later became a senior specialist at the Ukrainian Institute of Selection and Genetics. In 1936 he was named director of the All-Union Selection and Genetics Institute in Odessa. After being appointed (1938) president of the All-Union Lenin Academy of Agricultural Sciences, he was in a position to discredit scientists who doubted his "discoveries." Lysenko was finally denounced as a charlatan and disappeared from public view after Khrushchev fell from power in 1964.

McCauley, George Vest (Nov. 5, 1882 – April 19, 1976), U.S. physicist, designed and supervised the casting (1934) of the 200-in mirror disk that became the eye of the Hale telescope at Palomar Observatory in California. The 20-ton mass of Pyrex glass was carefully cooled over a period of 300 days, then shipped across country to the California Institute of Technology to be ground into shape. This monumental task, interrupted by World War II, was finally completed in 1948, when the 15-ton finished product was set in place. Thereafter, scientists were able to probe the secrets of the universe as never before. Following this triumph of engineering technology, McCauley supervised similar projects for such other observatories as Kitt Peak in Arizona, Mt. Wilson and Lick in California, and the Royal Greenwich in England. McCauley, who obtained his Ph.D. (1911) from the University of Wisconsin, spent nearly his entire career at the Corning Glass Works, which he joined in 1918.

Menzel, Donald H(oward) (April 11, 1901 – Dec. 14, 1976), U.S. astrophysicist, gained an international reputation for his studies of the Sun and its corona. In collaboration with Joseph C. Boyce he established (1933) the existence of oxygen in the Sun's corona, and some eight years later he and Winfield W. Salisbury made calculations that in 1946 resulted in the first radio contact with the Moon. Menzel personally viewed 15 total solar eclipses and developed (1938) the first coronagraph in the U.S. so that the Sun's corona could be studied when no eclipse was taking place. He was also involved in the establishment of the High Altitude Observatory in Colorado, the Sacramento Peak Observatory in New Mexico, and the Solar

Radio Observatory in Texas. Menzel received his Ph.D. (1924) from Princeton University and was associated with Harvard University during the major part of his professional career.

Minkowski, Rudolph Leo Bernhardt (May 28, 1895—Jan. 4, 1976), German-born astronomer, joined the faculty of the University of Hamburg after earning a Ph.D. in physics (1921) from the University of Breslau. After migrating to the U.S. in 1935 he specialized in astrophysical research at the Mt. Wilson and Palomar observatories in California. His spectroscopic observations of external galaxies led to the classification of two principal types of supernova, and his intensive study of remnants of supernovae in the Earth's galaxy led to an identification of the central star of the Crab Nebula. In 1960 he discovered the largest red shift for a normal galaxy. Other studies focused on planetary nebulae and on sources of X-rays and radio waves.

Monod, Jacques-Lucien (Feb. 9, 1910—May 31, 1976), French biochemist, shared the 1965 Nobel Prize for Physiology or Medicine with François Jacob and André Lwoff for discovering a new class of genes that regulate other genes. In *Le Hasard et la nécessité* (1970; *Chance and Necessity,* 1971), he asserted that all creation is the product of chance, that inanimate and animate beings differ only in the arrangement of their atoms, and that man is thus an accident in the universe. Monod graduated from the University of Paris (1931) and taught zoology there before moving (1945) to the Pasteur Institute in Paris, where he became head of the department of cellular biochemistry in 1954 and served as director general from 1971 until his death. He was also associated with the University of Paris (1959–67) and with the Collège de France (1967–73).

Nyquist, Harry (Feb. 7, 1889—April 4, 1976), Swedish-born communications engineer, gained wide acclaim for his practical inventions as well as for his theoretical studies. The "Nyquist criterion," which sets forth the conditions that must prevail to keep feedback circuits stable, has been used to study such electronic devices as amplifiers and to study certain human regulating processes. Nyquist established a quantitative explanation for thermal noise and determined the minimum band of frequencies required for communication signal transmission. After receiving his Ph.D. in physics (1917) from Yale University, he joined American Telephone and Telegraph Co., where he undertook extensive research on television and long-distance telephone circuits. In 1934 he moved to the Bell Telephone Laboratories and remained there until his retirement in 1954.

Onsager, Lars (Nov. 27, 1903—Oct. 5, 1976), Norwegian-born chemist, was awarded the 1968

Wide World

Lars Onsager

Nobel Prize for Chemistry for "the discovery of the reciprocal relations bearing his name which are fundamental for the thermodynamics of irreversible processes." His explanation of the movement of ions in solution as related to turbulences and fluid densities had an important effect on the development of physical chemistry and has been described as providing the fourth law of thermodynamics. Onsager's early work in statistical mechanics attracted the attention of the Dutch chemist Peter Debye, under whose direction Onsager studied (1926–28) at the Swiss Federal Institute of Technology in Zürich, Switz. He then went to the U.S. and taught at Johns Hopkins University, Baltimore, Md., and Brown University, Providence, R.I. He received his Ph.D. (1935) from Yale University, where he became professor of theoretical chemistry in 1945.

Penfield, Wilder Graves (Jan. 26, 1891—April 5, 1976), U.S.-born neurologist, gained international renown for his research on epilepsy and cerebral nerve cells. Using electric probes as stimulants, he was able to map the cerebral cortex and show a dependent relationship between specific areas of the brain and such functions of man as memory, speech, and physical movement. Applying this knowledge to corrective surgery, he cured or alleviated epilepsy in a large number of cases. In 1934 Penfield became a Canadian citizen and founded the Montreal Neurological Institute with a

$1.2 million grant from the Rockefeller Foundation. With Penfield as its director (until his retirement in 1960), the institute became one of the finest centers for brain surgery in the world.

Reiner, Markus (Jan. 5, 1886–April 25, 1976), Austrian-born engineer, obtained his doctor of technology degree in Vienna before World War I, then migrated (1922) to Palestine where for 25 years he was employed by the British in Jerusalem's department of public works. In 1926 he published a paper on the principles involved when an elastic fluid (a substance that flows only under a shear stress greater than a yield stress) flows through a tube. During Reiner's 1928 visit to the U.S., Eugene C. Bingham was so impressed by Reiner's remarks on flow and deformation of materials that he designated this new field of study rheology. Though Reiner is called the father of rheology, he did not give himself fully to academic pursuits until he became (1948) professor of mechanics at the Technion (Israel Institute of Technology) in Haifa, where he continued to teach until his death.

Ruzicka, Leopold (Stephen) (Sept. 13, 1887–late September 1976), Swiss chemist, was joint recipient of the 1939 Nobel Prize for Chemistry for his work on ringed molecules and terpenes. His research on natural odoriferous compounds led to his discovery of the unusual molecular structures of muscone and civetone, important to the perfume industry. In these molecules, carbon atoms are linked in rings larger than had been thought capable of existence. He also discovered the molecular structure of testosterone and other male sex hormones and succeeded in synthesizing them. Ruzicka, who was born in Croatia, became in 1917 a citizen of Switzerland, where he lectured at the Swiss Federal Institute of Technology in Zürich. In 1926 he became professor of organic chemistry at the University of Utrecht, Neth., but after three years returned to Zürich as professor of chemistry.

Schottky, Walter Hans (July 23, 1886–March 4, 1976), Swiss-born physicist, was a research scientist whose main contributions were in the areas of electron theory, ion theory, and electroacoustics. The term Schottky effect denotes the influence of an external electric field on the rate at which electrons are emitted from the surface of a heated metal. This principle, important to vacuum tube theory, was utilized by Schottky in developing the screen-grid vacuum tube, which was a much more efficient amplifier than earlier models. He is also credited with developing the superheterodyne receiver. Still other research involved thermodynamics and statistical mechanics. Schottky studied under Max Planck at the University of Berlin, and in 1927 he joined the Siemens Aktiengesellschaft in Germany.

Schulz, George J. (April 29, 1925–Jan. 15, 1976), Czechoslovakian-born physicist, made his most important contributions to science in the field of atomic-collision physics. After obtaining his doctorate (1954) from the Massachusetts Institute of Technology, he joined the Westinghouse Research Laboratories, where he made quantitative determinations of the cross sections of atoms for excitation by electron impact. He also devised ways to create low-energy electron beams of narrower and narrower energy spread, which made it possible to investigate the effect of sharp energy resonances on the scattering of electrons by atoms and molecules. In time Schulz established the resonances of numerous atoms and molecules, including that of helium at 19.3 electron volts. During the final decade of his life he taught at Yale University.

Slater, John Clarke (Dec. 22, 1900–July 25, 1976), U.S. physicist, was a theoretical scientist whose main work centered on the electronic properties of atoms. After studying individual atoms through the multiplet structure of their spectra, he focused his research on atoms in molecular combinations and in the solid state. Slater's lifelong interest in solid-state physics began about 1930 when he published "Cohesion in Monovalent Metals," one of numerous papers that have been viewed as important contributions to modern physics. He also gave his name to the Slater determinants, a concept from quantum mechanics that has found application in such fields as chemistry and metal physics. Slater received his Ph.D. (1923) from Harvard University and taught there from 1924 to 1930. He was associated with the Massachusetts Institute of Technology from 1930 to 1966.

Sparks, William Joseph (Feb. 26, 1905–Oct. 23, 1976), U.S. chemist, was co-inventor (with Robert M. Thomas) of butyl rubber, a synthetic produced by polymerizing isoprene with isobutylene. Butyl rubber, first marketed in 1943, found wide acceptance because of such special properties as low permeability to gases, excellent resistance to oxygen and ozone at normal temperatures, and good resistance to vegetable oils. Unlike natural rubber, it is not readily attacked by acids and alkalies. In addition, it is elastic, odorless, and nontoxic and can be worked without special machinery. Sparks received his doctorate (1936) from the University of Illinois and, except for a brief interval, remained with the Esso Research and Engineering Co. from 1936 to 1967.

Vinograd, Jerome Rubin (Feb. 9, 1913–July 3, 1976), U.S. chemist, was mainly concerned with problems of surface films and colloids before becoming engrossed in the nucleic acid aspects of molecular biology. His special interest became closed circular DNA (deoxyribonucleic acid).

Though DNA was known to exist as a linear molecule and occasionally also as a closed loop, Vinograd and two research assistants discovered a means of determining the proportions in which those loops can exist in relaxed or densely coiled forms. This finding provided another possible lead to understanding the relationships between the structure of DNA and its behavior in controlling genetic mechanisms in living cells. Vinograd obtained his Ph.D. (1940) from Stanford University and worked (1941–51) with the Shell Development Co. before transferring to the California Institute of Technology.

Wheeler, Sir (Robert Eric) Mortimer (Sept. 10, 1890–July 22, 1976), British archaeologist, was especially well known for the excavations he directed in the Indus Valley, which lies in India and Pakistan. He also did considerable research in Great Britain, continental Europe, and Africa. Wheeler became a familiar figure to the general public as a lecturer and through television appearances on such programs as "The Grandeur That Was Rome." During his career he was secretary of the British Academy (1949–68), director and president of the Society of Antiquaries, and trustee of the British Museum (1963–73). He became professor of ancient history to the Royal Academy in 1965, and was a fellow of University College, University of London, from 1922 until his death. Wheeler, who was knighted in 1952 and made a Companion of Honour in 1967, became a fellow of the Royal Society in 1968.

Whipple, George Hoyt (Aug. 28, 1878–Feb. 1, 1976), U.S. pathologist, shared the 1934 Nobel Prize for Physiology or Medicine with George R. Minot and William P. Murphy. Whipple's independent research with anemic dogs matched the findings of Minot and Murphy and established the fact that pernicious anemia can be controlled by a diet containing liver. This discovery signaled a major advance in the treatment of noninfectious diseases even though many years passed before the vitamin B_{12} in liver was identified as the extrinsic factor responsible for restoring blood to a healthy state. Whipple studied and taught at Johns Hopkins University and was director of the Hooper Foundation for medical research in California before moving to the University of Rochester in New York, where he served as professor of pathology (1921–55) and first dean (1921–53) of the School of Medicine and Dentistry.

Wiener, Alexander Solomon (March 16, 1907–Nov. 6, 1976), U.S. immunohematologist, co-discovered (with Karl Landsteiner and Philip Levine) the Rh blood factor while conducting experiments (1940) on rhesus monkeys. As Wiener pursued his research, he also identified the Rh factor in human

The New York Times

George Hoyt Whipple

blood, demonstrated that it was hereditary, and learned why the transfusion of a seemingly proper blood-type sometimes produced adverse effects. He also evolved methods to solve serious problems that arise during pregnancy when the mother's Rh-negative blood is in conflict with the Rh-positive blood of the fetus. Wiener received his medical degree (1930) from the State University of New York. He was long associated with the Jewish Hospital and Medical Center of Brooklyn and was involved in forensic medicine both as a teacher and as a serologist in the office of the medical examiner in New York City.

Wildt, Rupert (June 25, 1905–Jan. 9, 1976), German-born astrophysicist, was credited with two major discoveries. In 1938 he theorized that the masses of Jupiter and Saturn consist mainly of compressed hydrogen and therefore have low densities. The following year he concluded that the negative hydrogen ion is the essential radiation-absorbing element in the solar atmosphere. Both theories were later confirmed. Wildt earned his doctorate (1927) at the University of Berlin and conducted research at the university observatories in Bonn and Göttingen before moving to the U.S. in 1935. During his long association with Yale University (1946–73) he was a visiting professor at various other institutions and was a consultant to the National Aeronautics and Space Administration. The Royal Astronomical Society in London honored him with its 1966 Eddington Gold Medal.

Index

Index entries to feature and review articles in this and previous editions of the *Yearbook of Science and the Future* are set in boldface type, *e.g.,* **Astronomy.** Entries to other subjects are set in lightface type, *e.g.,* Radiation. Additional information on any of these subjects is identified with a subheading and indented under the entry heading. The numbers following headings and subheadings indicate the year (boldface) of the edition and the page number (lightface) on which the information appears.

Astronomy 78–263; **77**–263; **76**–264
climatology **78**–282; **76**–184
employment problems **76**–414
Formation of Stars, The **77**–76
holography use **77**–377
honors **78**–413; **77**–413; **76**–418
hydrologic research **77**–296
Molecules in Space **77**–104
Natural Satellites, The **76**–224
Other Civilizations in Space: The Search for Extraterrestrial Life **78**–282
planetary research **77**–394
red shifts **76**–221
Science in Colonial America **76**–18
space colonization studies **77**–11

All entry headings, whether consisting of a single word or more, are treated for the purpose of alphabetization as single complete headings and are alphabetized letter by letter up to the punctuation. The abbreviation "il." indicates an illustration.

Acknowledgments

4-5   Courtesy, NASA

6   Photos by (left to right, top to bottom) courtesy, Metropolitan Museum of Art, N.Y., photo by Lee Boltin; © National Geographic Society, photo by David Brill; Jack Couffer—Bruce Coleman Inc.; courtesy, Martin Marietta; John Marmaras—Woodfin Camp; Kent Reno—Jeroboam, Inc.

75   From T. D. Rees and C. C. Dupuis, "Plastic Reconstructive Surgery," 43:381, 1969, The Williams & Wilkins Co.

162-163   (Center) photograph by Bullaty Lomeo—The Image Bank

162   Photographs by (top) Paul Hosefros—NYT Pictures; (center) Russ Kinne—Photo Researchers; (bottom) R. L. Zentmaier—Photo Researchers

163   Photographs by (top) Peter Byrne—Photo Researchers; (center and bottom) Paul Hosefros—NYT Pictures

205   Based upon information prepared by Dr. R. F. Foster, Battelle Pacific Northwest Laboratories

211, 212   Adapted from "Final Environmental Impact Statement—Waste Management Operations," ERDA–1538, Hanford, Washington, vol. 1, fig. 11, 1–67 (page 211) and fig. 11, 1–52 (page 212)

213   Based upon projections by J. O. Blomeke, et al., Oak Ridge National Laboratory

215   Adapted from "High Level Radioactive Waste Management Alternatives," WASH–1297, USAEC, May 1974

216   Adapted from ARHL–D140, June, 1976

247   Adapted from "Catalysis," V. Haensel and R. L. Burwell, Jr. © Dec. 1971 by Scientific American Inc. All rights reserved

248   Adapted from "Structure of Hen Egg-White Lysozyme," C. C. F. Blake et al., Nature, 206:757, 1965

250   Photographs (top to bottom) Dennis di Cicco, Sky and Telescope; courtesy, Philip Johnson and John Burgee, photo by Richard W. Payne; courtesy, E. A. Pillemer and W. M. Tingey, New York State College of Agriculture and Life Sciences/a Statutory College of the State University Cornell University; courtesy, Wah Jun Tze, University of British Columbia

263   "Volcanic Dust, Sunspots, and Temperature Trends," Stephen H. Schneider and Clifford Mass, Science, 190:742, fig. a, Nov. 21, 1975, copyright American Association for the Advancement of Science

346   "Jackrabbit Ears: Surface Temperature and Vascular Responses," R. W. Hill and J. H. Veghte, Science, 194:436–438, photos, Oct. 22, 1976, copyright American Association for the Advancement of Science